THE GEOGRAPHY OF THE
FLOWERING PLANTS

". . . *that grand subject, that almost keystone of the laws of creation,*
Geographical Distribution."

CHARLES DARWIN
in a letter to Joseph Dalton Hooker in 1845.

By the same author

Features of Evolution in the Flowering Plants

Plate 1.

Forest
vegetation
in Java

(from Schimper, Pflanzen-Geographie)

THE
GEOGRAPHY OF THE
FLOWERING PLANTS

BY

RONALD GOOD, M.A., Sc.D.(Cantab.)

Professor Emeritus of Botany in the University of Hull

ILLUSTRATED BY
86 LINE-DRAWINGS
9 MAPS IN COLOUR
AND
16 PHOTOGRAVURE PLATES

LONGMANS

LONGMANS, GREEN AND CO LTD
London and Harlow
*Associated companies, branches and representatives
throughout the world*

First Published 1947
Second Edition 1953
New Impression by Photolithography 1961
Third Edition 1964
Fourth Impression 1969

SBN 582 44610 6

PRINTED IN GREAT BRITAIN BY
SPOTTISWOODE, BALLANTYNE & CO LTD
LONDON AND COLCHESTER

PREFACE TO THE THIRD EDITION

IN this, its third edition, *The Geography of the Flowering Plants* has again been revised throughout, and a good deal of new material, including some figures and many plant names, added. These additions are mainly concerned with the notable development that has taken place in the last few years, chiefly as a result of investigations into paleomagnetism and related matters, in the general attitude towards theories of continental movement. A brief formal account of this recent work is given in Chapter 20 but it has also been the chief motive for adding to the book an entirely new chapter, designed to give a more integrated and concise review than is readily available in other chapters of the facts, and some of the hypotheses, about those floras of the Southern Hemisphere which are of special interest in relation to theories of continental displacement, and most often mentioned in discussions about them.

Once more it is a pleasure to acknowledge the help which I have received from many friends and correspondents. I am particularly grateful to Prof. H. N. Barber, Prof. G. T. S. Baylis, Dr. S. T. Blake, Prof. V. J. Chapman, Dr. W. Curtis, Mr. E. E. Everist, Prof. H. B. Gilliland, Dr. H. S. McKee, Prof. W. R. Philipson, Prof. J. W. Purseglove, Prof. A. D. Skelding, Mr. J. S. Womersley, Mr. T. B. Worthington, and many of their colleagues, for their hospitality and generous help in enabling me to see so much of many floras of special interest to the plant geographer.

RONALD GOOD

Parkstone, February 1964

PREFACE TO THE SECOND EDITION

It was explained, in its preface, that for various reasons the first edition of this book depicted in the main our knowledge of the distribution of the Angiosperms as it was in 1939, and that more recent information would have to be dealt with on some later occasion. The demand for a new edition has, in very welcome fashion, provided this occasion, and I am most grateful to the publishers for allowing me to take full advantage of it.

In this new edition the book has been revised throughout, and parts of it, especially Chapters 4 and 20, largely rewritten. Its whole contents has been reviewed, and in many places elaborated by the inclusion of new material or by additional emphasis. Special care has been given to the floristic classification in Chapter 2 and its accompanying map (Plate 4) and it is hoped that in their improved form these will more completely meet the wider demand which clearly exists for a reasonably simple arrangement of this kind. Several of the weaker photogravure plates have been replaced; several text-figures have been added; Appendix B has once more been re-edited; a subject index has been provided; and the bibliography has been greatly enlarged. With regard to the last I regret that I have not been able to see a copy of item 117, which, I am given to understand, was originally announced under a different title.

Particular pains have been taken to bring the book up to date, or at least as up to date as the rapid development of the subject of plant geography permits, and to ensure its factual accuracy, and it is especially to these ends that I am in the debt of so many correspondents, both at home and abroad, for their ready and generous responses to my enquiries. I am particularly indebted to Mr. H. S. McKee, who has long constituted himself an invaluable and untiring intermediary in all matters Australasian, and to Prof. R. S. Adamson, Dr. C. E. P. Brooks, Mr. I. H. Burkill, Mr. E. J. H. Corner, Dr. P. Dansereau, Mr. W. N. Edwards, Mr. D. W. Ferguson, Prof. E. Hultén, Mr. L. A. S. Johnson, Prof. H. J. Lam, Mrs. M. R. Levyns, Mr. J. E. Lousley, Dr. H. E. Moore, junr., Prof. C. Skottsberg, Dr. W. A. Sledge, Dr. H. Sleumer, Dr. F. A. Stafleu, Dr. P. C. Tsoong and Dr. C. G. G. J. van Steenis. I am also most grateful to Mr. J. E. Dandy, Mr. A. W. Exell, Mr. C. E. Hubbard, Mr. N. Y. Sandwith, Mr. W. T. Stearn and other members of the staffs of the Herbaria at the British Museum and at Kew for always making so readily available to me their special knowledge and experience. I trust that all those mentioned, as well as the many others also who have helped me, will accept this warm expression of my thanks.

Since the first edition was prepared there has been completed an additional important general source of condensed information about the Angiosperms, namely Lemée's great *Dictionnaire descriptif et synonymique des genres de plantes phanérogames*. This is at present the most recent complete conspectus of the Flowering Plants and I have made considerable use of it, especially as a source of comparable figures.

It will be noticed that all specific epithets in this new edition have been spelt without capital letters, this being in accordance with the recommended practice now being generally adopted. As to nomenclature the same sources have been followed as before, except that I may here and there, and entirely on my own responsibility, have used names which are, perhaps, not in strict accord with the letter of the Rules.

RONALD GOOD

Hull, October 1952

PREFACE TO THE FIRST EDITION

THE manuscript of *The Geography of the Flowering Plants* was completed in the summer of 1939 and immediate publication was intended, but the vicissitudes of the war have caused its postponement until now.

In the seven years that have thus elapsed great changes have come about in the life of nearly every part of the world, and in two notable respects these changes are likely to increase interest in the study of plant geography. The spectre of starvation and the rigours of rationing have brought about a much more vivid appreciation of what man owes to the plant world; and the global military struggle has made familiar to the layman many of those more remote parts of the world (such as the islands of the Pacific Ocean) that are of special interest to the student of plant distribution.

On the other hand the war has brought chaos to the co-ordination of learning and research, and years are likely to pass before the advances in knowledge that may be expected from the opening up of hitherto little-known parts of the world can be fully recorded and integrated.

Therefore, although the text of this book has been as far as possible brought up to date, it must be regarded in the main as depicting the state of our knowledge at the outbreak of war, and subsequent advances must await full treatment at a later date.

This unavoidable delay in publication, though regrettable, has had one advantage. The plan of this book has permitted only a comparatively brief reference (notably in Chapters 3 and 14) to certain matters which are of considerable interest and about which the reader may well wish to know more, and it is now possible to refer to two other works in English which deal with them much more completely. These are the authorised translation of Wulff's *Historical Plant Geography* (610) and Cain's *Foundations of Plant Geography* (74). The latter, in particular, includes not only an up-to-date account of the evolutionary background to the subject (especially with regard to modern ideas on the origin of species), and of various questions relating to the distribution of plants in the past, but also a very extensive bibliography. Both books are valuable complements to *The Geography of the Flowering Plants*.

It is inevitable in a book of this kind that many facts are quoted without critical comment, since to verify them in detail would be impossible, but every care has been given to the selection of the sources from which they are taken. Also it must be remembered that there is no single complete modern revision of the whole group of the Angiosperms, nor, considering the amount of work it would involve, is there any such in prospect, and the literature is very scattered and often difficult to correlate.

As far as seems practicable the sources of all the major statements in the text are given in the selected bibliography at the end of the book, but there are four outstandingly comprehensive works to which I have had such constant recourse that they must receive special mention and acknowledgment here. They are *Index*

Kewensis (277), *Das Pflanzenreich* (156), *Die natürlichen Pflanzenfamilien* (159, 160) and Willis' *A Dictionary of the Flowering Plants and Ferns* (597).

Further, with regard to examples and statistics, it should be borne in mind that these are useful chiefly for illustrative purposes. Figures must, generally speaking, be looked upon as relative, and of most value as a means of comparison. To treat them as absolute and immutable would be to misinterpret both the figures themselves and their function, for even when they are computations made specially for this book, they are ultimately based on what are, in many cases, no more than personal estimates and opinions.

So many of my friends and colleagues have contributed, in one way or another, to the writing of this book that it is quite impossible to acknowledge in detail all the help I have received in this way, and I can only hope that they will one and all accept this general expression of my thanks.

I must, however, express my very special gratitude to my old master, teacher and friend, the late Sir Albert Seward, whose death in 1941 deprived the botanical world of one of its wisest and kindliest figures. It was characteristic of him that he should find time to read the whole lengthy manuscript critically at a period which must have been most inconvenient for him, and it is a peculiar satisfaction to me to have this opportunity of paying a personal tribute to his memory. His many suggestions and comments, especially in connection with the geological history of the Flowering Plants, were of the greatest service.

My very grateful thanks are due also to my former colleague, Mr. J. E. Dandy, who has devoted a great deal of time to reading the proofs. His ready and generous help has been invaluable in many problems, and particularly in those touching the vexed question of plant nomenclature. Concerning this matter the use of the names at present regarded as correct has sometimes led to the supersession of particularly familiar names, and where this has happened the latter have been added in brackets. In the case of British plants the nomenclature follows that of the recently published "Check List of British Vascular Plants" (98), except that I have retained initial capital letters for certain of the species names.

The numbers in brackets refer to the entries in the Bibliography, which includes also a number of general works on plant geography not specifically referred to in the text.

For the excellent plant drawings I am indebted to Miss Lorna Pillow.

RONALD GOOD

Hull, 1946

CONTENTS

PAGE

INTRODUCTION.—*The importance of plant geography; vegetation and flora; the Flowering Plants and their classification; the nomenclature of plants; the history of plant geography* 1

PART I

CHAPTER 1.—THE GEOGRAPHY OF THE WORLD 11
  Continents and oceans; islands; mountains; deserts; map projections; definitions.

CHAPTER 2.—THE DIVISION OF THE WORLD INTO FLORISTIC REGIONS . 22

CHAPTER 3.—SOME GENERAL ASPECTS OF PLANT GEOGRAPHY . . . 33
  The evolutionary background; differentiation; age and area; the cycle of distribution; endemism; discontinuity.

CHAPTER 4.—THE DISTRIBUTION OF FAMILIES 49
  Number, size and local representation of families; cosmopolitan families; tropical families; temperate families; discontinuous families; endemic families; anomalous families; southern families; details of some particular families.

CHAPTER 5.—THE DISTRIBUTION OF GENERA—I 84
  Number and size of genera; cosmopolitan genera; pan-tropical genera; temperate genera; other wide genera.

CHAPTER 6.—THE DISTRIBUTION OF GENERA—II 104
  Discontinuous genera.

CHAPTER 7.—THE DISTRIBUTION OF GENERA—III 132
  Endemic genera.

CHAPTER 8.—THE DISTRIBUTION OF SPECIES—I 154
  Number of species; distribution of species within genera; the significance of high species concentrations.

CHAPTER 9.—THE DISTRIBUTION OF SPECIES—II 174
  Cosmopolitan species; pan-tropical species; other wide species.

CHAPTER 10.—THE DISTRIBUTION OF SPECIES—III 189
  Endemic species.

CHAPTER 11.—THE DISTRIBUTION OF SPECIES—IV 226
  Discontinuous species; vicarious species or species pairs; narrowly restricted species; marine Angiosperms; mangroves; strand plants.

CHAPTER 12.—THE FLORAS OF THE SOUTHERN HEMISPHERE . . . 243

PAGE

CHAPTER 13.—THE HISTORY AND DISTRIBUTION OF THE BRITISH FLORA . 268

CHAPTER 14.—THE DISTRIBUTION OF PLANTS IN AN ENGLISH COUNTY . . 295

CHAPTER 15.—THE GEOLOGICAL HISTORY AND PAST DISTRIBUTION OF THE FLOWERING PLANTS 307
Geological history of the Flowering Plants; fossil floras; the Ice Ages.

PART II

CHAPTER 16.—THE FACTORS OF DISTRIBUTION—I 332
General review.

CHAPTER 17.—THE FACTORS OF DISTRIBUTION—II 350
Climatic factors.

CHAPTER 18.—THE FACTORS OF DISTRIBUTION—III 361
Edaphic factors.

CHAPTER 19.—THE FACTORS OF DISTRIBUTION—IV 369
The dispersal of plants.

CHAPTER 20.—THE FACTORS OF DISTRIBUTION—V 384
Changes of climate.

CHAPTER 21.—THE FACTORS OF DISTRIBUTION—VI 395
Geographical changes.

CHAPTER 22.—THE THEORY OF TOLERANCE 415

CHAPTER 23.—CONCLUSIONS 432

APPENDIX A.—STATISTICS OF THE WORLD'S LAND SURFACES . . . 437

APPENDIX B.—LIST OF DISCONTINUOUS GENERA 439

BIBLIOGRAPHY 445

INDEX OF SUBJECTS 467

INDEX OF PLANT NAMES 470

INDEX OF PERSONS AND PLACES 509

PLATES

PLATE

1. Forest vegetation in Java . . . . . . *Frontispiece*

2. Map of the world showing the distribution of vegetation . *Facing p.* 32

3. Map of the world showing oceanic islands and the − 600 ft. and + 600 ft. contours . . . . . . ,, 48

4. Map of the world showing floristic regions . . . ,, 64

5. Map of the world showing climatic provinces . . . ,, 80

6. A cactus landscape in Arizona . . . . . ,, 96

7. *Puya raimondii* in the Peruvian Andes . . . . ,, 112

8. The cactus-like tree *Euphorbia ingens* in the Transvaal . ,, 128

9. *Gunnera chilensis* in S. Chile . . . . . . ,, 144

10. Forest of *Eucalyptus regnans* in Victoria . . . . ,, 160

11. Stone-like plants in the Little Karroo . . . . ,, 176

12. *Protea cynaroides* at the Cape . . . . . . ,, 192

13. A giant Lobelia (*L. rhynchopetalum*) of the African mountains ,, 208

14. A giant Senecio (*S. keniodendron*) of the African mountains . ,, 224

15. Map of the world showing the distribution of the species of marine Angiosperms, excluding the genus *Zostera* . . ,, 240

16. Mangrove vegetation on the coast of lower California . ,, 256

17. Grass-trees (*Xanthorrhoea sp.*) on the slopes of Mt. Mitchell, Queensland . . . . ,, 272

18. *Liriodendron tulipifera* . . . . ,, 288

19. *Nipa* palms along the banks of a river in the Malay Pensinsula ,, 304

20. Map of the world showing the distribution of mean annual temperature . . . . ,, 320

21. Map of the world showing, in degrees Fahrenheit, the range of extreme temperature variation during the year . . ,, 336

22. An Asiatic giant bamboo (*Dendrocalamus giganteus*) . . ,, 352

23. Map of the world showing the distribution of annual rainfall ,, 368

24. Map of the world showing the seasonal distribution of rain ,, 384

25. A grove of palms (*Washingtonia filifera*) in California . ,, 400

xiii

ILLUSTRATIONS

FIG.   PAGE

1. Diagrammatic representation of the vegetation zones of latitude and altitude . 23
2. *Stylidium scandens, Stylidium tenellum,* and *Stylidium pycnanthum*   .   . 51
3. Map showing the distribution of the genera of the family Stylidiaceae .   . 51
4. *Drimys winteri*   54
5. Map showing the distribution of the family Winteraceae   54
6. Map showing the distribution of the family Pittosporaceae 56
7. *Cunonia capensis*   59
8. Map showing the distribution of the genera of the family Cunoniaceae.   . 59
9. *Lapageria rosea*   61
10. Map showing the distribution of the genera of the family Philesiaceae .   . 61
11. *Hypolaena fastigiata*   65
12. Map showing the distribution of the family Restionaceae   65
13. Map showing the distribution of the family Tropaeolaceae 67
14. Map showing the distribution of the family Palmae   76
15. *Oreocallis (Embothrium) grandiflora* 79
16. Map showing the distribution of the family Proteaceae   79
17. Map showing the distribution of *Berberis* and *Mahonia*   81
18. Map showing the distribution of the genus *Drosera*   87
19. Map showing the distribution of the genus *Vaccinium*   91
20. Map showing the distribution of the genus *Ribes*   93
21. Map showing the distribution of the genera *Euonymus* and *Celastrus* below the
    Tropic of Cancer   93
22. Map showing the distribution of the genus *Eucalyptus*   100
23. Map showing the distribution of the tribe Magnolieae   104
24. *Nepenthes gracilis* 106
25. Map showing the distribution of the genus *Nepenthes*   106
26. *Hibbertia volubilis* 108
27. Map showing the distribution of the genus *Hibbertia* 108
28. *Symphonia globulifera*   110
29. Map showing the distribution of the genus *Symphonia*   110
30. *Ancistrocladus heyneanus*   111
31. Map showing the distribution of the genus *Ancistrocladus* 111
32. *Hernandia peltata* 112
33. Map showing the distribution of the genus *Hernandia*   112
34. *Clethra tomentosa* 114
35. Map showing the distribution of the genus *Clethra*   114
36. Map showing the distribution of the genus *Colobanthus*   115
37. Map showing the distribution of the genera *Nothofagus, Hebe, Eucryphia* and
    Jovellana 116
38. *Eucryphia glutinosa*.   117

FIG.   PAGE
39. Map showing the distribution of the genus *Oreomyrrhis* 118
40. Map showing the distribution of the species of the series *Tetrapterae* of the
    genus *Sophora* 119
41. *Coriaria japonica* 121
42. Map showing the distribution of the genus *Coriaria* 121
43. Map showing the distribution of the genera of the family Empetraceae . . 122
44. Map showing the distribution of the genus *Sibthorpia* 122
45. Map showing the distribution of the genus *Phylica* 123
46. Map showing the distribution of the genus *Gentiana* 123
47. *Coprosma nitida* 124
48. Map showing the distribution of the sections of the genus *Coprosma* . . 124
49. *Collospermum montanum* 126
50. Map showing the distribution of the sections of the genus *Astelia*, and of the
    closely allied genus *Collospermum* 127
51. Map showing the distribution of the genus *Exocarpus* 128
52. Map showing the distribution of the genus *Gunnera* 128
53. Map showing the distribution of the genus *Metrosideros* 129
54. Map showing the distribution of the genus *Rhododendron* 168
55. Some characteristic members of the tribe Stapelieae 171
56. Map showing the distribution of the tribe Stapelieae 172
57. Map showing the number of genera and species in different parts of the range
    of the tribe Stapelieae 172
58. Map showing the distribution of the genera *Bryanthus*, *Harrimanella*, *Cassiope*
    and *Phyllodoce* 181
59. Map showing the distribution of the species of the section *Chamaepericlymenum*
    of the genus *Cornus* 232
60. *Phyllospadix scouleri* 238
61. *Cymodocea ciliata*, a tropical marine Angiosperm 239
62. Map showing the position of the island of New Guinea 263
63. Map showing the distribution of the species of *Primula* in the British Isles . 270
64. Map showing the distribution of the species of *Pinguicula* in the British Isles . 274
65. Map showing the distribution of the British species of *Erica* in Western Europe 278
66. Map showing the distribution of *Neotinea intacta* and *Arbutus unedo* . . 284
67. Map showing the distribution of *Saxifraga hirsuta* and *Daboecia cantabrica* . 292
68. Map showing, simplified, the distribution of subsoil types in the county of Dorset 296
69. Map showing, slightly simplified, the distribution of the primrose (*Primula
    vulgaris*) in Dorset 296
70. Map showing the distribution of *Clematis vitalba* in Dorset 298
71. Map showing the distribution of *Picris echioides* in Dorset 300
72. Map showing the distribution of *Molinia caerulea* in Dorset . . . 302
73. Diagrammatic representation of the upper half of the geological time-scale . 309
74. Map showing the past and present distribution of the genus *Liriodendron* . 313
75. Map showing the past and present distribution of the genus *Nipa* . . 319
76. *Nelumbo nucifera* 321
77. Map showing the past and present distribution of the genus *Nelumbo* . . 321
78. Map showing the extent of maximum Pleistocene glaciation in both hemispheres 325
79. Map showing the extent of the ice advance in North America during the maxi-
    mum glaciation 326

FIG.   PAGE

80. Map showing the extent of the ice advance in Europe during the maximum glaciation 328

81. Graph showing the variation in temperature in the Alps during the Ice Ages . 330

82. Diagram of Lang's Rain Factor 362

83. Diagram of a section of one hemisphere to show the position of the sial and sima 401

84. Reconstruction of the map of the world at different periods in geological history, according to Wegener's theory of continental drift 403

85. Map of the world showing the positions of the equator at various positions of the North Pole 412

86. Map of the world showing the positions of the equator at various positions of the North Pole 412

INTRODUCTION

The Importance of Plant Geography

PLANT geography is that branch of botany that deals with the spatial relationships of plants both in the present and the past. Its aim is to record, and then if possible to explain, the distribution of plants over the world's surface.

This book is arranged on a corresponding plan. The first part consists of a purely descriptive account of the facts of distribution in one great group of plants, and the second consists of a theoretical consideration of these facts and concludes with an attempt to give a generalised explanation of them.

Compared with many other aspects of botany, plant geography is remarkably free from technicalities and their attendant terminologies. It is naturally, too, an out-door subject rather than one involving exact experiment in a laboratory and its study needs neither complicated nor costly equipment. It therefore appeals not only to the trained botanist but also to many whose interest in plants, though just as real, is less academic, and especially those who delight in their gardens. For the same reasons it should be possible to prepare an account of the subject acceptable to all these, provided only that it incorporates, for the benefit of the less scientifically minded, an introduction to those aspects of biological thought and method of which some appreciation is necessary if the geography of plants is to be understood properly. Such an introduction is provided in these first pages, but they are in the nature of a preamble to the main parts of the book and the more scientific reader need not be detained by them.

Plant geography is so closely related, not only to many other branches of botany, but to zoology and anthropology, that it is a subject of great importance to man. The enormous advances that have been made in applied sciences make it ever more difficult to recognise in their proper proportions the foundations on which human civilisation rests and the influences that have determined the main trends of its development. Civilisation has been defined as man's gradual conquest of his environment, but how far this process has, in sober fact, gone is a matter for careful thought. In some ways certainly man's mastery over nature is complete enough. He has, for almost all practical purposes, annihilated space; he has explored and exploited the resources of the mineral world to a remarkable degree; he has gone far towards the control of infectious disease, especially in the warmer parts of the world.

These are great achievements, but they must not blind us to the fact that in other ways his efforts have been comparatively unavailing. His control of the elements, for example, can only be described as poor, and although he can often modify their dangers they not infrequently reveal their potentialities with disconcerting clarity.

Another direction in which he has been less successful, and which is of chief concern here, is his relation with the plant world, which still remains what it has always been, the only true basis of human economy. Naturally enough vegetation is as susceptible to man's destructive propensities as any other part of nature, and in many respects it can be as easily exploited by him, but unlike the rest he cannot entirely bend it to his will. Above all, there are two important things which, with all his knowledge, he cannot do—he cannot appreciably control, under all conditions, the speed at which crops mature and ripen; and he cannot grow every kind of plant

1

where and when he likes. In consequence the business of maintaining and distributing his food supplies requires a complicated prevision and an intricacy of movement which makes it extremely vulnerable to disruptive factors. For the explanation of this the reader must refer to sources where the problems are dealt with at greater length (290, 639), but at this particular juncture in world history the statement itself needs no special demonstration. In latter years the nations have presented one another with many and terribly imminent dangers, but behind them all has loomed the one ultimate and over-riding peril that the disorganisation of agriculture and transport arising from them may spread so widely and uncontrollably that there will come about, over much of the world, absolute dearth beyond remedy and the destruction by starvation of a great part of the human race.

Although modern conditions have accentuated this danger and contemporary events have made its possibility all too clear, it has always been in existence and the distribution of plants, which is one of the factual bases of it, has been a controlling influence in mankind's development throughout his history. It is no mere caprice that the earthly paradise depicted in the Book of Genesis—the Garden of Eden—is a place where, to use the words of the Authorised Version, there grew "every tree that is pleasant to the sight and good for food", because that is simply the pictorial rendering of an age-long ideal.

But apart from myth there is abundant evidence of the way in which plant geography has determined the course of history and the destinies of man. To consider this evidence at length would be equivalent to writing a history of the human race and is therefore impossible here, but the more salient points must be stated.

The natural vegetation of any part of the world can, in general, be described as belonging to one or other of three types only (Plate 2). It is either forest of a sort, grassland of a sort, or some kind of desert. There are, of course, considerable areas where somewhat intermediate conditions prevail, but from the human point of view these are the three main conditions. In the forests the plants are mainly trees; in the grasslands they are mainly grasses; while deserts may be described as areas where the total plant life and cover are scanty and incomplete, producing neither woodland nor pasturage. The potentialities of these three to a human population are obviously very different. Deserts are, by definition, unlikely to provide a sufficiency of food and such as there may be is likely to be of little value since it will not include the products of trees or grasses. Forest, while it may in total contain large potential supplies, offers many obstacles to exploitation by man, unless he is at one or other extreme of his development. A very primitive human society, sparse in numbers, may derive sufficient from it, and modern industrial societies can remove and destroy it, but to most peoples this type of vegetation is a serious barrier to progress, because it deprives them of two prime necessities, space for expansion and the opportunity for an economic form of agriculture by which their supplies may be increased in proportion to their growing needs. The grasslands, on the other hand, meet both these primary requirements, providing huge open spaces as stages for the playing of the human drama, and room wherein the most convenient and desirable forms of human food can be produced. It is here, too, that the climatic conditions most suitable for the human race are to be found.

If the world distribution of these three types of vegetation is studied, it is seen that it follows fairly closely the distribution of certain climatic values. Briefly, deserts are found where the prevalent conditions are excessive heat or cold, usually accompanied by lack of moisture, at least at some seasons. Forests, conversely, are found where precipitation is high and especially where temperature also is considerable. The climate of some forest regions is not in itself unsuitable for man, but, as has been said, the nature of the vegetation militates against him. Grassland, however, reflects medium climate values, where there is rain in sufficiency but not in excess and where the temperature is mild. In short it tends to have just the climate which is usually regarded as the best not only for the physical but also for the mental activities of mankind.

It may well be doubted whether primitive man consciously realised the climatic significance of the grasslands, but of their spatial advantages and of the ease with which animals could be hunted on them he must soon have become aware, and for this reason the association of man with this particular kind of vegetation is not hard to understand.

His dependence on the grasses for his own staple food, however, is an aspect of the subject which, by its very familiarity, excites much less interest than it deserves. To-day the pre-eminence of the grasses among the useful plants of the world is due to their double rôle of providing fodder from their vegetative parts and food from their fruits. The first of these two rôles is presumably the older, and with it the whole earlier history of mammalian evolution is intimately involved. The second is younger and its origin is mysterious. It is easy to imagine how, in the dawning of his intellectual powers, man might conceive the possibility of growing deliberately, in order to provide himself with food, plants whose fruits are large and conspicuous, but it is difficult to understand the circumstances by which his early agriculture became, as it did and as it has remained, concentrated upon the cultivation of grasses for the sake of their grain. For the most part the fruits of wild grasses are, in comparison with the fruits of many other plants, neither conspicuous nor bulky, and that their great potentialities as human food were so soon and so unerringly realised is one of the most intriguing sides of the story of primitive man, and may indeed be a valuable clue to problems which still remain to be solved.

But, however it may have come about, the development of mankind has been and presumably will long continue to be essentially a grassland development. Of the grazing or fodder aspect of this no more need be said here, but the subject of cereals as human food affords a peculiarly vivid picture of the influence of plant geography and a useful introduction to that study.

Although there are small but familiar exceptions it is true to say that even to-day, when diets have become so greatly diversified, the staple food of practically the whole human race is some kind of grain. Anything like a comprehensive list of the grains used would be lengthy, but of them all no more than half a dozen have an importance far greater than that of all the others put together. These are wheat, barley, rye, oats, rice and maize, the last named being on the whole less important than the rest. Broadly speaking the first four are crops of temperate regions, the last two of tropical countries. That is to say, these are their present cultivation zones, but it is of more particular interest to enquire into their natural ranges. In detail this is a subject of great controversy, but in general it may be said that wheat probably had its home somewhere in western or central Asia, barley and oats in rather more northerly parts of the same region, and rye somewhere more to the north again. Rice comes from the monsoon tropics of eastern Asia and maize, the only important New World grain, probably from somewhere in central America, though there is more than one opinion about this (481).

When maps showing the distribution of the earlier human civilisations are consulted it will be seen that these occur almost entirely in three parts of the world, namely western and central Eurasia, eastern Asia, and to a lesser extent in central America. That is to say, they have much the same natural distribution as the chief grain crops. This correlation can be elaborated in many interesting ways and one or two may well be mentioned here.

Africa has conspicuously never been the site of a comprehensive and powerful civilisation. Whether or not it may have been the cradle of the human race, as some believe, it long remained the home of a loose-knit collection of comparatively primitive races. Nor has it any outstanding cereal of its own. Most of the African peoples have their own peculiar grains, but none of these is of more than local significance and range, a point strikingly emphasised by the fact that the semi-industrialised Africans of to-day have adopted maize as their staple food and that its use is spreading to other parts of the population.

Temperate North America has contributed nothing of moment to the world's list of cereals and this is not unrelated to the fact that the native race of this part of the world was a scanty nomadic pastoral one, mainly without the localised and fixed type of agriculture which has always proved one of the foundations of human progress.

Until the period of European settlement the human population of Australia consisted of a sprinkling only of a race in a most primitive state of existence, comparable indeed to the Stone Age of Europe, and it is difficult to imagine that the absence of a well-characterised indigenous cereal is not a reflection of this low level of culture, or conversely, that the exploitation of some such crop plant would not have been accompanied by great changes in the mode and standards of life of the aborigines.

These instances show clearly enough, if only in one way, the relation between the distribution of plants and the development of man, but neither the one nor the other had grown up suddenly. Each is the outcome of a long and complicated series of events, extending in the case of the plants over many millions of years. Human history is much shorter and covers only the later chapters of the history of plants, but there is no doubt that where the two are concurrent a knowledge of each contributes greatly to an understanding of the other.

The plant geographer concerns himself not only with the distribution of plants in space but also with their distribution in time, and it is one of the purposes of this book to discuss some of the great changes in the distribution of plants that have taken place in the course of geological time. It will appear that the primary cause of these changes has been variation in the distribution of climatic values, but one of their most important aspects is that, acting through the intimate association already described, they have, during the short time that man has occupied the earth, been accompanied by equally great changes in the distribution of human populations. To this cause, for instance, are to be attributed at least two of the major features of human history—the repeated human migrations from the interior of Asia, which have occurred time after time almost throughout the historical period, and that gradual northward trend of the centre of world civilisation which is often called "the Northern March of Empire".

Thus it is to be seen in two quite different ways that plant geography is a subject so intimately connected with human affairs that however academic some aspects of it may seem, it is worth the careful attention of all whose aim and hope it is to reach some understanding of mankind and its difficulties. It can throw light not only on many present-day questions but also on many relating to the past. This being so, may it not also have some value as indicating the way in which some aspects of affairs at any rate may trend in time to come, and thus to do something towards lessening the greatest of all limitations under which man labours, his inability to see into the future?

Vegetation and Flora

Within the science of botany plant geography is most intimately connected with plant ecology, these together making up the wider subject of *geo-botany*, which comprehends all aspects of the relation between plants and the surface of the earth that is the substratum of their lives. Plant ecology is particularly concerned with the way in which plants are mutually related to one another and to the conditions of their habitat. Plant geography, on the other hand, is concerned primarily with the correlation between plants and the distribution of external conditions. The former is essentially physiological; the latter is essentially geographical. Expressed in another way, the difference is that between *vegetation* and *flora*, and a clear understanding of these two terms is important.

The chief features of vegetation reside in its quantitative structural characters because of their obvious influence on all other kinds of associated life. These structural characters are, as has been shown, closely related to climatic conditions, and hence the same kind of vegetation, that is to say the same kind of dominant growth form, tends to recur in many parts of the world. For example, deciduous woodland is found not only in the British Isles and other parts of Eurasia, but also in parts of North America, as well as elsewhere, and in all these places it possesses much the same general features and dimensions. An attempt to show the distribution of *vegetation* types in simple form is made in Plate 2, but it must be remembered that maps of this kind are seldom wholly satisfactory because of the ever-increasing difficulty of distinguishing between natural vegetation states and those induced by human activities.

The word *flora* is a purely scientific term and therefore has no common usage (which is itself an interesting commentary on the conception behind the word *vegetation*), and its meaning is best expressed by extending the example employed in the last paragraph. Although the deciduous woodlands mentioned there are alike in their vegetational features they will be found on closer examination to differ greatly and perhaps entirely in their floral (or floristic) constitution. The vegetation will be the same in all cases, but the actual kinds of plants which comprise it—and which together compose its flora—will be different. The beech of English woodlands is not the kind of beech which grows in the North American forests, nor do either of these occur in the southern hemisphere, where their place is taken by other related species. The distribution of *floras*, in contrast to that of vegetation, is shown in Plate 4.

Just as vegetation is chiefly a matter of quantitative characters so flora is chiefly a matter of quality, in the sense that it concerns the family relationships of the plant life rather than its visual resemblances. The flora of a region is the total of the species within its boundaries, but the vegetation is the general effect produced by the growth of some or all of these in combination.

The Flowering Plants and their Classification

The plant kingdom as a whole can be divided into two parts or sub-kingdoms—the Phanerogams, comprising all the plants which reproduce by means of seeds, and the Cryptogams, comprising all those which reproduce by means of simpler structures called spores. None of the latter, which include fern, mosses, seaweeds, fungi and the like are concerned here.

The Phanerogams or Seed Plants themselves consist of two groups. In one the seeds are generally borne in cones and are not protected by any exterior structures except in so far as the cones themselves may shelter them. This is the group of the Gymnosperms (a word meaning "naked-seeds"), and it includes the Conifers and their allies. With these also we are not concerned.

In the other group, which is immeasurably the larger, the seeds are borne in flowers and are protected by being produced in enclosed structures called carpels. This is the group of the Flowering Plants or Angiosperms (a word meaning "concealed seeds"), and it is with these alone that this book deals.

The Flowering Plants or Angiosperms are the dominant plant group in the world to-day and represent the highest expression yet attained of plant evolution. They have gradually supplanted all other groups in prominence, and now comprise the great bulk of the vegetation of the land on all but some of the smallest areas. Practically all the plants used and cultivated by man belong to this group. They range in form from gigantic forest trees to tiny ephemeral herbs lasting but a few weeks. They have colonised practically all the land, they are common in fresh water and are even to be found occasionally in shallow seas. It is difficult to say how many different species of them there are, but there may well be 250,000 or more.

For present purposes by far the most important general point about the Flowering Plants is that they represent the most modern type of plants and are the culmination, to date, of evolution in the plant kingdom. As might be expected from this they have a geological history much shorter than any of the other great groups of plants, and it is for this reason that this book deals with them alone. Time is a most important factor in matters of plant geography and it is therefore fundamentally unsound to treat together groups of plants whose length of history is widely dissimilar. To the older groups it is possible to apply generalisations which, owing to their shorter history, are quite inapplicable to Flowering Plants, and conversely much of what is true of these plants cannot be applied to other groups because these are of far longer ancestry.

With regard to the definition which was given above it must be remembered that many of the Flowering Plants which are grown in gardens, and particularly some of the shrubs, have come from regions far away, and when cultivated in countries which are to them strange lands they do not always find the conditions which will enable them to come into flower. Nevertheless these plants are true Flowering Plants, blossoming normally in their natural haunts, and the fact that they do not do so in gardens is no indication that they do not belong to this group. The only spore-bearing plants which are cultivated to any extent are some of the ferns, and their general characteristics are enough to distinguish them at sight from Angiosperms.

The primary classification of the Flowering Plants is into two great divisions, the Monocotyledons and the Dicotyledons, separated mainly by differences in the seeds. To the former, smaller, group belong such plants as grasses and lilies which, for the most part, have long narrow leaves with parallel veins; while to the latter and larger group belong, in general, the plants with broad and net veined leaves, including nearly all woody Angiosperms.

Each of these great divisions is classified into *orders*, based on very wide characters, chiefly of the flower. There are about a dozen orders of Monocotyledons and about forty of Dicotyledons. The order is too large a category to be of much practical importance and there will be no occasion to refer to it again.

Each order is classified into *families*. Some orders contain only a single family; others have as many as twenty or thirty. The word *family* here has exactly the same meaning as the older term *natural order*, and this emphasises the special feature of the family, namely that it is, broadly speaking, the largest category in which a general superficial resemblance reveals the close relationship between all its members. All classifications to-day are, theoretically at any rate, natural, in as much as they are based on characters presumed to indicate evolutionary relationship as well as mere similarity, but obviously the larger the category the more diffuse and uncertain will be the inter-relationships within it, and the importance of the family is that it is, in effect, the largest reasonably natural unit for most practical purposes. In short, it should be possible to regard the contents of any one family with some confidence as having had a fairly close community of origin and similarity of history.

Each family is made up of one or more *genera* (the plural of the word *genus*), and just as in the *family* there are brought together plants of a general degree of relationship, so in the *genus* there are brought together the plants of a more particular degree of relationship. In practice this means that a genus usually comprises all the plants closely resembling one another. Thus, all the pansies and violets form one genus, and the roses and willows respectively form others.

The *genus* may, above all others, be called the natural category. Families, despite their natural basis, are often so large and heterogenous that there may well be some confusion between mere resemblance and real affinity, and many families are not entirely free from the suspicion of being to some extent unnatural for this reason. Genera, on the other hand, are smaller, and for that reason alone tend to be more natural; but apart from this their characters usually emphasise this so much that for the most part they can be regarded reliably as true natural groups, that is to say as groups of plants the members of each of which have a common ancestry from a comparatively recent origin.

Finally, each genus consists of one or more *species*. In some ways the species is an unsatisfactory unit, for it is the subject of much controversy, and some reference to the cause of this must be made here. Difficulty arises primarily because the word has been current much longer than the idea of organic evolution, having been used originally to denote the different kinds of animals and plants which, according to the old cosmogony, had been *specially* created. In this sense the word had a normal conception and meaning, but unfortunately it continued in use after the doctrine of evolution became established and then came to mean (as far as can be expressed in words) any collection of individuals virtually like one another but more unlike any others and presumably the descendants of some one earlier individual parent. This is a theoretical definition, and thus the word species has come to have a subjective rather than an objective meaning.

It is this confusion that causes the practical problem. In the earlier view every species was an entity distinct from all others, with recognisable limits, and, having the same kind of origin, all were, in a sense, of equal value. In the later view the species is simply a collection of individuals related by descent, but how and to what extent it is usually impossible to say. Relationship can in fact only be estimated in terms of superficial resemblance, but the significance of similarity is a matter of personal opinion and hence it has come about that the word "species" scarcely means more at present than that it denotes a number of individuals which on account of their mutual resemblance are believed by fewer or more people to be descended from a single similar individual. This being so there is no real practical criterion of what constitutes a species and there are many different opinions. For this reason statements about species, and particularly estimates of their number, must always be treated with caution and regarded as indicative rather than absolute.

Families, genera and species are all three important in plant geography. A family is not only a collection of genera but there is usually running through it some fairly well-marked structural feature (such as the capitulum of the Compositae) which is more or less peculiar to it. Because of this the distribution of families is often of considerable interest with regard to the possible place of origin of the main types of Angiosperm structure, and their significance in the evolutionary story. The larger families, too, are often particularly characteristic of certain parts of the world, and this enables the salient features of different floras to be visualised in a way which is impossible with smaller categories.

The genus is the most natural category and can generally be accepted as combining together species which have had a common and close descent from a comparatively recent ancestor. This being a matter of great significance from the point of view of spatial relationships makes the genus the most important category for distributional studies.

The species is of value chiefly as a means towards statistical analysis. For such purposes, at any rate, species may be regarded as units of equivalent importance, and on this basis can be of great service in assessing geographical phenomena. For instance, to say that the flora of one region contains 100 species while that of another has 10,000, or to say that one genus has 5 species while another has 250, portrays the actual state of difference between the floras or genera in a particularly vivid way. Indeed, it is often only by using figures that qualitative resemblance or difference can be expressed quantitatively.

The Nomenclature of Plants

The nomenclature of plants, or the science of their names, is often a cause of bewilderment to those who are not familiar with its principles.

In the early days of botany, when the number of known plants was much smaller than it is to-day, there was no definite method of giving distinctive names to different kinds of plants and these could be distinguished verbally only by means of a short descriptive phrase embodying their more prominent characteristics. As the number of known plants increased this became more and more difficult because longer and longer descriptions became necessary, and after a while great confusion arose.

The credit for removing the difficulty belongs to the great Swedish botanist Linnaeus, who flourished about the middle of the eighteenth century and whose method of naming plants is reckoned to date from 1753 (461). His solution was what is termed the binomial system, by which each kind of species of plant is given two names and two names only, the combination of names given to one species never being given to any other. There was really nothing startlingly original about this procedure because it is what in fact is done in the case of human beings in most countries, and Linnaeus' two names were indeed almost exactly comparable with the surname and given names of a person. His genius lay in applying this system to plant species and genera, and more particularly in doing so in such a way that no two different species possessed the same name.

The names were not, of course, called surnames and given names, but *generic* and *specific* names. Each distinct kind of plant was called a species and the various species were collected into genera according to their mutual degrees of resemblance. The specific name thus corresponds to the given name and the generic name to the surname. An example will be the best way of making the working of the system clear. All the species of buttercup were collected together into a genus to which the name

Ranunculus was given, so that every kind of buttercup possessed the first or generic name of *Ranunculus*. Then each species was allotted a second and distinctive name, this being made as descriptive as possible and being reserved solely to the one species. The creeping buttercup, for instance, was called *Ranunculus repens* (the Latin for "creeping"), the hairy buttercup was called *Ranunculus hirsutus*, the bulbous buttercup *Ranunculus bulbosus*, and so on, and since each species had its own particular name confusion between them was avoided.

At first, and for a considerable period, this method proved almost perfect and in theory remains so to-day, but difficulties began to crop up when, after Linnaeus' death, others carried on his work. New species were constantly being discovered by all sorts of people, and it became the inevitable practice for the discoverer or describer of a new species to give it a name. There was no means of correlating this scattered work, and so it frequently happened that what was in fact one and the same species was given two or more different names by different workers ignorant of each others' actions. It then became necessary to decide which of the names was to stand and which were to be abandoned. In general the principle of priority was adopted by which the earliest or first-given name was chosen, but priority was often difficult to establish and gradually a great deal of confusion grew up. It is enough here to say that it ultimately became necessary to compile a most complicated set of rules for the naming of plants, but even so there are still great difficulties. It not infrequently happens that to fulfil these rules familiar and long-established names have to be replaced by new and strange ones, and this, when the reason is not fully appreciated, causes much confusion and sometimes much heart-burning. The changes are, however, made in good faith with the intention of trying to make things easier ultimately.

Another feature of Linnaeus' system which tends to be misunderstood to-day was his use of the Latin language for the purpose. The reason is really an excellent one, namely, that Latin was then and indeed is even now the nearest approach to a *lingua franca*. Latin was in fact used as a substitute for a universal language and in order to avoid the necessity of translating the names into various national tongues. It would probably have been impossible to invent any reasonable system of nomenclature without it, and it really needs no defence. Unfortunately, most of us are concerned only with our own language and in these circumstances the use of Latin seems pedantic. Quite apart from the fact that it is indeed not so, there is a stronger reason for using Latin names. The alternative to Latin names is to use national names; but national names have never been given on any system and have simply grown up by common usage which varies from place to place. Thus a plant may be known by several English names in different parts of the country and what may be intelligible in one part may be meaningless in another. Furthermore, all the English names are likely to be meaningless, let us say to a German or Russian. The use of Latin names avoids this difficulty because a species has one and the same Latin name throughout the world.

Specific names derived from human proper names, or from vernacular or generic names, used to be spelt with a capital letter, but this practice, which had little to commend it, has now been abandoned.

The History of Plant Geography

The history of the study of plant geography needs mention here only in so far as it throws light on the theoretical background of the subject and on its relations with other branches of knowledge and a longer account of it is given elsewhere (104, 300,

802, 803). In brief it falls into five periods. The first, and considerably the longest, is the pre-Darwinian period, which lasted from the earliest times to the middle of the nineteenth century. This was particularly the period of exploration and discovery and its essential achievement was the gradual description of the world's plant life, that is to say the accumulation of the main facts of plant distribution. The next period, the Darwinian, was a short but most important one reflecting, as it did, the great revolution in thought which its name implies. Darwin and his scarcely less notable contemporaries, Wallace, Huxley and Hooker, early realised that the geography of living organisms, which in terms of special creation might be a matter for wonder but not for speculation, provided, in terms of evolution, one of its most valuable lines of evidence, and it is only necessary to read the *Origin of Species* (177) itself to realise the change that evolution brought to plant geography. In this change Hooker was the pre-eminent botanist, and Turrill has given a very full account of his phytogeographical work (742). As evolution has ever since remained a fundamental tenet of biological thought plant geography is in one sense still in the Darwinian period, but it is more revealing to limit this stage to the years say from 1850 to 1875, which was the testing time of the new theory. The rest of the nineteenth century may be called the German period. During it a great many workers reinvestigated and reorganised the whole subject of the distribution of plants in the light of its new theoretical background and among them the German school of Grisebach, Drude, Engler and others was pre-eminent. With the turn of the century two new branches of botany— ecology and genetics—arose in spectacular fashion. The former in particular diverted to itself much of the interest formerly enjoyed by plant geography, and during this time, which may be called the period of ecology, floristic plant geography suffered a partial eclipse. Finally, the last 50 years have seen not only the rehabilitation of plant geography, mainly as a result of stimulating new theories relating to it, but what is even more important, much progress towards a proper synthesis of it with ecology, genetics and other aspects of botany which, far from being its rivals, are in fact its close allies. To-day, the study of plant geography has recovered much of the position it held seventy or eighty years ago. There is once more evidence that it may hold the key to much that is hidden and that it must therefore receive the proper measure of attention which it merits not only on this account but also because of its intrinsic interest.

PART ONE

CHAPTER 1

THE GEOGRAPHY OF THE WORLD

IN plant geography almost all aspects of the physical geography of the world are involved, but there are four subjects in particular of which an adequate understanding is so essential that a brief account of them is desirable here. They are the continents and oceans, the islands, the mountains, and the deserts.

Continents and Oceans

The continental land masses of the world are in effect six in number, namely, Eurasia, Africa, Australia, North America, South America, and Antarctica. The last named has now virtually no plant life and is covered with ice and snow, although it possessed a considerable vegetation in former ages.

The distribution of these masses in respect of the equator is such that the northern and southern hemispheres are almost exactly the opposite of one another, so that where there is land in the north, there is sea in the south, and *vice versa*. The Arctic Ocean in the north is balanced by Antarctica in the south, and so on. Arising from this, the distribution of the world's land masses can be described concisely in two useful ways. It may be pictured or represented by two cogwheels, each with three teeth, fitting into one another, the one wheel being the land of the northern hemisphere and the other the oceans of the southern hemisphere. A model made on these lines, with the land wheel black and the sea wheel white, is quite a good rough diagrammatic representation of the map of the world.

It will be apparent from this that the northern hemisphere is predominantly a land hemisphere and the southern one of sea, and in fact the general distribution of land can also be described as having the form of a more or less continuous northern ring from which three branches extend southward across the equator to varying distances.

This peculiar distribution of land leads to what is probably the most significant of all geographical features from the point of view of the general geography of plants and that which does more to explain the facts to be presented below than any other. It is that while in the higher northern latitudes there is a more or less continuous belt of land all round the world, this belt becomes more and more incomplete towards the south, until in southern temperate latitudes there is practically no land at all.

The three extensions southward from this northern belt are South America, Africa, and Malaysia with Australasia, and they differ considerably. The first reaches further south than the others and tapers to a point; the second is blunt and does not extend far beyond the Tropic of Capricorn; the third is intermediate in length and, beginning as an archipelago, ends in a detached continent.

But there is a further point about the continents which is apparent only if the

11

distribution of the contours of the seas is studied. If a bathymetric map of the world (Plate 3) is examined, it will be seen that along some parts of the edges of the continents the passage to great depths is very rapid so that deep water lies close to the actual outlines of the land, but that in other parts the seas, for a considerable distance out from the coast, are shallow, the sudden deepening being much further away. Always, however, there is some point at which the waters become suddenly much deeper. The full significance of this will be discussed at greater length in Chapter 21, but it will be clear enough here that this sudden deepening of the sea marks the real edge of the continents and that where this is far seaward of the actual coast line this is because the edges of the continents lie at such a level as to be shallowly submerged. In other words, the absolute level of the edges of continents varies considerably. In most places they stand clear of the water to their very boundaries, but in others they pass gently below the sea level before their actual abrupt edges are reached.

This being so, the seas of the world can be classified into deep seas or oceans proper, bounded by the true edges of the continents, and shallow or marginal seas which are really shallow flooding of the peripheral parts of continents. These latter are appropriately called epicontinental seas. As has been said, this distinction and its meaning will be referred to again later, but it is of immediate importance here in connection with the classification of the islands of the world, which must next be described.

Islands

The number of islands in the world is very great, but the absolute figure is of no particular concern here, their size and distribution being of much greater importance. Obviously all land masses are in a sense islands since there is none which completely girdles the earth, but convention restricts the use of the term to areas which are conspicuously less than those which habitually go by the name of continents. Greenland is generally described as the largest island and is considerably smaller than Australia or Europe, the least of the continents. Other large islands are Baffinland, Japan (three islands), Sumatra, Borneo, New Guinea and Madagascar, while on a somewhat lesser scale, Great Britain, Celebes and New Zealand (two islands) may be added.

Islands of what may be called second size are several in the Arctic, Ceylon, Cuba, Formosa, Fuegia, Haiti, Iceland, Ireland, Java, Luzon and Mindanao (Philippines), Newfoundland, Sakhalin, Sardinia, Sicily, Tasmania and Vancouver. Smaller again are Corsica, Crete, Cyprus, Jamaica, New Caledonia, Porto Rico, Trinidad, and a number of islands in the Malayan Archipelago, the Bismarck Archipelago and in the Solomons.

Lastly there are certain groups of still smaller islands and some very small isolated islands. These are too numerous to mention in detail, but this is a good opportunity for listing those of more particular botanical interest and giving a rough indication of their whereabouts. It is easiest to do this ocean by ocean, and it is perhaps worth while to recall that in a few cases islands which are habitually referred to in the singular, e.g. Lord Howe Island, are in fact small groups.

In the Arctic Ocean are Jan Mayen, half-way between Norway and Greenland, and Bear Island, half-way between Norway and Spitzbergen.

In the North (extra-tropical) Atlantic are, first, the three groups off Portugal and North Africa, namely Madeira, the Canaries and, furthest from land, the Azores. On the west side of this ocean are the Bermudas and the Bahamas.

In the Tropical Atlantic are the smaller islands of the West Indies; the Cape Verde Islands off Senegal; the group of Fernando Po and S. Tomé, in the

Gulf of Guinea; Fernando Noronha, off the point of Brazil; and Ascension and St. Helena.

In the Indian Ocean the Comoros, the Aldabras, the Seychelles and the Mascarenes (Mauritius, Réunion and Rodriguez) lie respectively north-west, north, north-north-east and east of Madagascar; Zanzibar is close to the African mainland a little south of the equator; Socotra lies off the tip of Somaliland; and there are several small islands off the south-east coast of Arabia and in the Persian Gulf. To the south-west of India and Ceylon are the Maldives and Laccadives and the Chagos Islands; the Andamans and Nicobars lie between India and Malaya, while south-west of Java are Christmas Island and the Cocos-Keeling Islands.

In the North (extra-tropical) Pacific there are three remarkable festoons of islands between China and Alaska, namely the Riukiu Islands between Formosa and Japan; the Kuriles between Japan and Kamchatka; and the Aleutians between Kamchatka and Alaska. The Bonin Islands are south of Japan.

Further south, within the tropics, the small islands are innumerable, since they comprise not only many in the Malayan Archipelago but almost all those further east (361, 546). Many of the latter are merely coral atolls and of little botanical interest, but the following groups are all of some, and mostly of considerable, importance. Across the Tropic of Cancer, and rather nearer America than Asia, lie the Hawaiian Islands. East of the Philippines come, first, Palau and Yap; next, the Marianne Islands and the Caroline Islands, and then the Marshall Islands. South of these, and east of the Bismarck Archipelago and the Solomons are the Santa Cruz Islands and, rather further off, the Gilbert and Ellice Islands. To the south again, and east of the northern part of Australia are, from west to east, the New Hebrides, the Fiji Islands, the groups of Samoa and Tonga, the Cook Islands, the Society Islands, the Tuamotu Islands and the Marquesas. Finally, far removed from all these across the ocean, are the four small Revilla Gigedo Islands, west of southern Mexico, and the more numerous Galapagos Islands, west of Ecuador.

In the South (extra-tropical) Pacific there are few islands but all of them are of interest. North-west of New Zealand are Lord Howe Island and Norfolk Island; north-east are the Kermadecs; to the east are the Chatham Islands and the Antipodes Islands; and to the south are Auckland Island and Campbell Island. Nearer the tropic and about half way between New Zealand and America are Pitcairn Island and Easter Island, famed for its strange statues. Lastly, rather more to the south and not far from the Chilean coast are the Juan Fernandez Islands.

Finally to be mentioned are the Falkland Islands and the tiny and very scattered islands situated in the great continuous sea surrounding Antarctica which it is convenient to call the South Temperate Oceanic Islands. The flora of these last is in total small but of peculiar interest (see p. 222) and it is appropriate to give a list of them here. Working east from the tip of South America they are South Georgia, Tristan da Cunha (with its close neighbours Gough Island, Nightingale Island and Inaccessible Island), Marion Island, the Crozets, the Kerguelen Archipelago, Heard Island, St. Paul and Amsterdam Islands, and Macquarie Island.

Islands are most often classified into two sorts, according to their positions in respect of continents. Some, including most of the larger islands, are parts of the shelves of continents and are separated from the mainland only because the intervening land is shallowly submerged. These are called continental islands and the British Isles, Japan and Borneo are good examples of them. Others, including the great majority of smaller islands, arise directly from the floors of the oceans and are separated from the nearest continents by deep water. These are called oceanic islands and are well exemplified by many of the smaller Pacific islands. Biologically this distinction, though somewhat arbitrary, is a very important one, because the criterion really employed is that of isolation. Continental islands, as integral parts of a continental mass, obviously have a close connection with the adjacent mainland, with which they are contemporaneous, and this is reflected in their plant and animal life. Oceanic islands on the other hand have no such connection, although they may lie fairly close to continents. They are independent of any large land mass and thus their biology presents features and problems of the greatest interest. In their cases isolation and age have been the predominant factors in controlling and determining their floras and faunas, which have been wholly derived from elsewhere.

Several different kinds of oceanic islands have been distinguished (314). First are certain large islands, composed in part at least of sedimentary rocks, which though situated fairly close to continents are separated from them by comparatively deep seas and which are clearly not parts of continental shelves. The most notable example is Madagascar, and the larger Caribbean islands are others. Iceland is similar but consists almost entirely of volcanic rocks. Second are certain similar but smaller and more isolated islands such as New Caledonia. Third are the small islands of igneous rocks arising abruptly from the beds of deep waters and exemplified by the Hawaiian Islands and St. Helena, which are in fact the summits of active or extinct volcanoes. Fourth are small isolated islands largely or entirely of coral rock which are believed to be the remains of coral atolls which have become well elevated above the present level of the sea, and of which there are many instances in the Pacific. Fifth are the coral islands or atolls proper of which there are enormous numbers, chiefly in the same ocean. Those of the third and fourth kinds are often spoken of as "high" islands in contradistinction to the "low", or atoll, islands. Biologically interest centres chiefly in the smaller islands because of their greater average isolation and wider variety, and it is to these, indeed, that the term "oceanic" is more loosely and generally applied. There is little or no geographical segregation between the kinds and since their differences are strikingly reflected in their floras it is important to realise to which class any individual island belongs. Thus the Seychelles consist of two groups, one of granite islands and one of coral atolls. The main distinction is also well seen in the Cocos-Keeling Islands (797) and the neighbouring Christmas Island (22), south of Malaysia, the former being coral atolls and the latter a high volcanic and coral rock island.

Oceanic islands and especially the more isolated of them have long been of particular interest to students of plant geography (323, 355, 374, 756) and a good deal will be said about them in due course. Darwin (177) first drew attention to the chief botanical features of the first four kinds of oceanic islands mentioned above, namely, that they have fewer species than similar sized areas on continents; that they have higher proportions of endemics; and that the order of importance and representation of the larger plant groups are often materially different from those usual on continents. These characteristics are repeatedly exemplified in the following chapters and for this and the other reasons given above there are tabulated here, together with their distances from the nearest large land surface, the most important of the oceanic islands (see Plate 3) to which reference will be made later. They are:

The Hawaiian Islands .	3,900 miles from Japan; 2,400 miles from America
Kerguelen . . .	2,500 ,, ,, Australia; 2,100 miles from Madagascar
Tristan da Cunha .	2,200 ,, ,, America; 1,800 miles from Africa
Tahiti . . .	2,200 ,, ,, New Zealand
Samoa . . .	1,700 ,, ,, ,, ,,

Fiji	.	.	.	1,300 miles from New Zealand
St. Helena		.	.	1,200 ,, ,, Africa
Ascension	.	.	.	900 ,, ,, ,,
New Caledonia	.	.	800 ,, ,, Australia
Rodriguez		.	.	800 ,, ,, Madagascar
The Azores		.	.	800 ,, ,, Portugal
The Galapagos Islands			650 ,, ,, America
The Bermudas		.	.	650 ,, ,, ,,
The Seychelles	.	.	650 ,, ,, Africa; 600 from Madagascar
The Kermadecs		.	.	600 ,, ,, New Zealand
Mauritius		.	.	500 ,, ,, Madagascar
Norfolk Island		.	450 ,, ,, New Zealand
Réunion	.	.	.	400 ,, ,, Madagascar
Juan Fernandez	.	.	400 ,, ,, Chile
Madeira	.	.	.	350 ,, ,, Africa
Lord Howe Island		.	350 ,, ,, Australia
Revilla Gigedo Islands			300 ,, ,, Lower California

Two more points about islands must always be remembered, namely, that their number and distribution depends to a large degree on the general water level of the oceans, and that they have not necessarily all existed as islands for the same length of time. The first of these points is sufficiently illustrated, as far as continental islands are concerned, by Plate 3 and what is said about it in Chapter 21. The same remarks apply to oceanic islands but much less obviously. Many of these arise abruptly from the ocean floor and only just break the surface or, as often in atolls, just fail to do so, and considering the depth of water concerned, the likelihood that there are other considerable submarine elevations which, nowadays, remain hidden below the surface, is clearly strong. A number of such "submerged islands" or *guyots*, as they are technically called, have now been detected in the Pacific (358, 835) and are a reminder that some of the islands listed above may not always have been so isolated as they appear to-day. A very interesting suggestion regarding these guyots is that they are islands which have become submerged through the rise of sea level caused by the accumulation of sediments on the ocean floor.

The age of islands is a much more thorny and controversial subject in which any estimates, such as those of Arldt (27), must depend very much on what their authors believe about various germane matters, such as those dealing with the history of the continental masses. It is probably safe to regard most oceanic islands as having existed in that form longer than most continental islands, and also to regard the first kind as the oldest and the atolls as the youngest, but beyond this there is little that can be said here, and there are almost certainly exceptions to all these statements.

Mountains

The importance of mountains in plant geography lies in the fact that, as altitude increases, the climate tends to become more and more temperate or frigid in character, so that a mountain at a lower latitude has, in its higher parts, a climate very like that prevailing at sea levels at higher latitudes. Owing to this a mountain nearer the equator is often able to support species or vegetation occurring at sea level further north. Moreover since high altitudes are usually combined into mountain ranges which may be of great length, the mountain systems of the world often provide connecting links or paths for the spread of plants.

In the broadest sense the great mountain systems of the world are only three, namely the western American system comprising the Rocky Mountains in the north and the Andes in the south; the Eurasian–Australasian system, comprising the Pyrenees, Alps, Caucasus, the plateaux of Central Asia, the Sino–Himalayan mountains, the mountains of Malaysia, and those of New Zealand; and the very different (both in size and form) African system, but the picture is too complicated to be painted in quite such bald terms, however desirable it may be to simplify matters, and a rather more detailed classification is required if all the necessary facts are to be revealed. On this basis the mountains are best described and arranged as follows.

The great western American chain consists of two parts with distinct names, the compound system of the Rockies in the north and the much simpler system of the Andes in the south, but these are really only portions of one great whole which reaches, in a more or less southerly direction, from Alaska in the north to Cape Horn in the south, that is to say through the whole length of the continent of America, and it is probable that the existence of this great transtropical "bridge" has had profound biological consequences. It is not unnaturally least obtrusive in the narrow isthmus of middle America, but even here it has elevations of over 12,000 ft. In the Rockies the greatest heights are in the extreme north-west (Mts. McKinley, Logan and St. Elias all approaching or exceeding 20,000 ft.) and in Mexico (Orizaba and Popocatepetl, both c. 18,000 ft.). In the Andes the highest mountain is Aconcagua, 22,800 ft., in latitude 33°, the most southerly of all the great Andean peaks. In eastern North America is the minor north-south range of the Appalachians, and in South America the south-eastern part of Brazil is also mountainous. It must also be remembered that Greenland is almost entirely an elevated plateau, but owing to the high latitude this is not very significant biologically.

In Europe the chief ranges are the Pyrenees, up to 11,000 ft.; the Alps, up to 16,000 ft.; the Apennines, up to 9,600 ft.; the Carpathians up to 9,000 ft.; and the Caucasus, up to 18,500 ft. All these run more or less west and east, as do also the Atlas Mountains, which although in Africa belong to the same general system, and which attain a height of nearly 14,000 ft. In addition to these, the Balkans are largely mountainous. In the north of Europe also there are two elevated regions, western Norway, where there is a height of 8,500 ft., and the Urals, where the highest point is some 5,000 ft. Both these latter systems run north and south.

In Asia the mountain systems are so vast and complicated that they can only be described in general terms. First, from the Bosphorus to north-west India there stretches a series of ranges, all running approximately west and east and mostly of medium height, but containing a few great peaks, such as Ararat, c. 17,000 ft., and with a notable outlier, the 13,000 ft. Jebel Akhdar, in eastern Arabia. Next, south-east of these, much of the Indian Peninsula is mountainous, culminating in heights of more than 8,000 ft. in South India and in Ceylon. The main ridge of this system is along the west coast of India. Lastly the whole of the vast triangle Afghanistan–Kamchatka–Siam is one huge and complex system of multitudinous mountain ranges which comprise the most extensive area of elevated land in the world as well as all the highest altitudes. Along most of the south side of this triangle runs the huge wall of the Himalayas, themselves a great plexus of ranges culminating in the extreme world height of Mt. Everest, 29,000 ft., and coalescing westwards with the mountains of Persia. Northwards the Himalayas pass into the highly elevated Tibetan plateaux and these again north into the plateaux and ranges of Central Asia, North China and eastern Siberia. The axes of all these are roughly west and east, but in Manchuria, Korea, Japan and Kamchatka they become more or less north and south in conformity with the coastline. Both Japan and Formosa have heights of over 12,000 ft.

Passing back to the south-east of Asia we find one of the major features of world relief. At the junction of Burma, Tibet and China the great west–east mountain chain, which we have traced all the way from the Pyrenees to and through the Himalayas, suddenly changes its course and its constituent ranges turn southwards, continuing through Burma, Siam and Indo-China. Many of the mountains reach a great height, but this region is not very well known and it is best to avoid using figures which may be misleading. The main line of this system is along its centre and runs right down the Malay Peninsula and into the Malayan Archipelago. The geography of this latter region is broken and scattered but it can be said that the main mountain line of the Malay Peninsula continues in a curve through Sumatra, Java and the Lesser Sunda Islands. In both the former there are heights of over 12,000 ft. Practically all the other great islands of the Archipelago are also mountainous, although the axes of their ranges do not follow any well-defined line. In Borneo, for instance, Mt. Kinabalu is over 12,000 ft., and there are peaks of more than 10,000 ft. in the Philippines. Further east again, in New Guinea, the general west–east trend of the mountains is once more apparent, and there are heights of more than 16,000 ft. The Solomon Islands have heights of over 10,000 ft., but the New Hebrides and New Caledonia, though much elevated, have no altitudes reaching the snow line, and the great Old World belt of mountains ends in the Southern Alps of New Zealand, culminating in Mt. Cook, over 12,000 ft., which are the counterpart of the Andean mountains in similar latitudes.

In Australia the main mountain system runs north and south along the east coast down into Tasmania and does not belong to the same orogeny, or phase of mountain building, as that just described. The highest point is Mt. Kosciusko in New South Wales, which, with a height of about 7,000 ft., reaches well above the snow-line. The mountains of Tasmania, rising to about 5,000 ft., narrowly fail to do so. Finally the Hawaiian Islands have peaks of more than 13,000 ft.

In Africa south of the Atlas ranges the mountain system is mainly different from elsewhere in the world. A ridge of elevated land runs north and south all the way from the Red Sea to the Cape but is broken up in a striking way. In the north is the plateau of Abyssinia, with peaks exceeding 15,000 ft., and in the extreme south-east the mountains of the Transvaal, Natal and the Cape Province also form a more or less definite whole, attaining locally heights of 11,000 ft., but in between the highest land consists mainly of a number of very distinct and isolated mountains surrounding Lake Victoria. Nothing quite like these mountains exists elsewhere and they are frequently referred to as "island mountains". Chief amongst them are Kilimanjaro, nearly 20,000 ft., Mt. Kenya and Ruwenzori, both nearly 17,000 ft., and Mt. Elgon, nearly 15,000 ft. In addition to these eastern mountains there is a secondary series of elevations along parts of the west coast which reach their highest altitude of nearly 14,000 ft., in the Cameroon Mountain. A third series, of widely separated mountain massifs, forms a line between Abyssinia and the Atlas Mountains, thus forming, as it were, stepping stones across the Sahara, and they are for this reason noteworthy. They are not very well known, but it is certain that some at least reach 12,000 ft. In Madagascar, too, there are considerable elevations.

Antarctica is also largely mountainous and said to contain peaks of more than 13,000 ft. (482).

Deserts

Everyone knows what is meant in general terms by the word desert, but it is difficult to define it scientifically. Heat and drought are the commonest

2

characteristics of deserts, but the two are not always combined, and deserts may, in fact, be either hot or cold, according to their latitude and altitude. In all, however, there is, for one reason or another, a deficiency of available moisture, and this is usually due to lack of rain. Botanically deserts have been defined as areas where, because of the climatic conditions, there is less than a continuous covering of vegetation, and this criterion includes also the entire absence of it. It is not easy, however, to know exactly where the line is to be drawn, and this definition breaks down if applied too narrowly.

Actually, although these points merit mention, there is no need here to attempt a rigid definition, and it will suffice to give a short survey of those parts of the world to which the name desert is generally applied. It may, however, be noted that they are, roughly speaking, those areas where the annual rainfall measures less than 10 in. (Plate 23).

Deserts are for the most part to be found on the leeward side of mountain ranges because the heights discharge the rain-bearing clouds from the sea before they pass further inland. This is specially true of the warm deserts, which may be mentioned first.

The North American warm desert of the Great Basin exemplifies this well, lying as it does between the constituent ranges of the southern Rockies. Another desert occupies parts of northern Mexico and the adjacent states of the Union. Both these have elevations of several thousand feet. In South America the arid parts of western Argentina are similar, but there is also the coastal and more tropical desert of Peru and northern Chile, sometimes described as the most absolute desert in the world (see p. 356).

The deserts of Africa and Asia must, in part at least, be considered together because the greatest desert in the world covers parts of both continents. This is the great series of varyingly dry regions which stretches, with but few breaks, all the way from the west coast of North Africa to north-eastern Mongolia, and which has six main constituent areas. Of these the Saharan, Arabian and Persian deserts are warm deserts, while those of Turkestan, Tibet and Mongolia (Gobi) are mostly cold deserts.

The Sahara is, in a popular sense, the most typical and absolute of all deserts, and over much of it the surface is mobile sand and bears no plant life. This is, however, by no means continuous but is broken by mountains and oases. The Saharan, Arabian and Persian deserts form a more or less single belt of dry lands all the way from north-west Africa to West Pakistan. It is also noteworthy that this great region is less intimately associated with mountain ranges than most deserts.

Much of the western part of southern Africa is also arid, and this area comprises the well-known Kalahari and Karroo deserts and most of South West Africa.

Finally, there is the great central warm desert of the interior of Australia, which covers much of western Australia and South Australia and the southern part of the Northern Territory. It illustrates well another feature often seen in deserts, namely, that they occupy the regions most distant from the coasts. The moisture-laden winds from the sea tend gradually to lose their water as they pass inland and distance has much the same result as that of a single mountain range.

The three chief cold deserts of the world have already been mentioned incidentally since they are part of the vast African–Asiatic desert. Among them, the Turkestan desert is the least extreme and has a fairly well-developed vegetation.

Both the Tibetan and Gobi deserts are good examples of cold deserts in which the low temperature is due to great elevation. Both, too, consist chiefly of the plateaux between mountains. The Tibetan plateau desert is often called "the roof of the world" and has an average elevation of some 15,000 ft. The Gobi desert in general exceeds 5,000 ft. The most important climatic feature of these deserts is the variation of temperature during the year, for a greater part of which they are exceedingly cold. Incidentally, even in warm deserts there is generally a great difference between day and night temperature.

In conclusion Antarctica is in one sense a cold desert because it is glaciated, and affords practically no niches for flowering plants, and the same is true of similar parts of the Arctic. In some other parts of the Arctic the precipitation is very low and something like desert vegetation results.

To summarise, the desert regions of the world comprise the warm deserts of North America, Mexico, Chile and Peru, Argentina, the Sahara, Arabia, Persia, West Pakistan, southern Africa and Australia; the cold deserts of Turkestan, Tibet and Mongolia; and the polar deserts of the Arctic and Antarctic.

There is considerable difference of opinion as to the length of time that the present deserts of the world have existed as such (34, 35). One view is that desert conditions have been a feature of the world throughout geological time, and that some at least of the deserts of to-day have been so far longer than the history of the Angiosperms. Another opinion is that desert conditions may have occurred at intervals throughout geological time but that all the present deserts are comparatively modern. Some, on the other hand, hold that desert conditions were unknown anywhere until late geological time. All that can usefully be said here on this issue is that the last would seem, on grounds of general evidence and experience, more unlikely than either of the other two, and that of these the first is perhaps the simpler proposition and therefore to be preferred in the absence of any definite evidence to the contrary. The present desert floras certainly suggest that they are not all the same age, for they vary in floristic diversity and in specialisation. Thus the desert floras of southern Africa are peculiarly rich in specialised xeromorphic groups, while the great African–Indian desert region and the Australian desert region are notably deficient in them.

Map Projections

It is almost impossible to depict exactly, on a flat surface such as a page of paper, the surface of a sphere, and maps of the world as a whole or of any large part of it therefore almost inevitably contain some distortion unless very complicated and impractical outlines are used. Various methods, often involving rather abstruse mathematics, are employed in order to reduce this distortion and one or two of these methods, or projections as they are called, require comment here.

The simplest method is perhaps that of picturing the world as it would appear if seen from a very long distance away, but since this view would reveal only the half of the sphere nearer the observer, the whole globe can only be shown thus by two separate circular maps. For most purposes this is a great drawback, but occasionally, as for instance when the polar regions are to be mapped, such a polar stereographic projection has its uses, and it is employed in one or two cases in this book.

The commonest of all projections is Mercator's projection, which shows the surface of the world in rectangular form, but this is only achieved at the expense of a seriously increasing distortion away from the equator. For everyday political maps whose interest centres in lower latitudes this disadvantage can be neglected, and this explains the constant use of this projection in simple generalised maps, but for scientific purposes it is almost useless since it distorts not only the relative position but also the relative size of land masses. Moreover, even this distortion is not constant but increases towards the poles. For these reasons Mercator's projection is particularly unsuitable for problems of plant geography and it is much to be desired that its use in this connection should cease.

For all but very special purposes Mollweide's projection, in one or other of its forms, is perhaps the most convenient since it removes many of the drawbacks of Mercator while still permitting a fairly simple total outline. Mollweide's projection shows the world as an ellipse having the equator as its longer axis. It is an equal area projection, so that the relative sizes of different parts of the world are true, and this is a point of great value. On the other hand, there is some distortion of shape, especially towards the ends of the ellipse, but if, as is usual, Africa is made the central feature, this disadvantage is much reduced.

Although far from perfect it is difficult to find a better projection than that of Mollweide if the whole world is to be covered and if the shape of the map is to remain continuous and simple, and since this is essential when biological problems are under discussion his projection is used almost exclusively in this book.

It need only be pointed out further that, with regard to maps showing less than the whole world, the smaller the area depicted the less important are problems of projections until, where quite small areas are concerned, the lines of latitude and longitude can be drawn truly horizontal and vertical without appreciable distortion.

Definitions

Most parts of the world have received their names without particular regard to biological problems, and hence, when these questions are at issue, it is sometimes necessary to refer to areas which are without convenient comprehensive names.

It is for instance useful to refer to the islands which lie in the eastern North Atlantic off the coasts of north-west Africa and Europe, that is to say the Azores, the Canaries, Madeira and the Cape Verdes, by the inclusive name of Macaronesia.

A more difficult case is that of the islands off the east coast of tropical Africa, which comprise Madagascar, the Comoros, the Aldabra Islands, the Mascarenes and the Seychelles, for there is no general term to cover them all. In the following pages they are considered to form the Madagascar Region and this name is used for them. Unless qualified it may be taken to include all these islands.

The name Malaya and its associated forms are also the source of some confusion. In this book the usage is to refer to that part of continental Asia south of the Isthmus of Kra as the Malay Peninsula; to the islands thence as far as and including New Guinea as the Malayan Archipelago; and to both together as Malaysia (702).

Australia and the lands neighbouring it on the north and east loom so large in the geography of the Flowering Plants, and will be referred to so frequently, especially in Chapter 12, that it is essential to have a term which can, when necessary, be used to cover them all, and Australasia is the obvious one. In the following pages, therefore, this word is used to mean the area comprising Australia, New Guinea, the Bismarck Archipelago, the Solomon Islands, the New Hebrides, New Caledonia, Fiji, Lord Howe Island, Norfolk Island and New Zealand. It may be noted that, except for the exclusion of Tonga, these are the lands of the south-west Pacific which are within, that is to say west and south of, the andesite line (see pp. 215, 405). Australasia so defined includes the whole of five of the floristic regions set out in the next chapter and parts of three others.

As a sequel to this, Melanesia, which on ethnological grounds is usually considered as including New Guinea, is here defined as consisting of the Bismarck Archipelago, the Solomon Islands, the New Hebrides and Fiji. Finally, the phrase "the Pacific Islands" is used, when necessary, to denote some or all the tropical or near-tropical islands north of New Guinea and east of New Guinea and Queensland as far as Easter Island.

CHAPTER 2

THE DIVISION OF THE WORLD INTO FLORISTIC REGIONS

Major Zonations

THE major and most obvious segregation of the plant life of the world to-day is into three latitudinal zones—polar, temperate and tropical. These, owing to the shape of the earth and its position in relation to the sun, are symmetrical about the equator. For most practical botanical purposes, however, this zonation is scarcely detailed enough and it is usual to incorporate a fourth zone and to speak of arctic (polar), temperate, subtropical and tropical zones.

A still fuller and more scientific classification is that quoted by Hansen (333), for example, which is as follows:

1. Equatorial zone .	.	0·0–15·0 degrees on either side of the equator
2. Tropical zone .	.	15·0–23·5	,,	,,	,,	,,	,,
3. Subtropical zone .	.	23·5–34·0	,,	,,	,,	,,	,,
4. Warm temperate zone .		34·0–45·0	,,	,,	,,	,,	,,
5. Cold temperate zone .	.	45·0–58·0	,,	,,	,,	,,	,,
6. Subarctic zone .	.	58·0–66·6	,,	,,	,,	,,	,,
7. Arctic zone .	.	66·5–72·0	,,	,,	,,	,,	,,
8. Polar zone .	.	72·0–90·0	,,	,,	,,	,,	,,

This would be a satisfactory and accurate indication of the major distribution of plants were it not that it ignores one factor which actually complicates it very much, namely, the influence of the elevation of the land. It is well known that at any latitude a sufficient vertical rise from sea level epitomises in a very short distance the climatic zonation which is to be observed at sea level between the latitude in question and the nearer pole. Since climate and vegetation are in general very closely correlated, it follows that a vertical rise similarly epitomises the botanical changes which are to be observed at sea level between the latitude in question and the nearer pole. This is illustrated by the familiar fact that as one ascends a mountain the plant life changes with increase in elevation until, if the rise is sufficient, a condition characteristic of polar latitudes is reached, so that the highest mountains, even if on the equator, have permanent ice and snow at their summits.

The vegetational zonation of mountains, and especially of tropical mountains, has been much studied and has been described and expressed in a number of classifications. The following, which is a combination of several, is a fairly familiar one. On a high mountain situated in the more equatorial parts of the tropical zone in the old world, for instance, the lowest levels, namely those between sea and 600 metres, are occupied by a truly equatorial vegetation characterised by palms and bananas; above them comes a tropical but less equatorial kind of vegetation in which tree-ferns and figs are prominent; above this is a zone of subtropical types like myrtles and laurels; above them another warm temperate zone of evergreen trees; next a zone of deciduous trees such as are familiar in temperate regions; then a zone of coniferous trees; then a zone of alpine shrubs; and finally a zone of alpine herbs. Above this there is no appreciable vegetation.

22

This zonation may be summarised with figures as follows:

0– 600 metres	. . . . .	Zone of palms and bananas
600–1,250 ,,	. . . . .	,, tree-ferns and figs
1,250–1,900 ,,	. . . . .	,, myrtles and laurels
1,900–2,600 ,,	. . . . .	,, evergreen trees
2,600–3,200 ,,	. . . . .	,, deciduous trees
3,200–3,800 ,,	. . . . .	,, coniferous trees
3,800–4,450 ,,	. . . . .	,, alpine shrubs
4,450–5,050 ,,	. . . . .	,, alpine herbs
5,050– ,,	. . . . .	Permanent ice and snow

Another and more extensive presentation of this zonation is illustrated in Fig. 1.

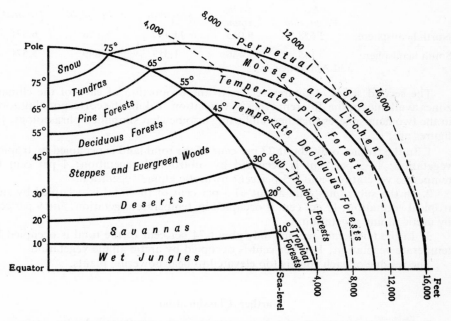

Fig. 1.—Diagrammatic representation of the vegetation zones of latitude and altitude.
(Redrawn from Herbertson's *Outlines of Physiography*, Edward Arnold & Co.)

It follows from what has been said that unless the relief of the land is very slight, each latitudinal zone of the world will afford suitable conditions for the appearance of plants in general characteristic of a zone or zones in higher latitudes. Subtropical plants will occur here and there in the tropical regions according to the relief; temperate plants will occur in both subtropical and tropical zones, and so on.

If the elevation is sufficient each type of plant or vegetation will, except for one important reservation, find the climatic conditions it requires at all latitudes nearer the equator. The reservation concerns "length of day" and the intensity of seasonal variation, because the shape of the world and its circling of the sun determine that both of these must depend upon, and vary with, latitude. This is why it is, in general, easier to grow tropical plants (which by and large are short-day plants) in hot-houses in temperate lands, than to grow temperate plants (which tend to be long-day plants) out-of-doors on high ground in the tropics.

From this there is to be drawn the very important conclusion that in no latitudinal zone is the total area exclusively available for the type of vegetation characteristic of the lowest levels in that zone. Some of it will be occupied by vegetation characteristic of the lowest levels of zones nearer the poles.

Detailed tables of figures relating to this interesting generalisation are given in Appendix A, but the two chief conclusions to which they lead may be summarised here.

The first relates to the absolute areas of the land occupied by the different kinds of vegetation on each side of the equator, and the figures show these to be, in thousands of square miles:

	No Vegetation	Arctic Alpine	Temperate	Subtropical	Tropical
North hemisphere	2,658	9,065	11,137	8,673	6,571
South hemisphere	155 add Antarctica	436	1,317	5,849	5,571

The second series of figures relates to the proportion of each of the climatic zones available for the different types of vegetation. Taking the corresponding zones in the two hemispheres together, and using a somewhat simplified phraseology, the figures are:

1. In the tropics only about 77 per cent of the total land is occupied by tropical vegetation; 17·5 per cent is occupied by subtropical vegetation; 4 per cent by temperate vegetation; and 1·5 per cent by arctic alpine vegetation.

2. In the subtropics only about 67·5 per cent of the total is occupied by subtropical vegetation; 17 per cent is occupied by temperate vegetation; and 9 per cent by arctic alpine vegetation.

3. In the temperate regions only about 74 per cent of the total is occupied by temperate vegetation; 18·5 per cent is occupied by arctic alpine vegetation.

The residue of each zone is too elevated to bear flowering plants.

Further Classification

The average range of species is comparatively small. No doubt a laborious computation could be made to give a fair idea of the actual dimensions involved, but in the absence of any such figure it is enough to say that the area occupied by any one of the vast majority of species (and, it may be added, of most genera also) is far less than that of any one latitudinal zone. As a result of this some or all the species present in one part of a zone are different from those in other parts of the same zone. Many factors help to determine the degree of this difference, and since these factors themselves show no regularity or constancy, it may be larger or smaller, so that the extent of geographical separation between two floras cannot alone be taken as a measure of the differences between them. Other means of estimation must be sought. From this it is also clear that the plant life of the world can be classified geographically, not only on a vegetational basis, but also floristically, that is, into distinct floras, and a classification of this kind is an important adjunct to plant geography. It is, however, not easy to make because of the absence of any ready means of estimating floristic differences and relationships.

The situation may be made clear by an illustration. Take the case of a botanist familiar with the British flora, who for the first time visits North America. There he will find many plants which he has not encountered before, but for the most part they will be so like those with which he is acquainted at home that he will be able to identify them fairly easily. If the same botanist now visits New Zealand he will again find many unfamiliar plants, indeed even more, but on this occasion his previous experiences will be of little or no help in diagnosing them. In short, the differences between the floras of the British Isles and New Zealand are greater than those between the floras of the British Isles and North America. This is clear enough, but the difficulty is to put an absolute value on these differences and to compare them with others, as for instance those between the floras of North America and New Zealand.

Actually the fact that species are not equally closely related to one another makes it almost impossible to measure floristic resemblances and differences, and all that can be done is to utilise such evidences as may be available (and these are more often than not imponderable and intangible) to make what can be no more than a rough estimate. Of these possibilities the evidence based upon the endemic or peculiar elements of a flora is perhaps the most fruitful, but even this has a strictly limited value. To know, for instance, that half the species of any particular flora are peculiar to it, is often of interest and value, but more than one flora may show a similar degree of endemism and the statement affords no indication of the relationship between them. Indeed, expressions based on endemism serve really only to show how distinct from all others any one flora may be and help little in deciding closeness of affinity. Nevertheless, figures relating to endemism are useful and are frequently quoted in later chapters.

Again it is necessary in making a floristic classification to estimate the relative importance of different floras, and here too endemism can be of only minor assistance. There are other difficulties which it does not touch such as deciding the comparative values of the floras of two regions of very different size or of two floras of which one is large and the other small. How, for instance, is the flora of St. Helena, with perhaps under 100 species, to be compared with that of all Brazil, with many thousands of species? Yet both have the same degree of endemism. Must they, on this account, receive equality of status? There are many questions of this sort and many are the attempts which have been made to solve them, most commonly by the use of formulae by which the various ingredients of a flora may be recognised and given some relative value, as, for instance, in the interesting studies by Exell (230) and Williams (780, 781). It is, however, no criticism of these essays to say that they are not likely to achieve anything more than a rough answer for the simple reason that the classification of plants, on which they must be founded, is man-made and far too clumsy to express all the relevant information.

On the other hand, if we picture, as is surely correct, the floras of different parts of the world meeting and mingling either mutually or unilaterally with one another in the course of time, it may be expected that while, in some circumstances and places, infiltration will be mutual and gradual, in others it will result in comparatively sudden changes of floristic composition, such points or lines of change marking, as it were, the advancing front of the more aggressive flora or the position of barriers which retard further progress. Such places are clearly of great help in determining the boundaries of floristic regions, and they have been particularly studied in respect of the Malaysian flora by van Steenis (702), who refers to them as "demarcation knots". It may well be that the geographical conditions of this part of the world give to these knots an emphasis which may not prevail everywhere, but they must clearly occur at least in some form all over the world, and they are so important a phytogeographical conception that the whole subject of them deserves very careful attention, because, apart from their aid in delimiting floristic areas they are likely to throw valuable light in the direction of migration. Van Balgooy's preliminary analysis of Pacific floras (44) also contains useful information on this matter.

But the difficulties need not be further stressed and in spite of them many floristic classifications have been made, one of the earliest and most illustrative of these being by Schouw in 1823. This is quoted below rather fully, not only for its intrinsic value as a forerunner of modern systems, but because it shows the character that may be imparted to a region by the strong development therein of particular plant groups (623). Schouw divides the world into twenty-five kingdoms, naming them, wherever possible, after their most characteristic plants, as follows:

1. Kingdom of saxifrages and mosses. Alpine arctic.
   a. Province of sedges. Arctic.
   b. Province of Primulaceae. Eurasian alps.
   c. Province of shrubby alpine Composites. American alpine.
2. Kingdom of Umbelliferae and Cruciferae. North Eurasia.
   a. Province of Cichoriaceae. North Europe.
   b. Province of *Astragalus*, halophytes, thistles. North Asia.
3. Kingdom of Labiates and Caryophyllaceae. Mediterranean region.
   a. Province of Cistaceae. Spain and Portugal.
   b. Province of *Scabiosa* and *Salvia*. South France, Italy and Sicily.
   c. Province of shrubby Labiates. Eastern Mediterranean.
   d. Province of North Africa.
   c. Province of *Sempervivum*. North African Islands and Morocco.
4. Kingdom of *Aster* and *Solidago*. Northern North America.
5. Kingdom of Magnolias. Southern North America.
6. Kingdom of Camellias and Celastraceae. China and Japan.
7. Kingdom of Scitamineae. India.
8. Kingdom of the Himalayas.
9. Kingdom of Polynesia.
10. Kingdom of the Malayan Mountains.
11. Kingdom of Oceania.
12. Kingdom of balm trees. South-west Arabia.
13. Kingdom of deserts. North Africa and North Arabia.
14. Kingdom of Tropical Africa.
15. Kingdom of Cactaceae and Piperaceae. Central America and Northern Tropical South America.
16. Kingdom of the Mexican mountains.
17. Kingdom of *Cinchona*. Northern Andes, lower levels.
18. Kingdom of *Escallonia* and *Calceolaria*. Northern Andes, higher levels.
19. Kingdom of the West Indies.
20. Kingdom of palms and Melastomataceae. Eastern tropical South America.
21. Kingdom of woody Composites. Middle Andes.
22. Kingdom of Antarctica. Patagonia, Fuegia and Falklands.
23. Kingdom of *Stapelia* and *Mesembryanthemum*. Extra-tropical South Africa.
24. Kingdom of *Eucalyptus* and Epacridaceae. Extra-tropical Australia.
25. Kingdom of New Zealand.

It is remarkable that at such an early date so complete a classification should have been made. It is naturally open to much criticism in the light of modern know-ledge, but its imperfections and incompleteness are largely due to the lack of knowledge of its time. In many respects it compares favourably with much more modern schemes.

Another, though much later, regional classification which deserves notice here, for much the same reason as did that of Schouw, namely that its approach to the problem is such as to throw into useful relief certain important facts, is that of Delpino (183). This in contrast to many others is a dichotomous classification and to that extent an obviously artificial one, but it has the two merits of being easy to visualise and remember and of showing what regions are analogous, not only above and below the equator but in other directions also. On the following page is a free and slightly modified rendering of Delpino's arrangement.

Modern attempts to divide the world up into more or less equivalent floristic units mostly trace back to Engler's scheme (220), and vary from it more in detail than in principle. No one of these however can be considered entirely satisfactory, especially from the point of view of this book, and the writer has therefore compiled the classification given below, which although based on those of Engler and others differs from them in a number of important respects. The object has been to divide the land surfaces of the world into a convenient but not too large number of regions, each of which may be regarded as supporting a flora of its own, that is to say a flora which is characteristic of the region; which, allowing for possible global floral migrations, has largely developed within the region; and which has, to a like extent, been conditioned by the history and circumstances of the region. This essentially historical and phylogenetic conception of the regions is of great importance not only as a step towards the broader understanding of plant geography in general, but also because it helps to lessen the problem of treating as equivalent, floras which are in fact very different in nature, size and richness.

Quite apart from the more theoretical difficulties to which allusion has already been made, it is extremely difficult in practice also, to make a floristic classification of this sort and although much care and attention has been given to it (see Preface) a few words of special explanation are called for here, particularly with regard to the changes which have been made since the first edition of this book.

First and foremost there is to be remembered the general lack of agreement in the literature as to where many of the boundaries between regions should be drawn. This is chiefly of interest here because it stresses what is really the inherent problem in such matters, namely that of deciding how and what criteria are to be applied, but it also means that in some cases decisions have had to be taken on general rather than particular evidences.

Second, it cannot be over-emphasised that the classification and its map depict a *world-wide floristic arrangement* and take no account of any extraneous and unrelated values. This is an important point because many similar classifications made by botanists of the northern temperate regions are marred by the exaggerated importance given to this part of the world, no doubt chiefly because these are better known botanically, but almost certainly also to some extent because of their pre-eminence in quite other respects.

Third, the map in Plate 4 is necessarily on a very small scale and in consequence the boundaries of the regions cannot in every case be made as accurate or as free from ambiguity as is theoretically desirable.

Fourth, it has been felt that pure convenience cannot always be ignored if the classification is to make its widest appeal, and a few boundaries have been deliberately drawn with this in mind, as is illustrated, both in general and particular, in the Malaysian region. This has been defined in accordance with the key maps in the first

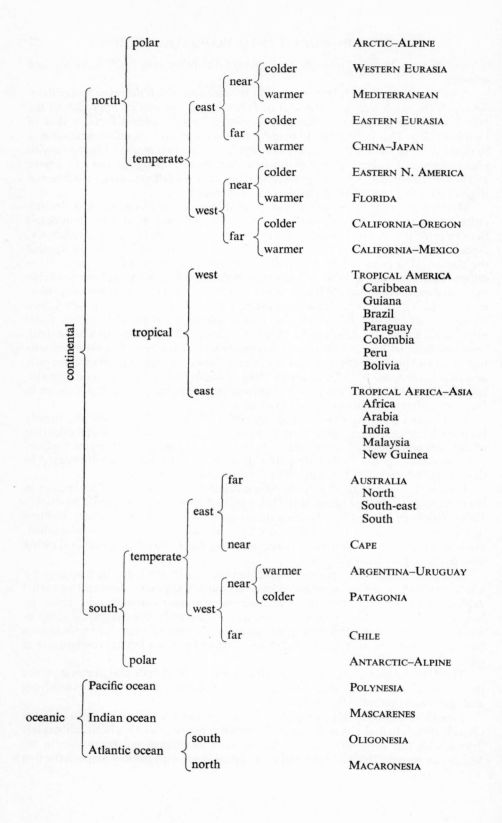

					ARCTIC–ALPINE
continental	north	polar			
				colder	WESTERN EURASIA
			near	warmer	MEDITERRANEAN
		east		colder	EASTERN EURASIA
			far	warmer	CHINA–JAPAN
		temperate		colder	EASTERN N. AMERICA
			near	warmer	FLORIDA
		west		colder	CALIFORNIA–OREGON
			far	warmer	CALIFORNIA–MEXICO

polar   ARCTIC–ALPINE

north

east   near   colder   WESTERN EURASIA
           warmer   MEDITERRANEAN
      far   colder   EASTERN EURASIA
           warmer   CHINA–JAPAN

temperate

west   near   colder   EASTERN N. AMERICA
           warmer   FLORIDA
      far   colder   CALIFORNIA–OREGON
           warmer   CALIFORNIA–MEXICO

tropical

west   TROPICAL AMERICA
         Caribbean
         Guiana
         Brazil
         Paraguay
         Colombia
         Peru
         Bolivia

east   TROPICAL AFRICA–ASIA
         Africa
         Arabia
         India
         Malaysia
         New Guinea

south

east   far   AUSTRALIA
            North
            South-east
            South
      near   CAPE

temperate

west   near   warmer   ARGENTINA–URUGUAY
           colder   PATAGONIA
      far   CHILE

polar   ANTARCTIC–ALPINE

oceanic

Pacific ocean   POLYNESIA

Indian ocean   MASCARENES

Atlantic ocean   south   OLIGONESIA
               north   MACARONESIA

instalment of the *Flora Malesiana* now being published, but this obviously desirable course begs at least two minor problems which deserve notice. Some writers (459, 514) consider that the flora of the small island of Botel Tobago, a little to the east of the south point of Formosa, has more affinity in some ways with that of the Philippines that with that of Formosa itself, but to attempt to show this on so small a map, however strong its justification, would only lead to confusion, and a more generalised boundary has been used. In the south-east of the region the line is drawn between New Guinea and New Britain and this again is certainly the most convenient way of dealing with the puzzling relationships of the latter, even if it does not do full justice to all the evidence. It may be added here that although many parts of the world have their similar problems the classification of the Pacific is especially difficult, not only because of the great isolation and tiny area of many of its land surfaces, but also because as yet little certain is known about their history, and the arrangement adopted here, though it now seems to be the most realistic, may need revision in the light of further information. The Pacific part of the world is undoubtedly of special significance in plant geography because there are reasons for supposing that it may hold the keys to many problems which at present perplex us, and it is promising that much more is now familiar about it than was the case some years ago. The war-time books of Merrill (514), and Osborn (546), for instance, are full of interesting facts, and other more particular references will be found in the bibliography, especially in connection with Chapter 21.

As regards the changes in the second edition only a few points need be mentioned. In Africa the northern boundary of the South African region was drawn more directly across the continent, the general convenience of this on a small map being felt to outweigh the advantage of attempting to show the transitional nature of the flora along the south-east coast. Rather similarly the word "transitional" was dropped from the titles of two of the regions because its retention tends to particularise these regions in a way which is perhaps not altogether justifiable. Chiefly because of its ambiguity the name of the East African Island region was changed to "the Madagascar region". In South America the earlier and unwieldy Brazilian region was divided into two, the Amazon region and the South Brazilian region, thus making, in the former, an entity properly and strictly comparable with the equatorial forest regions of West Africa and Malaysia. The boundaries of the Amazon region are, however, difficult to assess and those drawn are frankly somewhat tentative. The actual outlines of some of the regions were amended considerably in order to include within them, as seems most appropriate, such very isolated small islands as have an appreciable, though not necessarily characteristic, Angiosperm flora, as for instance the Chagos Archipelago and Christmas Island.

Lastly it will be seen that two regions, the Atlantic North American region and the Euro-Siberian region, have each been divided into two halves or subregions. This is not intended to suggest that they each contain two floras approaching regional status but is meant to emphasise that, largely on account of their exceptional extents, the one latitudinal and the other longitudinal, there is considerable difference between the two ends in each. It should also be noted that these are the only two regions which lie predominantly in the colder north temperate zone above latitude 50°, a value which, as is suggested in Chapter 9, may be of critical importance in plant geography, and it may well be that, on this account, the developmental histories of their floras, are at least sufficiently different from those of other regions to justify this slightly different treatment.

In this third edition there are only two changes of consequence—the Fiji Islands are transferred from Polynesia to Melanesia and Micronesia, to the floras of which region their plant life is closely related; and the boundary of the Patagonian region is drawn a little further north.

Certain other details about the regions will be referred to in Chapters 7 and 10 as they arise and it only remains to say here that, while the following classification and its accompanying map have been made primarily for the purposes of this book, they have, in this edition, again been revised with the particular hope that they may more widely meet the need which undoubtedly exists for a convenient classification of this kind.

CLASSIFICATION OF THE WORLD INTO FLORISTIC UNITS

(Plate 4)

BOREAL KINGDOM

1. Arctic and Subarctic Region

    a. Eurasian province
    b. Greenland
    c. Nearctic

2. Euro-Siberian Region

  A. European Subregion

    a. Western Europe
    b. Central Europe
    c. Scandinavia
    d. Russia
    e. Danube basin
    f. European alpine
    g. Caucasus

  B. Asiatic Subregion

    h. Western Siberia
    i. Altai–Trans-Baikalia
    j. North-eastern Siberia
    k. Kamchatka

3. Sino-Japanese Region

    a. Manchuria and South-eastern Siberia
    b. North Japan and South Sakhalin
    c. Korea and South Japan
    d. North China
    e. Central China
    f. Sino–Himalayan–Tibetan mountains

4. Western and Central Asiatic Region

    a. Armenian–Persian Highlands
    b. South Russia–Trans-Caspia
    c. Turkestan and Mongolia
    d. Tibetan plateau

5. Mediterranean Region

    a. Lusitania and western North Mediterranean coasts and islands
    b. Eastern North Mediterranean coasts and islands
    c. Morocco–Tunis
    d. Libya, North Egypt and Syria

6. Macaronesian Region

    a. The Azores
    b. Madeira
    c. The Canaries
    d. The Cape Verdes

7. Atlantic North American Region

  A. Northern Subregion

    a. Canadian Conifer province
    b. The Great Lakes
    c. The Appalachians

  B. Southern Subregion

    d. The Prairies
    e. Atlantic and Gulf coasts
    f. Mississippi basin

8. Pacific North American Region

    a. Southern Alaska and the Aleutian Islands
    b. Sitka, British Columbia, Washington and Oregon
    c. Californian coast
    d. The Great Basin
    e. Rocky Mountains
    f. Sierra Nevada
    g. Mexican Highlands

PALAEOTROPICAL KINGDOM

A. African Subkingdom

9. North African–Indian Desert
   Region
   a. Sahara–Arabia (except the
      south)
   b. Mesopotamia–South Persia–
      West Pakistan

10. Sudanese Park Steppe Region
    a. Senegambia–Sudan
    b. Upper Nile-land

11. North-east African Highland and
    Steppe Region
    a. Abyssinia and Eritrea
    b. Galaland and Somaliland
    c. Yemen and South Arabia
    d. Socotra

12. West African Rain-forest Region
    a. Upper Guinea
    b. Cameroons and Islands
    c. Congo Basin

13. East African Steppe Region
    a. Southern Portuguese East
       Africa
    b. The East African Steppes
    c. The East African high
       mountains
    d. The Central African lake zone
    e. The Rhodesias
    f. Angola

14. South African Region
    a. High veldt of the O.F.S. and
       Transvaal
    b. The Kalahari
    c. The Karroo
    d. Namaqualand and Damaraland
    e. Natal and eastern Cape
       Province

15. Madagascar Region
    a. Madagascar and the Comoros
    b. The Seychelles
    c. The Mascarenes

16. Region of Ascension and St.
    Helena

B. Indo-Malaysian Subkingdom

17. Indian Region
    a. Ceylon
    b. Malabar coast and southern
       India
    c. Deccan
    d. Ganges Plain
    e. Flanks of the Himalayas

18. Continental South-east Asiatic
    Region
    a. Eastern Assam and Upper
       Burma
    b. Lower Burma

    c. South China and Hainan
    d. Formosa and the Riukiu Islands
    e. Siam and Indo-China

19. Malaysian Region
    a. The Malay Peninsula
    b. Java, Sumatra and the
       Sunda Islands
    c. Borneo
    d. Philippines
    e. Celebes and Moluccas
    f. New Guinea and Aru

C. Polynesian Subkingdom

20. Hawaiian Region

21. Region of New Caledonia (with
    Lord Howe and Norfolk Islands)

22. Region of Melanesia and Micro-
    nesia

23. Region of Polynesia

NEOTROPICAL KINGDOM

24. Caribbean Region
    a. Mexican lowlands and coast
    b. South Florida, West Indies,
       Bahamas, Bermudas
    c. Guatemala–Panama
    d. North Colombia and North
       Venezuela

25. Region of Venezuela and Guiana
    a. Orinoco Basin
    b. Uplands of Venezuela

26. Amazon Region

27. South Brazilian Region
    a. Eastern coasts
    b. Uplands of Central Brazil

    c. Highlands of Eastern Brazil
    d. Grand Chaco

28. Andean Region
    a. Flanks of the Andes
    b. Montane Andes
    c. The Galapagos Islands
    d. Atacama Desert
    e. Chilean sclerophyll zone

29. Pampas Region
    a. Uruguay and South-eastern
       Brazil
    b. Argentine pampas
    c. Western Argentina
30. Region of Juan Fernandez

SOUTH AFRICAN KINGDOM

31. Cape Region

AUSTRALIAN KINGDOM

32. North and east Australian Region
    a. Northern forests
    b. Queensland forests
    c. South-eastern forests
    d. Tasmania

33. South-west Australian Region

34. Central Australian Region
    a. North and east savannas
    b. Central deserts
    c. South Australia

ANTARCTIC KINGDOM

35. New Zealand Region
    a. North Island
    b. South Island
    c. New Zealand Alps
    d. Kermadec Islands
    e. Chatham Islands
    f. Auckland and Campbell Islands

36. Patagonian Region
    a. Patagonia and Fuegia
    b. Southern Andes
    c. Falkland Islands

37. Region of the South Temperate
    Oceanic Islands

This floristic classification may be epitomised by saying that it divides the land surfaces of the world into 37 regions, which may, at least for theoretical purposes, be regarded as roughly equivalent in floristic value and importance, though not of course in size or, necessarily, in interest. Where appropriate, as in the discussion of endemics, the subject matter of later chapters is arranged under these regions, and further details concerning them will be noticed as occasion demands. The constituent provinces of each region have been listed for purposes of general interest and amplification and to provide a more detailed framework where such may be useful to add more detail to the treatment of the regions, but otherwise they will not receive further attention here.

PLATE 2

Map of the World showing the distribution of Vegetation. Simplified, chiefly after Brockmann-Jerosch in Rübel's *Pflanzengesellschaften der Erde*.

Areas correct Distortion increasing towards border of map.

Approximate Scale 1:100,000,000 (1600 miles = 1 inch) along Equator

on Mollweide's Homolographic Projection

tundra

desert and semi-desert

grassland

savannah

coniferous forest

other forest and woodland

Tropic of Cancer

Equator

Tropic of Capricorn

CHAPTER 3

SOME GENERAL ASPECTS OF PLANT GEOGRAPHY

The Evolutionary Background

THE short history of the study of plant geography in the Introduction is enough to show the enormous influence that evolutionary conceptions have had on the development of the subject, and it is no exaggeration to say that its whole background has become an evolutionary one, as, indeed, is true of any biological subject. Evolution is, as it were, the medium in which the picture of plant distribution is painted.

All the latter part of this book is devoted to a consideration of what are usually called the factors of distribution, that is to say the influences which may be looked upon as the immediate causes of the observed facts, but it will be clear from what has just been said that all these, critical as they may be, are to be regarded as secondary. Behind and beyond them is the infinitely broader cause inherent in the nature and course of organic evolution in general and of plant evolution in particular. Whatever the more precise explanation of them, the facts themselves are primarily due to something innate in the very order of nature. This something is the ubiquitous periodic production of new forms (which we call species, genera and families) by the processes of evolution. This is the general theme of which the so-called factors of distribution provide the variations.

Clearly then the study of plant geography must be approached with this evolutionary conception in mind, and such an approach at once reveals two of the most fundamental features of the subject. The first is that plant geography must always be regarded as a developmental study, and as dynamic rather than static. Whatever the particular facts under discussion it must always be remembered that they are not isolated and unrelated facts, but the culmination of a long series of events and changes which have been in operation at least for some time and often for very long periods. They are the outcome of that gradual change with time which is the essential feature of evolution, and if they are to be understood properly due account must be taken of the past as well as of the present. Second, it is manifest that time must always be one of the most important factors in all aspects of plant geography. Evolution is generally visualised as a continuous, though perhaps unevenly continuous, process and one in which the state of affairs is constantly changing, so that, in theory at any rate, the constitution and distribution of the world's plant life can only be described in relation to time itself, and it must not be assumed without other evidence that the circumstances controlling plant distribution to-day are necessarily those which have controlled it in the past.

The central problem of evolution has always been that of the methods by which new and distinct forms arise, that is to say of the processes involved in the "origin of species". It would be inappropriate, if nothing more, to discuss this huge subject at any length here, but it is also impossible to neglect it altogether because of its bearing upon a question to which, before commencing the study of plant geography, an answer is an urgent necessity. This is the question of whether a species originates

3

once and once only in the course of evolution or whether one and the same form may arise more than once at intervals of space and time. To give the problem greater definition, species may be said to consist of a number of closely similar individuals. Are these individuals all to be regarded as directly descended from a single and comparatively recent ancestor, that is to say as being *monophyletic*? Or are they to be regarded as having originated, some by one line of descent in one place and others by different lines elsewhere, that is to say as being *polyphyletic*? Is it, in short, safe to assume that all the individuals comprising a species are blood relations, or is it more likely that mere superficial resemblance is the chief bond between them?

A moment's reflection will show the importance of this question to the plant geographer. If a species is strictly monophyletic, then all its individuals are the descendants of one and the same ancestral plant and their total range, however extensive and peculiar it may be, must have grown by the processes of dissemination from the tiny area occupied by this ancestor. However wide may be the space between two or more individuals, this space must be the consequence of progressive geographical divergence in the course of time. If, on the other hand, a species is polyphyletic, then most of the features of its geography, however striking they may be, lose much of their interest and become almost meaningless and inexplicable, since there is nothing to show and no reason to suppose that the positional relationship between the individuals is anything but fortuitous.

In view of this it is obviously imperative before going further to come to some conclusion on this matter, and since this cannot be done without some reference to the subject of evolution in general and its theories, no further justification need be sought for making such a digression here.

Evolution is the natural antithesis of the conception of "special creation", which was the previously accepted explanation of the facts revealed by the study of animal and plant classification. Darwin (177), therefore, when he first propounded his views on evolution, was at some pains to do so in such form as would demonstrate, in the most telling fashion, the inadequacy of special creation as an explanation of the facts. He was also under the necessity of outlining some mechanism by which evolution might be supposed to come about, since without this his views would have been little more than academic. To meet these requirements he postulated his theory that evolution was brought about by "natural selection by survival of the fittest". The facts upon which he based this hypothesis were those of variation, the observed circumstance that no two individuals, even if of the same parentage, are ever exactly alike. He suggested that some of these differences would confer on their possessors advantages in the struggle of life, while others would be detrimental, and that since, as Malthus (480) had already shown, not all the individuals born can hope to survive, those best equipped would tend to be selected. This process he envisaged as accumulating with the passing of generations until some individuals had become sufficiently different from their earlier ancestors to merit recognition and description as new species.

There was nothing in the conception of special creation to preclude the possibility that similar individuals might have been created more than once and in different places, and in order to support his evolutionary views Darwin therefore devoted considerable time and space to an attempt to demonstrate that the weight of evidence was in favour of the opposite view, and that species were in fact normally monophyletic rather than polyphyletic. It was moreover important to do this from the point of view of the details of the suggested process of natural selection because, if this is indeed the mechanism of evolution, it is almost impossible to imagine that species can be anything but monophyletic. The chances that natural selection will, in two different parts of the world or at different periods, lead to exactly the same morphological result, can only be regarded as most improbable.

Perhaps on much the same grounds, Darwin and his contemporaries did not attach much importance to sudden and comparatively large evolutionary changes, but concentrated upon what are generally called "infinitesimal variations". If there is no theoretical limit to the magnitude of evolutionary change there must be visualised the possibility of some new form, widely different from anything hitherto existing, arising quite suddenly and unheralded, and there would be considerable difficulty in divorcing this kind of origin from the suggestion of an act of special creation. It was all-important rather, to show that evolution was an orderly process as opposed to the condition of arbitrariness, which must in one sense at least be inherent in the conception of special creation.

But it was also actually from the point of view of plant geography that Darwin saw the importance of demonstrating the monophyletic origin of species. As he himself expresses the point in the *Origin of Species*—"If the difficulties be not insuperable in admitting that in the long course of time all individuals of the same species belonging to the same genus have proceeded from one source, then all the grand leading facts of geographical distribution are explained on the theory of migration, together with subsequent modification and the multiplication of new forms." That is to say, given a monophyletic origin of species, the facts of plant and animal geography afford useful evidence in support of the theory of evolution.

It is for such reasons as these that the present-day reader of the works of Darwin and his contemporaries is often impressed with the extreme importance which is paid to minute variations and to the establishment of a general belief in the monophyletic origin of species, an importance which in the light of modern knowledge seems exaggerated. It seems so, however, only because the views that it seeks to establish have in fact been implicitly if not explicitly accepted by biologists for many years, and because it is difficult to realise, in the light of after-knowledge, how essential it was to establish them. It might therefore be deemed justifiable to accept these opinions as a general premise to a consideration of plant geography without more discussion, but the state of biological knowledge has advanced enormously since Darwin's time and it is necessary to be satisfied as to how far, if at all, these views now require modification (301, 739).

At the time when Darwin was writing his classics, knowledge concerning the cell and its structures was slight. It was but comparatively recently that the nucleus had been discovered and nothing was known of its internal organisation. Moreover, the work of Mendel on inheritance had still to be discovered by the scientific world. At this time, therefore, the evolutionist was unavoidably at a grave disadvantage because whatever mechanism he might suggest as being the vehicle of evolution, it was impossible to suggest any structural features in the living organism which might be the physical expression of it. Darwin fully realised this difficulty and indeed found it necessary later to augment his original exposition of Natural Selection by the additional hypothesis of "pangenesis" in which he tried to picture how reproductive cells might be capable of transmitting characters to their progeny. Incidentally it is no small measure of Darwin's greatness that his guesses in this matter have very largely been substantiated, though not exactly in the terms he employed.

It was partly due to this difficulty that while evolution as a general theory became widely accepted, a mechanism which stressed the importance of small variations was less acceptable. Indeed there gradually grew up the view that evolution proceeded rather as a result of larger and more sudden changes, called mutations (184). Such large changes were observed in many plants and it was found that their occurrence could be accelerated by certain experimental methods, but the mutationists were at first in much the same difficulty as Darwin because of their ignorance of cytology and genetics.

The enormous advances which have been made in these two subjects since the beginning of this century now enable a more scientific view to be taken of these apparently antagonistic opinions and it is clear that they are far less opposed than was originally thought, this conclusion being in great part the fruit of the remarkable investigations that have been made into the microscopic structure of the cell-nucleus.

It is now believed that the inheritance of characters between parent and offspring is by the agency of the chromosomes, which constitute the essential part of all cell nuclei. There is, moreover, reason to think that these characters are actually resident on the chromosomes in or as entities which are called *genes*, and that alteration in transmissible characters is due to actual alterations of some kind in one or more genes. When an individual differs markedly from its forebears in an inheritable character it is generally supposed that this difference originates as a definitive change in the nature or potentiality of one or more genes.

At first sight this "theory of the gene", as it is called, seems strongly to support the views of the mutationists, in as much as it puts into the general category of mutations all changes in characters since these must, by the nature of the case, be sudden and more or less sharply defined. But this is not quite a fair statement of the position. There are no particular limits in either direction to the magnitude of changes. Some may be large, but others are very small, and indeed are only to be compared with such minute modifications as were comprehended by Darwin in the phrase "infinitesimal variations". The fact of the matter appears to be that gene changes may be of almost any magnitude. If they are large, then they result in what is normally called a mutation: if they are small, they cause no more than minor variations. The distinction between them is primarily one of degree only.

The last 60 years or so have also seen the accumulation of a vast amount of information concerning the laws and phenomena of Mendelian inheritance, by which are expressed the ways in which the characters possessed by parents are distributed among and appear in their offspring. Here, again, there is more than one circumstance which may lead to the sudden and unexpected appearance of a form appreciably unlike any of its immediate ancestors which may in favourable conditions be the origin of a new species or at least of a new line of descent.

In brief it may be said that at the present time it seems that the novel morphological forms which are the basis of the recognition of new species arise chiefly by one or other of the following three processes:

1. By gene mutation.
2. By hybridisation, namely the combining together of the characters of relatively unlike parental forms (547), and by the segregation of such characters according to the laws of inheritance.
3. By changes in the number of chromosomes and genes (104).

Any further general consideration of the details of these processes would be beyond the scope of this book, and the reader who wishes to pursue the matter should consult some of the references given in the bibliography (19, 104, 301, 396,

697, 698), and textbooks of cytology and genetics. In particular Babcock's great study of the genus *Crepis* gives a most interesting insight into some of the processes of speciation (36). There are, however, a few particular aspects of the relation between evolution and plant geography which are so important that some further exposition of them is called for here.

Polytopy and Polychrony

The question whether species are normally to be regarded as monophyletic or as polyphyletic has already received some attention but there is more to be said about it if confusion on the matter is to be altogether avoided.

Both these words are among the older evolutionary terms, and in their earlier days at any rate were applied to the descent of large groups such as phyla or even of whole kingdoms, though their use has since become extended. They are in one sense the opposites of one another and describe, respectively, descent from a single ancestral source and descent from two or more different ancestral sources. What constitutes the appropriate degree of "difference" cannot be defined satisfactorily, but the implication is clear enough, namely, that the products of monophyletic descent are blood relations in a way in which the products of polyphyletic descent are not, or, to use the words of taxonomy, that the former constitute a natural group while the latter do not. The nouns monophylesis and polyphylesis, derived from these adjectives, are sometimes used.

The word *polyphyletic* can be disposed of here shortly. Anything to which it is properly applicable is by definition of mixed origin in the taxonomic sense and in matters of plant geography must be treated with all the caution and restraint that such a condition demands. The word *monophyletic*, on the other hand, needs more consideration. Much depends upon the exact interpretation put upon it, and the narrowness of its definition. In its strictest sense monophyletic suggests origin by a single and unrepeated act of species formation, or speciation, from a single individual ancestor, but this by no means exhausts the ways in which what must be regarded as a natural group as defined above may arise. To write in terms of species there are, indeed, three other possibilities. The first is that the individuals of a species may have come into existence by acts of speciation repeated at intervals of time by the same individual ancestor, or by one or more of that ancestor's immediate descendants. Species arising thus at more than one point of time are said to be *polychronic* and to arise by *polychrony*. The second possibility is that the individuals of a species may have arisen from a number of conspecific parents and hence, in more than one place. Species so arising in more than one place are said to be *polytopic*† and to arise by *polytopy*. Since it is difficult to imagine that polytopic origins can often be strictly synchronous, it may be assumed that polytopic species are also polychronic. In the strictest sense polychronic species are not polytopic but there is the third possibility of a combination of both these conditions. In all three the resultant species is monophyletic within the ordinary meaning of that word.

How does this relate to the main problem of the relative probability of mono-phylesis and polyphylesis? To answer this we must revert to p. 36. It will be noticed that the suggested primary causes of speciation there set out do not include "that

† There seems to be some confusion about the meaning of this word. The usage here accords with the discussion in Hayek (345) and with the definition in Daydon Jackson's *Glossary of Botanical Terms*. See also the *Oxford English Dictionary* under "polyphylesis."

accumulation of small variations" by which natural selection is presumed to operate, and this process, if indeed it exists at all, is believed now to play but a minor part in the origin of species. This is important, because this is, of all kinds of speciation, the one most likely to result in monophylesis, because of the very small chance that individuals arising in this manner in different places and circumstances would be sufficiently alike to be regarded as conspecific. On the other hand, the comparative abruptness of mutational change, both in time and degree, makes it very much easier to imagine their repetition, and the circumstances in which this may occur. It is largely to accommodate the possibilities inherent in mutation that the various shades of monophylesis just described have been distinguished.

It would seem then that the likelihood of some species being monophyletic in less than the strictest sense is much greater in the light of modern ideas of speciation than it used to be, but one must be careful not to swing too far in the other direction. We know that the same mutations may be repeated in a population under experimental control, but whether the same thing can and does happen in nature, and if so with what frequency, has yet actually to be demonstrated, and bearing in mind the extreme diversity of natural habitats where there is ordinary competition compared with that of cultivated conditions, it may legitimately be doubted whether it is ever likely to be more than rare. Moreover, the whole plan of character-discontinuity in organisms, which is the objective basis of classification, seems to be consistent with the opinion that polychrony, polytopy and, of course, all the forms of true polyphylesis, are, except perhaps in purely local circumstances, of comparatively unusual occurrence. Were they commonplace the fact would surely have revealed itself in the study of classification much more unmistakably before now, and indeed would be likely to make such classification even more difficult than it is. We must be prepared to accept the contingency of their occurrence and to judge each possible case on its merits in the light of this, but it seems doubtful whether it is necessary to regard them as of more than local significance, and as such unlikely to confuse the general picture of plant distribution, and especially discontinuous distribution, to any serious degree.

Differentiation and the Concept of Age and Area

It has already been suggested that if it can be conceded that mutations may be of any magnitude there is little cleavage between the selectionists and the mutationists. But if, on the other hand, it is maintained that evolution comes about largely or exclusively by mutational changes of the larger kind only, there is a great gulf between the two. Indeed the difference then involves the whole conception of the order in which the events of evolution have occurred. In terms of natural selection there is to be pictured a slow divergence of form, resulting from a gradual accumulation of difference and leading to the successive appearance of species, genera and larger categories in that order. Under such conditions it is possible to speak of evolution as working "upwards" from smaller to larger unities. In terms of large mutations the reverse holds. There is to be pictured sudden, abrupt and discontinuous divergence, without intermediate links, producing new forms which become at once foundation members of larger groups, which only subsequently resolve themselves into their constituent genera and species. Under these conditions it is possible to speak of evolution as working "downwards" from larger to smaller unities. The former process may be thought of as one of accumulation; the latter as one of differentiation. Whether there is indeed any clear antithesis between the two is a matter of debate, but there is at least an appearance of this, and in fact the Theory of Differentiation, which expresses only the latter view, is often used as an alternative to the Theory of Natural Selection.

The Theory of Differentiation has been long extant in one shape or another but as far as plant geography is concerned it is especially associated with the names of Guppy (324, 325, 326, 327, 328, 329) and Willis (784, 785, 786, 787), and more recently Croizat (163, 164, 165), who has dealt with the subject at great length as one of the main themes of his very wide-ranging survey of biogeography, and particularly of its evolutionary aspects. Guppy's interest in it lay chiefly in the light it seemed capable of throwing on the general history of the Angiosperms as a group and he defined it as the view that "the history of our globe, as far as secondary causes are in operation, is essentially the history of the differentiation of primitive world-ranging generalised types in response to the differentiation of their conditions". He was much impressed by the fact that the families of flowering plants tend to fall, on a combination of geographical and structural characters, into two classes, wide-ranging primitive families and restricted derived families, and he mentions in particular the families of the warmer zones, which are for the most part pan-tropical, and which show little association with the geographical distinction between the Old and New Worlds. He also emphasises, that as regards the larger groups, and especially again, the families, the principle that community between these families is an affair of the north is not true.

These circumstances he associates in an interesting way with the known course of climatic and plant history, and particularly with the belief that the earlier history of the development of the Flowering Plants was one of widespread genial and more or less constant climate, while their later history has been linked with great climatic diversity and austerity (see Chapter 19). A similar belief is arrived at on various grounds in the course of this book and is discussed at length in the final chapter, but the reason for mentioning it here in connection with differentiation is that Guppy associates it definitely with problems of species formation and in so doing makes a noteworthy contribution to the evolutionary background to the study of plant geography.

He (329) postulates for terrestrial plants "an era when uniformity in environment was the rule—an era, one might imagine, of great atmospheric humidity, when persistent cloud-coverings blanketed the globe and when the same equable temperature everywhere prevailed", and he pictures a plant organism "under such conditions as behaving very much like a ship in a calm, drifting in a morphological sense in all directions and displaying unchecked and irresponsive variations of the floral organs . . .". Again, he says, "this would imply that the mutations of the floral organs of our own day represent all that remains of the capacity for great morphological changes in the early ages of the history of the Angiosperms". In short, he expresses the view that changes in environmental conditions may be reflected in plants in the manner in which their evolution proceeds, so that while in one set of conditions one method of evolution may predominate, another may prevail when conditions become markedly different. He infers, indeed, that the past may well have seen certain periods and conditions in which species production was especially copious (654). It has already been said that there is some reason for supposing this to have been the case, but it is of particular interest to see this very important conception put forward in the vivid way quoted.

Willis's approach to differentiation was from a different direction. He tells, in some of his writings (786, 787), how increasing familiarity with tropical plant life soon caused him to abandon the Theory of Natural Selection, in which he had been nurtured scientifically, as an explanation of evolution, and how he began a search for something more satisfactory. This search led him to the mutationist point of view and to the Theory of Differentiation, and his work became more and more focused on the possibility of obtaining evidence which would demonstrate this view rather than that of the selectionists.

In this search he became attracted to some of the more statistical aspects of biology because he believed that the nature of the evolutionary process which had exclusively or mainly occurred was very likely to reflect itself in the proportionate numbers of species with various definitions and in the numerical relationships of their distributions. This belief was related to what he regarded as the essential features of natural selection, one, that it involved an enormous destruction of less "fit" forms which were *ipso facto* unable to survive, and another that it involved the general assumption that species would at once and almost inevitably be supplanted by their "fitter" progeny so that parent and offspring species would not as a rule coexist for any significant length of time. Of the first he could not, like so many others, find any evidence at all, and he was unable to understand, in the circumstances of the second, how the enormous numbers of existing species had ever accumulated, or indeed how the world had ever become populated so variously at all. Neither of these difficulties would have to be overcome if, on the other hand, a mutational method of evolution had prevailed, for this would not require the elimination of parental forms, which could instead go on living side by side with their progeny for an indefinite time and no doubt producing additional offspring in due course, so that far from there being an extensive elimination of species there would in fact be a rapid accumulation easily able in theory to account for the actual numbers extant. Not only so but this increase would, arithmetically, be of the nature of a geometrical progression or compound interest increase, approaching, if not reaching, the series value 1, 2, 4, 8, etc. Willis concluded therefore that if the existence of some such numerical series could be demonstrated then there would be strong presumptive evidence that mutational evolution and not selection had occurred. It should be added that he regarded the evidence of character-discontinuity as also showing that evolution had included or been composed largely of mutations of large magnitude and that the order of events had been that envisaged in the Theory of Differentiation.

Such geometrical progressions Willis claimed to find especially in two connections, namely, in the relative areas occupied by the constituent species of larger units, and in the numbers of species in genera. In these two cases respectively he found that the numbers of very widespread species and also of large genera were small; that the numbers having intermediate values were larger; but that the numbers of very restricted species and of very small genera were very much and disproportionately greater. The full story of the gradual elaboration of Willis's theories must be read in his own books (784, 786, 787), but these two aspects of it are so closely associated with plant geography in the Theory of Age and Area and in the problem of the so-called "hollow curves", that they must be considered with some care here.

The full presentation of the Theory of Age and Area appeared in 1922 (784), and in it the author postulated that, with certain reservations, the area occupied by a species is, within comparable circles of affinity, proportionate to its age, which is, of course, the time that it has existed. Actually this has long been something of an axiom in plant geography, as is clear from the writings of Hooker in the middle of last century, and there is the same conception, though its expression is rather different, in the principle, discussed by Babcock (36) in connection with the genus *Crepis*, that at any one time, in a large group of organisms showing close phylogenetic relations, the most conservative members will be found furthest from the centre of origin, and the most advanced nearest to it. Willis, however, puts the idea in the form of a much more definite proposition.

That age and area may be, and often in individual cases no doubt are, closely related is beyond question, and it would be difficult to find anyone who would deny this totally, but there are great differences of opinion as to what extent it is in fact true, and Willis's theory aroused unusual controversy, not always of the mildest kind. Two aspects of the presentation of the theory tended to increase opportunities for disagreement. Instead of making, without qualification, a comparatively simple and limited postulation, Willis not only made his theory too wide and was thus obliged to incorporate in the statement of it a number of troublesome reservations of which his critics were not slow to avail themselves, but he also associated with it some of the statistical arguments mentioned above, showing, in particular, that many facts of distribution, both geographical and taxonomic, were expressible by the sort of graph called the hollow curve.

Unfortunately this mathematical treatment did not enhance his theory. The real meaning and significance of the hollow curve was not at once apparent, and it was soon shown that similar curves could be obtained from many sources unconnected with plant distribution. Moreover, many botanists found it difficult to understand the importance which Willis attached to these curves, or their relation to the conception of Age and Area, and there was almost inevitably imparted to the theory a sense of unreality that was unfortunate. Many felt that if the theory was really sound it should not depend so much on this kind of evidence, and the result was that it met with considerable criticism.

The lapse of time and the more recent publication of the longest of Willis's book *The Birth and Spread of Plants* (787), combine to make possible now a more definitive appraisal of these two sides of his work than has hitherto been easy. With regard to the theory of Age and Area the idea of a relationship between the geographical extent of a species and the time that it has existed is undoubtedly sound in theory, but there is equally little doubt that in practice it is, owing to all manner of complicating circumstances, much less widely applicable than Willis maintains. Indeed it could only be of general application if it could be imagined that the circumstances in which evolution has proceeded have been uniform for vast periods of time, and this almost every aspect of plant geography disproves. It has therefore been said, with some truth, that the theory is no more than a well-known axiom in disguise, namely, that if two species with the same potentiality of movement begin to move at different times the earlier will, at any one future time, have extended further than the other. This criticism is perhaps over-severe, but it is nevertheless very difficult, in view of all the facts, both past and present, to see how the conditions necessary for this age and area relation can ever have prevailed to any appreciable extent. It must also always be remembered that the theory is not, in one sense, primarily a phytogeographical theory but was an integral part of the presentation of its author's views on evolution, which in the book just mentioned are fully set out as the Theory of Divergent Dichotomous Mutation. In this connection the reader may care to refer also to Rosa's Theory of Hologenesis (603).

The problem of the hollow curves was first analysed, in admirable detail, by Chamberlin (121) as long ago as 1924, and Nicholson has put the essential points even more concisely (537). In brief, Willis's contention is that the hollow curves are indisputable evidence that evolution has proceeded in such a way as to be expressed as an exponential or "compound interest" function, that is to say that they result only when a geometrical progression, such as might well exist if his views on evolution are correct, is plotted. This is, however, not the case. It is true that hollow curves are given by progressions of this sort but this is not the only source of them. They may also arise when frequency or probability distributions having a certain inherent limitation are plotted. This limitation is that the variate, or in other words the values concerned, shall not be less than one, all hypothetical lesser values being reckoned as one. This happens, for example, when the numbers of persons are concerned, since there cannot be a fraction of a person, and also when species are involved since biological classification does not recognise fractional species. The effect is to make the numbers reckoned as having the value of one disproportionately large and the graphic consequence of this is a hollow curve.

Hollow curves may therefore be the result of one or other of two quite distinct causes; they *may* result, as Willis says they do, from the multiplication of species or their areas according to a geometrical progression, but they *may* also express no more than an ordinary probability distribution without any exponential implication. At present it seems impossible to be sure which of these two a hollow curve belongs to, and until this can be done the hollow curve is in fact valueless as evidence either for or against Willis's theories. In this connection it may be remarked that the reader will find an interesting and simple account of many of the statistical aspects of plant distribution in a paper by Thacker (729).

Despite the considerable criticism that the detailed theory of Age and Area has received (62, 272, 283, 313, 622, 655, 656) it must always be remembered that Willis did the cause of plant geography a great service by publishing it. As a result the subject of plant distribution quickly became topical and gained once more the attention it had largely lost, and it served also to focus study on just those aspects of the subject where it was most needed in view of other modern theories. It must also be remembered that criticism of Age and Area does not necessarily imply criticism of or disbelief in its author's opinions concerning the processes of evolution.

Croizat's evolutionary views also grew from a dissatisfaction with the Theory of Natural Selection, and he has expressed them, not only in considerable detail in his *Manual of Phytogeography* (164), but at even greater length in his still more voluminous *Panbiogeography* (165). Differentiation, which he describes in the words "Form-making is an orderly process through time and over space. It takes place by the breaking down of an ancestral group (whatever its taxonomic rank) around essentially local centres of progressive differentiation", is one of the leading themes of the second of these books but more closely related to plant geography is his concept of the *genorheitron*, which he elaborates in the *Manual*. He defines this term as an evolutionary line of descent, or lineage, in which the components are not only time and structural change but also migrationary movement. In other words he points out, with considerable cogency, that in so far as the movements of floras and faunas are one of the normal features in the passage of time successive generations tend to occupy areas increasingly distant from the points of origin of their ancestors. Where, and when, migration is prolonged it ought therefore to be possible to correlate change of form and change of position in such a way as to arrive at some conclusions as to the directions in which the two changes have taken place and thus to throw light on the course of events in the past. This emphasis on geographical change as a concomitant of evolution parallel in many ways with morphological change is a valuable contribution to the philosophy of evolution, but its theoretical usefulness must not be allowed to exaggerate its practical value in relation to problems of phylogeny. In studying the distribution of plants it is easy to detect parallelism in sequences of morphological characters and geographical position but there is seldom enough satisfactory evidence to show in which direction the sequence should be read.

The Cycle of Distribution

The next question to be discussed is that of the geographical fate of species or genera after they have arisen by one or other of the processes of evolution mentioned, and in accordance with the conclusions arrived at there we may assume that this origin has been monophyletic.

If the monophyletic origin of species be accepted in its most extreme form it must be believed that a new species, when it first appears, does so as one or very few individuals only. In this condition it may be described as having no distribution in space, but this will persist only until such time as the first generation produces progeny. This stage is generally a very short one, for as soon as the species reproduces its range must increase, if for no other reason than that no two plants can occupy exactly the same position. If the new species is biologically sound and able to maintain itself normally among pre-existing species it will tend to increase its range further, roughly in accordance with the number of its individuals. At some point or other various external factors tending to restrict its spread will almost inevitably come into play, but for a time at any rate it will continue to increase its range at each reproduction. This checking point may come soon, in which case the species will never be widespread, or it may be long delayed, in which case the species will gradually attain a considerable range. In either case the first stage in its geographical history will be one of spread culminating in the attainment of an appropriate degree of distribution, and of an equilibrium in respect of associated species.

During this stage, however, the processes of evolution are continuing, and sooner or later the erstwhile new species will in turn produce new species itself. This it may do from individuals at any point of its range, or from individuals in certain parts of its area only, but whichever prevails the result will be that new specific distributions or ranges will arise within the area of the parent form or at least in close proximity to it.

There is good reason to believe that the life of a species has much the same course as the life of an individual, and that it passes fairly early through a stage at which it exhibits a maximum vitality. From a phyletic point of view this expresses itself in a maximum evolutionary activity, and hence we may characterise this second state in its history as that at which it produces a maximum of new forms.

As time goes on this vitality will appear to ebb, possibly because the original stock has produced all the new forms of which it is capable, or, to put it rather differently, will be passed on to succeeding generations and the original will gradually diminish and die out. It will pass in fact into what might be compared with a condition of incipient senility. Its powers of producing new forms will decrease or cease altogether and it will have greater and greater difficulty in maintaining itself against the competition of younger and more virile strains. This stage again may come soon or may be long delayed, but come it must, and the species will eventually die out altogether. Concurrently, and with the consequent diminution in the number of individuals, the range of the species will also tend to diminish until in the final stages both the plant and its range will disappear entirely.

From a geographical point of view this late stage is a very interesting one. Throughout its history the conditions in which the species exists are constantly changing through a variety of circumstances, and it is likely, and indeed almost inevitable, that the disappearance of the species will be a differential disappearance, that is to say will take place first in one part or another of its range rather than everywhere simultaneously. Geographically the result of this will be a strong tendency towards the development of a discontinuous range, one indeed which will consist of two or more disjunctive constituent parts. Such ranges form one of the most intriguing subjects of plant geography, and since on the assumption of a monophyletic origin they can scarcely arise otherwise than has been outlined their significance as an indication of the state of the species showing them is very great.

Ultimately, and for a varying time before its complete disappearance, the species will have but a very restricted range. If earlier it was discontinuous the further passage of time will see the gradual elimination of all but one of the constituent areas until eventually the range of the species returns to a condition comparable with that which it possessed at the earliest stages of its existence.

To summarise, it would seem therefore that the history of a species or genus, expressed in its geography, will normally consist of four successive stages, each represented by a different and well-marked condition, and this view has been called the Theory of Generic Cycles (104). The first stage may be called the juvenile stage, and during it the species is establishing itself and gradually extending its range from nothing to a maximum determined by various external conditions. The second stage represents the maturity of the species. During this it will exhibit a maximum phyletic activity and give rise to various new forms, numerous or the reverse. It will meanwhile in general maintain its maximum range, within or associated with which there will appear the incipient ranges of many closely related younger forms. It will, indeed, tend to show what may be described as a parental range inclosing a number of offspring ranges. In the third stage the species is passing gradually into obscurity. It no longer produces many new forms and it is giving place to the newer and more virile generations. For a time it may maintain its range, but sooner or later this must tend to decrease. This decrease is likely to be accompanied by a breaking up of the range into disjunctive parts owing to the disappearance of the plants earlier in some places than in others. The fourth and last stage marks the final disappearance of the species and the ultimate contraction of its range to vanishing point. As in the course of this extinction the range decreases, it approximates more and more closely in extent to that which the species possessed in the earliest stage of its career. Finally, for some time before final extinction the size of its range will be indistinguishable at sight from that of a species but newly formed.

It must not be supposed that all species follow exactly the same course in their development and decay, but there can be no doubt that this is a fair picture of their general prospects. The actual details will, however, obviously depend on many considerations. One or other of the stages may be unduly prolonged or much shortened; the length of them will always tend to be controlled by extraneous circumstances. Some species may never attain an appreciable range and may die out without showing either the second or third distributional stages. Others may early attain and long maintain a wide distribution. There is no doubt, too, that the matter of evolutionary vitality, as it has been termed, namely the ability to produce new forms, varies enormously not only among different kinds of plants but also in different circumstances and in different places (654), and it may well be that external changes may induce copious species production in forms which formerly gave rise to them but sparsely. It is difficult also to avoid the conclusion that certain parts of the world are, from time to time, peculiarly favourable for intense and rapid evolution.

The idea of this geographical life cycle in species derives in the main of course from the evidence of the geological record, of which the most striking features are the successive appearance of new groups, their rapid expansion, and their replacement one after another, though only after long passage of time, by something more highly differentiated. It is true that some types seem to have lasted much longer than others, though their constitution has changed, but there has apparently never been any progressive or absolute accumulation of types. Instead, one series gives way to another that replaces it, and it seems beyond doubt that in the course of geological time there is an almost complete "turnover" of plant types, so that unless we ascribe this to some form of periodic catastrophism something of the sequence of events outlined above would seem to be inevitable.

At the same time the theory of generic cycles has, for reasons of simplicity and clarity, been expressed above in terms which are frankly anthropomorphic, and Cain (104) has very properly commented upon this. It may, indeed, well be debated how much objective reality there is in such a phrase as "the senility of species", which, it should be noted, not only postulates the existence of entities called "species" but also endows them with certain physiological attributes, but it is nevertheless helpful to draw an analogy between the course of geographical history and some more familiar sequence of events, and for this reason the particular phraseology employed may be excused.

Such are some at least of the kinds of complications which may and do obscure the simplicity of distribution. Were it not for these complications it would no doubt be possible to describe and explain plant geography much more concisely and completely than it is at present, but it would certainly be a far less interesting subject.

Endemism

To quote the *Concise Oxford Dictionary* the word *endemic* means "Regularly found among (specified) people, in (specified) country". That is to say, it is applied to things which are peculiar to a given situation.

In botany the word *endemic* is applied to any species or other taxonomic unit which is so distributed as to be confined to one particular country or region. It will therefore be seen that without further qualification the word is almost meaningless because every species is confined to some area, though that may be a very large one. In the geography of plants and animals, therefore, the use of the word is restricted somewhat conventionally to species or other units having a comparatively or abnormally restricted range. It should also properly be used with due regard for the size of the taxonomic unit under consideration. Although it is generally indescribable in words, there is an average range of families, an average range of genera, and an average range of species, these being progressively smaller, and the best practical limitation of the use of the word endemic is to restrict it to units whose ranges are obviously less than the average for their kind. For example, it is appropriate and valuable to consider families which are found in only one continent as endemic because the average distribution of families is greater than this. On the contrary it is almost meaningless to speak of species in terms of continental endemism because comparatively few species are as widely or more widely distributed. Areas beyond a certain size will always tend to have a large percentage of endemic species for the simple reason that the great majority of species have ranges of less than these dimensions.

At the same time it is difficult to lay down any hard and fast rules and all that can be done is to bear in mind the importance of denoting in some way the sense in which the term endemism is used. It may be desirable to use it in one set of circumstances and indefensible in others.

It has already been explained that endemism may be particularly useful in the recognition of different floristic regions and also in determining or expressing the degrees in which floras are peculiar. In the first case it is often to be noticed that while one part of a large region possesses a high proportion of endemics another and adjacent region may have considerably fewer, and this is often a useful guide to the delimitation of the two. This is seen, for instance, between the Cape Region and other parts of South Africa, and between south-west Australia and some other parts of that continent.

The second case may be well illustrated by three island groups, the Galapagos, Juan Fernandez and Hawaii. The first has many endemic species but very few endemic genera, and even the endemic species are comparatively closely related to continental American types. Juan Fernandez is situated fairly close to Chile and has a small flora only, but this is peculiar, its endemics including numerous genera and even one family. The Hawaiian Islands are very isolated and have a flora much larger than those of the other groups. Moreover, it has a very high degree of endemism, about 90 per cent of its species being confined to the archipelago. There are also many endemic genera. Although the number of species in each of these floras is very different, the facts of endemism indicate clearly that the floras of Juan Fernandez and Hawaii have a much greater and more similar proportion of peculiarity than the Galapagos Islands. It is partly for this reason that, in the floristic classification given in Chapter 2, a higher rank is given to the former than to the last.

It is clear that species will be of such a narrow range as to merit the name endemic at two distinct periods of their existence, namely at the beginning and at the end, when they are very young and very old. A third possibility, that species may retain a very small area without expansion or contraction for a very long time, is a hypothetical contingency scarcely susceptible to proof or disproof, but the first two are very important in relation to other problems.

It is one of the principal features of plant geography that endemic (narrowly distributed) species are much more numerous than others and this may be explained in two completely different ways according to one's view of evolution. Those who favour the selectionist explanation contend that these endemics are for the most part almost extinct species, and regard their large numbers as evidencing that widespread extinction of forms which their theory requires. Those, like Willis for example, who favour a mutational view of evolution believe that endemics are mostly new species and that their superior numbers point to the kind of exponential increase that should be associated with such a process. This is why the discussion of endemism enters so largely into the presentation of evolutionary theories, each author trying to find, among the facts of endemism, the support which he seeks for his opinions.

Unfortunately there is no ready means, except in very rare cases, of knowing whether an individual endemic species is new or old and hence their value as evidence is strictly speaking, very little, however the more probable one or other mode of origin may be. It is nevertheless a common practice to distinguish these two sorts of endemics by name, if by nothing else, the "old" being referred to particularly as "relics", or even by the special name of "epibiotics" (594, 595).

It is important to remember that endemism may be qualitative as well as quantitative, though this condition cannot be expressed in exact numerical terms, this quality being the degree to which the endemics are in themselves peculiar or distinctive. For example two floras may well have the same proportion of endemic species, but while in one these species are all closely related to, and differ little from, other species which are not endemic, in the other they may be very different from other species in the flora, belonging largely perhaps to different genera or even larger taxonomic groups. The endemic species in this second flora clearly express a higher degree of distinctiveness and particularity than those in the first, and it is this difference that the concept of quality in endemism tries to express.

Discontinuity

Discontinuity, or disjunction as it is often called, is the occurrence of a species or other unit in two or more separated regions, and is by no means an uncommon phenomenon. Sometimes the extent of discontinuity is very small and the range as a whole is almost continuous; sometimes the discontinuity is great and even to be measured in thousands of miles. Between these two extremes there is almost every intermediate condition.

In theory, of course, all species are discontinuous to some extent in so far as they rarely if ever cover their general range so completely that the individual plants are actually in contact, and the greater the detail in which distribution is considered the more apparent this point of view will become. In general, however, and especially in considering the whole ranges of species and genera, it is impossible to take into account, or indeed to mark, this degree of discontinuity, and the term is restricted in practice to ranges which on a large and obvious scale consist of two or more parts. Even so the term remains comparative and this must always be remembered, and in reference to it the degree of discontinuity comprehended should if possible be stated explicitly.

Discontinuity is closely related to two matters which have already been mentioned in this chapter. The first is the problem of the monophyletic origin of species. If this view is maintained, then obviously the phenomena of discontinuity take on a very great interest and importance because it may be assumed that whatever is the present separation between the constituent areas they must once have been continuous, or at least the individuals contained in them must once have come from one ancestral plant. This being so, then the discontinuity has to be explained, and there must be taken into account all the factors which might possibly have caused it, and this often leads the investigator into fascinating by-ways of his subject. On the other hand, if species are polyphyletic or polytopic then discontinuity loses much of its potential importance because it can always be explained on the supposition that the same species has arisen independently in each of the separated portions of its total range.

As has been said, discontinuity is quite common, and appears in all sorts of forms, and it is unlikely that any serious critic would be found to maintain that all and every of its examples are due to the species concerned having had a polyphyletic origin. On the contrary, the detailed facts are generally such as to indicate very strongly that this is not the case and that discontinuity is the result of real disjunction.

Discontinuity is also closely related to the Theory of Generic Cycles outlined above and will be seen from it to be in some form or other an almost inevitable concomitant of the phase of senility. Hence discontinuity is only to be expected and is to be regarded as a normal phenomenon of distribution. It is of course affected, like the other phases, by all kinds of extraneous causes, and extreme discontinuity is no doubt to some extent abnormal, since it can arise only in definite circumstances. It is for this very reason of special interest and importance, particularly from a theoretical point of view.

Actually the present geography of the world is such that any unit with an extensive range must of necessity be discontinuous. Even northern circumpolar ranges are broken by the gaps of the north Atlantic and the north Pacific, and the increasing segregation of land makes this more and more noticeable the further south we go from the North Pole. The tropical region, for example, is divided by oceans into three main masses corresponding to the continents, while the same kind of segregation is seen even more markedly in the southern temperate latitudes. Hence all the plants which range completely over at least one major climatic world belt must be discontinuous in total distribution. Clearly, to include these under the consideration of discontinuity would make for complexity, and therefore it is a working convention that by discontinuity is meant only such disjunction as is, so to speak, over and above that due to major land and sea distribution. For example, units which are pantropical in range are not usually considered or treated as discontinuous. Their ranges are in fact of necessity discontinuous, but this is not their primary interest. On the other hand, units which are found only in certain parts of the tropics separated by areas of ocean are so considered.

It is also apparent that discontinuity can be water discontinuity, land discontinuity (where a unit is irregularly distributed over a large land surface), or a mixture of both. Each kind involves rather a different combination of considerations and in theoretical matters the distinction between them should not be lost.

PLATE 3

Map of the World showing, from various sources:

1. the 600 ft. submarine contour
2. land above 600 ft. in elevation
3. various islands mentioned in the text

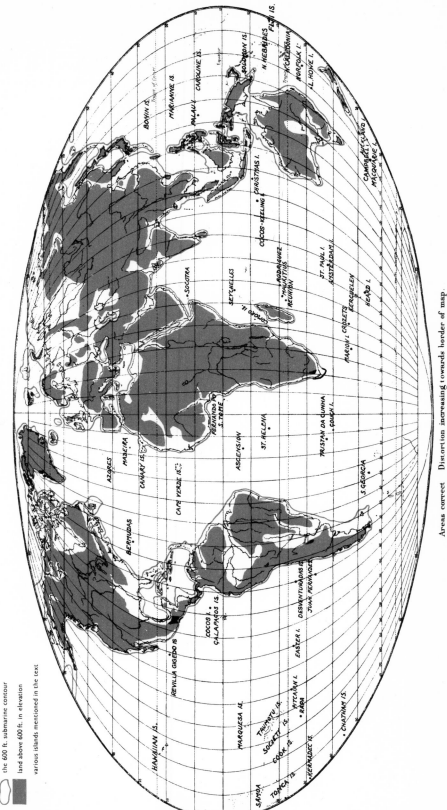

Areas correct Distortion increasing towards border of map.
Approximate Scale 1:100,000,000 (1600 miles = 1inch) along Equator
on Mollweide's Homolographic Projection

Copyright

CHAPTER 4

THE DISTRIBUTION OF FAMILIES

The Number and Size of Families

ESTIMATES of the number of families into which the Angiosperms should be divided vary considerably. Bentham and Hooker (56), whose system of classification is that most familiar to British botanists, recognised about 200; Engler's system (220), which is more generally used on the Continent, makes about 285; Lemée (452) admits over 300; while the new edition of Hutchinson's arrangement (394) includes 411. There is indeed a general tendency for the number to increase as time goes on, not only because new families are discovered but because better knowledge makes it ever clearer that the earlier conceptions of many families were too wide, and need to be restricted. This process of augmentation is, however, still far from complete and there is little doubt that the number of families usually recognised to-day is insufficient to give an entirely realistic picture of their relationships. Some families, as, for example, the Sterculiaceae and the Flacourtiaceae, contain numerous divergent subgroups, while others include either isolated and often monotypic subfamilies or conspicuous *genera incertae sedis* which may well represent distinct families. Certain other families again, which are commonly used, such as the Myoporaceae, Cornaceae and Loganiaceae, are notoriously unsatisfactory and are probably aggregations of genera whose claims to mutual relationship are very slight. Nor are the differences between the various systems in these respects merely those of simple addition or subtraction, for families recognised in one system need not necessarily be admitted in another, which itself may contain others not included in the first.

In a geographical review, therefore, where the main purpose is to describe the distributions of the various groups concerned, it is desirable to refer to as many families as seems reasonable, without attempting to follow any particular system of classification, and this is done below. In all about 435 families are mentioned, this number including, with one or two exceptions, all those in the four classifications noted above as well as some others which for various reasons call for recognition. It should be noted that as a result of this procedure individual families are normally defined in their narrow sense or, in the phrase of the taxonomist, *in sensu stricto*, and this is emphasised, where it seems especially necessary, by the use of an asterisk.

Families vary enormously in size, as is illustrated by the following figures, which are in round numbers based on Lemée (452). At one end of the scale is a family with more than 1,000 genera and 20,000 species and at the other there are several families (see below) which consist each of a single monotypic genus, and which are therefore of the smallest possible size, while between these extremes are others of almost every magnitude. Size can be expressed either in number of genera or in number of species, the former, since a genus may contain any number of species, being on the whole less expressive than the latter.

Heading the Dicotyledons and Monocotyledons respectively are two families considerably larger than any others, i.e.

		Genera	Species
Compositae	. .	1,000	20,000
Orchidaceae	. .	700	17,500

and these are followed by about twenty others having some 2,000 or more species, namely,

	Genera	Species
Papilionaceae .	440	10,750
Rubiaceae . .	500	9,000
Gramineae . .	600	7,500
Euphorbiaceae .	300	5,750
Labiatae . .	185	4,550
Scrophulariaceae .	235	4,150
Cyperaceae . .	90	4,100
Melastomataceae .	200	3,750
Myrtaceae . .	95	3,600
Asclepiadaceae* .	255	3,300
Acanthaceae .	250	3,100
Umbelliferae . .	350	3,050
Liliaceae . . .	200	3,000
Cruciferae . .	350	2,550
Solanaceae . .	88	2,300
Ericaceae . .	60	2,250
Piperaceae . .	5	2,200
Apocynaceae .	195	2,150
Rosaceae* . .	110	2,100
Mimosaceae . .	50	2,100
Palmae . . .	250	2,000
Araceae . . .	115	2,000

The Cactaceae are also credited by some with about 2,000 species but the peculiarities of this family make comparison of it with others difficult.

It may be added that, taking the total of known Angiosperm species to be about 225,000 (see p. 154), the average family size is 600 species.

The Local Representation of Families

Another interesting facet of the distribution of families is that of their proportionate representation in the floras of different parts of the world, which is usually expressed by a local version of the world order just quoted, that is to say by arranging the families according to the numbers of their species in the different floras.

If there were no widespread families at all the correlation between lists of this kind would be very small, and indeed absent except perhaps for almost adjacent regions. On the other hand, if a few families were greatly outstanding in ubiquity and size, they would everywhere head the lists. The truth lies much nearer the latter than the former. Almost everywhere Compositae, Gramineae, Leguminosae (in the wide sense) and Cyperaceae are among the first six, but thereafter much depends on whether the area concerned is temperate, in which case such families as Caryophyllaceae, Cruciferae, Ranunculaceae, Rosaceae and Scrophulariaceae rank high, or whether it is tropical, in which case such families as Orchidaceae, Euphorbiaceae and Rubiaceae take their places. Departures from the world norm are actually greatest in equatorial forest regions, where leguminous plants are unusually common and Compositae and Gramineae unusually few; in some extra-tropical parts of the southern hemisphere, especially Australia, where Myrtaceae, Proteaceae and certain other families replace many of those more familiar elsewhere, and in some isolated

Fig. 2.—A. *Stylidium scandens*, B. *S. tenellum*, and C. *S. pycnanthum*, somewhat reduced, after Mildbraed.

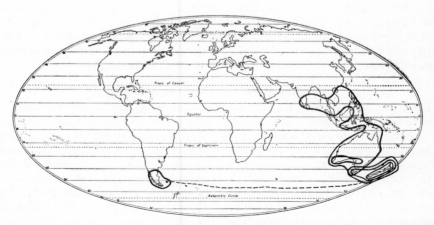

Fig. 3.—Map showing the distribution of the five genera of the family Stylidiaceae, i.e. *Stylidium*, Australia–Asia: *Levenhookia*, southern Australia: *Oreostylidium*, New Zealand: *Forstera*, New New Zealand and Tasmania: *Phyllachne*, New Zealand, Tasmania and S. America.

51

islands, notably New Caledonia where the Gramineae, Compositae and Papilion-aceae are remarkably few, and Hawaii where the Lobeliaceae are in the lead and Orchidaceae remarkably few.

Sprague (687) has made a useful contribution to this subject, though his estimates of family size have a basis different from those given above. After quoting a valuable series of figures he comes to several conclusions, which, it may be said, receive general support from many other lines of evidence. Chief among them are first, that the various floras of the world arose by segregation, under the influence of climate, from an ancient world-wide flora of a tropical or semi-tropical character, and second, that the history of the Flowering Plants in the two hemispheres has been quite different because of the near elimination of the southern cold flora during the Pleistocene as a consequence of the discontinuity of the land in the higher latitudes of that hemi-sphere.

The Geographical Classification of Families

Sundry attempts have been made to classify the families of Angiosperms accord-ing to their distributions but this is not an easy thing to do, partly because of the ill-defined taxonomic limits of some groups and partly because of the difficulty of determining the true status, in all parts of the world, of individual species. A particu-larly elaborate study of this kind had been made by Vester (750), who not only gives a map of each family but also a short verbal account of its distribution. Reference may also be made to papers by Axelrod (34, 35). Vester's work brings together in com-pact form a great deal of information, especially about the northern and southern limits of families, and, although many of the maps need correction, it is a source of great value. At the same time the degree of detail in his classification shows very clearly how hard it is to make anything of the sort both simple and complete. No two families have exactly similar distributions and there is almost infinite variety in detail. Moreover, though the total ranges of certain families may be much alike in outline they may differ considerably in many other respects, such as intensity of distribution, massing of species, proportions of endemism, ecological segregation and so on, all of which must be taken into account.

Here the main concern is to draw attention to the more prominent geographical features of each family as a contribution to the over-all picture of Angiosperm dis-tribution which it is the purpose of this book to draw, and on this basis geographical classification need not be so detailed. Indeed the main considerations are but two, the general degree of distribution and whether the families are essentially tropical or temperate, and combining these it is enough to divide the families under six heads—cosmopolitan or nearly so, tropical, temperate, discontinuous, endemic and anom-alous, subdividing each of these independently as required.

Cosmopolitan and subcosmopolitan families

These are the families which, in extent of range, cover the major portions of both the tropical and extra-tropical parts of the world, and the first question there-fore that may well be asked is whether there are any truly cosmopolitan, in the sense of ubiquitous, families. In so far as Antarctica and some of the Arctic regions are permanently glaciated and therefore virtually devoid of seed plants, there are none, but the term cosmopolitan in plant geography is generally used in a less rigid sense and thus to apply to distributions which cover all or nearly all those parts of the world where there is a reasonably well-developed flora of these plants, and within this definition quite a number of families fall.

Pride of place must certainly go to the Gramineae (343), the great family of which much was said in the Introduction. Not only do the grasses reach to the furthest land in the north and to the borders of Antarctica in the south, but their degree of distribution is usually particularly complete and continuous. Almost alone among the families of flowering plants they form the dominant element in vegetation over great areas of the world, and nearly everywhere else too, except perhaps in some forest regions, the proportion of these plants is high.

In general ubiquity the Compositae almost certainly rank next to the Gramineae. They are in fact much more numerous in genera and species but they never form so prominent a part of vegetation. Nevertheless the genera are well-scattered, and nearly every flora contains a good representation of them. In some places, especially within the drier mid-latitudes, the Compositae are particularly abundant, though there is no outstanding disproportionate local massing.

The Cyperaceae are another remarkably widespread family and, in many ways a counterpart, in rather damper conditions, of the Gramineae, but they are a much smaller family, especially in genera, with a narrower ecological range. Two very large genera, *Carex*, which is mainly temperate, and *Cyperus*, which is mainly tropical, account for most of the distribution.

In purely superficial extent of range the still smaller family Caryophyllaceae probably comes nearest to the Gramineae, for it has not only many arctic forms, but it is the only other family in Antarctica, as well as being a prominent feature in the floras of the South Temperate Oceanic Islands. It has not, however, anything like the same intensity and completeness of distribution, and there are many tropical areas, notably some of the forest regions and the western half of Australia, where it is almost or quite unrepresented. Moreover its breadth of range may to some degree be misleading since the family includes some of the most widespread weeds.

Seven families, in order of size Orchidaceae, Papilionaceae, Labiatae, Scrophulariaceae, Liliaceae*, Boraginaceae* and Gentianaceae*, come next to those above because they are, in the main, equally characteristic of both tropical and temperate regions, though in the Orchidaceae the actual number of species is immensely greater in the tropics. The first three have rather lower northern limits than the rest. The Gentianaceae is the smallest and most thinly spread of the six and owes its wide range chiefly to the development of a minority of notably arctic types.

Similar in general extent of range are the great, predominantly temperate families Cruciferae, Umbelliferae, Ranunculaceae and Rosaceae*. The first of these is probably the nearest approach to an exclusively temperate large family that there is, because its occurrences within the tropic lines are nearly all montane, though to a lesser degree this is true also of the other three. The family Rosaceae is the first to be mentioned in which there is an appreciable number of woody plants. Umbelliferae have a lower northern limit than the others. It is interesting also to note here that both the Cruciferae and Umbelliferae have closely related tropical families, the Capparidaceae and Araliaceae respectively.

Eight others are also predominantly temperate and almost as widely spread, namely Campanulaceae*, Juncaceae, Onagraceae, Polygonaceae, Cuscutaceae, Plantaginaceae (see p. 162), Hypericaceae and Primulaceae (see p. 74) but they are smaller and on the whole less evenly distributed. The first four are the most widely spread and the last two, especially, show considerable gaps. Each of them has one large genus covering nearly all the family range, and the Onagraceae and Polygonaceae are rather particularly characteristic of the western parts of North America.

The Ericaceae pose problems of great geographical interest. In its narrower sense

FIG. 4.—*Drimys winteri*, about natural size, after Baillon. According to Smith, in *Journ. Arnold Arboretum*, **24**, 1943, the plant depicted is the variety *punctata*.

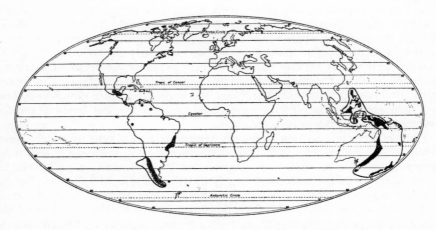

FIG. 5.—Map showing (black) the distribution of the family Winteraceae, mainly after Smith (677)

here used the family comprises three groups, the Rhododendroideae, the Arbutoideae and the Ericoideae. It is doubtful, however, whether the over-all differences beween these are in fact any less than those between them and two families recognised here as distinct, the Vacciniaceae and the Epacridaceae, and it is more satisfactory from a geographical point of view to think of all these as five groups of similar importance and more or less equal relationship. When this is done some very interesting facts emerge. In total area the five together are as completely cosmopolitan as almost any single family, but the five constituents have very different distributions. The Arbutoideae are almost world wide, but very predominantly north temperate and scarcely represented in Africa and Australia. The Rhododendroideae are similar but less widely distributed and are absent from Africa. The Vacciniaceae again have a very similar total range, though with representation in Madagascar but not in tropical Africa, but are conspicuously most strongly developed in tropical America and, to a lesser degree, in tropical Asia and Malaysia. The Ericoideae, in marked contrast are confined to Africa and Europe, with an enormous preponderance south of the Tropic of Capricorn. Finally the Epacridaceae are also southern, being essentially an Australasian group, having also a single monotypic genus in Patagonia. Thus, within a cosmopolitan whole, there are two northern groups, one trans-equatorial chiefly New World group, and two southern Old World groups (see p. 70). It should also be noted that these five comprise woody plants, many of them of a characteristic type, and constitute the most widely distributed of all such groups.

Four families, Convolvulaceae*, Malvaceae, Solanaceae and Urticaceae, are essentially tropical though they have a considerable and widespread temperate representation. They do not, however, reach quite such high latitudes as any of the foregoing. The temperate members of the Urticaceae are rather uncharacteristic of the family as a whole and thus illustrate a not uncommon condition, best seen in the next seven families.

These are the Rubiaceae, Euphorbiaceae, Linaceae*, Violaceae, Polygalaceae, Verbenaceae* and Lythraceae, though the last is rather less widely distributed than the rest. All but Linaceae are predominantly tropical families and their wide distributions are due in each case to the occurrence of one or two herbaceous types more or less unrepresentative of the family as a whole. In Rubiaceae the members of the *Galieae* are very unlike the numerous tropical woody genera; in Euphorbiaceae virtually only the highly specialised herbaceous species of the genus *Euphorbia* range into high latitudes; the herbaceous genera *Linum*, *Viola* and *Polygala* are almost the only temperate members of their predominantly woody groups; while in the Verbenaceae and Lythraceae there is a similar, though less marked, state of affairs.

Next come six families in which the main geographical feature is a preponderance south of the equator, and these are best dealt with in pairs. The Santalaceae and Thymelaeaceae* are both fairly evenly spread, though they have gaps, but are respectively most plentiful in Australasia and South Africa. The Geraniaceae* and Oxalidaceae are both greatly concentrated in South Africa and South America and are world wide only by certain species of the genera *Geranium* and *Oxalis*. The Crassulaceae and Portulacaceae are concentrated respectively in the South African, Macaronesian and Mediterranean regions and in South America and Australia, and are both cosmopolitan only because of the exceptionally wide range of one or two small aquatic members.

Four more woody families are sufficiently widespread to be included here though by the nature of the case they have not quite the same extent as many of those above. They are the Oleaceae, Caprifoliaceae, Celastraceae and Rhamnaceae, and the first two are chiefly temperate while the others are chiefly tropical. The Caprifoliaceae are much less completely distributed than the others.

Another five families may also be included here on the grounds that they are found practically all over the world within their ecological limits but which, on account of these, are certainly much less completely distributed than most of those mentioned above. Two of them, Chenopodiaceae and Plumbaginaceae, are rich in halophytes and are therefore mostly plentiful in either salt desert or coastal areas, and to a less extent the same is true of the Illecebraceae, but the Droseraceae and the Lentibulariaceae are chiefly marsh and bog plants and therefore absent from the more arid parts of the world. The Chenopodiaceae are described (222) as having ten main centres of concentration widely scattered over the world's deserts; the Plumbaginaceae and Illecebraceae are most developed in the Mediterranean and Central Asiatic regions; the Droseraceae are predominantly southern and especially Australian (222); the Lentibulariaceae are more evenly distributed but show one or two gaps.

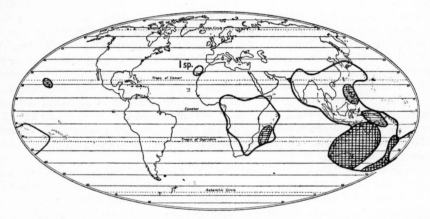

FIG. 6.—Map showing the distribution of the family Pittosporaceae. The areas of highest species concentration are cross-hatched: secondary concentrations are shown by horizontal lines.

The subject of edaphic limitation leads on conveniently to the last group of widespread families, the aquatics, in which it is seen in even more pronounced form. These number fifteen, namely:

Alismataceae, Callitrichaceae, Elatinaceae, Haloragaceae*, Hydrocharitaceae, Lemnaceae, Menyanthaceae, Najadaceae, Nymphaeaceae, Potamogetonaceae, Ruppiaceae, Zannichelliaceae and, less completely perhaps, Butomaceae, Ceratophyllaceae and Typhaceae.

Each of these occurs in fresh water (or rarely, in salt water also) in most parts of the world but the necessarily restricted nature of their habitats scarcely allows direct comparison with other families, and it would be unprofitable to try to assess how much more or how much less any one of them is in fact distributed. Their chief geographical interest is in relation to problems of dispersal (see Chapter 19). The largest of them, Hydrocharitaceae, has less than twenty genera, and the largest genus among them is *Potamogeton* with more than 100 species. The Haloragaceae include many species which are not aquatic, and owe their wide range chiefly to the genus *Myriophyllum*.

Tropical families

Because the area of land available within the tropical and subtropical zones of the world is nearly twice as great as that within the temperate and polar zones (see Appendix A) the families widely spread in and characteristic of the former naturally come, in point of distribution, next to those already discussed. There is, however, no very clear line of demarcation between the members of the two categories for the noteworthy reason that comparatively few families range widely through the tropics, that is to say well over all three constituent regions, without some, and usually considerable, extension into temperate latitudes, Indeed such families as the Orchidaceae, Rubiaceae and Euphorbiaceae, which are essentially tropical groups, are, as has been seen, so widespread actually as to merit the term subcosmopolitan. Hence the first families to be considered here under the "tropical" heading are those in which this latitudinal extension is most marked, though not to the degree which would place them in the previous category.

Ten of these families are familiar in the floras of north-west Europe because, in these latitudes, where the effect of the Gulf Stream is felt, they reach, if only by a single species, parallels higher than elsewhere. Perhaps the most remarkable instance is the Asclepiadaceae*, in which the genus *Cynanchum* reaches south Finland. Strangely enough this family is not present, even as adventive, in the British Isles. The other nine families, Amaryllidaceae*, Aquifoliaceae, Araceae, Aristolochiaceae, Cucurbitaceae, Dioscoreaceae, Loranthaceae, Tiliaceae and Ulmaceae, include members of the British flora.

The Eriocaulaceae and Lobeliaceae (see below) have an interesting point in common, namely, that the most northerly species in western Europe are found in North America also but not in eastern Europe or Asia, and in the former there is no representation between Britain and India.

More than a dozen families are of special note, particularly in contrast with those just mentioned, because they tend to reach their highest latitudes in North America and/or Asia, and north of the Sahara to be represented only by one or a few more or less isolated species. The best examples of these are:

> Acanthaceae, Apocynaceae, Araliaceae, Gesneriaceae, Lauraceae, Menispermaceae, Moraceae*, Sapotaceae, Smilacaceae, Vitaceae,

but the same feature appears in less striking form in:

> Amaranthaceae, Anacardiaceae, Buddlejaceae, Caesalpiniaceae, Capparidaceae, Commelinaceae, Mimosaceae, Nyctaginaceae, Strychnaceae.

The first and last but one of this latter group are especially American families. All but Strychnaceae are represented in temperate South America; of the first group all but Acanthaceae, Menispermaceae and Vitaceae are found in New Zealand, but of the second group only Amaranthaceae and Nyctaginaceae have a very slight representation there. Iridaceae and Rutaceae are rather similar, but they are on balance southern families.

The remaining families which, large or small, are found in all three main regions of the tropics, number sixty, and can be grouped in various ways. Here it is most appropriate in view of what has already been said to arrange them according to their latitudinal limits, and to do this with special reference to North America, where, for reasons perhaps associated with the Pleistocene glaciations, separation on this basis is particularly clear.

Three small families, Hypoxidaceae, Pontederiaceae and Xyridaceae, actually occur north of the Canadian border and the first is widest below the equator, reaching New Zealand.

Eight families reach to between 40° and 45° N. in the U.S.A. and for the most part occur in Japan also. The Agavaceae, Bignoniaceae, Passifloraceae and Sapindaceae reach as far south in Australasia as New Zealand; Annonaceae, Ebenaceae, Ehretiaceae and Melastomataceae reach temperate Australia. All these are considerable families, and among them Agavaceae, Bignoniaceae, Melastomataceae and Passifloraceae show preponderance in the New World, while Annonaceae and Ebenaceae are rather the reverse.

The four large families Palmae (whose northern extreme is actually in Mediterranean Europe), Malpighiaceae, Sterculiaceae and Marantaceae, and the much smaller family Simaroubaceae, reach between 30° and 40° N. in the U.S.A. The first is in New Zealand, and all but the Marantaceae occur in Australia. The Marantaceae and Malpighiaceae are predominantly American: Sterculiaceae richest in Africa.

The great predominantly southern family Myrtaceae resembles the palms (for which a southern preponderance is claimed on p. 73) in having its northern limit in Europe, but south of the tropics it is much more completely distributed.

Nine more families reach Japan but not (or scarcely only) the U.S.A., namely, Balanophoraceae, Meliaceae, Myrsinaceae, Olacaceae and Piperaceae, all of which are found in New Zealand; Flacourtiaceae, Triuridaceae (very local in Africa) and Zingiberaceae, which reach Australia; and Begoniaceae. Of these Myrsinaceae, Piperaceae and Begoniaceae are relatively few in Africa, Zingiberaceae are predominantly Asiatic (compare Marantaceae), and Flacourtiaceae are rich in Africa. Similar, but with their Asiatic extremes on the mainland, are Combretaceae and Icacinaceae, both with species in New Zealand.

A further twenty-one mostly somewhat smaller, families do not much, if at all, cross the tropic anywhere in the northern hemisphere, and these can be grouped according to their Australasian ranges as follows:

1. Dilleniaceae have their southern limit in Tasmania.
2. Bombacaceae, Burseraceae, Chailletiaceae, Chrysobalanaceae, Connaraceae, Erythroxylaceae, Guttiferae*, Hernandiaceae (if the Queensland genus *Valvanthera* is rightly attributed), Hippocrateaceae, Myristicaceae, Ochnaceae, Opiliaceae, Potaliaceae, Rhizophoraceae and Samydaceae occur in Australia.
3. Antoniaceae, Aptandraceae, Gnetaceae, Hugoniaceae and Ixonanthaceae do not reach Australia.

In addition to these there are 14 other tropical families which call for individual notice because they do not easily fit into any of the groups already mentioned. Nine of these are best described as incompletely pan-tropical because, while they occur in all three parts of the tropical zone, these are significant local gaps in their distributions. Podostemaceae, Tristichaceae, Rafflesiaceae (very scattered) and Zygophyllaceae are absent from parts of Malaysia and Australia; Theaceae* scarcely occurs in Africa or Australia; Taccaceae are absent from much of tropical America; Loganiaceae*, are absent from much of Tropical Africa, and Burmanniaceae and Thismiaceae are also incompletely distributed. Five others can only be described as anomalous, namely, the Aizoaceae and Molluginaceae, which are families of arid regions and predominantly African; the Cabombaceae which is a small but widely spread freshwater aquatic family; the Phytolaccaceae, which is a very small family of uncertain status in parts of the Old World tropics and the

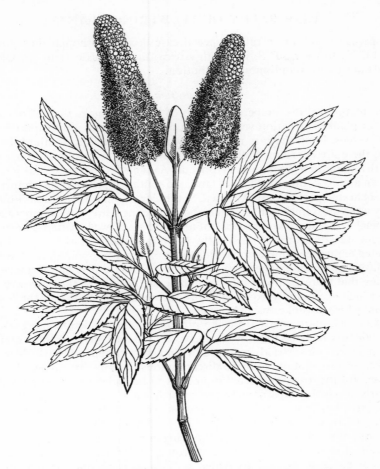

Fig. 7.—*Cumonia capensis*, about half natural size, after Baillon.

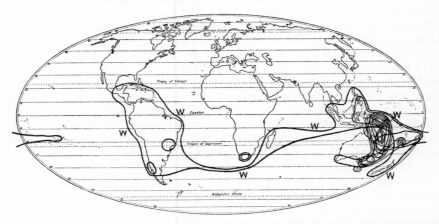

Fig. 8.—Map showing the distribution of the genera of the family Cunoniaceae. One genus, *Weinmannia*, represented by the letter W, is very widespread; all the rest are more or less narrowly endemic and much concentrated in New Guinea and Australasia.

Periplocaceae which are a rather special case because although they range from about 40° N. to over 30° S. in South Africa, they are essentially an Old World tropical family with a continuous distribution.

Temperate families

Four features of the temperate regions of the world make them, from the point of view of plant distribution very different from the tropics, quite apart from their climatic values. First, they are mainly in two parts, north and south of the tropics. Second, there are enormous differences of both area and latitudinal range between the north and south temperate (see Appendix A). Third, whereas the north temperate zone is an almost continuous belt of land, the south temperate zone comprises three widely separated parts, South America, South Africa, and Australasia. Fourth, and in many ways most important to remember, while there are in the temperate regions no tropical areas, there are, because of altitude, many well-scattered areas of temperate climate within the tropics. For this last reason the most widely and completely distributed temperate families are in fact more or less cosmopolitan and have already been considered under that heading. Again, because of the first circumstance, it is not surprising that there are no strictly pan-temperate families in the narrower sense of groups which are found throughout both the north temperate and the south temperate but which are unknown in between.

In short there are, apart from the predominantly temperate subcosmopolitan families already referred to, only about twenty families, most of them quite small, which are more or less strictly confined to temperate climates and which are neither so broken in distribution as to be discontinuous (as must be all purely southern temperate groups) or so restricted in area as to be endemic, and these fall simply and clearly into two groups, namely, those which, while mainly in the north temperate regions, extend on higher ground into or even across the tropics in places, and those which are strictly confined to north of the Tropic of Cancer.

Of the families in the first group, numbering thirteen, the Vacciniaceae (see above) is not only the widest, occurring all through the north temperate, throughout America as far as 40° S., in East Africa and Madagascar, and throughout tropical Asia and Malaysia to Queensland, but also the most anomalous, since its greatest concentrations are in the mountains of warm Africa and in Indo-Malaysia. The Berberidaceae also extend far to the south in America and cross the equator in both Africa and Asia (see p. 80 and Fig. 17). The Salicaceae are somewhat similar, but present in all Africa and absent from much of Malaysia and from Australasia. The Fumariaceae have southern extensions in both parts of the Old World but not in the New, and cover all Africa as well as parts of tropical Asia. Three families, Aceraceae, Elaeagnaceae and Philadelphaceae, are widespread in the north, the first and third reaching into Malaysia and the second into Australia. The Juglandaceae and Pirolaceae extend south in both America and Malaysia, the last-named only slightly so. Grossulariaceae (see Fig. 20), Polemoniaceae and Saxifragaceae* (now much dismembered) range widely through America only, and the Betulaceae does the same on a smaller scale.

The nine families of the north temperate which have no notable extensions into the tropics are Diapensiaceae, Parnassiaceae, Trilliaceae, and the monotypic Adoxaceae and Scheuchzeriaceae, all of which are more cold temperate, and Corylaceae, Cannabinaceae, Monotropaceae and Podophyllaceae, which are rather more warm temperate. The Diapensiaceae (with seven genera) is the nearest approach to a widely distributed northern arctic-alpine family.

FIG. 9.—*Lapageria rosea*, a familiar member of the Philesiaceae, slightly reduced, after Hutchinson.

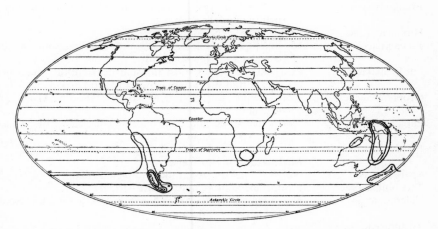

FIG. 10.—Map showing the distribution of the genera of the family Philesiaceae.

61

Discontinuous families

Speaking very generally the foregoing three categories account for the more widespread families, and there have now to be described those whose ranges are on the whole smaller. There are two classes of such families, the discontinuous, in which the actual areas occupied are in two or more distinct and separate parts, and the endemic, in which the total range is more or less strongly restricted.

The discontinuous families are best divided into groups by recalling and using for the purpose the two geographical circumstances that the temperate zones are separated by the intervening tropics, and that there are three separate land masses extending south from the almost continuous circumboreal belt, because many discontinuities are due to the restriction of families either to both of the temperate zones or to some or all of the three southern extensions. Apart from these discontinuity is usually the result of incomplete distribution within the north temperate or the tropical zones. It must be remembered that all pan-tropical families are in a sense discontinuous although they are more properly and usefully considered a class by themselves, and also that many of these and other families already dealt with are doubtless discontinuous to some degree, though not to the extent which makes it desirable to recognise them as such here.

It is convenient to record the discontinuous families in tabular form because this enables the very varied facts to be presented most simply and also indicates the relative prevalence of each kind. The table given here is capable of much greater subdivision but it is unnecessary to go into more detail because in many cases discontinuity is due to the distribution of particular genera, which receive further notice later on.

The Discontinuous Families of Angiosperms

A. Families of the north and south temperate regions:

Cistaceae	. .	North America and western Eurasia; South America
Empetraceae .	.	North temperate; South America and Tristan da Cunha
Fagaceae	.	North temperate and from Asia to New Zealand; South America
Frankeniaceae	.	North America; western Eurasia and Africa: South America; Australia and Tasmania
Hippuridaceae	.	North temperate; South America
Juncaginaceae		North temperate; Central and South America; South Africa; Australia and New Zealand
Lardizabalaceae	.	East Asia; Chile. A most unusual distribution which may indicate that the family is not a natural group
Orobanchaceae	.	North temperate; South America; ? South Africa and Australia
Papaveraceae*	.	North temperate and from North America to the Andes; South Africa; Australia
Posidoniaceae (marine)	.	Mediterranean; Australia
Sparganiaceae	.	North temperate; Australia and New Zealand
Tecophilaeaceae*	.	California; South Chile; South Africa
Valerianaceae	.	North temperate and from North to South America; South Africa; part of Malaysia
Zosteraceae (marine)	. .	North temperate; South Africa; Australia and New Zealand

B. Families of America and of Eurasia and/or Australasia:

   1. Families found entirely or predominantly in the northern hemisphere:

      a. America and western Eurasia:
         Platanaceae

      b. America and eastern Eurasia:

Calycanthaceae	Nyssaceae	Saururaceae
Hydrangeaceae*	Penthoraceae	Schisandraceae
Magnoliaceae*	Phrymaceae	

      c. America, western and eastern Eurasia:

Datiscaceae	Hippocastanaceae	Staphyleaceae
Styracaceae		

      d. Western America and Eurasia:
         Paeoniaceae

   2. Families found predominantly in the tropics:

Basellaceae	Illiciaceae (678)	Sauraujaceae
Bonnetiaceae	Roxburghiaceae	Symplocaceae
Chloranthaceae	Sabiaceae	Trigoniaceae

   3. Families found entirely or predominantly in the southern hemisphere:

Centrolepidaceae	Goodeniaceae (includes	Stylidiaceae (Fig. 3)
Corsiaceae	two species very widely	Tetrachondraceae
Donatiaceae	distributed on tropical	Winteraceae (Fig. 5)
Epacridaceae	shores)	(677)
Eucryphiaceae		

C. Families of America and of Africa and, in some, the Madagascar region:

   1. In Africa and the Madagascar region:

Canellaceae	Strelitziaceae	Velloziaceae
Hydnoraceae	Turneraceae	

   2. In Africa but not in the Madagascar region:

Bromeliaceae	Loasaceae	Rapateaceae
Caricaceae	Mayacaceae	Vochysiaceae
Humiriaceae		

D. Families of Africa and/or the Madagascar region and of Asia and/or Australasia and the Pacific Islands:

   1. In both Africa and the Madagascar region:

Aegicerataceae	Dipterocarpaceae	Pandanaceae
Alangiaceae	Flagellariaceae	Pittosporaceae
Aponogetonaceae	Leeaceae	Trichopodaceae
Barringtoniaceae	Musaceae	

   2. In Africa but not in the Madagascar region:

Ancistrocladaceae	Ctenolophonaceae
(Fig. 31)	Irvingiaceae
Aquilariaceae	

   3. In the Madagascar region but not in Africa:
      Nepenthaceae

E. Families found in all three parts of the southern hemisphere:

Cunoniaceae (Fig. 8)	Gunneraceae (Fig. 52)	Proteaceae (Fig. 16)
Escalloniaceae	Philesiaceae (Fig. 10)	Restionaceae (Fig. 12)

F. Other discontinuous families:

Atherospermaceae .	Tropical America; West Africa; Australia; New Zealand; New Caledonia
Clethraceae (Fig. 35)	America; Asia; Malaysia; Madeira
Cochlospermaceae .	Tropical America; tropical Africa and (if *Sphaerosepalum* is included) Madagascar; India and south-east Asia; tropical Australia
Coriariaceae (Fig. 42)	Central America and western South America; Mediterranean; East Asia; New Guinea; New Zealand, etc.
Cornaceae . .	North temperate; Asia to New Guinea; South America; South Africa and Madagascar; New Zealand, etc.
Cynocrambaceae .	Canaries; Mediterranean; Tibet; Japan
Elaeocarpaceae .	Tropical America and Chile; Madagascar; Mascarenes; Socotra; India and Japan to New Zealand and the Pacific Islands. Compare B3 and E above.
Haemodoraceae .	America; South Africa; Australia and Tasmania
Hamamelidaceae .	North America and Mexico; West Asia; India; Japan; Malaysia; Africa and Madagascar; and, if *Ostrearia* is rightly attributed, Queensland
Hydrocaryaceae .	Europe; parts of Africa; parts of Central Asia; eastern Asia.
Monimiaceae* .	America; Madagascar; Asia–Australasia
Myoporaceae . .	A dubious family, chiefly Australian and thence to Asia; Mascarenes; South Africa; West Indies
Petiveriaceae . .	Chiefly American but also in South Africa, eastern Australia and New Caledonia
Philydraceae . .	East and south-east Asia; New Guinea and eastern Australia; south-west Australia
Resedaceae . .	Western Eurasia and North Africa; eastern tropical and South Africa; south-west North America
Spigeliaceae . .	America; Madagascar; Asia–Australasia

Endemic families

As was explained in an earlier chapter the term "endemic" is not an absolute one but varies in value according to the circumstances of its use. Generally speaking the larger the taxonomic category concerned the wider the conception of endemism can be and in this chapter it is used to describe families which are found either within one of the continental land masses or within some area of roughly equivalent size. Many families are of course much more restricted even than this, and some are confined to single floristic regions, but to make the category less wide in scope would complicate things undesirably. It must also be noted that many families, which in this sense are endemic, are also, like various wide families, to some degree discontinuous, though not to the extent which would warrant including them in the last category in preference to this.

The endemic families are here tabulated geographically, and with them are given figures of the approximate number of species in each, since this is a matter of particular interest in more narrowly distributed groups. In connection with this table two families call for special remark, the Cactaceae and Bromeliaceae. The former is commonly reported as occurring in the Old World, but as far as can be judged, all these records are of adventive plants and the family is native only in the New World. Here, however, it has a much wider latitudinal range than any other purely American family and is also very much larger, and it has therefore been treated as an exceptional

PLATE 4

Map of the World showing Floristic Regions. Original.

1. Arctic and Sub-arctic
2. Euro-Siberian
    A. Europe
    B. Asia
3. Sino-Japanese
4. W. and C. Asiatic
5. Mediterranean
6. Macaronesian
7. Atlantic North American
    A. Northern
    B. Southern
8. Pacific North American
9. African—Indian Desert
10. Sudanese Park Steppe
11. N.E. African Highland
12. W. African Rain-forest
13. E. African Steppe
14. South African
15. Madagascar
16. Ascension and St. Helena
17. Indian

18. Continental S.E. Asiatic
19. Malaysian
20. Hawaiian
21. New Caledonia
22. Melanesia and Micronesia
23. Polynesia
24. Caribbean
25. Venezuela and Guiana
26. Amazon
27. South Brazilian
28. Andean
29. Pampas
30. Juan Fernandez
31. Cape
32. N. and E. Australian
33. S.W. Australian
34. C. Australian
35. New Zealand
36. Patagonian
37. S. Temp. Oceanic Islands

Areas correct   Distortion increasing towards border of map.

Approximate Scale. 1:100,000,000 (1600 miles=1inch) along Equator
on Mollweide's Homolographic Projection

Copyright

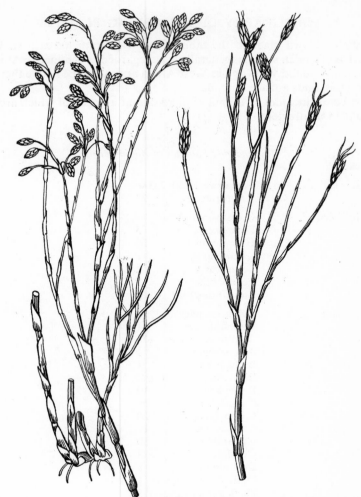

FIG. 11.—*Hypolaena fastigiata*, a typical member of the Restionaceae, about natural size, after Hooker.

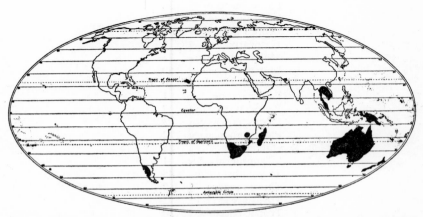

FIG. 12.—Map showing (black) the distribution of the family Restionaceae, partly after Hutchinson.

endemic with its own place in the tabulation. The Bromeliaceae, on the other hand, which is of similar size, has generally been regarded as confined to America, but the single species found years ago in West Africa appears to be native there and the family therefore finds a place on p. 63.

The list below includes 124 families in all, about a dozen of which are also discontinuous to a small extent.

The Endemic Families of Angiosperms

A. America:

1. General	. .	Cactaceae 1,250–2,000
		Krameriaceae 23
2. Northern	. .	Crossosomataceae 3
		Fouquieriaceae 5
		Garryaceae 20
		Koeberliniaceae 1
		Leitneriaceae 2
		Lennoaceae 5
		Limnanthaceae 5
3. Tropical	. .	Achatocarpaceae 10
		Agdestidaceae 1
		Alstroemeriaceae 175
		Asteranthaceae 1
		Batidaceae 1
		Bixaceae 1 or 2
		Brunelliaceae 10
		Cannaceae 50
		Caryocaraceae 20
		Cobaeaceae 17
		Cyclanthaceae 50
		Cyrillaceae 9
		Desfontaineaceae 3
		Dialypetalanthaceae 1
		Diclidantheraceae 3
		Goupiaceae 1
		Julianiaceae 5
		Lacistemaceae 20
		Lecythidaceae* 300
		Ledocarpaceae 1
		Lissocarpaceae 1
		Malesherbiaceae 25
		Marcgraviaceae 50
		Martyniaceae 10
		Pellicieraceae 1
		Picrodendraceae 3
		Plocospermaceae 3
		Pterostemonaceae 2
		Quiinaceae 25
		Stegnospermaceae 1
		Theophrastaceae 45
		Thurniaceae 2
		Tovariaceae 2
		Tropaeolaceae 30

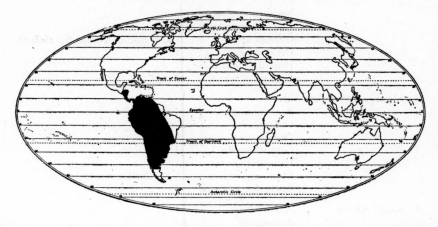

Fig. 13.—Map showing (black) the distribution of the family Tropaeolaceae, after Hutchinson.

4. Southern	.	.	Aextoxicaceae	1
			Calyceraceae	30
			Francoaceae	2
			Gomortegaceae	1
			Lactoridaceae	1
			Myzodendraceae	12
			Vivianiaceae	28
5. Others	.	.	Columelliaceae	2
			Heterostylaceae	1
			Nolanaceae	30
			Sarraceniaceae	10

B. Mediterranean in a wide sense, or at least centred there:

Cneoraceae 2
Cynomoriaceae 1
Globulariaceae 25
Punicaceae 2
Ruscaceae 150

C. Africa:

1. Tropical or tropical and southern Africa and the Madagascar region

Hydrostachyaceae 12
Montiniaceae 2
Myrothamnaceae 1
Selaginaceae 250
Sphenocleaceae 2

2. Tropical . . Barbeyaceae 1 and Arabia
Cyanastraceae 5
Dioncophyllaceae 3
Dirachmaceae 1 Socotra
Hoplestigmataceae 2
Huacaceae 2
Lepidobotryaceae 1
Medusandraceae 1
Melianthaceae 20 and South Africa

Nectaropetalaceae	6	
Octoknemataceae	5	
Oliniaceae	1	and South Africa; St. Helena
Pandaceae	1	
Pentadiplandraceae	1	
Scytopetalaceae	12	

3. Madagascar region only

Barbeuiaceae	1	
Chlaenaceae	30	
Didieraceae	4	
Geosiridaceae	1	
Humbertiaceae	1	
Medusagynaceae	1	Seychelles
Rhopalocarpaceae	5	

4. South Africa   .

Achariaceae	1
Bruniaceae	65
Geissolomataceae	1
Greyiaceae	3
Grubbiaceae	3
Heteropyxidaceae	2
Penaeaceae	30
Roridulaceae	2
Stilbeaceae	8

D. Asia:

1. Reaching Australia or New Zealand

Apostasiaceae	25
Sonneratiaceae*	12

2. Continental Asia, with Japan and Formosa

Bretschneideraceae	1
Cercidiphyllaceae	2
Circaeasteraceae	1
Dipentodontaceae	1
Eucommiaceae	1
Eupteleaceae	5
Pentaphylacaceae	1
Podoaceae	3
Rhoipteleaceae	1
Sargentodoxaceae	1
Stachyuraceae	5
Tetracentraceae	1
Trochodendraceae	1

3. Asia and Malaysia

Actinidiaceae	12
Crypteroniaceae	8
Daphniphyllaceae	30
Erythropalaceae	4
Pentaphragmataceae	15
Peripterygiaceae	5
Petrosaviaceae	3
Sarcospermataceae	8
Siphonodontaceae	3

4. Malaysia only   .   Gonystylaceae   22 and Solomons and Fiji
                     Lowiaceae   2
                     Scyphostegiaceae   1
                     Stenomeridaceae   1
                     Tetrameristaceae   2

E. Australasia and the Pacific Islands, or at least centred there:

1. Australia only   .   Akaniaceae   1
                     Austrobaileyaceae   1
                     Baueraceae   3
                     Brunoniaceae   1
                     Byblidaceae   2
                     Cephalotaceae   1
                     Chloanthaceae   60
                     Davidsoniaceae   1
                     Dysphaniaceae   6
                     Eremosynaceae   1
                     Gyrostemonaceae   5
                     Petermanniaceae   5
                     Tremandraceae   30

2. Others   .   .   Amborellaceae   1 New Caledonia
                     Balanopsidaceae   1 North-east Australia: New Caledonia, New Hebrides and Fiji
                     Cartonemataceae   8 Australia and New Guinea
                     Casuarinaceae   55 Australia, Fiji and New Caledonia to Burma
                     Corynocarpaceae   4 New Zealand, New Caledonia, New Hebrides, North Queensland, southern New Guinea
                     Degeneriaceae   1 Fiji
                     Eupomatiaceae   2 Australia and New Guinea
                     Himantandraceae   3 Australia and New Guinea
                     Oceanopapaveraceae   1 New Caledonia
                     Stackhousiaceae   25 Australia, New Zealand, New Guinea, Philippines, Palau and Yap
                     Strasburgeriaceae   1 New Caledonia
                     Xanthorrhoeaceae   12 Australia, New Caledonia and New Guinea

Anomalous families

There remain about ten families which do not easily fit into the foregoing classification (though most of them are fairly clearly related to groups therein mentioned) and which are therefore best treated separately here. In the main they are families which, less than world-wide, cannot be described satisfactorily as either tropical or temperate.

The Balanitaceae, Moringaceae, Pedaliaceae, Salvadoraceae and Vahliaceae belong to the tropics of the Old World but are mainly in arid countries and their distributions are therefore more or less continuous through Arabia and West Pakistan.

The Dipsacaceae and Tamaricaceae are found widely in Eurasia including India, and are also well distributed in Africa.

The family Hydrophyllaceae is, like the nearly-related Polemoniaceae, essentially

North American, but it includes one small genus (*Hydrolea*) which has species in all three sectors of the tropics. Balsaminaceae are in some ways an interesting contrast to Hydrophyllaceae in that they are essentially plants of the Asiatic and African tropics, but there are a few species which are widely distributed through the northern temperate regions.

As is shown by their maps in Vester (750) the distributions of Myricaceae and Buxaceae are, in differing respects, particularly anomalous, and inevitably raise a doubt as to whether these families as thus comprehended are really complete natural groups.

Southern families

Any general survey of the distribution of the families of Angiosperms such as has just been made leads directly to one of the most fascinating, and at the same time fundamental, problems of plant geography, the question of whether there is or is not recognisable a "southern" flora peculiar in origin to those parts of the world below the equator, and more particularly below the Tropic of Capricorn, and, if there is, what portions of the Angiosperms may be considered to belong to it. It is plain enough and will become even plainer as we go on, that a great many taxonomic units are to-day largely or entirely confined to this part of the world, but there are many others that are found in both extra-tropical zones, and others still which have, in addition, occurrences, usually at high elevations, within the tropics, so that it is certainly not possible to regard the northern and southern extra-tropical floras as two unrelated and isolated entities. There is in fact a continuity between them, and the problem, in its rather narrower expression, is to decide the relative significance of what at least appear to be two intermingled components.

It is well first of all to recall and to bear in mind one or two points of history. Because of the peculiar distribution of land and sea the land area of the northern flora is enormously greater than that of the southern (see Appendix A). Not only so but because of climatic conditions virtually nothing is known of the history of what, in the present connection, is likely to be the crucial part of the south, namely, Antarctica. The North has therefore at the outset an inherent predominance in many respects and this has been intensified by the fact that while this flora has been familiar to man for thousands of years and has been the subject of his interest ever since he became lettered, the southern flora has for the most part been known for less than 200 years. Added to this is the circumstance that the movement of almost all man-made influences has been predominantly in the one direction from north to south.

There is consequently an inherent tendency to assume that botanically, as well as in so many other ways, the south has been stocked from the north rather than the reverse, but this view has also in the past received a good deal of scientific support. Interest in the origin and migrations of floras quickened greatly after the coming of the Darwinian theory of evolution in the middle of last century and most of the great protagonists of that time had their views upon these questions (756), or at least realised how difficult they were. Hooker, who was one of the first to study the flora of the antipodes, was greatly impressed by the reappearance almost everywhere from Europe to Tasmania of genera, and sometimes even of species, belonging to the Scandinavian floras, as if, as he put it, there was a "continuous current of vegetation . . . along . . . the whole extent of that arc of the terrestrial sphere which presents the greatest continuity of land" (371), and from this there sprang the conception of the aggressiveness of the Scandinavian flora, an idea which, buttressed by such other observations as the extreme speed and ease of spread of many weed species emanating from the north, for long sustained belief in the overwhelming preponderance of north to south migrations. Even as recently as 1910 Thiselton-Dyer (730) expressed the opinion that the great floristic richness of certain parts of the south, such as South Africa, was due to the fact that they were *culs-de-sac* in which successive waves of migration from the north had piled up.

Gradually however this point of view underwent modification and it is interesting to note some of the stages by which this came about. Comparatively early the attribution of various northern Angiosperm fossils to typically southern families and genera came to balance the identification of southern fossils with northern plants, and although the value of these determinations is highly problematical (see Chapter 15) they served to adjust the focus a little. Much later came the change of ideas resulting from a better knowledge of both the past and present geology of many parts of the world and particularly from the doubts which began to be expressed concerning current beliefs regarding the permanence of continents and oceans, doubts culminating in the various theories now associated with continental drift, a conception which peculiarly involves the history of the southern land masses. In later years, too, the floras of the southern hemisphere and their resemblances and relationships to those of the north have been studied again and in great detail by many botanists, especially by Skottsberg, whose many writings on this subject (see bibliography) have done much to put it on a sounder basis, and who has, in particular, given a vivid impression of the successive floras which in the course of geological time have occupied Antarctica (659, 670). A useful survey of these and various related publications has also been given, with special reference to the crucial problem of bipolar plant distribution (see later), by Du Rietz (205). At the same time belief in the supposed greater migratory powers of the northern flora has been modified by such studies as those of Allan on the introduced plants of New Zealand (12, 13, 14, 15), in which he shows that the predominance of alien species is, for reasons more fully set out later (see Chapter 19), largely illusory and that they seldom make headway against native plants in their natural habitats. An interesting account of this particular change of outlook since Hooker's day has been given by Wright Smith (799).

These are some of the reasons why ideas as to the part which may have been played by the southern flora in the general development of the distribution of the Flowering Plants have so much changed in recent years. To-day opinions quite the reverse of those earlier held are not uncommon, as may be exemplified by reference to some of them. Croizat, in a discussion of the genera *Trochodendron* and *Tetracentron* (163), reaches the conclusion that not only certain families (he mentioned Cornaceae and Saxifragaceae especially), but most Angiosperm families, are united phylogenetically more closely with the southern hemisphere than they are to "holarctica". Camp, in a long survey of some of the more striking examples of distribution (108), goes even further and subscribes to the view that a study of distribution patterns in relation to phylogeny points to a southern origin of the Angiosperms as a whole. Gordon (309) has also made useful comments on this and its related problems.

More recently Croizat (165) has put forward, with a wealth of detail, the thesis that the Angiosperms originated in the southern hemisphere and that during the early stages of their history the distribution of land and sea was so different from that of to-day that they were able to spread through the tropics and over the world, from the south, by certain routes or, as he calls them, "gateways". Chief among these were the African "gate", the Western Polynesian "gate" and the Magellanian or South

American "gate". The evidence leaves little doubt that many genera, and even families, have indeed crossed the tropics by at any rate the second and third of these, but the geographical changes which Croizat considers necessary to sustain his theory, including as they do a much enlarged Antarctica and two transoceanic land-bridges, are so sweeping that they must be regarded with a measure of scepticism. This, however, does not detract from the originality of his thought and presentation, nor does it justify the dismissal of his opinions as unworthy of serious attention.

Whether or not one can, in face of so many facts concerning the tropical floras of the world, agree with some of the more extreme of these views, it is clear that the phytogeographical facts which may bear on this question of the southern floras and their history call for careful scrutiny here, and this can best be done by a further survey of the families from this particular aspect.

For this purpose southern families may be defined as those in which a considerable majority of the species are found below the equator and to some extent at least below the Tropic of Capricorn. In theory greatest species concentration and greatest superficial extent need not occur in the same hemisphere, that is to say a group may have most of its species on one side of the equator and most of its range on the other, but for simplicity these may, if any of them exist, be ignored here.

On this definition about 90 families may be described as "southern", and the easiest way to deal with them is to eliminate group by group from the discussion, especially since it will be found that interest mainly centres round a residue of a few, fairly large, families.

To begin with there are some eight endemic families partly or entirely in temperate South America (see above); about twelve in southern Africa (including Melianthaceae, Oliniaceae and Selaginaceae); seven in the Madagascar region; thirteen in Australia; three in New Caledonia, and one in Fiji. To these may be added five rather more widely endemic in Australasia, and three (Casuarinaceae, Philydraceae and Stackhousiaceae) which range from Australia or New Zealand northward across the equator. These in all account for over one-third of all the endemic families noted on pages 66–69 above.

Then there are nine families discontinuously distributed between South America and Asia/Australia, six of them quite small and three considerably larger, namely Epacridaceae, Goodeniaceae (ignoring the two pan-tropical shore species) and Stylidiaceae. These last three show a feature which is strikingly noticeable in many of the southern families, a considerable though absolutely minor extension northward across the equator into Malaysia and even into continental south-east Asia (see Figs. 3, 16).

Three families, Flagellariaceae, Pandanaceae and Pittosporaceae, range widely over the warmer latitudes of the Old World. The family Flagellariaceae is too small to have much numerical preponderance anywhere; the Pandanaceae are more evenly and widely spaced, but have most of their species in the south, including a notable number in the Madagascar region and comparatively few in Africa; the Pittosporaceae have a most remarkable distribution shown in Fig. 6, including a strong representation in Hawaii, and are predominantly Australasian.

Next are four families each of which, though totally widespread, has an enormous southern species concentration, either, as in the cases of Aizoaceae, Geraniaceae and Thymelaeaceae, in South Africa, or, in the Oxalidaceae, in both South America and South Africa. In view of what was said earlier about the Ericaceae it is perhaps fair to mention the Ericoideae here, as if they were a distinct family, for its South African concentration is very striking and it contrasts with the foregoing because of its comparatively restricted range north of the equator.

Two series of families remain. The larger consists of twelve which are chiefly notable because they are found in all three main sectors and of the extra-tropical south without having any very wide range above the equator, and in this sense they may be regarded perhaps as the most characteristic of all southern families. Four of them, Cunoniaceae, Proteaceae, Restionaceae, and the considerably smaller Philesiaceae, are illustrated here by maps and scarcely need further comment than perhaps to call attention again to their extensions north towards or into Asia. The family Petiveriaceae is also in all three southern sectors. Closely related to these are four families in which the southern predominance is, however, somewhat masked by their more considerable expression within the tropics. They are the Escalloniaceae, which in the New World extend to Central America; the Monimiaceae, which are also strongly represented in the New World; the Elaeocarpaceae, which have many points of particular interest including their occurrence in the Madagascar region but not in Africa, and the Dilleniaceae which are widely distributed in the tropics, though least be it noted in Africa, and which are definitely southern by virtue of the great genus *Hibbertia* (see Fig. 27) which has no counterpart north of the equator. Finally there are the two smaller families Haemodoraceae and Hypoxidaceae, together with the Zygophyllaceae, a family characteristic of arid countries, in total very widespread, but with a majority of species in the south, especially in South Africa and Australia.

Seven families forming the second series remain to be mentioned. The Haloragaceae, Juncaginaceae and Droseraceae (see Fig. 18) are very widespread but all three have the great bulk of their species south of the tropics and are indeed most characteristic of Australia. Also widely distributed but with a much more restricted range in the north temperate are the much larger families Rutaceae and Araliaceae. The limits of the former are not too well-defined but it is clear that the great bulk of the species of the genera usually assigned to it are southern and the family is particularly conspicuous in the floras of South Africa and Australia. It may be that a future re-estimation of the family will make it even more obviously southern than it is now by the removal from it of some of the northern genera. The Araliaceae is a well-defined family but its genera are much confused, and this is unfortunate because the reputed distributions of many of them are of exceptional interest. As a whole the family has a notable Australasian preponderance and is particularly significant in New Caledonia and the Pacific Islands.

It may cause surprise that the Palmae should be claimed as a southern family but there are cogent reasons for doing so. True, the overall distribution of the family is fairly symmetrically pan-tropical and there is no really outstanding concentration of species in the south, but it shows (see pp. 75–77) several points in common with many of the foregoing families. The family is less well-developed in Africa than in America and Asia; but it is notably rich in the Madagascar region; it is strongly associated with New Caledonia and some of the neighbouring parts of Australasia; and certain constituent parts of the family, and particularly the Areceae, are much more strongly represented south of the equator than north of it, and there is no corresponding group in the north.

Lastly there is the largest of all the families to be mentioned here, the Myrtaceae, which though pan-tropical and even with some extra-tropical northern representatives is in total overwhelmingly southern. In one half of the family, the Leptospermoideae, one of the two constituent groups is exclusively Australian, and the other, which includes the great genus *Eucalyptus*, very largely so. In the other half are various instances of relationship between South America and Australasia. There is notable paucity in Africa and also, in this case, in the Madagascar region.

Space will not permit us to pursue this very interesting subject of the southern flora here, though one or two other families, e.g. Portulacaceae, Strelitziaceae and Lobeliaceae, might have been mentioned, but enough has been said to show how considerable a factual basis it has, a basis that the progress of phylogenetic taxonomy is likely to widen. It must be remembered also that only whole families have been alluded to and there are many individual genera, as for instance *Acacia* and several of those familiar in the north temperate zone, whose details suggest that the families to which they belong, or at least parts of them, may also have had a southern, origin. There is still too much to be learnt about the course of botanical events south of the tropics to justify any dogmatic statement but we can at least be reasonably sure that the southern flora, that is to say the flora now characteristic of the southern temperate regions, is not the derivative of the north that it was long believed to be (see Chapter 12).

Details of some Particular Families and other large Groups of Genera

The total range of a family is simply the sum of the ranges of its constituent genera and species, and except in very small families reveals little about the relative and proportionate distribution of these minor units, which is actually often the most noteworthy feature in their distribution as a whole. Moreover, this varies greatly, with the result that families whose total ranges are very similar are often very distinct in terms of the distribution of their genera. Indeed, it would be quite possible to arrange all the families actually on this basis, but this would occupy too much space here. As a substitute, the remainder of this chapter is devoted to a review of 5 particular families and 2 comparable lesser groups which, taken together, illustrate most of the salient features that a classification of this kind would show. These are the Primulacea, Palmae, Proteaceae, Lobeliaceae, Berberidaceae, the Bambuseae, and the arborescent members of the Compositae.

The Primulaceae

The Primulaceae may be described as an outstanding example of a family made up of a few, and comparatively widely different, genera which vary considerably in distributional extent. Its total range is practically world-wide, but most of the genera are much more restricted. The classification used here is that of Pax (218), with the figures brought reasonably up to date.

There are twenty-two genera, namely, *Primula, Dionysia, Douglasia, Androsace, Cortusa, Stimpsonia, Ardisiandra, Soldanella, Pomatosace, Bryocarpum, Dodecatheon, Cyclamen, Lysimachia, Trientalis, Asterolinon, Pelletiera, Glaux, Anagallis, Centunculus, Samolus, Hottonia* and *Coris*. Most of them are temperate genera and generally familiar, so that a glance at the list shows how varied an assortment of types may go to make up a family which is nevertheless a well-defined natural group.

The world-wide distribution of the family is due chiefly to the exceptionally wide areas of *Anagallis* and *Samolus*. *Anagallis* especially is a genus of disturbed ground and much of its range may be adventive, but *Samolus* appears to be truly and naturally more or less cosmopolitan with species in both northern and southern temperate regions.

Primula is by far the largest genus, with several hundreds of species. Geographically it is both discontinuous and locally centred. It ranges throughout the northern temperate regions with some extension into the tropics and has also one species at least in temperate South America, but the vast majority of its forms are confined to the great Sino-Himalayan mountain region. This latter region has been carefully explored only in recent years, and the discovery and frequently the subsequent introduction into European gardens of many new *Primula* species has been a marked feature in the horticultural history of this century. The genus *Androsace*, though smaller than *Primula*, closely resembles it, but is generally regarded as confined to the northern temperate zone.

Lysimachia is also a large genus and is found in almost all the temperate and subtropical parts of the world, as well as on some tropical mountains. The remaining genera are all small in species number, less widely distributed and fall into several groups, each of special interest. Three are widely discontinuous, namely *Hottonia*, with two species in eastern North America and in Europe; *Dodecatheon*, with about fifteen species in North America and in eastern Asia; and *Douglasia*, which has one species in the Alps and Spanish Mountains and five in arctic and western North America. *Glaux*, 1 sp.; *Centunculus*, 3 spp., and *Trientalis*, 3 spp., are fairly widespread in the northern temperate zone. *Dionysia*, 23 spp., is found in western and Central Asia and *Cortusa*, 2 spp., comes from some of the mountains of Europe and Asia. *Cyclamen*, with 12 spp., *Asterolinon* with 2 spp., *Coris* with 2 spp. and *Soldanella* with 7 spp. are all found only in Europe and the Mediterranean region, the last-named being one of the few genera endemic to the European Alps. *Bryocarpum* and *Pomatosace* are each monotypic (of one species only) of the Sino-Himalayan mountains; and *Stimpsonia*, also monotypic, occurs very locally in China and on the Riukiu Islands. *Pelletiera*, 2 spp., is found only in temperate South America, and, finally, the monotypic genus *Ardisiandra*, belonging to the same part of the family as *Primula*, is confined to some of the mountains in western and eastern Tropical Africa.

The family thus illustrates the following points. It consists of comparatively few but markedly distinct genera. The genera vary in size from monotypes to one with hundreds of species. There is discontinuity both within the northern temperate zone and between the north and south temperate regions. It is in total world-wide but only by the exceptional ranges of one or two forms. Endemism is fairly well marked, and one genus, *Primula*, is an outstanding example of a group with the bulk of its species massed in one part of the world. The family is very predominantly temperate in character.

The Palmae
(Plate 25)

The family Palmae, containing that remarkable and almost unique group of plants known as the palms, differs from the Primulaceae in almost every way. It is a large group both in genera (about 250) and species (about 2,000) but it is at the same time a very natural one with a most distinctive appearance. Its geographical range also is distinct (Fig. 14), being rigidly limited by climatic conditions and almost entirely within the tropics. Indeed the Palmae are one of the most exclusively tropical of all the larger families. Such climatic limitation is never absolute in a family of any size, and to this the Palmae are no exception, having a slight representation in several subtropical and even warm temperate regions, but this only emphasises the tropical character of the family as a whole.

Within the tropics the distribution of the palms is almost ubiquitous, though they are said to be absent from a few small areas such as the Galapagos Islands, but by the nature of the case it is divisible into three parts. Rather more than one third of the genera are confined to the New World; a rather larger proportion to Asia, Australia and the Pacific Islands; while only about one-seventh are restricted to Africa and the Madagascar region. Fewer than half a dozen genera range over more than one of these areas and none is found in all three. *Phoenix, Borassus* and *Calamus* are found in both African and Asiatic sectors. *Raphia* is in both American and African sectors, and *Elaeis* was formerly credited with the same distribution, but the American plants have now been made the genus *Corozo*. Apart from these the most widely spread are some half dozen which range from south-east Asia to Australia or Polynesia.

The genera vary greatly in size. The largest is *Calamus* with some 250 species; *Bactris, Daemonorops, Geonoma* and *Pinanga* have about 100 each; while *Chamaedorea* and *Licuala* are not much smaller. On the other hand, about seventy-five genera are monotypic, and more than fifty others are generally reckoned to have fewer than 5 species each.

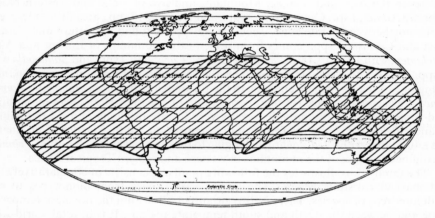

Fig. 14.—Map showing (shaded) the general latitudinal distribution of the family Palmae.

The absence of wide genera has already been remarked, but in addition to this the number of genera with narrow ranges, namely endemics, is very large. Using the term endemic in quite a conservative sense, over 100 merit it, and these are well scattered, few warm regions being without them. They are least plentiful perhaps in Malaysia, though there are some 30 confined to this great region as a whole, and most abundant and conspicuous in certain small insular areas. Thus in the Seychelles and Mauritius all the genera are endemic, and in New Caledonia 12 out of 15 genera are endemic. In Madagascar 13 out of 18 are found nowhere else, and among other regions Central America, the West Indies, New Guinea and, especially, the Pacific Islands are notable for endemic genera.

Species endemism is even more marked and it has been calculated that no less than 95 per cent of all species in the family are so narrowly distributed. Not only this, but in nearly 150 genera there are none but endemic species. In Hawaii, Madagascar and the Mascarenes, and New Caledonia all the native species are endemic, while even in such continental regions as Central America, South America and tropical Africa the percentage is over 90. Similarly in New Guinea and the Pacific Islands; but in other parts of Malaysia the proportion of endemic species (as also of endemic genera) is lower than almost anywhere else, as, for instance, 50 per cent in Java and 38 per cent in Sumatra.

Even more noteworthy is the relationship between endemism and geographical isolation in the form of insularity, which is seen in both genera and species. Nearly forty genera are restricted to what may reasonably be called small islands. There are, for instance, twelve endemic genera (with about 25 species) in New Caledonia and nine among the smaller islands associated with Madagascar, including six on the Seychelles alone. There are also about six on various small islands of the Pacific as well as three on the tiny Lord Howe Island, between Australia and New Zealand, one on Cocos Island (America) and one on Juan Fernandez.

This marked restriction of many palms to small islands is still better seen in the species, as the following table shows:

Species of Palms on Small Islands

Hawaiian Islands *c*. 30, with very segregated distributions (668)		Fiji . . . . . 9 Solomons 8	
Bismarck Archipelago . . 12		Seychelles 7	
Mauritius 11		Trinidad 7	

4 species each on Martinique, Samoa, the Carolines, Lord Howe I., the Comoros, and St. Marie de Madagascar.

3 species each on the Andamans, the Nicobars, Aru, Ternate.

2 species on the Guadeloupe, Ceram, Nossi Bé, Tobago, Palau and St. Vincent.

Among the islands from which single endemic species have been recorded are: St. Thomas, Barbados, the Isle of Pines, Mergui, Bird Island, Bermuda, Fernando Po, Corisco, Key, Bougainville, Billiton, Christmas, Grenada, Croker Island, Batjan, Norfolk, St. Kitts, the Kermadecs, and one or two single islands of the Tuamotus.

Finally, a point of considerable local interest in the distribution of the palms is the isolated occurrence (not shown in Fig. 14) of a small grove of palms belonging to the genus *Livistona* on the Macdonnell Range near Alice Springs in the dry heart of Australia.

To summarise, the Palmae are a very natural group of considerable geological age, with a very isolated systematic position—features once vividly described by Hooker, in a letter to Darwin (397) in the words "a very ancient group and much dislocated, structurally and geographically". The genera vary greatly in size, but an unusually large number of them are very small. The family is rigidly limited geographically to the warmest parts of the world's surface except for one or two quite minor extensions. No single species or even genus covers anything approaching the whole range of the family and widespread genera and species are very few. Such as there are show discontinuity over two of the three major land divisions of the tropics. Endemism in both genera and species is exceptionally high and is accompanied by an almost unique degree of geographical isolation, a number of species being confined to islands so small as to be difficult to find even in the largest atlases, a state of affairs all the more remarkable because the fruits of only a very few species of palms are known to be capable of drifting unharmed in sea water.

The Proteaceae (578, 674, 836)

(Plates 12, 15, & 16)

This family, which has 60 genera and 1,400 species is best known for the relationship it shows between southern Africa and Australia, but undue emphasis on this point has tended to obscure the main geographical feature of the group, namely, that it is one of the best examples of a large southern family well represented in all the continents below the equator.

As will be seen from the map (Fig. 16) there are three extensions northwards from the main areas of distribution, one in each continent. That in America is largely due to the genus *Roupala* which is well represented in Brazil and other parts of the neighbouring tropics, and in this continent the southern species are comparatively few. These show, however, a strong relation with Australia, *Gevuina*, *Lomatia*, *Oreocallis* and *Orites* being discontinuous between the two continents.

The northern extension is least in Africa, though there are some fifty species within the tropics here, and this, in view of the great development of the family in South Africa, has often caused comment (31). There are no species in the west African forests though the genera *Protea* and *Faurea* occur in the savannas of French Guinea: on the east *Protea* reaches Eritraea and *Faurea* is found in Abyssinia (456). There is one endemic genus, *Dilobeia*, in Madagascar and also one species of *Faurea*.

As in the New World the northward extension of the family in Asia is due to one large genus, *Helicia*, (and its split, *Helicopsis*) which covers the whole of the monsoon region from South India, Sikkim and southern Japan to the Bismarck Archipelago and eastern Australia as far as New South Wales. In the eastern part of the Old World, however, the more equatorial species are much in a minority (even though there are some forty species of *Helicia* in New Guinea) because of the strong development of the family in Australia and New Caledonia. There are two species in New Zealand and the family also reaches Palau, Fiji and Samoa.

The relatively enormous massing of the species of the family in South Africa and in Australia, which is so frequently cited, may be gauged by the statement that about two-thirds of the species are Australian and about one-quarter South African, so that only one-twelfth is left in the whole of the rest of the family area.

The family is divided into two subfamilies, the Persoonioideae and the Grevilleoideae, and the relative distribution of these can be best visualised by saying that the former has no American representatives and that the latter has no African representatives. It will be seen from this that the former is the characteristic group of South Africa, and the latter of Australia. The segregation between the two is, however, not complete, because no fewer than fourteen genera of the Persoonioideae are found in Australasia, sometimes in considerable numbers of species.

The family as a whole therefore exhibits (apart from almost indisputable evidence of a southern origin) major discontinuity between Africa and Australia; extension north across the equator in all continents; massing of species in Africa, Australia and New Caledonia; minor discontinuity between Australia and New Caledonia and between Australia and New Zealand; well-marked systematic segregation between America and Africa and less marked segregation between Africa and Australia.

The Lobeliaceae

The Lobeliaceae, which have been monographed by Wimmer (794), illustrate many points of interest of a rather different kind. In total the family has a very wide range throughout the tropics, and over much of the warm temperate and even temperate parts of the world, but in the latter is represented by comparatively few small herbaceous forms. The main feature of the family is the occurrence in many isolated regions of endemic genera or species with peculiar growth forms, many of which may be described as giant herbs, though some of them are branched shrubs or even small trees.

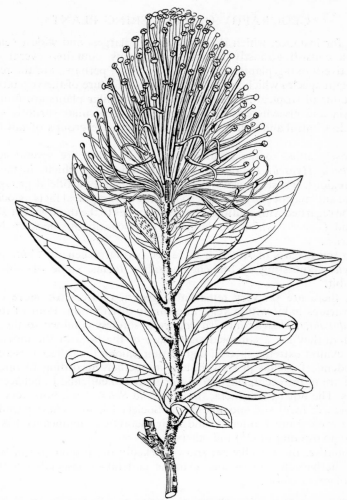

FIG. 15.—*Oreocallis* (*Embothrium*) *grandiflora*, a typical member of the Proteaceae, about half
natural size, after Baillon.

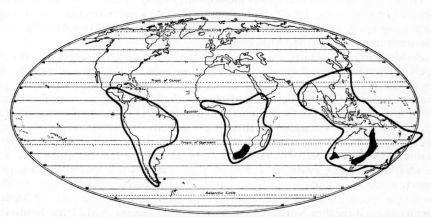

FIG. 16.—Map showing the distribution of the family Proteaceae. The solid black areas are those
of greatest species concentration.

Lobelia, for instance, which is the central and largest and widest genus of the family, while consisting mostly of herbaceous forms, contains several groups of very distinctive-looking plants. Best known of these, perhaps, are the remarkable columnar giant species which are so conspicuous a feature of the vegetation of the high mountains of tropical Africa (Plate 13), but similar plants are found also in parts of Asia and elsewhere (660). There is also a peculiar shrubby species on St. Helena. In Central and South America, too, there are groups of tall herbs and shrubs.

Very closely allied to the small herbaceous Lobelias are several genera, i.e. *Grammatotheca*, *Hypsela*, *Laurentia*, *Monopsis* and *Pratia*, chiefly in the southern temperate regions. These, however, are almost certainly artificial groups derived from *Lobelia* and may be polyphyletic, so that the geographical facts associated with them must be regarded with caution. The same applies to the three genera *Downingia*, *Howellia* and *Legenere* which are described as discontinuous between North and South America.

In the tropical parts of America there are two large genera, *Centropogon* and *Siphocampylus*, consisting of branched shrubby forms, some of which have a climbing habit.

Finally, there are six very remarkable genera of trees, or more commonly shrubs, of various habit with a very noteworthy distribution. Four of them, *Clermontia*, *Rollandia*, *Delissea* and *Cyanea*, are absolutely confined to the Hawaiian Islands, where they are a conspicuous feature of the flora of the mountains and where they exhibit extreme specific segregation among the different islands. There are also endemic Lobelias in Hawaii, and altogether, according to one estimate (691), there are in the archipelago no fewer than 150 endemic Lobeliaceae including varieties. The other two genera, *Apetahia* and *Sclerotheca*, both very small, are similar in growth form and endemic to the Society Islands. These peculiar Pacific genera have excited much interest, and their theoretical significance has been discussed at length by Guppy (325) and others.

To summarise, the Lobeliaceae show markedly the production of widespread generalised herbaceous forms and extreme endemism associated with marked peculiarity of growth form.

The Berberidaceae*

The sister genera *Berberis* and *Mahonia*, which make up the family Berberidaceae in its most proper sense, have distributions well illustrating many features of Angiosperm geography, and a detailed recent revision by Ahrendt (9) enables these to be seen much more clearly than hitherto.

Berberis (Fig. 17), which, with about 500 species, is much the larger, has two very widely separated areas of species concentration, namely the great mountain complex of the Himalayas and western China and its southern counterpart the great Andean system of South America. Rather more than half the species are found in the former and from it the genus spreads in small numbers in almost all directions. Eastward it ranges across China, where there is a considerable number of species, decreasing rapidly to a few in Japan, a few in Formosa and one in the Philippines: to the south-east there is a species in Java and Sumatra; and to the south there are a few species in India and Ceylon. To the north there are very few species, but the genus seems to extend to about the latitude of 50° N. On the west the genus ranges, by about two dozen species, through west Central Asia to central Europe and the Mediterranean (where it reaches North Africa) to a terminal species in Madeira. South from

PLATE 5

Map of the World showing Climatic Provinces. After Supan in Bartholomew's *Physical Atlas*, vol. III.

1. Arctic
2. West European
3. East European
4. West Siberian
5. East Siberian
6. Kamchatkan
7. Sino-Japanese
8. Asiatic Mountain and Plateau
9. Aral
10. Indus
11. Mediterranean
12. Saharan
13. African Tropical
14. Kalahari
15. Cape
16. Indo-Australian Monsoon
17. Inner Australian
18. S.W. Australian

19. East Australian
20. New Zealand
21. Polynesian Tropical
22. Hawaiian
23. North Canadian
24. N.W. American Coastal
25. Californian
26. N. American Mountain and Plateau
27. Atlantic American
28. West Indian
29. Tropical Cordilleran
30. S. American Tropical
31. Peruvian
32. North Chilian
33. South Chilian
34. Pampa

Areas correct   Distortion increasing towards border of map.
Approximate Scale 1:100,000,000 (1600 miles = 1 inch) along Equator
on **Mollweides Homolographic Projection**
Copyright

about the middle of this western extension the genus extends down into East Africa as far as Tanganyika by an isolated species in eastern Arabia and to others south from Somaliland.

In America *Berberis* occupies the whole western side of South America from Costa Rica to the Falkland Islands but its centre of concentration, in which there is something less than half of the total number of species, is in the mountains between the Equator and the Tropic of Capricorn. From here there is a strong extension to the south and a rather weaker one westward to cover the rest of temperate South America. There is one outlying species on Masafuera in the Juan Fernandez group. In North America there are also two outlying species, one in New Mexico and southern Colorado and one in the east, chiefly along the Alleghenies. The species of the Old and New World are completely segregated taxonomically except that the last-mentioned belongs to an Old World group.

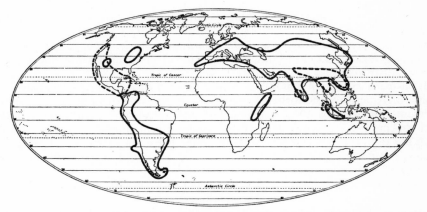

FIG. 17.—Map showing the distribution of *Berberis* (continuous line) and *Mahonia* (broken line), after Ahrendt (9).

Mahonia (Fig. 17), which differs from *Berberis* mainly in being spineless and in having pinnate instead of simple leaves, has about 100 species, and its distribution is much narrower and more widely discontinuous. Its area of greatest concentration in Asia is much the same as that of *Berberis*, and it stretches thence eastward to four species in Formosa and one in the Philippines. To the south and south-east it occurs in continental tropical south-east Asia and there are outlying species in Sumatra and in southern India, but it does not extend northward or westward. In the New World it does not occur in South America at all but has a continuous range from Cuba and Mexico north-westward to California and as far as British Columbia, an area from which *Berberis* is virtually absent.

Thus the family as a whole is incompletely north temperate: has extensions southward beyond the equator in all three tropical sectors; but is absent from Australasia. The larger genus is almost discontinuous because of its restricted distribution in North America. The smaller genus, *Mahonia*, is completely discontinuous between America and Asia.

The Bambuseae

Although it is not formally recognised above as a separate family, this very well-marked section of the Gramineae, comprising its woody members the bamboos,

6

has a very interesting geography particularly illustrative of certain features not uncommonly seen in the distribution of families and referred to elsewhere in these chapters.

The bamboos consist of upwards of fifty genera and of about 500 species, and are found in general throughout the warmer parts of the world, though their northern and southern limits are very uneven longitudinally. In the northern hemisphere they reach as far as 45° in Asia (the Kuriles), and 40° in eastern North America, but there are no native species in Europe, south-west Asia or in North Africa, their extreme in this sector being about 18° in the Sudan, south of the Sahara (compare various families above). In the southern hemisphere they reach about 43° in Chile; they are in all parts of southern Africa; but in Australia they extend no further than about 18° in Queensland.

Unless the somewhat doubtful American species are correctly associated with the Asiatic species of *Bambusa*, only the more or less pan-tropical genus *Arundinaria* is found in both Old and New Worlds. *Oxytenanthera* occurs in Africa and Asia; *Schizostachyum* in Madagascar, Asia and some of the Pacific Islands including Hawaii; and *Cephalostachyum* and *Ochlandra* are both in Madagascar and Asia. No other genus occurs in more than one sector of the tropics and some are quite narrowly distributed.

It has been calculated that 90 per cent or more of the 500 or so species are either Asiatic or American, the former being much more numerous than the latter. The representation of the bamboos in tropical Africa is remarkably small and one of their most striking features, consisting of only about 6 genera and 14 species, which is much less even than that of Madagascar, where there are 9 genera and perhaps 30 species. There are 3 species (of *Arundinaria* and *Bambusa*) in the northern part of Australia.

As for the Pacific the genus *Greslania*, which is a dwarf form scarcely typical of the group, is endemic in New Caledonia: there are believed to be bamboos in the Solomon Islands; and *Schizostachyum glaucifolium* occurs in Hawaii, Fiji, Samoa and is possibly on other islands too. The absence of bamboos from New Zealand is interesting compared with their presence as far as 43° S. in Chile. This suggests the possibility that they are foreign to the south temperate flora but have been able to enter it from the tropics in the New World, where there is land continuity, but not in the Old World where there is marked insularity.

Arborescent Compositae

In the northern extra-tropical regions the Compositae consist so predominantly of herbaceous plants that it is easy to forget that in some other parts of the world, and especially in Australasia, woody members of the family are not uncommon. Some of these are only small shrubs but the largest of them properly merit the description of trees. Certain of these such as the giant species of *Senecio*, which are a familiar element in the flora of the mountains of tropical Africa (see pp. 202–206), and *Vernonia arborea*, which is said to reach a height of 100 ft. in the forests of some part of tropical Asia and Malaysia, are members of large and widespread genera, but for the most part they belong to genera which are without herbaceous species. It is difficult to draw a hard and fast line between large shrubs and small trees but about thirty genera, belonging to nearly a dozen sections of the family, have been described as comprising woody plants including trees or small trees, and the geographical distribution of these genera is of great interest.

Olearia which, with over a hundred species, is much larger than any of the others and shows a wide range of size, is specially characteristic of Australia and New Zealand and is found also in New Guinea. Of the rest, some sixteen, with an average species content of about ten, have continental distributions, chiefly in South America. The remaining dozen, however, which are nearly all smaller, have remarkable insular ranges.

Three of them—*Commidendron, Melanodendron* and *Petrobium*—are endemic to St. Helena, where, in Melliss's time (509) nine of the ten native composite species were woody, six of them trees. Three more—*Wilkesia, Argyroxiphium* and *Hesperomannia*—are endemic to the Hawaiian Islands: while three others—*Robinsonia, Rhetinodendron* and *Dendroseris*—are endemic to the Juan Fernandez Islands. The remaining three are *Brachyglottis*, a New Zealand monotype: *Fitchia* which has six species on islands in the Pacific between 130° and 160° W. and 15° and 30° S. (see p. 145); and *Scalesia*, the remarkable woody endemic genus of the Galapagos Islands, which includes several species described as trees. *Dendroseris* and *Fitchia*, it may be noted, are the only arborescent members of the Liguliflorae.

Remarkable as the Compositae are in this respect they are not the only predominantly herbaceous group with arborescent, or at least large woody, representatives on tiny islands, other instances being *Plantago* (see p. 163), *Chenopodium* (p. 219), *Melanoselinum* (p. 135), *Dendrosicyos* (pp. 138, 201), *Dorstenia* (p. 201) and the Lobeliaceae (see p. 78, above), and the presence of these plants on remote and, often, geologically young, oceanic islands raises fascinating problems, not only of plant-geography but also of evolution in the Flowering Plants.

CHAPTER 5

THE DISTRIBUTION OF GENERA—1

WHEN classification was discussed in an earlier chapter, it was pointed out that, from a geographical point of view at any rate, the genus is the most important and illuminating of all categories. The species is, generally speaking, too small a unit to be of much use in the consideration of world-wide problems, and it is moreover an ultimate category not amenable to further statistical analysis. It is encumbered, too, by the confusion arising from the divergence of opinion as to its value. The family, on the other hand, is more often than not too large a category for convenient handling and the total number of families is small. It is, certainly, like the genus composed of constituent units (the genera) and can be analysed in various ways, but the relationship between genera is not even theoretically constant.

The genus, on the contrary, tends to possess the advantages of both the family and the species without their disadvantages. Genera are mostly of convenient size, both taxonomically and geographically, and are made up of constituent parts, the species, which, at least in theory, all possess the same value. Moreover, the conception underlying the genus is very definitely monophyletic, that is to say, the genus more than any other category is presumed to consist of forms closely related not only by structure but also by descent from a common ancestor.

For these reasons genera need special attention, and the next three chapters, which describe their distribution, are to be regarded as among the most important in this book.

Number and Size of Genera

Taxonomically the size of a genus is reckoned by the number of species it contains, and genera vary enormously in this respect. A great many are monotypic, that is to say consist of only one species: at the other extreme are several genera containing upwards of or more than 1,000 species. It is obviously difficult to give definite figures because of the differences of opinion which often exist as to what does or does not constitute a species, just as it is often difficult to say how many genera there are in a given family. There are striking examples of both these points. The most recent revision of the family Cruciferae (222) puts the number of genera at over 300, but these are in general so closely similar to one another that the suggestion has even been made that they really constitute only one enormous genus. Again, *Mesembryanthemum* used to be treated as a single genus with some hundreds of species, but it is now (222) generally split up into many genera, most of which are very small. It is important to bear these difficulties in mind because of the constant quotation of figures in this and succeeding chapters. Such quotations are in the opinion of the writer quite essential in order to give some measure of reality and precision to what would otherwise be merely generalised statements, but all such figures are open to some degree of criticism. It must be remembered, therefore, when reading them, that they cannot claim to be definitive or absolute and are of value only in so far as they afford a useful means of comparison between genera. They can but represent one opinion on what may be, and often are, controversial questions. The figures actually used are taken not only from the writer's own compilations, but from various other sources, prominent among them being Lemée's dictionary (452) which is the most up-to-date source of its kind, and the works mentioned at the end of the Preface to the first edition.

Estimates of the total number of genera of Flowering Plants known to-day are generally in the neighbourhood of 12,500, giving an average content of about eighteen species each.

According to Lemée fourteen genera have more than 1,000 large species each, these being led by *Astragalus*, with some 1,800, and *Senecio* with 1,500. Then come *Eugenia*, *Piper* and *Ficus* with between 1,250 and 1,500 each; followed by *Bulbophyllum*, *Carex*, *Dendrobium*, *Epidendrum*, *Eupatorium*, *Euphorbia*, *Psychotria*, *Rhododendron* and *Solanum*. The estimated numbers appear in some cases to be on the conservative side, for *Senecio*, *Carex* and *Euphorbia*, for instance, have often been credited with many more and the same is doubtless true of others. On the other hand, a recent estimate for *Ficus* (151) puts the number of species in the genus at only 900. The reference to large species is necessary because there are certain genera, notably *Salix*, *Hieracium*, *Rubus* and *Crataegus*, which are extremely polymorphic and have been divided into huge numbers of closely similar forms. If these are regarded as normal species then the genera containing them are certainly among the largest but they are more reasonably treated as micro-species, and it is relevant to point out that at least certain of these genera depart from the normal in some aspects of their reproduction, so that there may be a real reason for the usual practice of regarding them as special cases.

For the rest there are genera of almost every species number down to the extreme condition of monotypy. These last are particularly numerous, some compilations estimating them at one-third of all genera, while the number of ditypes (two species) is also high, perhaps, according to the same compilations, one-eighth of all genera, so that the two may account for half the total. With increase in species-content so there is decrease in numbers, as is shown by the following figures.

Quoting again the figures derived from Lemée there are some 470 genera in all with 100 or more species each. Of these 270 have between 100 and 200 species each, among the more familiar being *Anemone*, *Asclepias*, *Asparagus*, *Buddleja*, *Coleus*, *Crinum*, *Eschscholzia*, *Linum*, *Lysimachia*, *Olearia*, *Phacelia*, *Restio*, *Rhus*, *Thunbergia* and *Verbena*. About 100 genera have between 200 and 300 species each, including *Aconitum*, *Calamus*, *Calceolaria*, *Clerodendrum*, *Cynanchum*, *Dianthus*, *Eriogonum*, *Gladiolus*, *Hoya*, *Jasminum*, *Pelargonium*, *Penstemon*, *Plectranthus*, *Strychnos* and *Tibouchina*. About 65 genera have between 300 and 500 species each, including *Allium*, *Campanula*, *Diospyros*, *Eucalyptus*, *Helichrysum*, *Hibiscus*, *Justicia*, *Lobelia*, *Mimosa*, *Passiflora*, *Pedicularis*, *Ranunculus*, *Smilax* and *Vaccinium*. Some 30 genera have between 500 and 1,000 species each, namely, in alphabetical order, *Acacia*, *Anthurium*, *Aster*, *Begonia*, *Cassia*, *Centaurea*, *Croton*, *Dioscorea*, *Erica*, *Gentiana*, *Habenaria*, *Impatiens*, *Indigofera*, *Ipomoea*, *Loranthus*, *Mesembryanthemum*, *Miconia*, *Myrcia*, *Oncidium*, *Oxalis*, *Panicum*, *Peperomia*, *Pleurothallis*, *Polygala*, *Primula*, *Quercus*, *Salvia*, *Sedum*, *Symplocos* and *Vernonia*.

The types of distribution exhibited by these largest of genera are extremely varied and many of them will be mentioned again in due course, but the following table, in which the numbers of genera are slightly rounded off, is a useful summary:

1. More or less cosmopolitan	. .	50
2. Tropical		305
a. pan-tropical 135		
b. only in the Old World . . 85		
c. only in the New World . . 60		
d. America and *either* Asia or Africa 25		
3. Temperate		90
a. wide temperate 20		
b. north temperate . . . 45		
c. only in the Old World . . 18		
d. only in the New World . . 7		
4. Southern		30
		475

Distribution of Genera

The same broad geographical classification which was used for families may be employed for genera, but the size and relative importance of the categories work out rather differently. This is owing, first, to the natural fact that the average range of genera is much smaller than that of families, and, second, to the arbitrary limitation to be attached to endemism. In the families, it will be remembered, endemism was measured in continental terms, but this is much too wide a conception for genera, and something smaller must be taken. Taking the general purpose of this book into consideration, we cannot do better than to interpret generic endemism broadly in terms of the thirty-seven regions which were outlined in the floristic classification in Chapter 2. Not only will this provide a suitable conception but it will also serve usefully to throw into relief many features in the floras of these regions. In this account of the distribution of genera then, endemic genera are those which are confined to one only of the floristic regions of the world as outlined in the scheme given there, or whose ranges are not much greater than the average size of the continental regions therein mentioned.

But with such a conception of endemism it is clear that there will inevitably be many genera which, though too widely distributed to be considered endemic, will nevertheless be far from completely spread through any one major climatic zone. It will be found, on this account, that a category which in the case of the families was almost negligible, namely the "medium wide" category, is in the genera of much greater size and importance, especially from many theoretical points of view. So much so indeed that it must receive very detailed treatment.

Genera may then, for our present purpose, be divided into the following categories:

> Cosmopolitan and subcosmopolitan
> Tropical
> Temperate
> Other wides
> Discontinuous
> Endemic

This arrangement is roughly one of diminishing areas, and it is therefore convenient to take the categories in the order given, as was done for the families. The number of families is such that it was possible to mention each one individually. This is manifestly impossible with the genera, and instead a rough estimate of the number of genera in each category is given together with examples from among the more familiar. In special cases all the genera are mentioned.

Cosmopolitan and Subcosmopolitan Genera

What was said, under the heading of families, about the use of the terms cosmopolitan and subcosmopolitan is even more to the point in respect of genera. Families, especially if they are large, may contain genera of widely different tolerances and may therefore be found in very diverse circumstances, but the species of genera usually follow a much closer pattern of environment and it is rare to find a genus equally well represented at sea level in all the various parts of both the tropical and temperate zones. Indeed, if we define a cosmopolitan genus in its strictest sense, as one

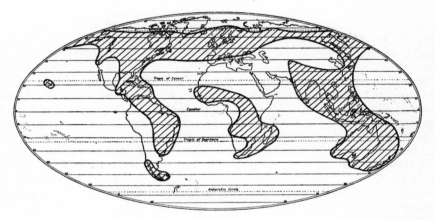

Fig. 18.—Map showing (shaded) the distribution of the genus *Drosera*, after Diels and Irmscher.

which is found in both high and low latitudes and which has roughly equal numbers of localised species in all the major parts of the world, then perhaps there is only one, *Senecio*, to be mentioned, and it should not be forgotten that this belongs to a family in which generic distinctions are notoriously hard to draw. *Euphorbia* is in some ways a better example but here there is a distinct falling off and specialisation in the colder zones. There is a similar diminution in *Solanum*, which, in addition, is unbalanced by its preponderance in the New World. *Carex*, on the other hand, which in simple terms of extent is almost certainly the most widespread genus, is unbalanced because its low altitude tropical representatives are comparatively few. These four are, as might be expected, very large genera, but four others, notably smaller, namely *Polygala*, *Scirpus*, *Drosera* and *Utricularia*, are also exceptionally well distributed in a native state. In fact, the last two are, in view of their peculiar specialisations, the most noteworthy of the eight.

Going now to the opposite extreme, and considering as at least subcosmopolitan all the genera which are considerably more than purely tropical or purely temperate in distribution, a number of different types can be recognised.

Nearest to the above, at least in mere extent, are those large genera, which although essentially temperate in character, have nevertheless a notable distribution through the more elevated parts of the tropics, namely *Anemone, Bromus, Cardamine, Clematis, Convolvulus, Cuscuta, Cynoglossum, Deschampsia, Eleocharis, Galium, Geranium, Hierochloe, Hypericum, Juncus, Luzula, Plantago, Poa, Polygonum, Ranunculus, Rhamnus, Rubus* and *Teucrium*. It is particularly difficult to draw any hard line between these and the first group of temperate genera on p. 91 below, with which the link is almost unbroken. The converse of these is seen in a smaller group of large genera, which, essentially tropical, have also a considerable extension into higher latitudes, namely *Andropogon, Aristida, Aristolochia, Cynanchum, Cyperus, Eragrostis, Eupatorium, Heliotropium, Panicum, Smilax, Sporobolus* and *Stipa*. This again is a difficult group to define because there are tropical genera with almost every kind of extension north and south, and the distinction here can be little more than arbitrary, a point which should be recalled when tropical genera are under discussion.

Another conspicuous group consists of very widespread, but in species numbers often very small, genera, which are either completely aquatic or are at least characteristic of subaquatic habitats. These are *Apium, Callitriche, Ceratophyllum, Cladium, Elatine, Hydrocotyle, Leersia, Lemna, Limnanthemum, Limosella, Ludwigia, Montia, Myriophyllum, Najas, Nasturtium, Nymphaea, Phragmites, Potamogeton, Rhynchospora, Ruppia, Samolus, Tillaea, Vallisneria, Wolffia* and *Zannichellia*.

It would seem that the only other small genera which can claim to be of comparable distribution are *Anagallis, Calystegia, Cynodon* and *Prunella*, but these serve the useful purpose here of bridging the gap between the foregoing and another large group of very widespread genera, those which are found to-day practically all over the world but which owe a now indeterminable part of their ranges to introduction as weeds or crops or as more miscellaneous adventives. These amount to at least 30, are nearly all medium size, rather by the nature of the case are chiefly typical of temperate climates, and include numerous grasses. They are *Agrostis, Agropyron, Amaranthus, Anaphalis, Arenaria, Atriplex, Avena, Bidens, Centaurea, Cerastium, Chenopodium, Coronopus, Celosia, Datura, Erigeron, Erodium, Festuca, Gnaphalium, Glyceria, Lepidium, Lolium, Oxalis, Phleum, Polycarpon, Portulaca, Rumex, Sagina, Sonchus, Spergula, Stellaria* and *Taraxacum*.

All the foregoing may be described as cosmopolitan, and the term subcosmopolitan is best and most conveniently confined to those genera which are incomplete in their distribution in the sense that they are but poorly represented in, or even completely absent from, one major region or broad type of habitat. Such genera, which number about 24, fall into a number of smaller groups according to the details of their geographical deficiencies. *Brachypodium, Impatiens, Lysimachia, Mentha, Schoenus, Swertia* and *Typha* are notably deficient in warmer America; *Parietaria, Sambucus, Scutellaria* and *Vaccinium* are so in Africa; and *Linum, Salix, Sanicula, Satureja* and *Stachys* are the same in tropical Asia and/or Australasia. *Orobanche, Sagittaria* and *Verbena* are almost absent from the tropics of the old world. *Eriocaulon* and *Lobelia* are an interesting pair in which the chief feature is absence from western Eurasia except for occurrences on the Atlantic margin. Finally there is an important minor group of halophytic and desert genera, *Frankenia, Limonium, Salicornia, Spergularia, Suaeda* and in less degree *Salsola*, which in superficial area are fairly world wide but which are restricted to certain kinds of soil condition only.

To summarise, the genera which are so widely distributed that they are notably more than either pan-tropical or wide temperate, and are therefore treated here as cosmopolitan or subcosmopolitan, number about 130. This is probably about 1 per cent of all genera, a figure which demonstrates vividly how few genera have succeeded in spreading themselves with any degree of completeness over all the available land surfaces of the globe, or to put it another way, how few genera have exploited both tropical and temperate conditions. When the aquatic genera, which are rather a law unto themselves, special groups like the halophytes, and the numerous instances including weed species, are subtracted from the total, this circumstance becomes even more striking.

Pan-tropical Genera

Of genera which are found in all three sectors of the tropical zone (America: Africa–Madagascar: Asia–Australasia), and which may thus, in one sense at least, be considered as pan-tropical, there are many familiar examples, but to give anything in the nature of a complete account of this kind of distribution is difficult, partly because the published data, especially the less recent, are seldom detailed enough to reveal the actual extent of range in the countries concerned, and partly because the tropics have, like the temperate regions, weed species of their own, so that it is often impossible to know whether a genus is of natural occurrence or not. For these reasons emphasis here is laid on the various types of pan-tropical distribution and the quotation of examples of these is confined to genera in which the facts are generally held to be beyond dispute.

Nor is it easy to arrive at any very exact figure of the numbers of these genera, but it would seem that rather more than 250 are pan-tropical in the sense used above. Somewhat fewer than half of these have more than 100 species each; the rest are of all sizes, including even monotypes, such as *Gyrocarpus*. Some have probably little geographical significance. Uncertainties of classification make it impossible to say just how the leading families are represented in this total, but it is safe to say that the Leguminosae (comprising Mimosaceae, Caesalpiniaceae and Papilionaceae) and the Gramineae stand out conspicuously. A rough compilation shows, indeed, that about 40 genera of the former group are found throughout the tropics and that nearly three-quarters of these have at least one pan-tropical species each, while a recent revision of the subfamily Panicoideae of the Gramineae (222) shows that it, alone, contains some 24 pan-tropical genera. This exceptional position may, in the former, be due largely to the number of species which are tropical strand plants, and in both cases in some measure to human exploitation, but this is certainly not the whole explanation. It may be added that the Compositae and Orchidaceae, the only conspicuously larger comparable groups, contain very few pan-tropical genera, a distinction which may reflect major historical differences.

The pan-tropical genera as a whole can be classified in much the same way as were the cosmopolitan ones, into three main headings—those evenly distributed with much the same species numbers in all sectors; those in which the species numbers are either notably higher or notably lower in one or more sectors; and those which are associated with particular edaphic conditions.

The evenly spread genera are not unnaturally mostly large genera (more than 100 species), and are exemplified by *Bauhinia, Costus, Dalbergia, Dioscorea, Eugenia, Hibiscus, Justicia, Mimusops, Peperomia, Phyllanthus, Psychotria, Rhynchosia, Strychnos* and *Vitex*, but there are quite a number of smaller ones, including *Corchorus, Erythrina, Fleurya, Geophila, Melothria, Ocimum, Ruellia, Tacca* and *Vanilla*.

The variations among the unevenly distributed genera are best set out in tabulated form as follows:

1. Genera with most of their species in the New World.

    e.g. the large genera *Cassia, Chrysophyllum, Cordia, Croton, Erythroxylum, Hyptis, Ipomoea, Mikania, Mimosa, Pavonia, Vernonia* and the smaller genera *Coldenia* (with only one species in the Old World), *Hybanthus, Sauvagesia* (pan-tropical by only one species) and *Tetracera*.

2. Genera with most of their species in the two sectors of the Old World.

    e.g. the large genera *Ampelocissus, Aneilema, Barleria, Bulbophyllum, Clerodendrum, Commelina, Crotalaria, Jasminum* (the one species in America is but doubtfully native), *Randia* and *Tephrosia*, and the smaller genera *Ehretia* and *Morinda*.

3. Genera with an outstanding proportion of species in Africa–Madagascar.

    e.g. the large genera *Combretum, Eulophia, Hermannia, Indigofera* and *Pavetta* and the smaller genera *Cassipourea, Hypoxis* and *Rinorea*.

4. Genera with an outstanding proportion of species in Asia–Australia.

    e.g. the large genera *Acacia, Diospyros, Ficus, Ixora* and *Sterculia*, and the smaller genera *Gnetum, Laportea, Uncaria* and *Ziziphus*.

5. Genera which are least strongly represented in Africa–Madagascar.

    e.g. the large genera *Begonia, Marsdenia, Piper* and *Pithecellobium* and the smaller genera *Caesalpinia, Cleidion* and *Crataeva*.

6. Genera which are least strongly represented in Asia–Australia.

    e.g. the large genera *Dorstenia* (one species only), *Eriosema* (one species only), *Hippocratea* and *Xyris*, and the rather smaller genera *Aeschynomene, Biophytum* and *Dalechampia*.

No strict comparison of the relative importance of these various categories can satisfactorily be given because of the many different factors which would have to be taken into consideration, but the impression is that the first is the most considerable and that the last two are the smallest, and this seems to suggest that such real segregation as there may be is chiefly between the New World and the Old.

In the third class of pan-tropical genera the subdivisions parallel those already used for the cosmopolitan genera, namely, aquatics, adventives, and desert plants and halophytes, except that the latter are represented here chiefly by members of the tropical strand flora. The aquatics are very few, presumably because such plants are less controlled by temperature factors and thus tend to have a wider latitudinal range. *Pistia* is perhaps the best known and is notable in being monotypic. It may be added that the rather similar *Eichhornia*, now seen in many parts of the tropics, has spread adventively from America, and thus leads conveniently to this next category of genera which now occur more or less throughout the tropics mainly because of the wide distribution of one or more species which are either weeds or actually subjects of cultivation. Among the former there may be mentioned *Ageratum, Cassytha, Catharanthus, Celosia, Dactyloctenium* (one species only), *Gynandropsis, Quamoclit, Sida* and *Waltheria*, and among the latter *Cocos, Coix, Gossypium, Terminalia* and *Urena*.

Pan-tropical genera of arid conditions again are very few also perhaps because their climatic relations give them a wider tolerance to temperature and only *Glinus* (which has one species in America and one in the Old World), and *Tribulus* need be mentioned. The tropical coastal plants are of special interest to the plant geographer because of their connection with problems of dispersal and they are discussed at greater length in a later chapter. By the nature of their habitat they cannot of course compare in extent of occupation with many other types and they are often discontinuous, but rather less than a dozen are found, within these limitations, in all three sectors of the tropics. They may conveniently be divided into genera, including *Dodonaea* and *Scaevola*, which are pan-tropical only because one or more of their species are widespread coastal species; genera of mangroves which occur in both western and eastern hemispheres, namely *Avicennia* and *Rhizophora*; and one or two genera consisting only of single coastal species, as in *Remirea* and *Suriana*.

At this point, as we are about to pass from what have been described as tropical genera to those categorised as temperate, it is well to stress again that there is by no means so clear-cut a distinction between the two as this method of treatment might suggest. This is chiefly because many tropical genera have a minority of temperate species and *vice versa*, rather than to the fact that any considerable number of genera can be said to be neither tropical nor temperate but something in between. It is true that there are some genera which are more particularly characteristic of mid-latitudes, such as *Rhus*, *Vitis* and *Lespedeza*, but it would be very misleading to separate these as a third category. Indeed the small representation of such a type is probably a matter of considerable significance in the historical evolution of the Angiosperms, reflecting, among other things, the shape of the earth and the consequent ever-critical nature of the middle latitudes (see p. 177).

Temperate Genera

The circumstances of world geography and relief are such that it is difficult to include, in one category, all the genera to which, broadly, the term "temperate" might be applied. For instance genera which are found in all temperate regions are of necessity almost world-wide and have in fact already received notice; while those confined to temperate latitudes are discontinuous, and are dealt with in the next chapter. There remain, however, two great groups of genera which may appropriately

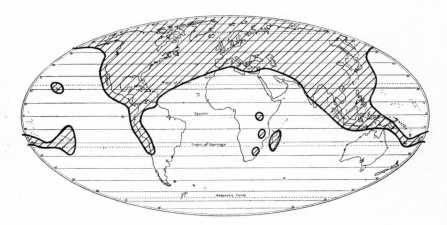

Fig. 19.—Map showing (shaded) the distribution of the genus *Vaccinium*.

be called temperate genera in the narrower sense and which may therefore be considered here. The first of these consists of genera found throughout the northern extra-tropical latitudes, and also to some extent, but incompletely, in the more elevated regions of the tropics, sometimes actually reaching the southern temperate zone. The second consists of genera distributed through but entirely confined to the northern extra-tropical zone, that is to say, to the northern temperate and arctic regions. Many of the members of these groups will be familiar, at least by name, and it is rather surprising to find that they do not number more than about 165.

There are also a few genera, of which *Vaccinium* (Fig. 19) is perhaps the best example, which are equally characteristic of the northern temperate regions and of some parts, but not all, of the tropics, especially the more mountainous. In this genus many species have, for instance, been described from New Guinea, and other parts of Malaysia also have their representatives. There are also many species within the tropics of America. It is least in evidence in Africa, where it is to be found only on the east, but there are a number of species in Madagascar.

The first group can be divided into a number of subgroups according to detail, and these can be tabulated, with examples, as follows:

1. Genera so widely spread, either naturally or as adventives, as to be almost sub-cosmopolitan:
     Epilobium, Hordeum, Trifolium, Urtica.

2. Genera with some extensions southwards in all directions, usually to certain tropical mountains only:
     Artemisia, Berberis, Rhamnus, Rosa, Sambucus, Thalictrum.

3. Genera extending south in America and Asia:
     Prunus, Viburnum.

4. Genera extending south in America and Africa:
     Astragalus, Sedum, Silene.

5. Genera extending south in America only:
     a. Into the tropics—
          Cotoneaster, Juglans.
     b. Into temperate South America—
          Alnus, Draba, Lathyrus and *Vicia, Menyanthes, Pinguicula, Ribes*
          (Fig. 20).

6. Genera extending south in Asia and also in Madagascar:
     Celastrus, Euonymus (Fig. 21).

7. Genera extending south in Asia only:
     Acer, Androsace, Pirola.

8. Genera extending south in Africa only:
     Allium, Arabis, Cirsium, Crepis (36), *Subularia.*

The genera which range more or less completely through the northern extra-tropical regions, either at all or some latitudes, can be divided into three according to their constitution. First are those in which the species are fairly numerous and in which the generic area is much greater than that of any one species. This is by far the largest group, and its 65 or so genera include many that are familiar. Mostly they call for no special comment and are well exemplified by:

     Aquilegia, Epipactis, Fritillaria, Iris, Spiraea, Trollius and *Veratrum.*

A few are found in part of North America only, while *Dracocephalum* and *Scrophularia* are rather special cases because in each only one species is American. Conversely in *Erythronium*, *Polemonium* and *Solidago*, all but one or two species are

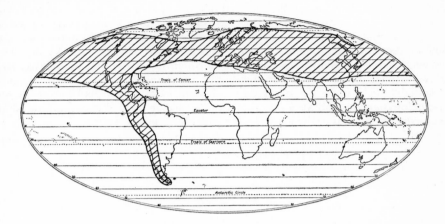

FIG. 20.—Map showing (shaded) the distribution of the genus *Ribes*, after Hutchinson.

American. In some others, among them *Asarum*, *Cornus* and *Cypripedium*, there are very few, and sometimes only one, species in Europe.

Second are the genera with more than one species, but in which a single species

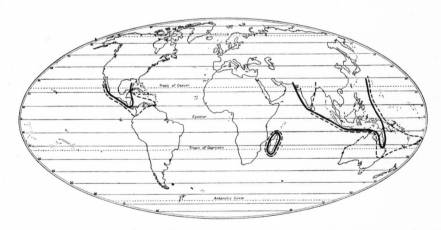

FIG. 21.—Map showing the distribution below the Tropic of Cancer of the genera *Euonymus* (continuous line) and *Celastrus* (broken line), after Bader.

is more or less circumpolar and accounts for most of the generic range. These number about twenty and include *Diapensia*, *Dryas* and *Phyllodoce*. It must be remembered that the ranges of the most northerly of these species may be small.

Finally, there are the genera, such as *Adoxa*, *Calypso* and *Loiseleuria*, which consist of only a single more or less circumpolar species each.

Other Wide Genera

Under this general heading are included all the continuously distributed genera which are, on the one hand, too restricted to merit inclusion in any of the foregoing categories, but which are, on the other hand, too wide in range to be treated as endemics. Not only are these very numerous, but they show almost every variation in range, so that any cursive account of them would be almost impossible. It is essential, therefore, to tabulate them, and in order to do this they must be classified somewhat rigidly. It is also desirable to give rough figures so that the relative size and importance of the different groups can be appreciated.

Actually there are eight main types of wide, continuous distribution in the sense defined above, and although they can be further divided according to detail it is convenient to arrange their description under these heads. They are:

> American wide genera
> North Pacific wide genera
> Eurasian wide genera
> African　　,,　　　,,
> Asiatic　　,,　　　,,
> African–Eurasian–Australasian wide genera
> Asiatic–Australasian–Pacific Islands wide genera
> Australasian wide genera.

American wide genera

The number of genera confined to America but so widely distributed there as to cover more than one floristic region is about 350 (excluding the more widespread tropical genera, which are dealt with later), and they fall into the following four groups:

1. Genera more or less completely distributed throughout North America. These number about 70 and include:

   > *Ceanothus, Heuchera, Liatris, Monarda, Rudbeckia* and *Symphoricarpos.*

2. Genera found in North and Tropical America. These number about 40 and include:

   > Predominantly northern genera—*Helianthus, Kalmia.*
   > Predominantly tropical genera—*Agave, Echeveria.*

3. Genera found in tropical and temperate South America. These number upwards of 200 and include:

   > *Adesmia, Alstroemeria, Ananas, Bromelia, Escallonia, Hippeastrum, Mutisia, Salpiglossis, Tropaeolum.*

4. Genera found throughout America from north to south. These number about 80 and include:

   > *Cereus, Echinocactus* (42° N. to 39° S.), *Gaillardia, Godetia, Gonolobus, Helenium, Krameria, Metastelma, Mentzelia, Oenothera, Opuntia* (from 50° N.), *Petunia, Phoradendron, Tagetes.*

Some of these genera, such as *Gaillardia*, have minor gaps in their range.

North Pacific wide genera

The wide North American genera and those of Eurasia (below) are linked up by a small group, the members of which are found on both sides of the Bering Strait and which may for this reason appropriately be called North Pacific genera. They number about a dozen.

First come three large genera, *Castilleja*, *Phlox* and *Penstemon*, each with numerous species in the western parts of North America, and with one species in north-east Asia. In *Castilleja* and *Phlox* this latter species is confined to Asia, but *Penstemon* includes one species which ranges from Alaska to Japan.

Bryanthus (Fig. 58) is fairly widespread in Eastern Asia but only just reaches America; *Chamaerhodos* ranges from Mongolia to western North America; *Coelopleurum*, *Physocarpus* and *Romanzoffia* are found in north-east Asia and in western North America; and *Erioblastus*, *Leptarrhena* and *Merckia* are monotypic genera distributed narrowly on both sides of the Strait, the last being arctic. *Smilacina* (*Tovaria*) as maintained by Krause (222) may also be included here. It ranges from the Himalayas more or less continuously eastward to Central America.

The four genera *Claytonia*, *Dodecatheon*, *Menziesia* and *Zygadenus* may also be mentioned here because, although they range throughout North America, they have also one or a minority of species in north-east Asia.

Eurasian wide genera

Strict adherence to the definition of endemism given earlier would necessitate treating even the genera which range eastward right from the North Atlantic to the North Pacific as endemic owing to the exceptional width of the Euro–Siberian region. A warning was, however, given in Chapter 2 that this region might on account of its size have sometimes to be treated as a special case, and there is good reason for doing so now. Not only are the actual ranges of these genera far greater than those of the average run of endemic genera as defined, but also to call them endemic without qualification is to distort the general picture of plant distribution and to overshadow what is certainly their most important feature, namely, their relatively great longitudinal range and their more or less complete occupation of the Old World northern temperate zone.

The genera which thus extend across the great Eurasian continent north of the tropics and the subtropics number, at a rough estimate, about 100, and among them the families Cruciferae, Gramineae, Compositae and Umbelliferae are conspicuous. At both ends of their range, and more especially in the west, they often show a tendency to extend south into warmer latitudes. The group naturally includes many genera familiar to European botanists either as garden plants or as native wild plants and as far as possible the following examples have been drawn from these:

Doronicum, *Eranthis*, *Hedera* (occurs also in Macaronesia), *Hypecoum* (sometimes made a separate family), *Lamium* (especially in the west), *Morina* (sometimes made a separate family), *Neottia*, *Paris*, *Syringa* (especially eastern), *Tulipa*.

African wide genera

Here are included the genera which are widely distributed in Africa (generally with the exception of the north) and in the Madagascar region. They total between 200 and 300 and are of three main geographical types, excluding the wider genera *within* the tropics, which are dealt with later.

1. Genera found in tropical and southern Africa only. These number more than 100 and include:

   Babiana (discontinuous between Socotra and southern Africa), *Eucael*, *Fadogia* and *Voandzeia*, predominantly tropical.

Blaeria, Cliffortia (768), *Protea, Stapelia* and *Ursinia,* predominantly southern.

2. Genera found in Africa and in the Madagascar region. These number about 100 and include:

Myrothamnus in tropical Africa and Madagascar only.
Clematopsis, Faurea, Hydnora and *Sparrmannia* in tropical and southern Africa and Madagascar.
Aristea (769), *Lightfootia* and *Selago* with a similar distribution but predominantly found in southern Africa.
Angraecum, Disa, Philippia and *Stoebe* more or less throughout Africa and the Madagascar region, *Philippia* being characteristic of the latter and *Disa* and *Stoebe* of southern Africa.
Himantochilus is found in tropical Africa and the Mascarenes only.
Agauria is found in tropical Africa, Madagascar and the Mascarenes.

3. Genera found in South Africa and Madagascar, and occasionally in the Mascarenes. These number about 20 and include:

Alberta, Cassinopsis and *Trichocaulon.*

It is noteworthy that many of the genera here shown as in Madagascar or the Mascarenes are found also in South Africa, and this relationship is perhaps more significant than that between tropical Africa and the islands. It is true that the Madagascar region has many other genera in common with tropical Africa, but these extend more widely also, and therefore, as regards this chapter, appear in other categories.

Asiatic wide genera

This group is a large one calculated to contain between 350 and 400 genera, and is moreover difficult to define numerically because the limits of the genera tend to be in regions where it is hard to trace them accurately. One definite fea r . however, is that to all intents and purposes all the genera are limited westwe India, that is to say hardly any reach warm Central Asia. Actually several such ave been described, including *Skimmia,* which ranges from Afghanistan to the Malayan Archipelago, but these serve only as exceptions that prove the rule.

This fact points the way towards a classification of the whole group into distributional types, which is best done by recognising two main types, the first of which shows ranges from India, China or Japan to the Malayan Archipelago and the second from some part of the south-east Asiatic region similarly to the islands. The former are apparently more than twice as numerous as the latter, and both are constantly increasing because of new records in Malaysia.

In the first, the largest number consists of genera which range from India only, the Indo-Malaysian genera proper. It is probable that these amount to at least 200, and many of them touch south-west China. Several of the Dipterocarpaceae, such as *Dipterocarpus, Hopea* and *Shorea,* are good examples, as are also several other genera containing important timber trees such as *Mesua, Tectona* and *Walsura. Mangifera* seems to belong here as far as its natural range can be ascertained, and other examples are *Colocasia, Daemonorops, Hodgsonia* and *Hydnocarpus.* A few genera, including *Osmelia,* range eastward from Ceylon and do not occur in the Indian Peninsula proper. Two other smaller groups in this main type which are related to the above are genera ranging from India and China and from India, China and Japan respectively. The first includes *Beaumontia, Dichroa* and *Eriobotrya,* and the

Plate 6. A cactus landscape in Arizona. The large columnar species is *Carnegiea gigantea*: in the foreground are two species of *Opuntia*

(*Photo: Josef Muench*)

second *Camellia, Daphniphyllum, Heterosmilax* and *Michelia*. Finally there are some genera distributed from China and Japan respectively into Malaysia. The former include *Anneslea* and *Cratoxylon* and the latter *Broussonetia* and *Cladopus*. *Actinidia* and *Thladiantha* exemplify genera which range from north Asia to the Archipelago.

The second of the main types could also be classified into three, though on a smaller scale, according to whether they are, in south-east Asia, found in both Burma and Indo-China or in only one of these, but it is doubtful whether the facts are sufficiently well known to make this worth while here. Examples of this type as a whole are *Achasma, Barclaya, Dendrocalamus, Duabanga, Feroniella, Gigantochloa, Indorouchera* and *Payena*.

In addition to these two main types there are a few genera which must be reckoned as wides because they are found in more than one of the floristic regions that cover tropical continental east Asia, namely India, south-east Asia and the southern part of the Sino–Japanese region. It is, however, interesting to note, especially in relation to the numbers in the main types, that the genera to which a range of this kind has been attributed probably number scarcely a dozen, among them *Chaydaia* and *Pentasacme*.

The very interesting subject of the detailed distribution of all these genera within the Archipelago is too complex to be dealt with here in what is but a general survey, but it is worth noting that while many genera occur fairly generally on all the larger islands, an appreciable number tend to be found either in Java and Sumatra *or* in Borneo *or* in the Philippines (see p. 141). Of the more generally distributed genera most seem to extend all the way to New Guinea.

It should also be noted that these genera include examples of various types of discontinuity, as for instance, *Sarcosperma* (444); *Herpysma* and *Triplostegia* (700); *Itoa, Rhodoleia, Scutinanthe, Trichadenia* and *Wightia*.

At first sight the different groups mentioned above are not easy to visualise, and it is therefore useful to summarise them and to repeat the approximate numbers of genera in each. They are:

1. Genera ranging from India, China and Japan to the Malayan Archipelago, 250–300.
   a. Genera ranging from India to the Archipelago, most numerous.
   b. Genera ranging from India and China to the Archipelago.
   c. Genera ranging from India, China and Japan to the Archipelago.
   d. Genera ranging from China to the Archipelago, comparatively few.
   e. Genera ranging from Japan to the Archipelago, comparatively few.
2. Genera ranging from south-east Asia to the Malayan Archipelago, 100–150.
3. Genera in continental tropical east Asia only, few.

African–Eurasian–Australasian wide genera

This very comprehensive category includes all those genera which, present in Africa, range continuously thence either to Eurasia only, or further through Malaysia into Australasia, and, it may be, to the Pacific Islands. From many points of view the category is important and interesting, but any estimate of numbers is difficult, especially because it is often impossible to say how complete the distribution of a genus is over the arid regions which link Africa and India. The total seems to be about 150, and it must be remembered that this excludes nearly all the more characteristic genera of the Old World tropics because these are, by the nature of the case, discontinuous, and dealt with in the next chapter (see p. 109 and Appendix B).

7

In general the category comprises two main types of range, namely genera more characteristic of the temperate regions, but with extensions into the tropics, and genera more characteristic of the tropics and reaching continuously all or part of the way from tropical Africa to Australasia and the Pacific Islands.

There must be included in the first of these a rather special group of genera which range from Europe and the Mediterranean southward through Africa. *Adenocarpus*, *Asterolinon* and *Crambe*, with most of their species in the north, are good examples of one extreme and these reach no further than the northern tropics. *Punica* has a rather similar range, but extends well eastward into Asia, and its distribution is no doubt confused by long cultivation. *Dianthus*, which extends to Japan, reaches as far south as the Cape (222). At the other extreme are genera like *Erica* and *Gladiolus* (also in Madagascar), both of which are concentrated in South Africa, but extend, chiefly up the east side of the continent, practically all over Europe and western Asia. Between these extremes are such genera as *Holcus* and *Romulea*, which occur in Europe and the Mediterranean region and also in South Africa, but which appear to be more or less absent in between.

The second main type, consisting of essentially tropical genera, is much larger and can be divided into four. First there are the genera which are practically confined to Africa, but which extend therefrom into Arabia. Here belong *Aloe*, *Catha* and *Kniphofia*. Next comes the largest group of all, containing genera which range continuously from Africa to India. Some of these, like *Cometes* and *Salvadora*, occur only in the tropical parts of Africa; others, like *Vahlia*, extend to the south of the continent. *Echinops*, *Hyoscyamus* and *Reseda* exemplify genera found in Europe and the Mediterranean as well as in tropical Africa. *Caralluma* ranges from South Africa up the east coast and all over North Africa to India. A third minor type comprises genera of similar distribution, but extending still further into tropical Asia. Examples of these are:

> *Asparagus*, South Africa, Mascarenes to Malaysia.
> *Boswellia* and *Cistanche*, Africa to China.
> *Maerua*, Africa, Madagascar and Mascarenes to Siam.
> *Pereploca*, Macaronesia, tropical Africa to China.

Finally, there are the widest ranging genera of all—those extending from Africa all the way to Australia or the Pacific. It is difficult to estimate the number of these, but they include:

> *Ceropegia*, Macaronesia and South Africa to Australia.
> *Loranthus*, Africa and Madagascar to the Pacific Islands.
> *Melhania*, Africa and Madagascar to Australia.
> *Viscum*, Africa and Eurasia to Australia.

Of all these very varied groups, that of the genera ranging from Africa to India is by far the largest, comprising about one-third of the total, but taking the category as a whole there is represented in it almost every degree of distribution from Africa towards Australia and the Pacific islands.

Asiatic–Australian–Pacific Islands wide genera

In one sense this category is the counterpart of the last in that it includes genera with much the same kind of distribution, but with the emphasis on the east and southeast rather than the west. Moreover, although it contains genera which may well have originated in Asia and have spread thence southward, it certainly comprises many which originated in Australia or the Pacific islands and have ranged thence into Asia.

This category is best divided into three groups. In each of these the genera are represented in some part of continental Asia or Malaysia, but in the first they occur also in *both* Australia *and* the Pacific islands: in the second they are found also in Australia *only*, and in the third in the Pacific islands *only*. Each of these three groups can be further subdivided according to whether the Asiatic distribution includes India, China or Japan or whether it is limited to Malaysia and south-east Asia. A further distinction can be drawn in each subgroup between the genera which are predominantly Asiatic and those which are predominantly Australian. It should be noted that genera which, in Malaysia, are found only in New Guinea, are not included because they have a special relevance to the problems of relationship outlined in Chapter 12 and are therefore best included under the next heading of Australasian wide genera. It should also be remembered that though the number of predominantly Australian genera has tended to increase through recent new records from Malaysia it is often difficult to say whether these occurrences are natural or the result of introduction (305, 306).

1. Genera of Indo–Malaysia, Australia and the Pacific Islands:
   a. Genera ranging from India and/or China–Japan:
   (1) Genera predominantly Asiatic or Malaysian:
   > e.g. *Ailanthus, Aleurites, Andruris, Cryptostylis, Dendrobium, Dischidia, Dysoxylum, Helicia, Hoya, Nipa, Pachygone, Parsonsia, Polyosma, Rhodamnia, Scyphiphora, Semecarpus.*
   (2) Genera predominantly Australian:
   > *c.* 3—*Haloragis, Microtis, Styphelia.*

   b. Genera ranging from Malaysia and/or south-east Asia:
   (1) Genera predominantly Asiatic or Malaysian:
   > e.g. *Aglaia, Alphitonia, Fagraea, Geodorum, Homalanthus, Loeseneriella, Ryssopteris, Taeniophyllum.*
   (2) Genera predominantly Australian:
   > *c.* 12—*Baeckea, Casuarina, Centrolepsis, Eucalyptus, Flindersia, Lepidosperma, Leptospermum, Macadamia†, Melaleuca, Mitrasacme, Stackhousia, Thelymitra, Trachymene.*

2. Genera of Indo–Malaysia and Australia:
   a. Genera ranging from India and/or China–Japan:
   (1) Genera predominantly Asiatic or Malaysian:
   > e.g. *Aegialitis, Areca, Knoxia, Licuala, Livistona, Philydrum, Stemona.*
   (2) Genera predominantly Australian:
   > *Stylidium* is apparently the only example.

   b. Genera ranging from Malaysia and/or south-east Asia:
   (1) Genera predominantly Asiatic or Malaysian:
   > e.g. *Apostasia, Bromheadia, Caryota, Durandea, Kibara, Myrmecodia, Nauclea, Stemonurus, Tecomanthe, Tetrastigma, Vanda.*
   (2) Genera predominantly Australian:
   > *c.* 6—*Calogyne, Citriobatus, Grevillea, Patersonia, Ptilotus, Thysanotus.*

3. Genera of Indo–Malaysia and the Pacific Islands:

   a. Genera ranging from India and/or China:

      Acanthophippium, Bikkia, Ceratostylis, Chrysoglossum, Kingiodendron, Pangium, Sarcolobus.

   b. Genera ranging from Malaysia and/or south-east Asia:

      Amaracarpus, Ascarina, Berrya†, Carruthersia, Cloezia†, Couthovia Cypholophus, Desmos†, Discocalyx, Dolicholobium, Drymophlaeus† Endospermum, Grammatophyllum, Gulubia, Heterospathe, Hydnophytum Metroxylum, Sarcanthus, Wenzelia, Xanthophytum.

The total number of genera in this category appears to be about 200 and the groups 1*a* (1), 1*b* (1), 2*a* (1), 2*b* (1), are by far the largest. Group 3 also contains a fair number but the remaining subgroups are small. It is interesting that various genera, especially in group 3, indicated by † are notably discontinuous.

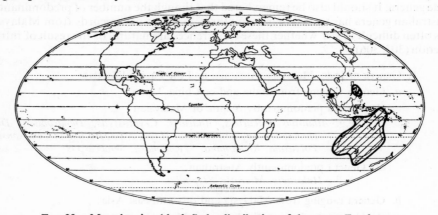

FIG. 22.—Map showing (shaded) the distribution of the genus *Eucalyptus.*

Because of the exceptional interest of the genus *Casuarina* from the point of view of comparative morphology, it is worth while to give a slightly extended description of its distribution, for the details of which I am indebted to Mr. L. A. S. Johnson. The genus has two distinctive sections, one with 40 species and the other with 14. The former comprise 20 in western Australia, about 15 in eastern Australia, and 4 in Java, New Guinea and New Caledonia; and it also includes the now widely planted *C. equisetifolia,* the native range of which is probably from Burma to Australia and Polynesia. The latter section has only one species in Australia (in northern Queensland) and the rest range over the Malayan Archipelago and eastward to Fiji. It will be noted that the genus is not native in New Zealand. It should be added that a fossil from the Miocene of Patagonia has been identified as belonging to this genus (834).

The genus *Eucalyptus* (Fig. 22), which has several hundred species, is also of outstanding importance from many points of view and it is therefore of interest to give a summary of the natural occurrence of the genus outside Australia, which from information kindly supplied by Dr. S. T. Blake is as follows:

E. deglupta	. .	Philippines, New Britain and north-east New Guinea.
E. alba	. .	Timor, Wettar, Flores, Sumba, south-east New Guinea and coastally in Australia from 124–152° E. longitude.

E. confertiflora	.	South-east New Guinea and Australia to about 20° S.
E. papuana	.	South-east New Guinea and locally in all the northern parts of Australia.
E. tereticornis .	.	South-east New Guinea and eastern Australia as far south as Victoria.
E. polycarpa .	.	South-east New Guinea and north-east Australia to about 20° S.
E. ampupa	.	Timor.
E. sp. .	.	South-east New Guinea and perhaps Queensland.
E. sp. .	.	Lesser Sunda Islands.

Australasian wide genera

These are the genera found only within the geographical area defined on p. 20 as Australasia but which occur in more than one of the floristic regions which contribute to it. It is difficult to say just how many such genera there are, partly because several of the floras concerned are still imperfectly known, and partly because it is not always clear whether a genus is native in any particular place or not, but the following, reasonably complete, list contains 154, and they are of special interest in relation to the problems discussed in Chapter 12.

These genera vary greatly in their details and for present purposes it is best to arrange them on the rather arbitrary basis, first of whether they are found in the two major land masses concerned, Australia and New Guinea, or in only one, or in neither, and second, whether, in similar terms, they are found in New Caledonia and New Zealand.

1. Genera found in both Australia and New Guinea:
   a. Genera found also in both New Caledonia and New Zealand:
   > *Acianthus, Arthropodium, Calochilus, Corynocarpus* (also in the New Hebrides), *Epacris, Hedycarya, Pterostylis.*

   b. Genera found also in New Caledonia but not in New Zealand:
   > *Amyema, Bubbia, Castanospermum, Cupaniopsis, Dallachya* (also in Fiji and Tonga), *Euroschinus, Geigera, Geitonoplesium, Halfordia, Lomandra, Spiraeanthemum* (also in New Hebrides, Fiji and Samoa), *Stenocarpus, Tapeinosperma* (also in New Hebrides and Fiji).

   c. Genera found also in New Zealand but not in New Caledonia:
   > *Ackama, Dichelachne, Microlaena, Olearia, Raoulia, Ripogonum.*

   d. Genera of Australia and New Guinea only:
   > *Agonis, Backhousia, Banksia, Bouchardatia, Carronia, Cartonema, Ceratopetalum, Cleistochloa, Cycnogeton, Daphnandra, Dissiliaria, Drakaea, Ectrosia, Epiblastus, Eupomatia, Eustrephus, Gillbeea, Gompholobium, Haemodorum, Helmholtzia, Himantandra, Hymenosporum, Hydriastele, Kentia* (? also Norfolk Island), *Kissodendron, Lechenaultia* (also on Timor), *Linospadix, Mackinlaya, Neosepicaea, Osbornia, Phacellothrix, Piptocalyx, Schelhammera, Tecticornia* (also on Madura), *Toechima, Torrenticola, Tricoryne, Trochocarpa, Vandasia* and *Velleia.*

   e. Others:
   > *Fenzlia* (also in the Carolines and Marianas), *Paphia* (also in Fiji), *Ptychosperma* (also in the Bismarcks and Solomons), *Pullea* (also in Fiji).

2. Genera in Australia but not in New Guinea:
   a. Genera found also in both New Caledonia and New Zealand:
   > *Dracophyllum, Lyperanthus, Orthoceras, Pomaderris, Prasophyllum, Rhagodia.*

b. Genera found also in New Caledonia but not in New Zealand:
  Actinotus (? native), *Argophyllum, Balanops* (also in the New Hebrides and Fiji), *Campynema, Geissois* (also in the New Hebrides and Fiji), *Lagunaria, Ricinocarpus, Stypandra, Zieria.*

c. Genera found also in New Zealand but not in New Caledonia:
  Aciphylla, Adenochilus, Amphibromus, Archeria, Caleana, Celmisia, Chiloglottis, Craspedia, Cyrtostylis, Ewartia, Forstera, Hemiphues, Herpolirion, Hydatella, Hymenanthera (also Norfolk Island), *Liparophyllum, Logania, Pennantia, Pentachondra, Persoonia, Phebalium, Plagianthus, Poranthera, Swainsona.*

d. Others:
  Lysiana (also in the New Hebrides).

3. Genera in New Guinea but not in Australia:

a. Genera found also in New Caledonia and New Zealand:
  Meryta (also in the Marianne Islands).

b. Genera found also in New Caledonia but not in New Zealand:
  Agatea (also in the Solomons and Fiji), *Antholoma, Belliolum, Delarbrea, Dubouzetia, Sphenostemon, Trimenia* (also in Fiji).

c. Genera found also in New Zealand but not in New Caledonia:
  Carpodetus, Macropiper (also in Norfolk Island, Lord Howe Island and the Society Islands), *Tupeia.*

d. Others:
  Airosperma (also in Fiji), *Antiaropsis* (also in the Bismarck Archipelago), *Astronidium* (also in the Caroline Islands and Samoa), *Bleekeria* (also in the Marianne Islands), *Calycacanthus* (also in the Bismarck Archipelago), *Eurycentrum* (also in the Solomon Islands), *Finschia* (also in the Bismarck Archipelago, the Solomon Islands, the New Hebrides and the Caroline Islands), *Lepinia* (also in the Solomon Islands and the Society Islands), *Merrilliodendron* (also in the Marianne Islands), *Moerenhoutia* (also in the Caroline Islands, the Society Islands and Samoa), *Peckelia* (also in the Bismarck Archipelago), *Peckeliopanax* (also in the Bismarck Archipelago), *Plerandra* (also in the Solomon Islands and Fiji), *Ptychococcus* (also in the Bismarck Archipelago and the Solomon Islands), *Sararanga* (also in the Solomon Islands), *Tripetalum* (also in the Bismarck Archipelago).

4. Genera in neither Australia nor New Guinea:

a. Genera of New Caledonia and New Zealand:
  Earina, Knightia, Xeronema.

b. Genera of New Caledonia and the New Hebrides:
  Alphandia, Chambeyronia, Cyclophyllum, Dizygotheca, Strobilopanax.

c. Genera of New Caledonia and Fiji:
  Buraeavia, Piliocalyx, Storckiella.

d. Others:
  Carmichaelia (New Zealand and Lord Howe Island), *Exorrhiza* (New Hebrides and Fiji), *Kermadecia* (New Caledonia, New Hebrides, Fiji and Samoa), *Melicytus* (New Zealand, Norfolk Island, Fiji and Tonga), *Phormium* (New Zealand and Norfolk Island), *Rhopalostylis* (New Zealand and Norfolk Island).

Summary

In order to bring together in conveniently abbreviated form all that has been said in the foregoing pages about the widely distributed genera of Angiosperms, it is desirable to conclude this chapter with a summary of the facts and figures which have been described and discussed. This summary, which comprises all the genera which are neither discontinuous nor endemic, is as follows:

1. Cosmopolitan or very wide genera . . . . *c.* 130
2. Tropical genera . . . . *c.* 250
3. Temperate genera . . . . *c.* 165
4. Other wide genera:

    a. American genera . . . . . . *c.* 350
    b. North Pacific genera . . . . . . *c.* 12
    c. Eurasian genera . . . . *c.* 110
    d. African genera . . . . *c.* 250
    e. Asiatic genera . . . . *c.* 370
    f. African–Eurasian–Australasian genera . . . *c.* 150
    g. Asiatic–Australasian–Pacific Islands genera . . *c.* 220
    h. Australasian genera . . . . . . *c.* 60

Total . . *c.* 2050

From this table it therefore appears that about 15 per cent of all genera may be regarded as wide genera, leaving about 85 per cent for discontinuous and endemic genera.

CHAPTER 6

THE DISTRIBUTION OF GENERA—II

Discontinuous Genera

THE facts of discontinuous distribution are among the most remarkable in all the geography of the Flowering Plants and on this account alone would demand special attention here, but there is a second and related reason why a careful survey of them is particularly desirable. Discontinuity is a matter which bears upon many problems (especially those concerning the distribution of land and climate in the past) beyond the confines of botany, and it has therefore, not unnaturally, attracted the attention of many who are not botanists, and their statements regarding it are not always to be taken at their face value. Thus there has arisen a certain amount of confusion regarding the facts, and a general survey which reviews the subject as critically as possible may serve also to dispel some of this. Since the story of discontinuity in general is largely the story of generic discontinuity in particular, this chapter comprehends the most important part of such a survey.

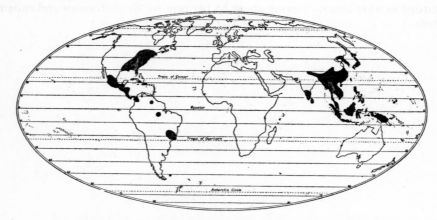

FIG. 23.—Map showing (black) the distribution of the tribe Magnolieae.

When one plant group is found distributed over two or more widely separated regions its discontinuity is significant, in theory at all events, only if it can be assumed that its range was formerly continuous and that the subsequent disjunction has resulted from natural causes. Expressed rather differently, discontinuity is of interest, from most points of view, only when it can be assumed that the group exhibiting it is of monophyletic origin and has had therefore not only a common ancestry but also a single point of origin. It is by the quotation, as discontinuous, of genera which do not fulfil these conditions that confusion has chiefly arisen.

The greatest difficulty lies in deciding which genera are to be regarded confidently as monophyletic groups, because here the only possible criterion is that of

104

personal opinion, but there are two types of genera which must almost certainly be excluded. The first comprises those which consist of two or more very distinct subgenera separated by characters which in other cases are often regarded as of full generic value. Not uncommonly such genera are described as discontinuous because each of the subgenera has a distinct range, but if the relationship between them is open to doubt, so also of course is their discontinuity, and reference to it is merely misleading.

The second case is much commoner and especially concerns certain large and particularly "natural" families. In these families the constituent species are all so much alike that it is very difficult to group them into separate genera and it becomes necessary, in order to do so, to emphasise and rely too rigidly upon characters so detailed and minute that their value as criteria of true relationship can only be described as very doubtful. Thus in some families especially the genera as commonly defined can but rarely be accepted as monophyletic units. This is true, for instance, in the Compositae, where one of the most prevalent types of generic distinction is the minute morphology of the style arms; and, again, in the Acanthaceae, where minor characters of the anthers are much used. Sometimes, of course, other and more practicable features come into play, but the general result is that nearly all the discontinuities recorded for these and a few other families must be treated with reserve.

Another common difficulty is that of deciding whether or not a plant is of natural occurrence in all parts of its range. The heather and certain heaths, for instance, are often quoted as striking examples of wide discontinuity on the strength of their occurrence in eastern North America, but investigation shows that they are by no means free from the suspicion that the American plants are in fact intentional or unintentional introductions from the Old World and that they do not, therefore, confer discontinuity in the phyletic sense on the genera to which they belong.

Misidentifications and errors of fact also lead to misunderstanding. Slips of the pen or tongue have frequently attributed to genera discontinuity which in fact they do not possess. In collecting plants and in dealing with them subsequently data sometimes get misplaced: these errors may eventually pass into print, and once this has happened it is not at all easy to correct them. As regards identification, a wrong conclusion as to which of two genera a new species belongs may lead to great geographical confusion.

It was the realisation of these difficulties that prompted the present writer, many years ago, to review all the genera which had from time to time been described as exhibiting wide discontinuity, that is to say discontinuity of approximately continental or oceanic dimensions, and to compile a list of those which could with reasonable confidence be looked upon as good and reliable instances of it, omitting those which for such reasons as have just been mentioned were to be regarded at least with suspicion. In short, the object of the review was to produce a list of all the genera whch could be safely quoted as examples of widely discontinuously distributed monophyletic groups. The list first appeared in 1927 (285), and there were revisions of it in the first and second editions of the present book. A fourth version of it is given here in Appendix B. This course of printing the list separately has been adopted because to have incorporated it in the text of this chapter would have overburdened this with detail and would have made the cursive reading of it almost impossible. The following pages include, however, a more generalised account of the list and of the classification and figures that it presents, and the Appendix can be used to amplify this as may be felt desirable.

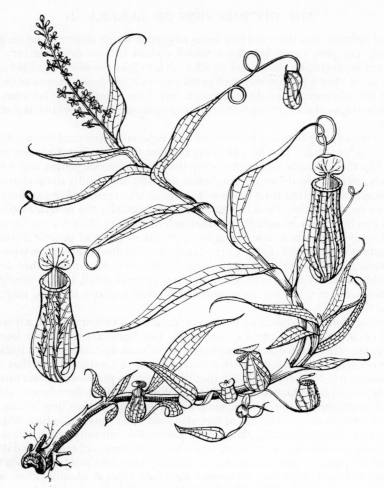

FIG. 24.—*Nepenthes gracilis*, much reduced, after Engler.

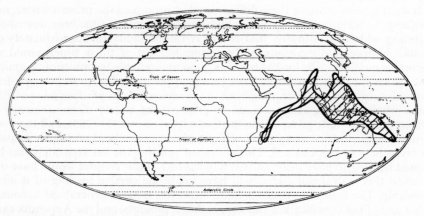

FIG. 25.—Map showing (shaded) the distribution of the genus *Nepenthes*, mainly after Hutchinson.

The distribution of land and sea and the zonation of climate are such that the discontinuous genera of the Flowering Plants are of five main types, i.e.:

1. Genera entirely or predominantly confined to the northern temperate regions.
2. Genera entirely or predominantly confined to the tropical zone.
3. Genera entirely or predominantly confined to the southern temperate regions.
4. Genera occurring in both northern and southern temperate regions.
5. Genera of various distributions but all occurring in the exceptionally isolated Hawaiian Islands.

Discontinuous genera of the north temperate zone

The northern temperate discontinuous genera comprise, as might be expected from the huge extent of this area, several very distinct types, including some which range over the whole of it and rather fewer which occur at both ends of the Eurasian continent, but the commonest discontinuities are between America and Europe and America and eastern Asia respectively.

The latter is one of the most familiar and important of all and, from the time that Asa Gray (312) first drew special attention to it, has been much studied and discussed (458). These genera number about eighty and there is reason to believe that they may be survivors of a very ancient circumboreal flora which has failed to persist in Europe and western Asia. They can be further classified according to the details of their Asiatic distributions, some occurring only on the continent; some in Japan; and others in both. Some of them, moreover, have marked extensions southward into the tropics of one or both hemispheres. The Japanese components are discussed by Hara (335, 337).

The total number of genera in this northern temperate category is about 125, and the following are some of the best examples of them:

Liquidambar . .	According to most authorities there are three species—one in North and Central America, one in south-western Asia, and one in Formosa and south China.
Meconopsis . .	Taylor (723) regards this genus as consisting of one western European species and about forty in the Sino–Himalayan mountain system. Some taxonomists include also two western North American species.
Corema . .	A genus of two species—one in North America from Newfoundland to New Jersey and the other in the Azores, Spain and Portugal (Fig. 43).
Platanus . .	There are four species in western North America and Mexico, one in eastern North America, and one in the eastern Mediterranean and in Asia Minor. Seward (636) gives an interesting map of the past and present range of this genus.
Clintonia . .	This genus has six species—two in western North America, two in eastern North America, one in the Himalayas and one in east Asia.
Paeonia . .	According to Stern (708), this genus has some thirty species, of which about a dozen are in Asia; seventeen in south Europe, the Mediterranean region and the Caucasus; and two in western North America. See also Barber (47).
Menispermum .	According to Diels (218) there are two species—one in eastern North America and one in north-east Asia, north China, Korea and Japan.

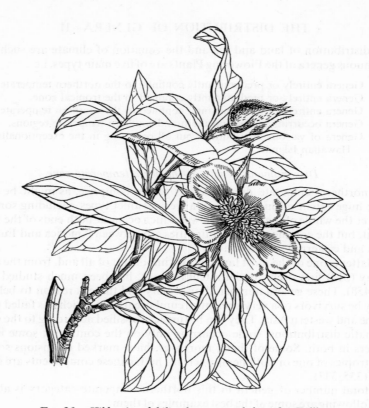

Fig. 26.—*Hibbertia volubilis*, about natural size, after Baillon.

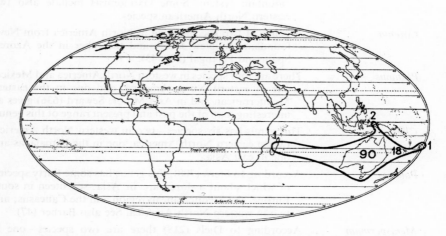

Fig. 27.—Map showing the distribution of the genus *Hibbertia*, partly after Hoogland. The figures are the numbers of the species in the different parts of the range.

| *Liriodendron* . | . | One of the most striking and often quoted instances of discontinuity. There is one species in eastern North America and one very narrowly distributed in eastern China (Plate 18 and Fig. 74). |

Chiogenes . . There is one species throughout eastern North America and one in Japan. Some consider the latter to be only a variety of the former.

Magnolia . . According to Dandy and Good (332) there are some species in eastern North America and a larger number in eastern Asia, both groups having an appreciable extension into the tropics (Fig. 23).

Discontinuous genera of the tropical zone

The tropical genera considered here as discontinuous comprise those which, while not completely pan-tropical, nevertheless occur in two or more of the main land divisions of this zone. Whether or not it is to be interpreted as a measure of the relatively great age of the tropical flora as a whole, the fact remains that the genera of this category are far more numerous than those of all the others put together, amounting indeed to nearly two-thirds of the total.

The three most obvious subdivisions are composed of genera found in America and Africa (e.g. Figs. 28, 29), in America and Asia (e.g. Fig. 75), and in Africa and Asia (e.g. Figs. 30, 31) respectively, but not all the genera which have to find a place can be included in these, and it is necessary to recognise two further groups, one of genera more widely, but still discontinuously and incompletely, distributed over the tropics (e.g. Figs. 32, 33), and one to include still more anomalous cases.

Of the three first divisions that of the African–Asiatic genera is more than twice as large as the other two together, and in this connection it is relevant to remind the reader that this is the only case in which the two constituent land masses are actually contiguous. Of the two divisions involving the New World that of the American–African genera is nearly three times as large as that of the American–Asiatic and Australasian groups.

The two divisions involving Africa can each be further classified according to whether the genera occur on the continent only; on the continent and in the Madagascar region; or on the islands only. Specially remarkable is the small but distinct group of genera which are found in America and elsewhere only in Madagascar.

The actual ranges of these various tropical types are sufficiently indicated by the titles of the divisions to which they belong and it is unnecessary to quote many examples of them apart from four of which figures and maps are given here. These are:

Nepenthes . . A well-known genus of pitcher-plants with well over fifty species ranging from South China to north-eastern Australia, and in addition one species in New Caledonia, one in the Seychelles and one on the eastern side of Madagascar (Figs. 24, 25).

Cunonia . . A genus with about a dozen species in New Caledonia and one in South Africa. The latter is illustrated in Fig. 7 and the distribution of the genera of the Cunoniaceae in Fig. 8.

Hibbertia . . In some respects like the last, but much larger. There are nearly one hundred species in Australia, about eighteen in New Caledonia, one in Fiji (702), two in New Guinea (266) and two in Madagascar (Figs. 26, 27).

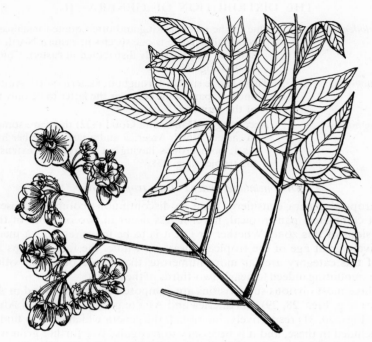

FIG. 28.—*Symphonia globulifera*, about half natural size, after Engler.

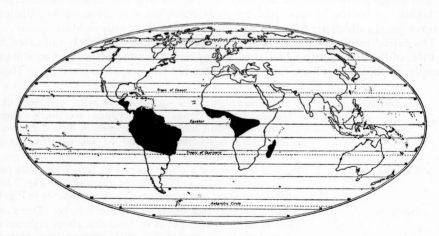

FIG. 29.—Map showing (black) the distribution of the genus *Symphonia*, after Hutchinson.

FIG. 30.—*Ancistrocladus heyneanus*, about half natural size, after Engler.

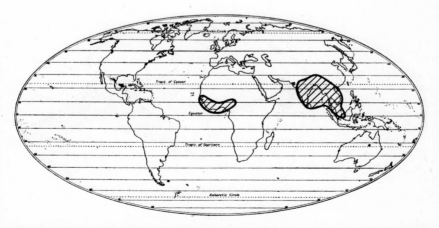

FIG. 31.—Map showing (shaded) the distribution of the genus *Ancistrocladus*, after Hutchinson.

Fig. 32.—*Hernandia peltata*, somewhat reduced, after Seemann.

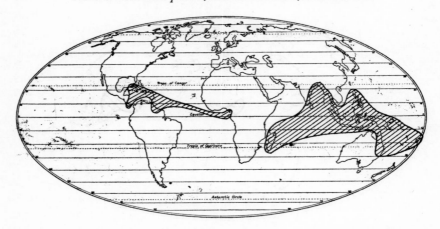

Fig. 33.—Map showing (shaded) the distribution of the genus *Hernandia*, after Hutchinson.

Plate 7. *Puya raimondii* in the Peruvian Andes

(*from Weberbauer in Vegetation der Erde*)

Nelumbo	.	According to Irmscher (398) one species extends from the Caspian to Japan and through Malaysia to Australia and a second from North America to Brazil (Figs. 76, 77).
Nicotiana	.	The natural distribution of this genus is now hard to trace but according to Goodspeed (308) three-quarters of the 60 or so species are in America, and one-quarter (the section *Suaveolentes*) in Australia and the Pacific. Of the latter *N. fragrans* occurs only on the Isle of Pines off New Caledonia, in the Loyalty Islands and in Tonga, though it is introduced in the Marquesas. *N. debneyi* is found in eastern Australia from Sydney almost to Cairns and also on Lord Howe Island, and is introduced in New Caledonia. The rest of the section is confined to Australia. In America the genus is found from Argentina to the southern United States and California.

The more widely ranging discontinuous genera of the tropics are by the nature of the case much more miscellaneous and admit of no general description. Some idea of their details will, however, be apparent from the following, which are some of the more outstanding of them:

Clethra	.	This genus is almost confined to America and Asia, but one species occurs on Madeira (Figs. 34, 35).
Turnera	.	There are many species in tropical America, and in addition one that ranges from the Seychelles and Réunion to Indo–Malaysia.
Kalanchoe	.	A large genus with all but one of its species in the Old World. The exception is a plant found locally in Brazil. It is usually described as distinct and as a native, but it is possibly adventive.
Styrax .	.	Very like *Clethra* in that all but one of its species are American or Asiatic, but the exception in this case is found in the Mediterranean region.
Weinmannia	.	A large genus with the great majority of its species in tropical America, but it is also fairly well distributed in the Madagascar region and in Malaysia and the Pacific Islands, and there are one or two species in New Zealand (Fig. 8).

The anomalous discontinuous genera of the warmer parts of the world are even more miscellaneous and nearly every one of them has its own particular interest, and at least the following call for special reference here:

Aldrovanda .	.	A monotypic aquatic genus recorded from the warmer parts of Europe, north-east Asia, Japan, India, central Africa, Timor and Australia.
Canarina	.	There are three species according to a recent study by Hedberg (350). One of them is found on four of the Canary Islands; and two are in East Africa from Abyssinia (Ethiopia) to Tanganyika.
Cohnia	.	This genus has been recorded from the Mascarenes and from New Caledonia. This is a very extraordinary range and the relationships of the genus need further study, but it is notable that a somewhat similar distribution is attributed to some other genera (296), and particularly to the next.

8

Fig. 34.—*Clethra tomentosa*, about natural size, after Bailey.

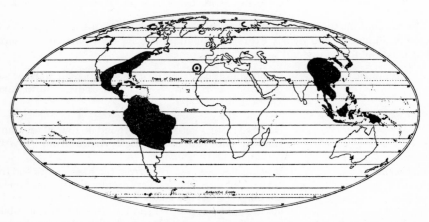

Fig. 35.—Map showing the distribution of the genus *Clethra*, mainly after Irmscher.

Cossinia	. .	This genus is now recorded from the Mascarenes, New Caledonia and Fiji, and the species from the last of these is said to be closely related to that from the Mascarenes (679).
Kissenia	. .	According to Dandy (170) this genus is found only in southern Arabia and Somaliland and in the south-western part of South Africa. The plants in the two areas are much alike and may represent only one species.
Pelargonium .	.	A large genus with the great majority of its species in South Africa, whence it extends to Madagascar and up the east coast of Africa to Arabia and western India. There are also several species in Australia and one occurs in Australia, South Africa and on the Tristan da Cunha islands.
Pharnaceum and *Hypertelis*		Together these form a natural group of species almost entirely confined to Africa and Madagascar, but with one, now very rare, on St. Helena.

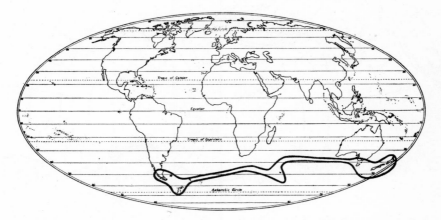

Fig. 36.—Map showing the distribution of the genus *Colobanthus*, from various sources.

Phylica	. .	A genus of some seventy species which according to Pillans (561) has one species on St. Helena, one on the islands of the Tristan da Cunha group and on Amsterdam Island, one in Madagascar, Mauritius and Réunion, two in Madagascar only and the remainder in southern Africa, nearly all of them at the Cape (see Fig. 45).

Discontinuous genera of the south temperate zone

It will be remembered that of the three land extensions south from the north circumboreal belt those in America and Asia and Australasia are much longer than that in Africa, and it is, therefore, not surprising to find that among the discontinuous genera of the southern temperate regions (e.g. Figs. 37, 40), which number some fifty in all, those confined to America and to Australasia are much the most numerous. Some are confined to Africa and Australasia, but other types are scarcely represented. A very few are anomalous.

The genera of the first of these groups are of special interest and importance in relation to the past history of Antarctica and have been much studied in this connection. The writings of Skottsberg in particular (see bibliography) on this subject are of first importance and should be consulted by all who are interested in the great problems they involve.

These genera can be further subdivided according to whether they are found in Australia and New Zealand or in only one of these. The first condition is, with twenty-one genera, much the commonest, and that of occurrence in Australia only is the rarest.

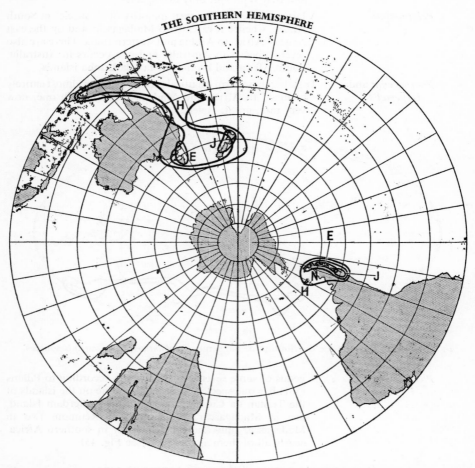

FIG. 37.—Map showing the distribution of the genera N, *Nothofagus*; H, *Hebe*; E, *Eucryphia*; J, *Jovellana*.

The general features of these southern temperate genera are fairly adequately displayed by their classification, but the following may be noticed in detail as specially noteworthy examples of the group:

Colobanthus . Most of the species are confined to New Zealand, but one is common to New Zealand and Australia. There are also at least two ranging from New Zealand to South America and occurring also among the South Temperate Oceanic Islands and on Antarctica.

Haloragis . . According to Tuyama (744) this genus has 59 of its 80 species in Australia, whence it extends to Rapa on the east and to Japan northwards, the latter chiefly by two exceptionally widely distributed species. There are also three species on the Juan Fernandez Islands. The genus thus well illustrates the not infrequent extension of an Australasian group far north of the equator, and the much rarer condition of occurrence in Juan Fernandez but not in continental America.

FIG. 38.—*Eucryphia glutinosa*, about natural size, after Hutchinson.

Lilaeopsis . . A genus of rather problematical species constitution and according to Hill (359) recorded from North America, Mexico, South America and the Falklands as well as from Australia, Tasmania and New Zealand.

Nothofagus . . This genus contains the southern beeches which are distinct from, though closely related to, the northern beeches of the genus *Fagus*. This antipodal relationship has long made *Nothofagus* particularly interesting to plant-geographers and this interest has increased in recent years by the recognition that there are numerous species of the genus living in New Guinea (703, 704, 705) and in New Caledonia

(51), and also by the identification of fossil pollen as belonging to the genus from parts of the southern hemisphere where *Nothofagus* does not now occur (157). There are now said to be eleven living species in western South America from 38° S. southward; five in New Zealand; three in Australia (one South Queensland, one Victoria and Tasmania, one Tasmania); five in New Caledonia, and about twenty in New Guinea.

Oreomyrrhis . . According to Mathias and Constance (499) this genus has, in the New World, two species in Central America, one along the Andes, and one in Fuegia and the Falkland Islands. In the Old World there are two in Formosa, one in extreme North Borneo, five in the mountains of New Guinea, seven in Australia and Tasmania, and two in New Zealand (Fig. 39).

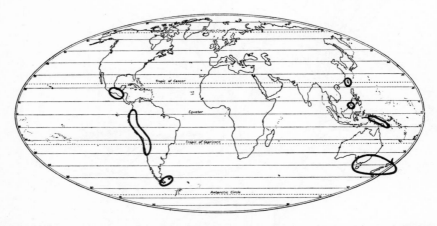

Fig. 39.—Map showing the distribution of the genus *Oreomyrrhis*, after Mathias and Constance.

Fuchsia . . Most of the hundred or so species occur in America and especially in the tropical parts, but there are five, including *F. procumbens*, in New Zealand and one in the Society Islands (529).

Jovellana . . A genus closely related to *Calceolaria*, with one or two species in Chile and a few in New Zealand (Fig. 37).

Phyllachne . . This genus has three species in New Zealand and Tasmania and one in Fuegia, the latter being the only member of the family (Stylidiaceae) in the New World (284) (Fig. 3).

Drimys and . . Most of the species are in the eastern part of the Malayan
Pseudowintera Archipelago and especially in New Guinea, but there are others in Australia, New Zealand, and in parts of South and Central America (Fig. 5).

Restio . . . A large genus confined to South Africa and Australia and well represented in each. The family to which it belongs (Restionaceae) has, in general, much the same distribution.

Carpobrotus . This is one of the modern segregates of the large genus *Mesembryanthemum*. It has about a dozen species in South Africa, several in Australia and one in Chile.

Pringlea . . "The Kerguelen cabbage", a monotypic genus once thought to be confined to the island group of that name but now known also from Heard Island, Marion Island and the Crozets. It thus combines wide discontinuity with a very small actual area of occurrence.

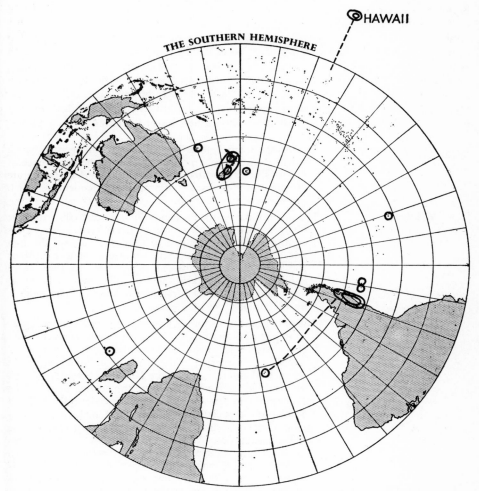

FIG. 40.—Map showing the distribution of the thirteen species of the series *Tetrapterae* of the genus *Sophora*.

Discontinuous genera of the north and south temperate zones

The fourth great category, of genera found only in the north and south temperate zones, is particularly hard to estimate because of the difficulty of determining the real status of many plants which occur more or less naturally in the temperate parts of the southern hemisphere. Frequently plants which seem, at first sight, to be native there, turn out on further investigation to be, in all probability, adventives, and therefore not to be reckoned as authentic cases of discontinuity. There is also the problem of deciding which of the many genera that extend with more or less marked gaps along the Andes are in fact sufficiently discontinuous to merit inclusion. When these two difficulties in particular are allowed for, the number of genera in the category appears not to exceed about sixty.

These are best further divided according to their ranges below the equator. Some occur, for instance, in all three parts of the southern hemisphere, others in only two out of three, and still others in only one. In all there are seven possible combinations and of these six occur, the only case of which there appear to be no examples being that of distribution in the northern temperate zone and in South America and South Africa. The commonest state is that of occurrence in the north and in South America only, and this is doubtless correlated with the exceptional ease of migration along the great line of the Rockies and the Andes. Details of the numbers in each of these several types must be sought in the Appendix, but the following may be cited as specially interesting examples of the category as a whole:

Triglochin . .	Among the many interesting features of this genus, which merits a careful geographical study, are the occurrence of several species in both the northern and southern temperate regions and the presence of a number of endemics, which are annuals, in Australia.
Frankenia . .	The wide total range of the genus (398) is due to the extensive distribution of a single species which is found more or less continuously from Europe to Central Asia and through Africa to the Cape, but there are also a number of other species in the Mediterranean region. Besides these there is a large group of species in Australia, another in Chile, and a smaller one in western North America. The genus is also recorded from St. Helena.
Coriaria . .	The only genus of its family and one of the most remarkable examples of discontinuity (288). The few species are found (Figs. 41, 42) from the tropic in Mexico through Central America, in western South America to about 45° S., in the western Mediterranean, in the Himalayas, western China and Burma, from Japan south to the northern part of the Philippines, in New Guinea, in the New Hebrides, Fiji and Samoa and especially in New Zealand, including Stewart Island, the Chatham Islands and the Kermadecs. The Australasian and American species are more or less identical but the species of the Northern and Southern Hemispheres belong to different sections of the genus. It is interesting to note that nitrogen-fixing root nodules are known in many of the species (77).
Myosurus . .	A very small genus found in the northern temperate zone and in all three parts of the southern temperate regions.
Eryngium . .	This genus has an unusual distribution and is a somewhat anomalous member of this category though it cannot be fitted in better elsewhere. It has one species concentration in western Eurasia and the Mediterranean, and another, larger one, in America, especially in the tropics. There are

FIG. 41.—*Coriaria japonica*, about half natural size, after Bailey.

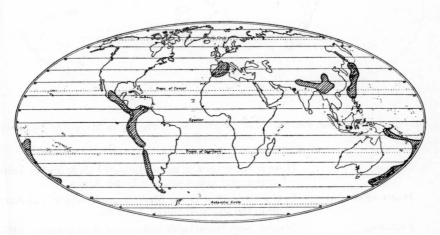

FIG. 42.—Map showing (shaded) the distribution of the genus *Coriaria*.

one or two species in Australia and New Zealand. The genus is absent from Asia except in the west; from tropical and south Africa; and is only slightly represented in North America.

Papaver . . Almost entirely a northern genus and centred in the Mediterranean region, but there is one species in South Africa and Australia.

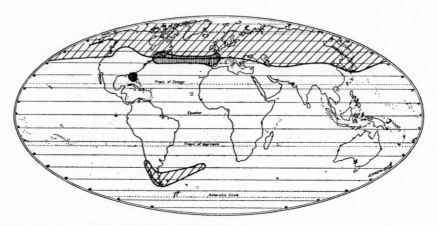

FIG. 43.—Map showing the distribution of the three genera of the family **Empetraceae**: Wide diagonal shading—*Empetrum*; close vertical shading—*Corema*; solid black—*Ceratiola*.

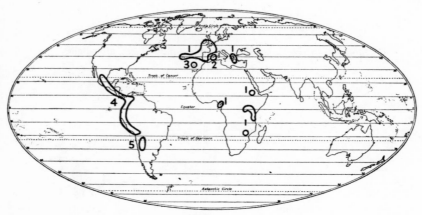

FIG. 44.—Map showing the distribution of the genus *Sibthorpia* and its five species (numbered), after Hedberg.

Oligomeris . . There is one species in the south-west U.S.A. and in western Eurasia, and about seven in South Africa.

Damasonium . . Two species occur in the Mediterranean region and there is one in the southern half of Australia.

Empetrum . . Another very remarkable instance of discontinuity (286). It is a genus of two species and is completely circumpolar in the north. Elsewhere it is found only in temperate South America, including the Falklands, and on the Tristan group (Fig. 43).

Honkenya . . Widely distributed in the northern temperate regions and occurs also, apparently native, on the coast of Patagonia. It is a monotypic genus but its subspecies and forms are also completely segregated geographically.

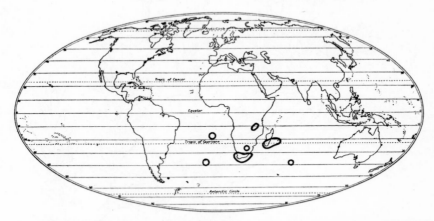

FIG. 45.—Map showing the distribution of the genus *Phylica*, mainly after Suessenguth.

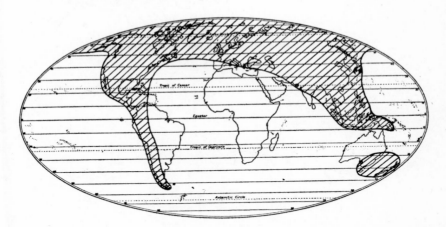

FIG. 46.—Map showing (shaded) the distribution of the genus *Gentiana*, mainly after Irmscher.

Littorella . . A genus of two species, one of which is found in Europe and in eastern North America and the other in Patagonia. It thus combines two distinct types of discontinuity.

Sibthorpia . . Hedberg (348) considers that this genus has five species, one in Greece, western Europe, the Azores, and some of the tropical African mountains; one in the western Mediterranean; one in Madeira; one from Mexico to Bolivia, and one from Bolivia to 30° S. (Fig. 44).

Fig. 47.—*Coprosma nitida*, about natural size, after Hooker.

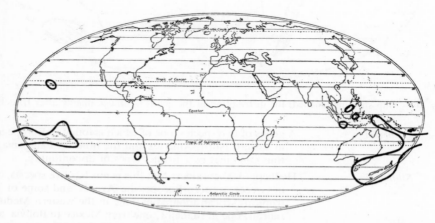

Fig. 48.—Map showing the distribution of the genus *Coprosma*, after Oliver and Bader.

Discontinuous genera present in Hawaii

The last of the five categories, that which concerns certain plants found in the Hawaiian Islands, is scarcely comparable with the others but it is, nevertheless, of considerable interest, especially from the point of view of the relationships of the southern floras of the Old World (see Chapter 12). It is made necessary by the extraordinary isolation of these islands and by their position roughly equally distant from Asia and America. As will be seen later, these islands have many endemic genera and their flora also includes others which are cosmopolitan, pan-temperate or pan-tropical. The fifty-odd genera which comprise the present category are therefore those genera of the flora which, outside the islands, have a fairly restricted distribution and which thus are of special interest as a clue to the general affinities of the flora.

In this connection it is most noteworthy that of these genera thirty-odd are found elsewhere only in the Old World, compared with about half a dozen found only in the New World. The rest are found in both. The category as a whole includes some genera with very remarkable distributions, and in particular the following deserve notice:

Acaena . . This genus is chiefly to be found in South America, temperate Australia, Tasmania and New Zealand, but occurs also in the South Temperate Oceanic Islands, at the Cape (1 sp.), in California, in New Guinea and on the Hawaiian Islands. The New Guinea plants belong to a widespread species which is described as occurring also in Australia, New Zealand and through the oceanic islands to South America.

Coprosma . . According to Oliver (541) about 40 out of the 90 species of this genus are in the New Zealand region, reaching to the Kermadecs, the Chatham Islands, the Auckland and Campbell Islands and Macquarie Island; and nearly 20 are endemic to the Hawaiian Islands. There are seven in south-east Australia and Tasmania, three on Lord Howe Island and two on Norfolk Island. In Malaysia Oliver gives two in New Guinea, one on Mt. Kinabalu in Borneo, and one in Java. The remainder range from the New Hebrides eastward through the Pacific islands to Pitcairn Island, and there are two species on Juan Fernandez. In recent years a few more additional species have been added, notably from the mountains of New Guinea; from Rapa; and from Kerguelen (818). The distribution of the genus as given by Bader, is shown in Fig. 48.

Pittosporum . . A genus distributed widely in the tropical and south temperate zones of the Old World, but massed in Australasia. Secondary species concentrations are found in Madagascar, the Philippines, New Guinea and Hawaii and there is an outlying species in Macaronesia (296).

Cuphea . . Another large genus, exclusively American except for one species which is found in Hawaii and also on the Galapagos Islands.

Astelia . . According to Skottsberg (664 and in litt.), there are nine species in New Zealand, six in Hawaii, two in Australia, one in Australia and New Zealand, one in New Guinea, one in New Caledonia, one in Tahiti, one in the Marquesas, one in Rapa, one in Réunion and Mauritius, and one in temperate South America (Figs. 49, 50).

Nertera . . This genus, which is related to *Coprosma*, is centred in New Zealand with some representation in tropical Asia. It includes one very widespread species recorded also from Australia, Tasmania, Hawaii, South America and Tristan da Cunha, and another in Australia only.

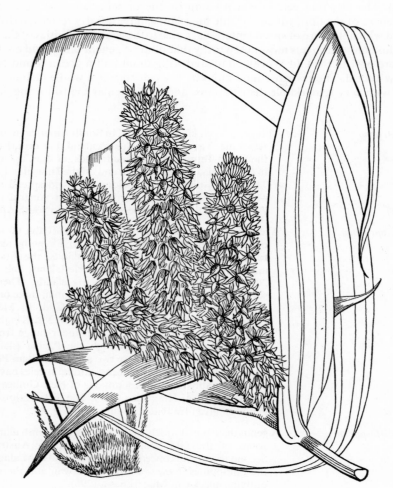

FIG. 49.—*Collospermum montanum*, somewhat reduced, after Seemann.

Exocarpus . . Stauffer, in his recent monograph (694), admits 26 species in three subgenera. Two species range widely over Malaysia, one of them from Annam to New Guinea, and the other from the Philippines and Borneo to Australia. One species occurs locally in Queensland and in Norfolk

Island and New Caledonia; and there are eight in Australia and Tasmania. There are five more species in New Caledonia, three in New Guinea, three in Hawaii, one in Rapa, one in Fiji, one in Lord Howe Island and one in New Zealand (Fig. 51).

Gymnelaea . . In Johnson's revision of the Oleaceae (410) this genus is credited with five species in New Caledonia, three in New Zealand, one in New Zealand and on Norfolk Island, one in south-east Australia and Tasmania, and one in Hawaii.

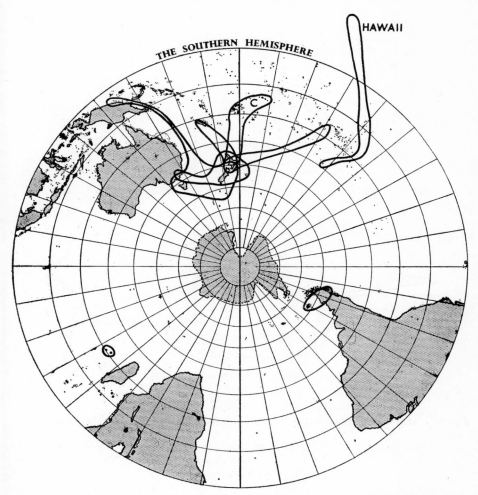

Fig. 50.—Map showing the distribution of the seven sections of the genus *Astelia*, and of the closely allied genus *Collospermum*, C (Fig. 49).

Santalum . . St. John (689) says that of the still-existing species one, *S. album*, is found from Java to Timor, there are two in New Guinea, three in Australia, one in Fiji, one in New Caledonia and the New Hebrides, seven in Hawaii, one on

Henderson Island, one on Juan Fernandez, and one, *S. insulare*, on Tahiti, Raiatea, the Austral Islands, Rapa and the Marquesas.

Gunnera . . According to Skottsberg (666) this genus is chiefly South American with a minor group in New Zealand, Tasmania and the Malayan Archipelago. It occurs also in Africa and Madagascar, and in Hawaii (Plate 9, Fig. 52).

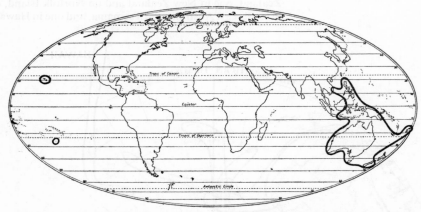

FIG. 51.—Map showing the distribution of the genus *Exocarpus*, after Stauffer.

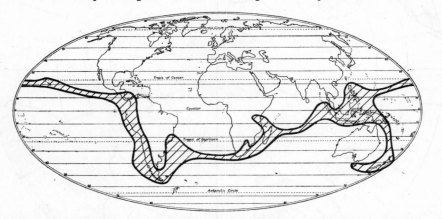

FIG. 52.—Map showing (shaded) the distribution of the genus *Gunnera*, partly after Hutchinson.

Metrosideros . This is not a very clear-cut genus but a recent study (812, Fig. 53) shows that it is centred in New Guinea 13 spp., New Caledonia 10, and New Zealand 12. Westward of this it is found in the Moluccas, Java and Sumatra; northward it is found in the Bonin Islands 1, and the Hawaiian Islands 4; and eastwards it extends to the Marquesas, Gambier Island and Rapa, mainly through the wide distribution of *M. polymorpha*, which is also in Hawaii. There are two local species in Australia, one in the north-west and one in the north-east, and there is one in the Cape flora of South Africa.

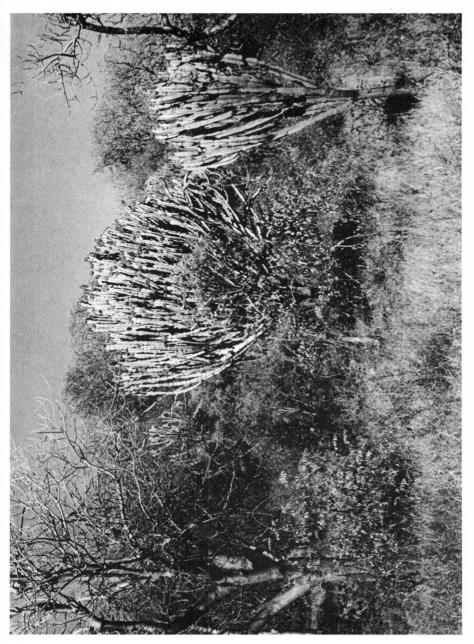

Plate 8. The cactus-like tree *Euphorbia ingens* among other vegetation in the northern Transvaal. Note the terminal flower clusters on the centre specimen

(Photo: M. R. Levyns)

Elaeocarpus . . There is unfortunately no convenient revision of this genus but about 500 species have been described and these, except for a very small number of wides, are distributed roughly as follows. The great centre of concentration is the Malayan Archipelago and especially New Guinea with 120, Philippines 65, Borneo 65. South-east Asia and Burma and Malaya each have more than 30, and there are 20 or more in China and Japan, in eastern Australia, in New Caledonia, and in Celebes and the Moluccas. Madagascar has 18, Fiji 18, India and Pakistan 16, and the rest are more thinly scattered over other islands, including three in New Zealand. According to Smith (681) there are 4 in the Solomons, 2 in the New Hebrides, 4 in Samoa, and 1 in Samoa and Tonga. There is an endemic species in Socotra.

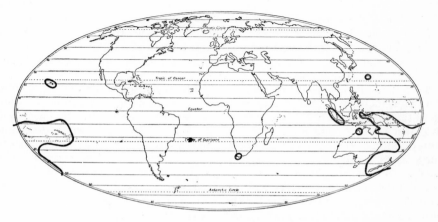

FIG. 53.—Map showing the distribution of the genus *Metrosideros*, after Bader.

Suttonia . . Found only in Hawaii and in New Zealand and as a different subgenus in each.

Dianella . . According to Schlittler (827) this genus occurs in Hawaii; north-west tropical South America; the Madagascar region; and from Ceylon, Nepal and South Japan to Tasmania, New Zealand and the Society Islands, but 16 of the 24 species are confined to Australasia. The genus has more lately been recorded from Rhodesia (778).

Three other genera of this category, all of them large, deserve mention together because of their high proportions of endemic species and great development on the islands of Malaysia and the Pacific, namely *Pandanus* and *Freycinetia*, which are closely related members of the same family of Monocotyledons, and *Cyrtandra*. All three have been discussed at some length, especially from the point of view of the problems which the details of their endemism present, by Guppy (325).

The most widespread of these is *Pandanus*, which ranges from Tropical Africa, through Madagascar and the Mascarenes (where it is strongly represented), over

9

tropical south-east Asia, and Malaysia, where it has a great number of species especially in the Malay Peninsula, the Philippines and New Guinea, to New South Wales in Australia and far over the Pacific. From this last vast region more than one-fifth of all its species have been described. *Pandanus* has only a single species in Hawaii, but it extends east as far as the Marquesas and Rapa. Many of its species have been described as endemic on tiny islands, but a handful of species are widely distributed coastal plants. A considerable majority of its total species are south of the equator. *Freycinetia* is geographically a lesser version of *Pandanus* having much the same limits in the east but extending westward only as far as Ceylon. In the north it reaches Formosa and in the south New Zealand. Many more species have been described from the Philippines and New Guinea than anywhere else, and there are several in Hawaii. Like *Pandanus* it has most of its species south of the equator. *Cyrtandra*, which is as far removed taxonomically from the others as can well be imagined, ranges south and east from China, Siam and the Malay Peninsula to Australia and far across the Pacific to the Marquesas. Almost all its species, however, are in Malaysia and the Pacific Islands, the former having about twice as many as the latter, and in contrast to the two preceding genera, Hawaii, where all the species are endemic, is one of the greatest centres, the only larger ones being the Philippines and New Guinea. Its species are almost equal in numbers on both sides of the equator with perhaps a slight preponderance in the north.

Finally the inclusion of the genus *Edwardsia* of Salisbury requires explanation. This genus includes various species which are more commonly regarded as belonging to the large genus *Sophora* which has been exhaustively studied by Dr. Tsoong, who most kindly provided the following information. The genus *Edwardsia* cannot in his opinion be sustained, but its geographically most interesting species constitute a new series, *Tetrapterae* of *Sophora*. This series comprises thirteen species distributed as follows (see Fig. 40)—two on Hawaii, one on Lord Howe Island, one on the Chatham Islands, three in New Zealand, one on Réunion, one in temperate South America, one in temperate South America and on Gough Island, two on Juan Fernandez (one on Masafuera and one on Masatierra), and one on Easter Island. A closely related series containing two other species of *Edwardsia* occurs in continental Asia. There are two other related monotypic series, one of which is found on coasts throughout the tropics, and the other in Korea.

The complete list as given in Appendix B contains 765 genera. For the reasons given earlier this is almost certainly an appreciable underestimate of the total number of discontinuous genera in the Angiosperms, and hence it can at least be said that these amount to more than 5 per cent of all genera. Among them tropical genera predominate strongly.

It would be particularly interesting to calculate the number of discontinuous genera in the different families, but the method of classification of certain families makes it almost impossible to do this. It is, however, possible to calculate the relative and absolute frequency of the different families represented in the list, and this reveals some interesting facts.

The Leguminosae, using that term in its comprehensive sense, is the most frequent group and is followed in the order named by the Compositae, Euphorbiaceae, Rubiaceae, Liliaceae, Scrophulariaceae and Apocynaceae. Taking into account what has been said about the Compositae in particular, the number here is remarkably high and indicates that, as might be expected from its size, this family probably actually has more discontinuous genera in total than any other.

It is more interesting to note that, as the list stands at present, some of the smaller families show by far the highest *proportion* of widely discontinuous genera. Saxifragaceae, Gentianaceae, Sterculiaceae, Rutaceae, Olacaceae, Meliaceae, Oleaceae, Rhamnaceae, Aizoaceae, Simaroubaceae, Combretaceae and Rhizophoraceae, for instance, have very high figures, but even these are exceeded by the Magnoliaceae and by the Berberidaceae in the wide sense.

Mention of the Rhizophoraceae, the family containing the mangroves, serves as a reminder that one very special kind of discontinuous distribution has received practically no notice above. This is the discontinuity which is generally and indeed almost inevitably shown by wide ranging plants whose habitats are in, or closely associated with, shallow marine waters. Such plants fall into three groups, namely, the marine Angiosperms, which live actually submerged in the sea; the mangroves, which inhabit muddy tidal shores; and certain so-called strand plants, which grow either on, or just inland of, sandy shores. Each of these groups contains many genera which are discontinuous and form a conspicuous element in at least the tropical category of the list given in Appendix B. It is clear, however, that their discontinuity is of a very particular and special kind, and for this reason and also because it is, more often than not, a matter of individual species, more detailed consideration is deferred to a later chapter, where it will be described at some length.

CHAPTER 7

THE DISTRIBUTION OF GENERA—III

Endemic Genera

ENDEMIC genera have been defined, for present purposes, as genera either actually confined to one floristic region or having distributions not greatly exceeding the average size of a region. This latter qualification is necessary because many genera, while comparatively restricted in range, actually extend over parts of two regions. On the other hand, many are so local as to occupy much less than the whole of an average region.

Taking into account the figures already given for other categories, it would appear that about 10,000 genera are endemic in the sense just defined, and for the purposes of the short and formal survey which is all that is possible here they can be dealt with most conveniently if they are classified according to the thirty-seven regions which form the basis of the floristic arrangement used here. Here and there it is necessary for special reasons to depart from this treatment, but on the whole it not only permits the easy handling of this great mass of genera but also provides a useful opportunity for drawing attention to special features of interest in the floras of these regions.

As far as possible figures are again quoted, but they are intended only to give some idea of relative numbers. The various examples selected for mention include, whenever possible, those most likely to be familiar to the general reader.

It should also be borne in mind that the inclusion of a genus in any particular regional account does not necessarily mean that it is exclusively confined to that region but only that the region in question is that of which it is most characteristic. Many genera naturally extend somewhat beyond the limits of the region in which the bulk of their range and/or the majority of their species occur.

Arctic and Sub-arctic Region

The arctic provides an excellent instance of the limitations to the use of endemism in estimating floristic rank, because, though it is commonly agreed that the arctic flora is a sufficiently distinct entity to be reckoned as a major unit in floristic classification, it has, in fact, practically no endemic genera. A few, including *Arctagrostis* and *Parrya*, have been described as such, but they are small and not too well defined. It is in this negative quality that the chief interest of the arctic flora lies, because the proportion of endemism in a flora tends to increase with the degree and duration of its isolation. There is good reason to believe that the arctic flora, in its present form, is one of the youngest and perhaps the youngest in the world. It also shows a minimum amount of isolation, consisting merely of the most resistant elements of the northern temperate flora and their derivatives (see pp. 177 *et seq.*), and the boundary between the two indeed is largely a subjective one. It should also be borne in mind that the arctic region, except for Greenland, which is almost covered by an ice-cap, is a small one and that the polar region proper is occupied by the Arctic Ocean.

132

Euro–Siberian Region

It was found convenient to deal with the genera which range throughout this exceptionally extensive region in the last chapter, and attention is here confined to genera which are endemic to one or other part of it.

One good reason for dividing this very elongated region into two is that, although these are clearly but parts of one whole, conditions at the two ends of the region are very different. In the west the influence of the Gulf Stream results in a considerable latitudinal depth of comparatively genial climate, especially in winter, and this, coupled with an absence of barriers, not only gives room for a wide development of deciduous forest vegetation but also adds to the general flora a noteworthy element from the Mediterranean region to the south. On the east the coast is entirely icebound in winter and the climate of the interior is one of the most severe in the world, characterised by enormous seasonal variation in air temperature above a subsoil which, for the most part, is permanently frozen. Moreover, the direction of continuous mountain ranges not only narrows the region geographically and restricts it vegetationally largely to coniferous forest, but cuts it off from easy general infiltration from China on the south, where the East Asiatic deciduous forest flora is found.

The dividing line between the two subregions (see p. 29) follows the longitude 60° E., partly because such a line is easily recognised and drawn on maps, partly because it follows, reasonably closely, the main physiographic feature of the Urals, partly because, so doing, it marks also the boundary between Europe and Siberia, and partly because it marks, more or less accurately, the limits of various constituents of the European deciduous forest flora.

It is not surprising, in view of these conditions, that the flora of the western part of the region is much richer than that of the eastern part, and this is shown by the fact that while Europe has between fifty and one hundred endemic genera, according to taxonomic taste, and some of these not of the smallest size, Siberia appears to have very few, perhaps no more than a dozen or so, and nearly all of them monotypic. The former include *Bulbocodium, Lunaria, Melittis, Physospermum, Stratiotes* and *Pulmonaria*, the last with about a dozen species being perhaps the largest. These are scarcely to be distinguished from genera characteristic of Europe, but which extend somewhat into western Asia, such as *Astrantia, Eremurus, Laburnum* and *Vinca*. Strictly confined to Europe and actually even more strongly localised are about twenty genera found only in one or other of the mountain systems, among them *Erinus, Nigritella, Ramonda* and *Soldanella*. *Bryonia, Carlina* and *Crithmum* exemplify genera which are very familiar in west Eurasia but which extend also to Macaronesia.

None of the Siberian endemic genera is important or familiar, and *Borodinia, Macropodium* and *Redowskia* are examples of the Cruciferae which seem to provide the bulk of them. Certain other genera, however, are rather characteristic of this subregion though they extend outside it, and of these there may be mentioned *Bergenia, Caragana* and *Rheum*.

Sino–Japanese Region

This region consists of three main parts—the elevated area of the Sino–Himalayan–Tibetan mountains; the rest of China except the south; and an insular area, Japan. The flora is, on the whole, homogeneous throughout except that the inclusion of the total Himalayan complex brings in extraneous elements to some extent. To regard these mountains as a single whole, however, makes for a very useful simplification and does not obscure any very salient facts.

The total number of endemic genera in this considerable region is almost certainly 300 or more, though most of them are small, but it is difficult to give exact figures because its limits are not everywhere political boundaries. Whatever the number may be the genera divide fairly simply into groups. Comparatively few range over the whole region, but these include *Caryopteris, Euptelea, Helwingia, Metaplexis, Reevesia, Stachyurus* and *Tricyrtis*. More are found in China and Japan, thus covering nearly all the region, and among these are *Akebia, Callistephus, Chimonanthus, Hosta, Liriope, Lycoris, Nandina, Paulownia, Platycodon, Rehmannia, Rhodotypos, Rodgeria* and *Rohdea*. Genera confined to China number well over 100 but the southern part of this country belongs to another region. Chinese genera include *Hovenia, Kerria, Kolkwitzia, Litchi, Poncirus, Saruma, Veratrilla* and *Xanthoceras*. A few small genera are confined to Korea and Japan. Japan has some seventy-odd endemic genera, among them *Anemonopsis, Chionographis, Fatsia, Kirengeshoma, Pteridophyllum* and *Trochodendron*. Sakhalin, which is partly in the region, has at least one endemic genus.

The Sino–Himalayan mountain system and indeed the whole region, is the native land of many highly-prized garden plants, but its strictly endemic genera do not number more than a hundred, most of its characteristic genera having wider ranges. Among more familiar examples are *Davidia* (sometimes made a separate family), *Leycesteria, Maddenia, Nardostachys, Nomocharis, Stranvaesia* and *Triplostegia*. Several genera, while massed in the Himalayas, extend somewhat out of the region, as, for instance, *Cremanthodium* (287), which can be included here only by stretching a point, as one or two of its more atypical species reach well into Tibet and North China, and *Codonopsis*, which actually reaches Japan. *Meconopsis* also is essentially a Himalayan genus but, in fact, on account of a species in Europe, discontinuous.

On the south the region shows considerable linkage with its neighbours. A number of genera are, for instance, described as ranging from India to Japan, and in another direction a handful of genera extend south towards Malaya, among them being *Aspidistra* and *Schizophragma*, and there are several genera confined to Japan and Formosa. On the other hand there is a conspicuous demarcation line between Korea and Japan, the latter having 260 genera not in the former, and the former 60 genera not in the latter (Hara, 335, 336, 337).

Takhtajan (717) has suggested that the Angiosperms originated in a monsoon country with a warm subtropical climate such as prevails for instance in the southern part of this region, and particularly in southern Yunnan, and Fedorov has given an interesting account of the rain forest in that part of China (234, 235).

Western and Central Asiatic Region

This region, which comprises the Caucasus, Armenia, part of Persia, part of Russia, and part of Tibet, as well as the rather indeterminate countries between east Europe and China, is difficult to deal with because its limits bear little relation to political boundaries, a point which always complicates the investigation of plant distribution. It consists of dry mountainous areas or of actual deserts some of which are salt, and the vegetation is comparatively limited and specialised.

As far as any estimate can be of value it appears to contain about 150 endemic genera, of which Tibet has perhaps a dozen, and these are almost all small and specialised. Halophytes and xerophytes are well represented, and more than a third of the total belong to the Cruciferae, a family of notoriously difficult generic distinction. Chenopodiaceae and Umbelliferae are also plentiful, and these three families together account for more than half the total. Most of the genera are fairly well distributed, but some, like *Dorema*, are restricted to the western part and others, like *Ostrowskia, Potaninia* and *Tetraena*, to the east.

Cannabis and *Spinacia* are almost the only very familiar genera. The former, as far as its native range can now be determined, is confined to the region, but the latter extends into Mesopotamia. *Exochorda* extends eastwards into China, and *Phelipaea* is a true endemic parasitic genus.

Mediterranean Region

The actual area of land within this region is small, being confined, except for the larger part of the Iberian Peninsula, to the littoral zones of the Mediterranean, and it has a very specialised type of vegetation (215, 489), which is reflected in a high proportion of endemic forms. Furthermore, the boundaries between it and the neighbouring regions are not always clear and many genera characteristic of the Mediterranean in fact extend far beyond it. This is specially noteworthy in the north, where many Mediterranean genera range far up into western Europe and some actually reach the British Isles, where, as will be seen later, they form an important element in its flora. Among these are *Anthyllis, Atropa, Bellis, Hippocrepis, Jasione, Medicago, Ophrys, Origanum, Tamus, Ulex* and *Verbascum*. Among others, mainly represented in Britain by garden plants only, are *Centranthus, Crocus, Galanthus, Gypsophila, Helleborus, Lavandula, Muscari, Narcissus* (241) and *Nigella*.

Including these the total number of Mediterranean genera is probably about 250. Among them *Aethionema* and *Cistus* stand out as exceptionally large genera, the former having more than fifty species. The latter, though rather smaller, is perhaps the most characteristic of all Mediterranean plant groups because it contributes so largely to the peculiar type of vegetation known as the "maquis". Among other fairly well known examples are *Aubrietia, Galega, Malope, Phillyrea, Pisum, Rosmarinus* and *Santolina*, all of which range fairly widely over the region.

As examples of rather more restricted genera there may be mentioned—*Helxine* on Corsica and Sardinia; *Triplachne* on Sicily; *Astrocarpus* in Spain; *Argania* in North Africa; *Drosophyllum* in south Spain and neighbouring North Africa and several notable monotypic genera of Cruciferae in south Spain. There are also a few genera, mostly Umbelliferous, recorded only from Syria.

On the east side the region connects up with Central Asia by several genera such as *Chionodoxa, Cicer, Danae* and *Michauxia*, but it is difficult to classify genera here, because while parts of the coast of Asia Minor belong floristically to the Mediterranean region the interior belongs to Western and Central Asia. On the west side the region shows relationship with Macaronesia in the presence of several genera, including *Ecballium, Echium* and *Ruscus*, which occur in both.

Macaronesian Region

The degree of generic endemism in this region is low and chiefly of interest in relation to its distribution among the island groups. In all there are less than thirty endemic genera. Of these about half are confined to the Canaries, including *Phyllis, Plocama* and *Semele*. A few are confined to Madeira including *Musschia* and the remarkable arborescent umbellifer *Melanoselinum*. Two only are found on the Cape Verdes, and there is none on the Azores. Of the rest three, including *Isoplexis*, inhabit the Canaries and Madeira; *Lytanthus* is in the Canaries and the Azores: and *Aichryson* ranges over the Canaries, Madeira and the Azores.

It should be noted that the Canaries, though volcanic, are in the position of continental islands, and that they have most endemics, while the most isolated group, the Azores, has none.

Atlantic North American Region

The endemic genera of this region probably number between one and two hundred. It must, however, be remembered that many genera characteristic of eastern North America extend right across the continent and have, therefore, been considered among the wide genera in Chapter 5.

Some of the endemics, like *Baptisia* and *Robinia*, are almost extensive enough to rank as wides, but there are others which are very narrow. *Franklinia* is a particularly interesting case because it appears to be one of the few genera which have actually become extinct in a wild state during the historical period. One single plant of a single species was discovered in the eighteenth century on the Atamaha River in Georgia (240), and from this tree the existing garden individuals are all descended. The original wild tree, however, has disappeared and apparently no other has ever been seen.

Among other genera confined to the Atlantic States of North America are *Ceratiola, Dionaea, Dirca, Gatesia, Hudsonia, Meehania, Neviusia, Pleea, Sanguinaria, Sarracenia* and *Uvularia*.

Pacific North American Region

Various estimates go to indicate that there are at least three hundred endemic genera in this region. The richest part is certainly California (530, 823, 828), but many genera extend nearly all over it. It is, however, safe to say that the number is greater in the south than in the north.

Eschscholzia and *Abronia* are good examples of wider endemics, while *Sidalcea* and *Tolmiea* exemplify genera of the more northern parts. Others, chiefly of the south, are *Choisya, Darlingtonia, Dendromecon, Lewisia, Nolina, Romneya* and *Umbellularia. Sarcodes* is a remarkable saprophytic plant from the Sierra Nevada.

As is usual, a number of genera mainly characteristic of the region show transition with its neighbours. *Yucca*, for instance, though characteristic of the south-western U.S.A., extends widely east in the southern part of its range. *Bigelovia*, similarly, has one species in the east. *Zinnia*, again, is centred in the southern part of the region but has one species which extends right down to Chile. *Garrya* reaches Mexico and the West Indies; and *Calochortus* reaches Guatemala.

North African—Indian Desert Region

This region, though one of the largest, has, as might be expected from the nature of its climate, a comparatively restricted vegetation, and the number of its endemic genera, none of which is large, probably does not much exceed fifty. Among them the Cruciferae and Compositae are particularly well represented.

Some of these genera are relatively widespread, as, for instance, *Anastatica, Londesia* (which reaches Mongolia), *Ochradenus* (which reaches Abyssinia), *Savignya* and *Neurada* (which is sometimes reckoned a family of its own), but others are confined either to the western part from Morocco to Arabia (e.g. *Cornulaca* and *Zilla*) or to the eastern part from Persia to Afghanistan (e.g. *Fortuynia, Reptonia* and *Zataria*).

Among more restricted endemics are *Mecomischus* from the Sahara; *Saltia* from Aden; *Omania* and *Xerotia* from Arabia.

At the other extreme there are certain genera which though ranging variously beyond the strict limits of this region are nevertheless very characteristic of it, and among these *Daemia, Glossonema* and *Leptadenia*, all belonging to the Asclepiadaceae, may be cited.

Endemic Genera of Tropical Africa

This is one of the points at which it is convenient to depart from a rigid regional classification, because the different regions into which tropical Africa is divided are so closely related that many genera are not markedly confined to one of them although they are not found outside the tropical parts of the continent. They therefore can scarcely rank as wides, and must receive notice here.

These more extensive endemics probably number several hundred but most of them are small, although *Ritchiea*, for instance, has upwards of fifty species. They include *Cola, Erythrocephalum, Khaya, Margaretta, Monotes, Octoknema, Oricia, Pleiotaxis* and *Ricinodendron.*

Some are confined to the mountains and occasionally show some discontinuity. *Thunbergianthus*, for instance, is recorded from the island of S. Tomé in the Gulf of Guinea and from Ruwenzori; and *Pseudagrostistachys* from S. Tomé, Fernando Po and the Ruwenzori region.

Even with the more narrowly distributed endemic genera of tropical Africa it is convenient to modify the regional classification slightly and in two instances to combine together a pair of separate regions. These pairs are the Sudanese Steppe Region and the West African Forest Region, and the North-east African Highland and Steppe Region and the East African Steppe Region, respectively. By reckoning these four as two double regions an important point is emphasised, namely the occurrence of two well-marked floras, one covering what may be called western tropical Africa and the other eastern and southern tropical Africa, and the advantage of doing this outweighs the drawback of departing from the more rigid regional arrangement, and also simplifies the presentation of the relevant facts.

Sudanese Park Steppe Region and West African Rain-forest Region

The total number of endemic genera in these two portions of the African continent appears at present to be about 250, but knowledge of the flora here has increased in late years and this may well prove to be an underestimate. Whatever the number may be, however, there is no doubt that the majority of them belong to the forest rather than to the steppes, not because the forest flora is richer but because the steppe flora is mainly part of one which covers much of the African tropics.

Moreover, except to the specialist, the genera are not very familiar and there need only be mentioned *Anisopus, Carpodinus, Maesobotrya, Napoleona* and *Oldfieldia.*

Several genera, including *Heteradelphia* and *Principina*, are confined to the small islands in the Gulf of Guinea.

North-east African Highland and Steppe Region and East African Steppe Region

Taken together these two regions represent eastern and southern tropical Africa, and reach from the Red Sea to south Angola. The north-east part divides very clearly into two areas, the highlands of Abyssinia and the lowlands of Eritrea and Somaliland, and the flora of the first is closely related to the rest of tropical Africa, while that of the second is more nearly allied with that of the North African-Indian desert region.

The total number of endemic genera in this double region is probably of the order of 200, with the same reservation as in West Africa.

The north-east region does not account for more than about fifty of these, and nearly half of this group are confined to the island of Socotra, which for its position has a remarkably peculiar flora, including *Dendrosicyos*, an arborescent genus of Cucurbitaceae. The rest are fairly evenly divided between Abyssinia and Somaliland, examples of the former being *Afrovivella* and *Hagenia*, and of the latter *Drakebrock-mania* and *Poskea*. *Oreophyton* and *Edithcolea* range southward into East Africa proper, and *Morettia* connects the region with that of the African-Indian deserts.

The endemic genera of the rest of eastern and southern tropical Africa are practically all small and unfamiliar and scarcely form a conspicuous element in the flora. This is due chiefly to the great mingling of floras which has taken place here, and especially to the extension northward in East Africa of many genera more particularly characteristic of the southern parts of the continent.

The more strictly endemic genera are for the most part found either on the east side of the continent (Kenya to Nyasa) or in Angola and northern South West Africa. The former include *Saintpaulia* (*S. ionantha* has become a familiar house-plant) and *Synadenium*, and among the latter are *Corynanthe* and *Umbellulanthus*.

Madagascar Region

This region comprises Madagascar and its small islands; the Comoros between Madagascar and the mainland; Aldabra and the Seychelles to the north; and the Mascarenes to the east.

The number of endemic genera is large and the total for the whole region may be well over 200 (296) of which the great majority are found on Madagascar itself, or, as in the case of a few small genera, on the very tiny islands close to it, but estimates of the total vary considerably (554).

The most striking element in the endemic flora of Madagascar is that of the seven genera which make up the endemic family Chlaenaceae, and of which *Rhodo-chlaena* is perhaps the chief. Perrier de la Bathie (554) has described the distribution of these in some detail. He divides the island into two main floristic regions, an eastern, windward region, including all the mountainous parts, in which the vegetation is evergreen; and a smaller leeward region, where the vegetation is deciduous. The species of Chlaenaceae are massed particularly in the northern corner of the island and in the mid-latitudes of the eastern region. In the west, which is the part where human influence has been greatest, there is only one genus of four species.

Among other endemics are *Asteropeia* (sometimes made a separate family), *Bembicia*, *Boutonia*, *Hydrotriche*, *Stapelianthus*, *Vomitra* and the extraordinary cactus-like *Didierea*. *Symphytosiphon* is said to be confined to the small island of Nossi Bé.

Certain genera, among them *Dicorypha*, *Humblotidendron* and *Ravenea*, are found on both Madagascar and the Comoros, while a few others, including *Cremocarpus*, are confined to the latter.

Lomatophyllum, *Oncostemon* (which has been described as the largest genus which is confined to islands) and *Poupartia* exemplify a small group of genera which range over Madagascar and the Mascarenes. *Brandzeia* appears to be the only genus restricted to Madagascar and the Seychelles.

The endemics of the Mascarenes number about thirty and are variously distributed. For example *Cylindrocline* and *Roussea* (sometimes made a separate family), occur on Mauritius; *Hyophorbe* and *Pyrostria* on Mauritius and Rodriguez; *Mathurina* and *Scyphochlamys* on Rodriguez; *Fargesia* and *Guya* on Réunion.

There are about a dozen endemic genera in the Seychelles. *Medusagyne*, which is found only on a single island, forms an exceptionally local family, while *Deckenia* and *Lodoicea* are noteworthy genera of palms.

Region of Ascension and St. Helena

In area this is probably one of the smallest of all the regions, comprising only two small islands. Its natural flora is also extremely small to-day because the rich native vegetation of the larger island has gradually become almost exterminated (741). There is, however, still enough left to show that the original flora was almost entirely distinctive and peculiar. The degree of specific endemism indeed must have been very high (see p. 206), although the number of endemic genera was perhaps not considerable.

To-day there are known only five endemic genera, all from St. Helena. They are *Mellissea*, *Nesiota*, *Commidendron*, *Melanodendron* and *Petrobium*, the last three exemplifying the woody members of the Compositae which are, and still more were, a feature of the flora.

South African endemic genera

Once again, in the case of South Africa it is desirable to depart from the regional classification. Two regions cover the southern part of the African continent (395, 562), but they are very different from one another. The Cape region, which actually constitutes a separate floristic kingdom, consists only of the south-west part of the Cape Province and is thus one of the smallest continental regions, but it has one of the most remarkable, and perhaps the richest, of all the world's floras. It is also of special interest because it has contributed much to the beauty of European gardens. The South African region, on the other hand, has not a particularly rich flora and represents the meeting ground of elements from the more tropical north and from the specialised Cape flora to the south (68). The latter on the whole predominate, or at least do so over much of this region, and it may be regarded more particularly as related to the Cape flora. For this reason alone there would be grounds for combining the two here, but there is also an important practical reason for so doing.

The combined area of both is roughly that of the erstwhile Union of South Africa, and the flora of this political area has been analysed in great detail by Phillips (557), so that by combining the two regions a great number of statistics are conveniently to hand. According to Phillips the flora of the Union of South Africa contains about 1,500 genera with native species, and of these some 500 are endemic, giving a proportion of about 30 per cent, a figure perhaps not exceeded anywhere. The flora also includes a number of endemic families, but these are for the most part small. As might be expected, the endemic genera vary greatly in size from monotypes, of which there are about 200, to genera with over one hundred species. Among these latter are *Agathosma*, *Aspalathus* and *Heliophila*, and other large genera are *Gasteria*, *Lachenalia* and *Leucadendron*. The endemics are specially numerous in certain families. For example *Elegia*, *Hypodiscus*, *Thamnochortus* and *Willdenowia* belong to the Restionaceae; *Lebeckia*, *Podalyria*, *Priestleya* and *Rafnia* to the Papilionaceae; *Grisebachia*, *Salaxis*, *Scyphogyne*, *Simocheilus* and *Sympieza* are closely related genera of the Ericaceae; and *Chrysocoma*, *Eriocephalus*, *Metalasia*, *Oldenburgia* and *Relhania* belong to the Compositae. Among other endemic genera belonging to less conspicuous families are *Duvalia, Freesia, Galtonia, Mimetes, Pectinaria, Prismatocarpus, Rochea, Roella, Roridula, Sarcocaulon* and *Strelitzia*. It must also be remembered that many of the genera included in wider African categories are in fact almost entirely confined to this part of South Africa.

The case of *Mesembryanthemum* (Plate 11), one of the most characteristic of all South African genera, requires special comment. In its old conception of a single huge genus of several hundred species, *Mesembryanthemum*, although almost entirely confined to South Africa, was not entirely so since a handful of species extended its range to a considerable distance elsewhere. In recent years, however, this huge genus has been split up into about one hundred smaller genera, mostly of only a few species each. Of these practically all are confined, often very narrowly, to South Africa and have the effect of appreciably increasing the number of genera endemic to that botanical kingdom.

Indian Region

This region divides latitudinally into three distinct parts—the subtropical flanks of the Himalayas, the Indian Peninsula proper, and Ceylon, and the first and last of these are botanically of the greater consequence. Floristically the northern and eastern limits of the region are fairly accurately marked by the southern boundary of the distribution of the Cupuliferae.

Hooker (376), to whom we owe so much of our knowledge of the Indian flora, emphasises that the subcontinent is essentially a meeting place of floras from the west, the north and the east, and that it has little real botanical character of its own, as is reflected in the small size of the endemic element. The total of endemic genera within the region is probably not more than 150, of which the great majority are monotypic and very local. About 20 are confined to Ceylon; a somewhat similar number occur in both India and Ceylon; and the rest are fairly evenly divided between the Himalayas and the peninsula.

The endemics of Ceylon, among which members of the Dipterocarpaceae are conspicuous, include the largest of all, *Stemonoporus*, with a dozen or more species, *Hortonia, Nargedia* and *Schumacheria*. Genera of both India and Ceylon include *Heylandia, Lagenandra* and *Zeylanidium*. Among the Indian endemics are *Blepharistemma, Cruddasia, Hitchenia* and an interesting small group of Asclepiadaceae in the wide sense, among them *Utleria*, generally described as the only arborescent member of the family. Among the endemics of the Himalayas may be mentioned *Amphicome, Dittoceras* and *Dodecania*.

Continental South-east Asiatic Region

This region comprises the Andamans and Nicobars, Burma, tropical China, Formosa and the Riukiu Islands (492), Hainan, Siam and Indo-China, and has a vegetation comparable in luxuriance with that of Malaysia. Floristically, however, it is not an outstanding region, and indeed might be described as transitional or intermediate between the rich floras of Malaysia in the south and of China in the north. Furthermore, it is still far from completely known. The floristic boundary between this and the Indian region is well marked.

As might therefore be expected the degree of endemism is not remarkable, and is also very difficult to estimate, but the number of endemic genera is probably now over 250, though nearly all of these are small and localised. *Parabarium* is one of the largest, and others that may be noted are *Bousigonia, Schizocapsa, Tirania* and *Trisepalum*.

Numerous genera link the region with its neighbours north and south and a small but conspicuous group links it with the Indian region. Some of these range from India to Siam, and others to the Malay Peninsula, among them being *Pentasacme*, *Sapria* (Himalayas and Siam) and *Sphinctacanthus*.

There are one or two endemic genera in the Riukiu Islands but the Andamans and Nicobars have none.

Malaysian Region

For many reasons, and especially for those connected with theories of palaeo-geography, Malaysia is, quite apart from its great floral richness, one of the most interesting parts of the world.

A bathymetrical map of the world, such as Plate 3, shows that the western part of the Malayan Archipelago, comprising Java and Bali, Sumatra and Borneo, or the Sunda Islands as they are called, is separated from the mainland of Asia by seas less than 600 ft. deep, and these islands are therefore generally regarded as rising from a continental shelf, the Sunda shelf, which is a prolongation of the Asiatic continent. Some authorities regard the Palawan-Calamian groups of the Philippines as also belonging to this shelf (512), which is believed to have been wholly exposed as land as lately as the Pleistocene (506) and in part perhaps even more recently (53, 676). Similarly in the eastern part of the Archipelago, the islands of New Guinea and Aru are adjacent to Australia and are commonly spoken of as rising from what is called the Sahul shelf which also is thought to have been dry land in the Pleistocene. Between are many islands separated from these two shelves, and for the most part from one another, by much deeper water, and these, which include the Philippines, Celebes, Ceram, Timor, the Lesser Sundas, the Moluccas and Kai, make up what has been called a "zone of disquiet relief", which it is believed has been insular since the early Tertiary. This zone is sometimes called "Wallacea".

It is thus seen that the Malayan Archipelago has three parts, a western, Asiatic zone; an eastern, Australasian zone; and an intermediate zone. It has also long been realised that the flora and fauna of the region show a similar segregation, although this is sometimes rather obscure, and many attempts have been made to draw imaginary lines marking the junction of the western and eastern biota (95). One of the earliest, and perhaps the best known of these is "Wallace's Line" which ran between the small islands of Bali and Lombok, east of Borneo, and between Celebes and the Philippines. This, it will be noted, actually marks the edge of the Sunda shelf and was based largely on the facts of animal distribution. The later line of Weber put the chief division east of Timor, west of Buru and Halmahera, and between Halmahera and the Philippines, and therefore followed fairly closely the western edge of the Sahul shelf.

Latterly both these lines have been amended in detail, Wallace's line to run along the Mindoro Strait and between Formosa and Botel Tobago, and Weber's to run east of Halmahera, Obi, Ceram, Kai, Timorlaut (Tanimbar) and Timor (514). These old and new lines and the extent of the shelves are well portrayed in a map by van Steenis (699), and are again reviewed in the *Flora Malesiana* (702), which accepts a third line, that of Zollinger, as best dividing the archipelago into western and eastern parts from a botanical point of view. This line runs round the east of Timor-laut, westwards through the Sunda Sea, north through the Macassar Strait, and east between the Philippines and the Moluccas, thus putting all the Sunda Islands, Timor and the Philippines into western Malaysia, and including Celebes and the

Moluccas in eastern Malaysia. These lines have been discussed by de Beaufort (53) in relation to animal distribution.

It is outside our province here to discuss the merits of these lines further, but they help us to visualise what is the most important botanical feature of the region as a whole, namely that the flora consists of two different elements which may be called the Asiatic and the Australasian, and that the middle part of the archipelago particularly shows a considerable mingling of them. It is also generally true to say that the Asiatic element is by far the larger and more extensive and that this predominates in the west, while the Australasian element is most in evidence in the east. What has been said also makes clear that any comprehensive botanical account of the region is impossible within the space available here and that it is possible only to refer to some of the leading features. What has been said should be borne in mind, especially in relation to the subject matter of Chapter 21.

The *Flora Malesiana* divides Malaysia, for practical analytical purposes, into three parts, namely, southern Malaysia comprising the islands from Java to Timor-laut inclusive; western Malaysia, comprising the Malay Peninsula, Sumatra, Borneo and the Philippines; and eastern Malaysia, comprising Celebes, the Moluccas, Kai, Aru and New Guinea. Within these three parts the numbers of strictly endemic genera, that is to say genera confined to one island or island group, vary considerably. In southern Malaysia the number is only about 15, including 10 in Java: in western Malaysia there are at least 150, including 60 in Borneo, over 40 in the Malay Peninsula, more than 30 in the Philippines, and nearly 20 in Sumatra; in eastern Malaysia there are 150, of which no fewer than 140 are in New Guinea (see Chapter 12). These total more than 300, and remembering that there are others which, though more widely distributed, are nevertheless still confined to Malaysia as a whole, it would seem likely that the total number of endemic genera in the region may approach 500.

Of the wider endemics there may be instanced the larger genera *Anerincleistus, Anplectrum, Boerlagiodendron, Cyrtandromoea, Elettariopsis, Hallieracantha, Kibessia, Pterisanthes, Schismatoglottis* and *Trichotoria,* and the smaller *Althoffia, Aphanomyrtus, Connaropsis, Dryobalanops, Durio, Gynotroches, Lunasia, Matthaea, Ochthocharis, Pangium, Paraboea, Prainea, Rafflesia, Sindora* and *Trigoniastrum.* In addition there are examples of distribution over almost every combination of two or more islands. *Philbornea* and one or two others, for instance, form a group recorded only from Borneo and the Philippines.

The *Flora Malesiana* also gives an important brief analysis of the geographical affinities of the total flora, estimating that of 2,178 genera native to the region—

> about 25 per cent are widely spread from Asia through Malaysia to Australia;
> about 25 per cent are essentially Asiatic;
> about 40 per cent are either actually endemic or at least essentially Malaysian;
> 4·3 per cent are Australian;
> 1·4 per cent are Pacific–Subantarctic.

Merrill's extensive studies of the plant life of the Philippines (510, 511, 512, 514) have made this one of the best known and documented of the constituent Malaysian floras, and show it to be not only particularly rich but also, as adumbrated above, of special interest with regard to the question of the paths of plant migration in the archipelago. Thus, although the flora of the Philippines has most in common with that of western Malaysia, it nevertheless possesses an Australian element typified by the occurrence of members of the Myrtaceae (see Fig. 22). There is also in the flora of the northern islands a distinct Himalayan element, which is an attenuation of a corresponding element in the flora of Formosa. In this connection it has been maintained (459, 514) that the flora of the small island of Botel Tobago is more closely allied to that of the Philippines than to that of Formosa (see p. 29).

The climatic conditions throughout the Malayan Archipelago are in general constant and nearly all the islands are heavily forested, but Timor and its immediate associates are exceptional. Here the climate is effectively much drier and closely resembles that of the north of Australia, and it is interesting to note that the vegetation is similarly parallel, being a much more open one in which species of *Eucalyptus* are conspicuous (755).

New Guinea, because of its position in respect of the rest of Malaysia, Australia and the Pacific islands, is one of the most important parts of the world from the point of view of historical plant geography, and the remarkable number of its endemic genera is of great interest. It is therefore satisfactory that a feature of the last decade has been a considerable advance in our knowledge of its flora. The results of this are discussed more fully in Chapter 12 but it is appropriate to remark here that one of the most valuable of them has been to show that the Australian element in the New Guinea flora is even less significant than has generally been supposed.

The Polynesian Subkingdom
(24, 190, 513, 514, 515, 546, 634, 635)

The next four regions all fall within what, using the definition given on p. 21, are called the Pacific islands, or "Polynesia" as it may be thought of in the broadest sense. Although the floras of these regions vary much in size they are all of considerable interest, and it is desirable to give as complete a list as possible of their endemic genera. The information is, however, scattered and confusing, and allowance must be made for this, but a recent study by van Balgooy (44) has usefully collected together much of it.

Two of the regions, Hawaii and New Caledonia, have rich and remarkable floras: the larger island groups of Melanesia and Micronesia also have important floras; but that of Polynesia calls for comparatively little comment. Indeed there is virtually no Polynesian flora in the aboriginal sense of the word, what there is being almost wholly derived, but this is in itself something of considerable significance. This state of affairs is well illustrated by an overall summary of endemic genera in the four regions, which shows that, of some 225 genera about 120 are in New Caledonia only: over 40 in Hawaii; and 13 in Fiji, leaving no more than 50, all of them very small, for the rest of this great area.

Only fourteen of these endemic genera occur in more than one of the four regions, namely:

Alphandia, Chambeyronia, Cyclophyllum, Dizygotheca, and *Strobilopanax* in New Caledonia and the New Hebrides.
Buraeavia, Piliocalyx and *Storckiella* in New Caledonia and Fiji.
Crossostylis in New Caledonia, in Fiji and in Polynesia.
Veitchia in New Caledonia, the New Hebrides and Fiji.
Belliolum in New Caledonia and the Solomons Islands.
Phyllostegia in the Hawaiian Islands and the Society Islands.
Pritchardia in the Hawaiian Islands and Fiji.
Pelea in the Hawaiian Islands and the Marquesas.

The distribution of all the genera over the families is interesting. At least thirty-five of them are palms, which is perhaps not so surprising in view of what is said in Chapter

4, but more than twenty belong to the Rubiaceae. Others particularly well represented are Araliaceae, Rutaceae, Euphorbiaceae, Myrtaceae, Apocynaceae and Compositae though the last has few outside Hawaii. The Gramineae, on the other hand, are represented only by two genera on New Caledonia.

Hawaiian Region

The physical facts regarding this whole area have been brought together in masterly fashion by Zimmerman (807). He describes it as a great chain of eighteen islands, several satellite islands, and various islets, reefs and shoals, stretching for about 1,500 miles in a north-west to south-east direction, but the name Hawaii is more properly applied to the eight islands at the south-east end, which are much bigger than the rest. There is no evidence that they are of continental origin or character, or that they were ever joined together in an elongated subcontinental land mass. He also points out that although the Hawaiian Islands are separated from any major land mass by great distances (see p. 14) there is a coral atoll 600 miles to the south-west and this, in turn, is not much more than that distance from Palmyra Island which itself is much less isolated, so that the actual gap between landfalls is much less than is commonly assumed. It is believed that no part of the islands is more than 5 million years old and that the main islands are Pliocene or younger and mostly Pleistocene.

The number of endemic genera is twenty-eight (807) which is generally considered a proportion of about 20 per cent, and one or two families are particularly prominent. For instance, *Brighamia, Clermontia, Cyanea, Dellissea, Rollandia* and *Trematolobelia*, which include the largest endemics, are all woody members of the Lobeliaceae (see p. 80), while *Raillardia* is one of at least six Composite genera. On the other hand, the orchids are but poorly represented, and there is in general a lack of endemic genera belonging to the Monocotyledons.

For the rest *Kadua, Schiedea* and *Stenogyne* are among the largest and others are *Bobea, Hillebrandia, Labordea* and *Nothocestrum*.

Region of New Caledonia

In our regional classification there are here included, for convenience, Lord Howe Island and Norfolk Island, which would otherwise have to be treated separately since they are equally isolated from more than one other region. They are two of the most interesting oceanic islands in the world but it must be enough here to deal with them merely by the statement that the former has five endemic genera, *Colmeiroa* (see p. 151), *Denea, Hedyscepe, Howea* and *Negria*, and the latter apparently only one, *Streblorrhiza*, now extinct in a wild state. The genus *Lagunaria* is characteristic of these two islands, but occurs also in coastal Queensland, a little within the tropics.

The flora of New Caledonia (322), which, though oceanic in isolation is continental in structure, is of the greatest interest not only for its marked endemism but also because of its floral relationships (296). It contains well over 100 endemic genera in nearly thirty families and this probably means upwards of 20 per cent of the genera native to the island.

Moreover, the quality of the endemism is high, several of the genera forming separate families or being almost distinct enough to do so. Naturally enough the endemics are relatively unfamiliar but notable among them are *Arthroclianthus, Canacomyrica, Cocconerion, Codia, Coronanthera, Exospermum, Greslania, Hachettea, Maxwellia, Montrouzeria, Neoguillauminia, Oncotheca, Oxera, Pancheria, Paracryphia* and *Sparattosyce*.

Plate 9. Gunnera chilensis in S. Chile

(from Karsten & Schenck, *Vegetationsbilder*)

Region of Melanesia and Micronesia

The following is believed to be a reasonably complete list of the genera which have been described as endemic to this rather dual region, but it must be borne in mind that the floras of the Bismarck Archipelago, the Solomon Islands and the New Hebrides are still far from completely known.

Fiji—Five palm genera (*Goniocladus, Goniosperma, Neoveitchia, Taveunia, Vitiphoenix*): five Rubiaceous genera (*Gillespiea, Hedstromia, Readea, Squamellaria, Sukunia*): *Amaroria, Degeneria* and *Pimia*.

Solomon Islands—*Paragulubia, Pritchardiopsis, Rehderophoenix* and *Strongylocaryum*.

New Hebrides—*Physokentia, Trichochilus*.

Caroline Islands—*Palaua* and *Trukia*.

Fiji and New Hebrides—*Exorrhiza*.

Bismarck Archipelago—*Clymenia*.

Marianne Islands—*Guamia*.

Bonin Islands—*Boninia*.

Bonin Islands and Caroline Islands—*Bentinckiopsis*.

Because of their proximity to the Marianne Islands and their comparable insularity, the Bonin Islands are included in this region but, as Hara (336, 337) has pointed out, the affinity of their flora is with Japan rather than elsewhere, as indeed might be expected from their latitude.

Region of Polynesia

There appear to be only nine or ten genera endemic to this region, *Fitchia* being the most noteworthy. This genus of arborescent composites has, according to a recent revision (120), six species scattered over the area 130–160° W. and 15-30° S., namely two on Tahiti, one on Rarotonga (an escape on Hawaii), one on Raiatea, one on Mangareva and one on Rapa.

The remaining endemic genera are *Coralliokyphos* and *Sarcopygme* in Samoa, *Tahitia* on the Society Islands, *Pelagodoxa* (and perhaps *Cyrtandroidea*) in the Marquesas: *Metatrophis* (and perhaps *Lautea*) on Rapa, *Apetahia* on Tahiti and Rarotonga and *Sclerotheca* on Raiatea, Rapa and the Marquesas.

Endemic genera of tropical America

Just as in Africa, there are in tropical America many endemic genera with ranges that transcend the limits of any one region. Some of these approach in extent of distribution genera which elsewhere have been described as "wides", but they vary a great deal and it is more generally convenient to include them here as a special more widespread type of American endemics, and this may be justified on the grounds that their interest lies more in the fact that they are confined to tropical America than in the fact that they do not happen to be confined to one region.

This reflects to some extent on the value of the regions as defined in the floristic classification, but enough has already been said to show that these are indeed real entities. It seems rather that in the tropics of the New World, which form an extensive and homogeneous area, geographical segregation and isolation has never been very great and that, as a result, endemism is, as it were, on a rather wider scale.

The total number of genera unknown outside tropical America appears to be about 3,000 and it may be that upwards of one thousand of these are distributed over two or more of the regions here defined and must therefore be considered here.

10

Their ranges vary enormously but various influences lead to the predominance of three main types. First, there are the genera which extend practically all over the whole area including Central America and the West Indies. Next, there are those confined to the western, Andean, side of the land but which extend so far north and south that they cover two or more floristic regions. Finally, there are the genera which are mostly to be found within the great area of Brazil but which extend thence varyingly westward or north-westward.

These groups as a whole include many large and familiar genera and especially many of the choice orchids commonly grown in hothouses in Europe. Among good examples are:

1. Genera found more or less throughout tropical America:
   Caryocar, Cecropia, Gloxinia, Lycaste, Maranta, Monstera, Ochroma, Oncidium, Tecoma, Theobroma.

2. Genera chiefly in Brazil but extending west and north-west therefrom:
   Cattleya, Cephalocereus, Jacaranda, Jacobinia, Laelia, Miltonia.

3. Genera found chiefly in western tropical America:
   Cinchona, Cosmos, Phytelephas.

Caribbean Region

This region consists of two well-marked areas, isthmian America and the West Indies, and the former has a close relationship with western North America. Owing to the absence of modern floras it is difficult to estimate the total number of endemic genera, but it is probably considerably more than 500. *Bouvardia, Guajacum, Hura* and *Swietenia* (which is actually said to reach Peru) exemplify genera found more or less throughout the region.

More than half the endemic genera are confined to isthmian America and particularly to Mexico, and the latter include *Dahlia, Dictyanthus, Euchlaena, Martynia* and *Polianthes.*

The West Indies have about 180 endemic genera but most of them are quite small, the largest, *Wallenia*, having only about thirty species, and only about half a dozen others having ten or more. These larger genera are mostly some of the thirty-odd which are more or less widely distributed over the archipelago and which include *Bontia, Catesbaea, Lagetta, Pinillosia* and *Spathelia*. Of the total no fewer than 80 have been described from Cuba, compared with 28 from Haiti, 7 from Porto Rico, 4 from Jamaica, 3 from Trinidad and 2 from Tobago. The remaining twenty-five or so are practically all found in Cuba and on one, or more rarely two, of the other large islands. *Ulbrichia* is confined to the tiny Beata Island close to San Domingo.

Agave is a good example of a genus which extends rather beyond the strict limits of the region, being centred in Mexico but ranging deep into the U.S.A. and to northern South America. *Furcraea* is similar but less northerly.

The region includes, on the Pacific side, Guadalupe Island and the Revilla Gigedo Islands but these have no endemic genera.

The Bahamas are said to have one or two endemic genera but the Bermudas have none.

Region of Venezuela and Guiana

Although there are sufficient reasons for maintaining this area as a distinct floristic region, it is not surprising that its relationships with the next two, the

Andean and the Amazon, are very close, and its endemic genera appear to be few, most probably fewer than one hundred. Moreover, none of these are either well-known or familiar plants, and there need only be mentioned *Heliamphora*, *Manicaria* and *Voyria*. Botanically the most remarkable part of the region is the mountainous area along the boundaries of Venezuela and Brazil where the endemics include *Leitgebia*, *Ledothmnus*, *Stenopadus* and several members of the Rapateaceae, and about this more will be said in Chapter 10.

Endemic genera of Brazil

The two floristic regions which cover the States of Brazil, Paraguay, and other border areas, have one of the richest floras in the world but also one of the least completely known, and they are considered together here, because although they are both physiographically and floristically quite distinctive, it is not always easy to be sure which genera are strictly confined to one or the other.

A compilation based on Lemée (452) shows that the total number of endemic genera in Brazil is about five hundred, though a number of others probably do not extend very far beyond this country. The chief families represented are, as might be expected, the Compositae, Orchidaceae, Euphorbiaceae and the three leguminous families, and, more notably, the Asclepiadaceae, Bignoniaceae and Melastomataceae. The largest endemic genera are *Cambessedesia*, *Chaetostoma*, *Diplusodon*, *Ereman-thus*, *Kielmeyera*, *Lavoisiera*, *Lychnophora*, *Nidularium*, *Promenaea*, *Sinningia* and *Tremblya*, but none of these has more than about fifty species. Indeed the total number of species in all the endemic genera is probably not more than about 1,250, a very small proportion of the whole flora, and this reflects very clearly the comparatively wide distribution of most tropical American genera, as mentioned on p. 145 above.

The Amazon region is the third of the great equatorial forest areas and is a simpler and better-defined unit than either of the others because it consists exclusively of the vast basin of the Amazon river system. An important environmental factor in it, which also makes it somewhat different, is the extensive flooding to which, on account of the general lowness of level and the slowness of drainage, much of the region is regularly subjected, and the vegetation can primarily be divided into that above the level of the flood-waters (igapo) and that below it (ete). Here there are probably about one hundred endemic genera, all quite small, and including *Dilkea*, *Hevea* (the Para rubber) and *Lissocarpa*.

The South Brazilian region comprises three main constituent parts, the forested mountains of the eastern coasts, the open woodlands of the caatingas, and the savannas of the campos. The flora is large and the number of endemic genera appears to be about four hundred, among them being *Albertinia*, *Antonia*, *Arachis* (to which the ground-nut belongs), *Barjonia*, *Castelnavia*, *Diclidanthera*, *Fernseea*, *Fragariopsis*, *Gearum*, *Hymenolobium*, *Itatiaea*, *Leptotes*, *Mauritiella*, *Nautonia*, *Pamphilea*, *Pygmaeorchis*, *Sapucaya*, *Schlumbergeria*, *Seris*, *Soaresia*, *Spathicarpa*, *Tetra-plandra*, *Tetraulacium* and *Wunderlichia*.

The islands of Fernando Noronha (4° S. 32° W.) and South Trinidad (20° S. 30° W.) have no endemic genera.

Andean Region

Although the whole Andean region from Colombia to southern Chile is to be regarded as a single elongated region, it is convenient to consider it here as made up of two rather distinct parts, tropical and temperate, and these are fairly clearly marked politically. In the northern tropical part are the montane portions of four countries, Colombia, Ecuador, Peru and Bolivia, while the southern part consists essentially of Chile (though it includes also the western part of Argentina) and may be referred to by this name. The Andean region as defined in our classification also includes the Galapagos Islands.

The flora of the tropical Andes is very rich and also, on account of the range of elevation, very varied. Each constituent country has many endemics, so that the total is probably several hundreds, and they are found chiefly on the tropical flanks of the mountains, the highland element in the flora having generally a wider range. Among the more familiar endemic genera are *Cochlioda*, *Desfontainia* and *Eccremocarpus*.

The flora of the Galapagos Islands (434, 709, 715) is of great interest from the point of view of its species but contains very few endemic genera, *Leiocarpus* and *Scalesia* being the only important ones. It is chiefly for this reason that the archipelago has not been given any regional rank.

The flora of Chile has been analysed in some detail in connection with the flora of temperate South America as a whole (291), and from this and more recent sources it appears that there are about 125 endemic genera, a high percentage considering the size of the flora as a whole. *Jubaea*, *Lapageria* and *Lardizabala* are noteworthy examples, the first-named being one of the few palms found outside the tropics, and others include *Berberidopsis*, *Fascicularia*, *Francoa*, *Schizanthus* and *Tecophilaea*.

Pampas Region

This region comprises that part of South America east of the Andes and between the tropical Brazilian flora on the north and the temperate Patagonian flora on the south. Its core consists of the great grass plains of the pampas proper, so vividly described by Hudson (383) and others, but there also falls within it much of drier western and northern Argentina, as well as the southernmost two provinces of Brazil. The botany of the Argentine part of it has been well described by Cabrera (100).

The flora is not particularly rich and the endemic or near endemic genera, which are all small, probably do not number more than about fifty, including several in the Cactaceae. Others are *Deinacanthon*, *Holmbergia*, *Jodina*, *Synandrospadix* and *Tricomaria*.

Region of Juan Fernandez

The Juan Fernandez Archipelago, which lies 400 miles off the coast of Chile, and in which the two largest islands, Masatierra and Masafuera, are 90 miles apart, has a very remarkable flora which has been particularly studied by Skottsberg (658). It has a very high degree of endemism including about fifteen genera. Among them are *Juania*, a palm; *Lactoris*, which forms an endemic monotypic family; and one or two remarkable Composites, including *Dendroseris* and *Rhetinodendron*.

This region, as here defined (see Plate 4), also includes the tiny Desventuradas Islands (S. Ambrosio and S. Felix) which lie about 500 miles north of Juan Fernandez and 600 miles from the coast of Chile. Their flora (667) is very small, but includes three endemic genera, of which one, *Thamnoseris*, is regarded as most closely related to *Dendroseris*, already mentioned.

Other American endemic genera

As in tropical America there are, in temperate South America, a number of genera which, while not falling under any one region, must nevertheless be considered as endemics. These consist chiefly of genera characteristic of the temperate Andes but which extend therefrom eastward across Argentina and Patagonia for various distances.

In all there are about eighty such genera, and among them are *Azara, Cajophora, Myzodendron, Nassauvia* and *Triptilium.*

Australian endemic genera

The Australian continent supports one of the most peculiar and, in places, one of the richest of the world's floras (110). Indeed, its very degree of peculiarity, which it can scarcely be doubted results from some long geographical isolation of the continent, combined with its relative unfamiliarity, makes for difficulty because the flora is in general so different from others (its only considerable relation being with that of South Africa) that there is a natural tendency to regard it as a single unit, whereas in fact there is room for a classification quite as detailed as that of other continental areas of comparable size. Another complicating factor is that the flora is unevenly distributed. It is richly developed in the east and south-east, and also in the south-west, but it is less so in the middle parts of the south coast, and is poor in the interior and over much of the north. There is also a great range of latitude and the flora of northern Queensland is, if but for this one reason, very different from that of Tasmania or that of the south-west. This and other aspects of the phyto-geography of Australia have been discussed recently in a long paper by Burbidge (94).

The constantly recurring theme in nearly all that has been written about the Australian flora is the aridity of the country and the related xerophily of the plant life, a characteristic which is reflected in the general absence of deep shade even where the vegetation is of trees. Andrews (23), for instance, maintains that the "real" Australian flora is essentially one of barren waste places, and Lawson (449) also stresses its striking and varied xerophily as one of its main features. The facts relating to the climate and the correlation of the vegetation with it, are perhaps most prominent in the western part of the continent and for this region have been admirably set out by Gardner (262). In connection with their studies of the South Australian vegetation Crocker and Wood (161) conclude that the general aridity is the result of post-Pleistocene desiccation which has wiped out most of the prior flora, at any rate over much of the interior. The highest rainfall is along the coast of northern Queensland and here the vegetation is comparatively luxuriant and has much in common with that of New Guinea. Here in particular there is, in the flora, a striking mixture of Malaysian and Australian types and Cambage (106, 107) believes that here again the vegetation is in nice balance with existing climatic values, so that any diminution of rainfall would cause a waning of the Malaysian element and *vice versa.* This is a point of special interest in connection with theories of continental movement, according to some of which the position of Australia has altered considerably during the latter part of geological time (see Chapters 12, 21).

The recognition here of three regions in Australia, northern and eastern, south-western, and central, expresses the main segregation of the flora and climate, and also the outline of the geological history of the continent (357), in which a chapter of special significance to the Angiosperm flora was the long submergence of much of mid-Australia with consequent isolation of the west from the east, but, as with other continents, there are many genera which range much more widely than over any one of these three, although nevertheless restricted to the continent, and these must be noticed first.

The endemic genera of Australia number about 500, a figure representing about

30 per cent of all native genera. As is the case in South Africa many of them are large and well-marked and of these most are so wide-ranging that they cover all or parts of two or more of the three floristic regions into which the continent is divided. Many, indeed, are found almost all over it except in the more arid parts of the centre and north.

Among the largest endemic genera are *Boronia, Dampiera, Daviesia, Eremophila, Goodenia, Hakea, Pultenaea* and *Prostanthera*, and among others worthy of note are *Angianthus, Billardiera, Bossiaea, Calythrix, Caustis, Comesperma, Conospermum, Darwinia, Humea, Isopogon, Mirbelia, Spyridium, Thomasia, Verticordia* and *Xanthosia*. Of smaller endemics a few, such as *Correa*, are predominently eastern, but in most the highest species concentration is in the south-west, good examples of this being *Dillwynia, Jacksonia* and *Kennedya*.

Some of these smaller endemics are more or less widely discontinuous within the continent, nearly all of them between the south-west and the south-east and east, e.g. *Aphanopetalum, Amperea, Conostephium, Eriochilus, Labichea, Lambertia, Macarthuria, Monotaxis, Monotoca, Oxylobium, Petrophila, Strangea, Tetratheca* and *Xylomelum*. *Byblis*, with one species in the south-west and one in the north-west, illustrates a rarer kind of discontinuity.

It must also be noted that several other large genera fail to be endemic to Australia only because a single species has been found elsewhere, sometimes in circumstances which suggest that it may not be native, namely *Xanthorrhoea* (1 sp. in New Caledonia): *Banksia, Gompholobium, Haemodorum, Lechenaultia* and *Velleia* (1 sp. each in New Guinea): *Hemiphues* and *Swainsona* (1 sp. each in New Zealand): *Lomandra* (1 sp. in New Caledonia and New Guinea); and *Ptilotus* (1 sp. in New Guinea and elsewhere in Malaysia).

North and East Australian Region

This is an unsatisfactory region because of its enormous latitudinal range (compare eastern North America), and it is only to be expected that the flora of northern Queensland which is well within the tropics, will be very different from that of the mountains of the south-east, or of Tasmania which lies beyond 40° south.

The region as a whole has rather more than 150 endemic genera, but few, if any, of them cover it all. Some such as *Angophora* (close to *Eucalyptus*), *Anopterus, Archontophoenix, Bauera, Blandfordia, Doryphora* and *Telopea* are fairly widespread: some, exemplified by *Doryanthes, Gymnostachys* and *Monococcus* range through southern Queensland and New South Wales: others found only in Queensland include *Carnarvonia, Darlingia, Fitzalania, Micraira*, and *Thozetia: Atkinsonia, Piptocalyx* and *Richea* are some of those in the south; and *Pachynema* is one of the few found in the north.

Tasmania, in the extreme south-east has ten endemic genera, all but one of them monotypic, namely *Agastachys, Anodopetalum* (the notorious "Horizontal" which forms almost impenetrable thickets), *Bellendena, Cenarrhenes, Hewardia, Milligania* (4 spp.), *Nablonium, Prionotes, Pterygopappus* and *Tetracarpaea*.

South-west Australian Region (262)

This region stands out among the Australian regions in the richness of its flora and in its high degree of endemism, and it is, indeed, perhaps the only flora which compares (as it does in this and many other ways) with that of the Cape Region of South Africa. Each, it will be noted, occupies the extreme corner of a continental mass.

Its endemic genera, however, do not give a real picture of its peculiarity, because some of the most characteristic genera actually range far outside it and have already been mentioned, and this peculiarity will be plainer when the species are discussed.

The number of genera more or less strictly endemic to this region is about 125 and by the nature of the case they are mostly restricted in range. They vary considerably in size, the largest being *Dryandra* with more than fifty species and *Conostylis* with about thirty-five. *Anigozanthos, Beaufortia, Chamaelaucium*, have a dozen or more species each and the smaller endemics include *Baxteria, Cephalotus, Dasypogon, Diplolaen, Dipteranthemum, Emblingia, Franklandia, Hemiandra, Kingia, Nuytsia, Rhizanthella, Sollya* and *Stirlingia*.

Central Australian Region

The boundary between this and the better-known regions to the west and east is not very definite, and it is therefore difficult to say just how many genera are found only within it, but the number appears to be about forty, many of them in the families Chenopodiaceae, Compositae and Cruciferae. Examples are *Babbagia, Embadium, Macgregoria, Newcastlia, Rutidosis, Threlkeldia* and *Uldinia*.

New Zealand Region

For many reasons, chiefly connected with its position, the flora of this region is of special interest to the plant geographer, and it has been so much studied that its constitution now is well known (129, 219). This will be discussed in more detail in Chapter 10, but it can be said here that the number of endemic genera is about thirty. They are, however, all quite small, and nearly all the endemic species for which the region is remarkable, belong to non-endemic genera. Indeed the contrast between the degrees of generic and specific endemism is very marked. It should, however, be noted that *Celmisia* (more than 50 species), except for one species in Australia, and *Carmichaelia* (over 20 species), except for its occurrence on Lord Howe Island, are entirely New Zealand genera. *Phormium, Rhopalostylis, Pleurophyllum* and *Stilbocarpa* would also be endemic were it not that the two first are also found in Norfolk Island, and the last two on Macquarie Island.

Two monotypic endemics, *Coxella* and *Myosotidium*, both coastal and now becoming rare, are confined to the Chatham Islands; and two others *Plectormirtha* and *Elimgamita*, are only in the Three Kings Islands, just off the North Island, and are practically extinct. The rest are all restricted to the main islands and include *Colensoa, Entelea, Haastia, Hoheria, Ixerba, Leucogenes, Notothlaspi* and *Oreostylidium*. Five of the endemic genera are the only representatives of their families in the New Zealand Region, namely, *Dactylanthus* (1 sp. Balanophoraceae), *Tetrapathaea* (1 sp. Passifloraceae), *Rhabdothamnus* (1 sp. Gesneriaceae), *Plectomirtha* (1 sp. Anacardiaceae) and *Alseuosmia* (4 spp. Caprifoliaceae).

Finally, the genus *Corokia* affords a good example of the problem made for plant-geographers when opinions about generic limits vary. *Corokia* was long regarded as endemic to New Zealand and the Chathams, but later a species was described from Rapa, though the genus concept had to be widened to permit its inclusion. Recently another species has been described from New South Wales. Moreover, it has been suggested that the genus, if it includes these three, should also contain an endemic genus of Lord Howe Island (*Colmeiroa*). Thus in this much-widened form the genus

Corokia is found in Australia, Lord Howe Island, New Zealand, the Chatham Islands and Rapa, but in its narrowest and original sense it is still a New Zealand endemic.

Patagonian Region

This region, which may be described as comprising the lowland parts of extreme southern America, has a small flora with a few almost or quite endemic genera, among which *Lebetanthus, Magallana, Niederlinia* and *Saxifragella*, and a small group of Cruciferous genera, may be noted. Some of those already mentioned for Chile and Argentina perhaps actually fall mostly within this region but as they have already been referred to they need not be considered again. The most isolated part of the region, the Falkland Islands, has no well-marked endemic genera at all. The question of the boundaries of the Patagonian region and its subdivisions have been discussed by Beetle (55), Donat (194) and Skottsberg (663).

Region of the South Temperate Oceanic Islands

The flora of this region is extremely small, but it is of exceptional interest for many reasons and will be considered in greater detail in Chapter 10. The genera number about fifty, of which only two are endemic, namely *Lyallia* on Kerguelen and *Pringlea*, on several islands, and therefore discontinuous and already mentioned. The others are for the most part very widespread genera and the Gramineae and Cyperaceae are conspicuous among them.

The proportion of endemic genera in the two hemispheres

This lengthy account of endemic genera may fitly be concluded by an attempt to estimate the number of such genera in each of the two hemispheres, northern and southern. It is not altogether easy to make this computation, because several regions lie across the equator, but if some arbitrary proportionment of these is adopted it appears that there are about twice as many endemic genera in the southern hemisphere as there are in the north. This is using the term endemic as it has been defined for the particular purposes of this chapter. If it is made more narrow in conception, then the disparity in numbers is certainly accentuated, and of extremely restricted genera the great majority are undoubtedly southern.

These bare figures are sufficiently noteworthy, but the position can only be appreciated properly if the relative areas of land in the two hemispheres are taken into account. It was seen in Chapter 2 that the land area open to plant habitation in the north is about 38 million square miles, while in the south it is only 13 million, a proportion of nearly three to one, and it would appear therefore that the density of frequency of endemic genera is six times as great in the south as in the north.

There are good reasons, chief among them being the variation in size of the regions and the differences in the conception of genera, why it is unwise to read too much into the figures and facts set out in this chapter, but on the other hand some generalisation seems to be fully justified. It is clear that in certain parts of the world generic endemism, that is the number of endemic genera and the total of the species they contain, is considerably higher than elsewhere. These parts are isthmian America, the Andes, South Africa, Madagascar, south-west Australia, eastern Australia and Malaysia (especially New Guinea), to which, though rather different because of their smaller areas, Hawaii and New Caledonia must be added. Of all these areas the South African is certainly the most remarkable not only because of its floristic wealth but also because it is almost or quite the least isolated geographically. A lower but still notable degree of generic endemism is seen in western

North America, the West Indies, southern Brazil and south-east Asia. Somewhat lower again are China and Japan and Europe and the Mediterranean, though it may be suspected that the intense study which the floras of the latter have received has inflated their figures somewhat. For the rest there are of course parts of the world such as the arctic and the African–Indian deserts where it is scarcely surprising that generic endemism is low, but there are others where the figures are notably less than might, for various *prima facie* reasons, be expected, prominent among these being eastern North America, Venezuela and Guiana, the Amazon, Argentina, tropical Africa generally, India and New Zealand. Finally in relation to these statements it must be borne in mind that generic endemism is neither necessarily nor commonly any measure of specific endemism, which is discussed in a later chapter, and the parallels and contrasts between the two are one of the interesting problems of plant geography.

CHAPTER 8

THE DISTRIBUTION OF SPECIES—I

THE number of families of Flowering Plants is such that it was possible in Chapter 4 to mention them individually. The number of genera is so much greater that even in three chapters only a few of them could be mentioned, but it was possible to make a complete statistical analysis of them. The number of species, however, is so huge that even this is impossible, and only a very generalised survey is possible, in which it is difficult to decide what should be included and what should be left out. Whatever else may be desirable, the essential purpose of such a survey is to demonstrate what is certainly the most conspicuous general feature in the distribution of species, namely that there are representatives of almost every kind of range that the geography of the world permits, and the illustration of this leading fact is the main theme of this and the next three chapters. It must not be supposed, of course, that all these types are represented in anything like even proportions, some are much more common than others, but at the same time it is true to say that there are no particular types of specific distribution which are overwhelmingly more prevalent than others that are properly comparable, nor are there any very conspicuous types that are greatly under-represented. In short there is no simplification of the overall distribution pattern because of the outstanding prominence of a few distribution forms.

That many genera consist of but one species, and that the ranges of others are but the sums of the superposed ranges of their constituent species, are enough indication that there is no real difference between the distribution of species and that of genera, except, of course, that the latter is usually more extensive. This being so, much the same treatment and arrangement can be adopted with regard to species as was used in the case of genera, and if this framework is supplemented by particular reference to certain especially important aspects of species distribution, the main purpose mentioned above can be sufficiently achieved. The subject matter of these four chapters dealing with the distribution of species therefore begins with a discussion of the subject of species numbers in general. This is followed by the description of the distribution of the species in each of a few large genera, selected for their variousness in this respect. Wide species are dealt with next; then comes a survey of endemic species, arranged as far as is appropriate, according to the thirty-seven floristic regions, and finally certain particular matters of species distribution receive special notice.

Number of Species

It is possible to make a reasonably up-to-date estimate of the number of species of flowering plants at present known from such a source as Lemée's dictionary (452). This work, in nine volumes, includes particulars of all described genera, and from the information given it would appear that the grand total of species is about 225,000, and the grand total of genera about 12,500, giving an average of eighteen species per genus. Within these totals the figures for Dicotyledons are several times those for Monocotyledons. Taking into consideration how many parts of the world have yet to

154

be completely explored botanically, it seems likely that the total number of species in existence is appreciably higher than this, and that it probably exceeds a quarter of a million. Jones, calculating on a slightly different basis, has (413) arrived at the same figures except that he believes a quarter of a million Angiosperm species to be already known.

The numerical distribution of these species over the world's surface, or what may more shortly be called the species density from place to place, is a subject which has long attracted attention as one likely to reveal facts of importance in the study of plant geography (116, 550), and among later references to it are those of Szymkiewicz (716) and Wulff (801). The latter paper, from which many of the figures quoted below are taken, is the more elaborate study and concludes with an attempt to map the world on the basis of species density using different shadings and colours for different concentrations.

Unfortunately the results are disappointing, for the subject is one beset with difficulties which, as will be seen, render it, except in special circumstances, a less valuable aid in plant geography than might at first sight be expected. In the first place the necessary totals of species can be obtained only from complete floras or floral lists, and even to-day these are readily available only for certain parts of the world, and not necessarily those of greatest interest in this connection. Even the lists which do exist should only be compared with great caution partly because they are seldom contemporaneous and partly because they are the work of many different authors with various ideas about the value of species. Then again it is not always clear from quotations whether totals represent all vascular plants or only Angiosperms, and if the latter, whether these include introductions as well as the native species which alone are significant. Indeed, in the floras of many parts of the north temperate regions, e.g. Great Britain, it is probably no longer possible satisfactorily to separate one from the other. There is also the difficulty that more often than not floras are of political rather than natural areas.

But even more important, the figures, whatever their provenance and reliability may be, mean little unless they are expressed in some way which takes into account the size of the areas concerned, in other words unless they are expressed as values of relative density, and this has seldom been done.

Some of the broader aspects of the relation between area and species population have been conveniently summarised by Williams (780), who, applying statistical methods, constructed a curve based upon the numbers of species present in a great number of areas ranging in size from a few square inches to many thousands of square miles. He shows that the resultant curve consists essentially of three parts and the explanation of this appears to be as follows.

In any very tiny area such as that of a few square inches there is probably only a single individual plant representing a single species, but as area increases the likelihood that the number of species present will rise grows, the augmentation in theory following a probability formula which the writer discusses. This first part of the curve, therefore, shows a fairly steep and even rise up to a point at which it begins to flatten out, showing that the rate of increase has sharply changed. This point of change appears to be that at which the area is of such a size that all the species immediately available to inhabit it in fact do so. That is to say, if an area is ecologically simple there will soon be reached the point at which all the normal species inhabiting that kind of habitat appear in the area concerned. In brief it represents not only the maximum population of a simple habitat but also the average size of such habitats.

The second and more gently rising part of the curves follows, and results from the fact that, beyond the point just described, the larger the area is, the greater will its ecological diversity tend to be, and therefore the greater the number of species it will contain. Judging from the curve this relation holds good over a very wide range of area size, a circumstance which is probably related to the fact that the average area of occupation of species is comparatively small, so that with areas above a certain size increase in population continues because the boundaries extend to places where some or all of the original species are replaced by others.

Finally the curve enters a third phase and becomes irregular and of little value partly because areas above a certain size tend to contain all possible kinds of habitats but chiefly because in such enormous areas quite new factors, such as those of relative isolation and independent evolution, come into play.

To recapitulate, as long as an area comprises only one kind of habitat its species population increases rapidly with enlargement according to a certain formula of probability. In large areas species population continues to increase, though more slowly, because, generally speaking, area increase here means also increase of ecological diversity. This increase does not, as might be expected, die out beyond a certain point because the average distribution of species is comparatively small. Finally, however, entirely new factors destroy the validity of the curve.

This work of Williams is a very useful presentation of a difficult subject but it gives perhaps too simplified a conception of the situation as it strikes the plant geographer who is concerned mainly with the medium and large areas such as counties, provinces and countries which compose the second and main part of the curve, and two complicating factors in particular need to be emphasised. One is that while larger areas are admittedly likely to be more heterogeneous ecologically than smaller ones, this is effectively true only when areas of the same general type and of similar latitudes and longitudes are compared. A single European parish is probably more heterogeneous than vast tracts of the Sahara; nor is there, although the respective figures may be interesting, any direct basis of comparison between an area in North Africa and one of similar size in South Africa. The second point is that isolation and its attendant climatic effects influence comparatively small areas as well as very large ones.

An enormous amount depends also on where the boundaries of areas are drawn. With islands and with strongly circumscribed natural continental areas there is not much difficulty but often the arbitrary use of artificial boundaries is very misleading, a point which may be illustrated by two examples. The county of Dorset whose area is less than 1 per cent of the British Isles contains upwards of, or even perhaps more than, two-thirds of all the native British species. In the same way any parish of average size in Dorset probably contains upwards of or above half the county flora. The reason is that both the county and the parish are but constituent parts, above a critical minimum in size, of a more or less homogeneous whole.

The second example is taken from North America. Here the state of Arizona is reported to contain about 3,300 species, and the neighbouring state of New Mexico about 3,000. Yet the population of the two combined is said to be no more than 4,000. Clearly this is because the boundaries of these states have little or no relation to the distribution of the plant life of the continent. The same kind of result is obtained if two English counties are similarly combined.

But despite these difficulties and the many possible sources of confusion there is much of interest to be learnt, especially about some wider issues, from a study of species density, and the following summary, in which some of the less debatable figures are used, is intended to illustrate not only the limitations but also the potentialities of the subject. In this summary are given the approximate areas in square miles, the approximate numbers of species, and positive relative density figures obtained by dividing the former into the latter and thus representing the number of species per square mile.

1. Figures showing great differences in density between areas unlike in size, structure and kind:

	Area in sq. mls.	Species	Density
Canada, North-west Territory	1,300,000	400	0·0003
Canada, Eastern Arctic .	420,000	286	0·0007
Tibet	460,000	700	0·0015
Nigeria	370,000	3,150	0·008
Chile	290,000	5,500	0·02
Switzerland	16,000	2,600	0·16
Cuba	44,000	8,000	0·18
Formosa	14,000	3,265	0·23
Panama	31,600	7,500	0·25
New Caledonia . . .	7,200	2,600	0·36
Isle of Wight . . .	150	850	5·7
Cape Peninsula . . .	200	2,500	12·5
Principe I.	12	275	23

2. Figures showing comparable densities in areas of very different size and situation:

	Area in sq. mls.	Species	Density
Spain	200,000	5,000	0·025
Victoria	88,000	2,200	0·025
Korea	85,000	2,165	0·025
Madagascar . . .	228,000	6,000	0·026
California	160,000	4,729	0·029

3. Figures showing different densities in areas comparable in size but not necessarily in kind:

	Area in sq. mls.	Species	Density
a. Italian Somaliland . .	220,000	600	0·003
Germany	226,000	2,600	0·012
France	213,000	3,800	0·018
b. Kuriles	34,000	770	0·0225
Sakhalin	30,000	1,166	0·037
Sierra Leone . . .	28,000	1,685	0·06
Austria	32,000	2,300	0·07
Portugal	35,000	2,700	0·08
Ceylon	25,500	3,000	0·12

4. Figures showing different densities in areas geographically related but different in size and kind:

	Area in sq. mls.	Species	Density
Australia	2,975,000	12,000	0·004
South Australia . . .	900,000	2,200	0·0023
Western Australia . .	975,000	4,400	0·0045
Queensland	670,000	4,400	0·0068
New South Wales . .	310,000	3,700	0·012
Victoria	88,000	2,200	0·025
Tasmania	26,000	1,200	0·045

5. Figures showing somewhat similar densities in areas relatively similar in position and kind, though varied in size:

	Area in sq. mls.	Species	Density
Texas	266,000	4,900	0·018
Utah and Nevada . .	185,000	3,600	0·018
New Mexico . . .	122,000	3,000	0·025
Colorado	104,000	2,900	0·028
California	160,000	4,729	0·029
Arizona	114,000	3,300	0·029
Illinois	58,000	1,785	0·031
Oregon	97,000	3,100	0·031
Indiana	36,350	1,900	0·052

Selected figures like the above give little idea of whether there is any underlying order in the distribution of densities, or whether indeed any particular parts of the world are notably richer in species than the rest, but some reply to these questions can be gained by arranging all the available figures in a single list according to the sizes of the areas concerned and beginning with the largest. When this is done it is seen at once that, in general, the density increases as the areas get smaller, that is to say the smaller the area the greater its species density. The significance of one aspect of this will be considered in a moment but meanwhile a more careful inspection shows that here and there are densities which are either higher or lower in the table than is appropriate to the size of the areas concerned. Italian Somaliland and Kerguelen, for example, and various arctic or subarctic regions have densities lower than most places of their size, as a result presumably of their difficult climatic conditions. On the other hand, certain areas have densities much higher than the average appropriate to their size. Prominent among these areas are the Union of South Africa, the Balkans, the Malay Peninsula, Borneo, the Philippines, New Caledonia and Cuba. The figures for these coupled with what is in general known about the species population of certain areas not specifically represented in the tables, such as parts of Australia where the density is notoriously high (23), enables the following general statement to be made with a reasonable degree of confidence.

The species density increases rapidly and fairly regularly from the poles towards the equator down to about 35°, but then in many places falls rapidly owing to the prevalence of arid regions. Within the tropics it rises again to a maximum in the equatorial zone. There is difficulty in making an absolute estimate of what this second maximum may be because in so many places the floras are far from completely known, but such evidence as there is suggests that it is probably not appreciably higher than some of the greatest densities elsewhere. There seems little doubt that the highest densities of all are found in certain comparatively limited areas of the southern warm-temperate and sub-tropics.

Reverting again to the table of diminishing areas it is very noticeable that the smaller areas at the end, which have in general the higher densities, are islands, and this is likely to give the impression, which should be corrected, that, other things being equal, the species density on islands is greater than on continents. This is not so and, indeed, the paucity of species on the more remote oceanic islands has long been recognised (177) as one of their most significant and peculiar features (see Chapter 1). The table gives the erroneous impression simply because the only areas of small size from which there are commonly quoted figures happen to be isolated oceanic islands, this being because by the nature of things an island has an individuality and familiarity often quite out of proportion to its size. For example, it is of general interest to know how many species there are on an oceanic island, but it is rare that corresponding figures are available for areas of similar size on continents. It is due to this lack of comparative figures that such islands appear to have exceptional species density, and comparison with continental areas of similar size would almost certainly show many more species in the latter, provided, of course, that reasonably similar circumstances prevailed in both.

How much the density on small or very small islands may differ is shown by the following tabulation:

   a. Density below 0·1:

      Kerguelen, Falklands.

   b. Density from 0·1 to 0·25:

      Ascension, Auckland, Bahamas, Fiji, Galapagos, Hawaii, New Hebrides, Sardinia, Sicily.

   c. Density from 0·25 to 0·5:

      Corsica, Crete, Cyprus, Macquarie, New Caledonia, Réunion, Samoa, Socotra.

   d. Density from 0·5 to 1·0:

      Azores, Campbell, Canaries, Carolines and Palau, Easter, Fernando Po, Tahiti, Tristan da Cunha.

   e. Density from 1·0 to 10:

      Bermudas, Juan Fernandez, Madeira, Mauritius, Micronesia, Rodriguez, Seychelles, St. Helena, S. Tomé, Tonga, Trinidad.

   f. Density more than 10:

      Annobon, Lord Howe, Norfolk, Principe.

Having discussed some of the smallest areas let us turn in conclusion to the opposite end of the scale and see what information can be gathered about the species density of some very large areas and especially of the three main constituents of the tropical zone. Here some of the difficulties already stressed are particularly great but something may be attempted. One estimate (696) gives a figure of 15–20,000 and hence a density of 0·0022 for the whole huge area, 8 million square miles, of the U.S.S.R. Wulff gives a figure for India, Pakistan and Burma of 20,000 species, which yields a density figure of 0·013, but the area on which it is based is very heterogeneous. In India in the narrowest sense, that is to say the peninsula south of the Indus and Ganges plains, there are perhaps not more than 4,000 native species (376) giving a density figure of only 0·005. At the same time it is only fair to say that the floras of both the Himalayas and Ceylon are rich and redeem much of the balance for India in the wider sense. Wulff also discusses China and concludes that its flora also contains about 20,000 species which gives a density of about 0·005. Van Steenis (702) considers that 27,000 is a conservative estimate for Malaysia, which gives a density of 0·02, but judging from the figures of constituent areas the total seems quite likely to be as high as 40,000, in which case the figure is 0·033. In the New World there is less to go upon but it is generally believed that Brazil contains not less than 40,000 species which gives it a density figure of 0·012, and this figure probably remains much the same if the rest of tropical America is included. In tropical Africa, however, the facts seem to be very different. Thonner (734) some fifty-five years ago, estimated the total of species at over 18,000, and even a generous proportionate increase would raise this only to 25,000 now. A figure of this sort is supported also by estimates for some particular constituent areas, and general recognition that the proportion of species widely distributed through tropical Africa is relatively high. Certainly such evidence as there is indicates that the total flora is not likely to be more than 30,000, and even this figure gives a density of only 0·005, which seems to show quite conclusively that the species population of this, the most extensive sector of the tropics, is much lower than that of either of the other two sectors, in both of which, it must not be forgotten, it is likely that just as high a proportion of the total flora remains as yet unknown. This relative paucity of the tropical African flora is a general phenomenon though it is especially evidenced by the relatively scanty representation there of some of the most characteristic and elsewhere plentiful tropical plant groups, notably the orchids, palms, bamboos and aroids. It is also in remarkable contrast with the flora of South Africa, which is one of the richest in the world, and the reasons for this difference merit very careful study. In general African paucity is most often considered likely to be due to climatic changes in the continent, and this view has been put most definitely in the work of Aubréville (29, 30) who suggests that it is due partly to great movements of climatic zones over the continent (and in particular a movement of the equator southwards) and partly to the "désertification", or increase of aridity, of large areas by causes associated with the presence of man. With regard to this last, however, it should be noted that this process would seem to favour the spread of savanna conditions, and it is in some forms of this vegetation that the tropical African flora actually finds its richest expression. It would also seem that there is little doubt that the paucity has some connection with the geological and physiographic history of Africa since the early days of the Angiosperms, during which it appears to have been much more isolated than either of the other tropical sectors. A very useful summary of what we know about the continent from this point of view has been given by Moreau (525) and many of the leading facts have been brought together more lately by Boughey (80, 81, 82). Aubréville has also discussed some aspects of this problem in another connection (31), citing various groups of the tropical forest flora which, present in America, the Madagascar region and Asia, are nevertheless relatively or entirely absent from Africa, among them the Lauraceae, Magnoliaceae and the genus *Symplocos*. He concludes that the equatorial flora of Africa has not, at least since the beginning of the Tertiary, been in broad and prolonged contact with the subtropical floras to the north and south, but separated from them by seas or deserts.

Cailleux, in a brief but estimable outline of the fundamentals of biogeography (101), makes a major contribution to this subject of the richness of floras. He thinks that 10,000 sq. km. is a suitable working area and illustrates several treatments on this basis, but he also gives a map of the whole world, with figures of appropriately varying size, of *the species number per 10,000 sq. km.* for many regions, and this map gives a very clear general impression. The highest figures (420 and 380) are in Central America, though eastern Brazil with 370 and Cuba with 350 are not far behind. The only other figures over 300 are 320 for Borneo and for the Cape of Good Hope. For south-east Asia and the Malay Peninsula, Java, Madagascar and the Philippines, and Burma the figures are, in that order, between 290 and 250. The figures for the south temperate compare in general with those of the north temperate but there is unfortunately no figure for south-western Australia.

Such are some of the facts and figures relating to the numerical distribution of species. It would be unwise, for the reasons given, to read too much into them or to base any very profound deductions upon them, but three points, each with a

Plate 10. Forest of *Eucalyptus regnans* in Victoria

(*Photo: Victorian Railways*)

different implication for the plant geographer, seem to emerge fairly clearly. They are that in the absence of adverse conditions the highest species concentrations are found in the warm temperate and in the equatorial zones, and that these are probably much of the same order; that islands do not show, in general, any higher concentrations than those of corresponding continental areas; and that of the three great parts of the tropical zone the flora of tropical Africa is much poorer in species than that of either America or Asia, and that the two latter have very similar values, possibly with Asia a little in the lead area for area.

The statistical comparison of floras

Clearly related to the numerical values of different floras is the problem of comparing them in a way which may be at once concise and realistic. The aim is, generally, to estimate the comparative degrees of relationship between floras in order to determine which have the greatest measure of affinity (and hence are likely to have had the most recent community of origin) and which are the more original and least derivative, questions which are very difficult to answer. For instance, how can a flora of 100 species be compared with one of 1,000 or perhaps 10,000 species? How can the relative degrees of endemism be equated? How does the proportion of wide species affect the matter? And how does relative size of area and consequent density influence the result? These are but a few of the questions which many have tried to answer, without, it must be admitted, very much success. It is not necessary to review these attempts, which often involve complicated statistics, here, but the reader may be referred to the interesting method of presenting the facts, so that their value may be estimated in various ways, outlined by Exell and Williams (230, 781, 782) who in the course of their remarks illustrate many of the difficulties just mentioned and some of the ways in which they may be met.

Many similar aspects of the relation between area and species population have been studied by Jaccard (402) in particular. He stresses the distinction between the number of species present in an area, or the floristic *richness*, and their taxonomic diversity, or floristic *composition*, and believes that the relation between these two can be expressed by a single figure, the generic coefficient, which is the number of genera proportional to every hundred species, or in other words, the quotient, expressed in whole numbers, when the number of species is divided *into* the number of genera. This coefficient, its author states, is higher when uniformity of habitat prevails and lower when there is ecological diversity, and for areas of roughly similar ecological values the coefficient diminishes with increase of area, because of the resulting greater floristic diversity, and he develops these themes in a number of ways. He also states that the coefficient is higher in islands than in continental areas of the same size, because of the greater frequency in the former of monotypic or ditypic genera, a conclusion of particular interest here in view of what is said about islands elsewhere.

Distribution of Species within Genera

Genera vary enormously in the relative distribution of their constituent species, and even those which are alike in total range are often quite dissimilar when the actual distribution of their species is taken into account. In some genera there is a fairly high proportion of wide species; in others the species are practically all, and in some cases entirely, endemics. In the former the wides may be of comparable range and fairly evenly scattered, or there may be one or more which exceed the rest and

11

which may even attain the whole area of the genus. In the latter endemics may be found in all parts of the genus area, or they may be massed in one part of it. Some genera illustrate several of these features to some degree.

In order to illustrate these and other more detailed points, eight large genera have been selected and the detailed distribution of their species is here described. They have been chosen as covering between them most of the world and most aspects of interest in the geography of species. Two, *Plantago* and *Juncus*, are almost world-wide, but chiefly temperate, genera; two, *Begonia* and *Dioscorea*, are almost pan-tropical; *Drosera* is predominantly a southern genus; *Viola* is a widespread but discontinuous temperate genus; and *Rhododendron* and *Erica* have each great numbers of endemic species in one particular region.

The distribution of the species of Plantago

The genus *Plantago*, which has been revised by Pilger (218), has about 250 species and is a good example of a genus which is actually found, owing to the cosmopolitan range of one or two widely introduced species, almost all over the world, but which is essentially temperate in its natural distribution.

The total range is almost world-wide except that in many parts of the tropics the genus is represented only by the adventive species, *P. major* and *P. lanceolata*, and even these are absent from the low-lying parts of tropical America.

About twenty species can be said to have a wide range, and of these the only marked examples are *P. media* in Eurasia, *P. asiatica* from the Himalayas to Java, *P. macrocarpa* from Kamchatka to north-western America, *P. erosa* from Ceylon to western China, *P. depressa* in central and eastern Asia, *P. hirtella* from Mexico to Uruguay and *P. triantha* in Australia and New Zealand.

Nine species have discontinuous ranges, namely, *P. maritima*, northern hemisphere and Patagonia; *P. durvillei*, California and the tropical Andes; *P. heterophylla*, North America, Uruguay and Paraguay; *P. trimenta*, Chile and Juan Fernandez; *P. crassifolia*, Mediterranean and South Africa; *P. canescens*, eastern Siberia and north-west America; *P. amplexicaulis*, Canaries and Mediterranean; *P. ovata*, Canaries and western and central Asia; and *P. lanigera*, New Zealand and New Guinea.

This leaves over 200 species of what may be called endemics, that is to say, species more or less rigidly confined to one region. The distribution is as follows:

Western North America	5
Eastern North America	15
Mexico	5
Western tropical South America	39
Temperate South America	42
Europe, Mediterranean and west Asia	42
Central Asia	10
East Asia	10
Formosa	2
Java	2
Madeira and Canaries	4
Tropical African Mountains	2
South Africa	4
Madagascar	1
Australia	16
New Zealand	4
Hawaii	9

together with the following very narrowly distributed species:

P. fernandezia	. . . .	Masatierra.
P. hedleyi	. . . .	Lord Howe Island.
P. robusta	. . . .	St. Helena.
P. rupicola	. . . .	Rapa Island.
P. rapensis	. . . .	Rapa Island.
P. aucklandica	. . . .	Auckland Island.
P. picta	. . . .	E. Cape Island, New Zealand.
P. pentasperma	. . . .	Amsterdam Island.
P. stauntoni	. . . .	St. Paul Island.

Among more recently described species are *P. palustris* from a mountain top in New South Wales and *P. gunnii* from mountain summits in Tasmania.

The distribution of the species of Juncus

In contrast to *Plantago*, *Juncus* has very few species which are anywhere adventive. As revised by Vierhapper (222), the genus has about 225 species, and of these something between one-third and one-half are wides—a very high proportion.

The widest of all is *J. bufonius*, which is almost cosmopolitan. It is worth noting that this is the only member of the genus which is a common weed of cultivated land and its great range may be to some extent adventive. This latter is true also of certain other species such as *J. tenuis*, which is widespread in America and introduced here and there in the Old World; *J. capitatus*, which occurs naturally in Newfoundland, Europe and Africa, and which is introduced into Australia; and the Eurasian *J. inflexus*, which is introduced in South Africa and New Zealand. *J. articulatus* and *J. bulbosus* are both characteristic of the temperate parts of the Old World but have a limited distribution in North America.

Other wides include a conspicuous group of arctic-alpine species with a more or less circumpolar range and which occur also in some or all of the north temperate mountains, among them being *J. triglumis* and *J. biglumis*.

Among more temperate northern species are *J. conglomeratus* and *J. gerardii*, and on a narrower scale *J. compressus*.

Several species range more or less continuously from North to South America as, for instance, *J. dichotomus*, *J. andicola* (from Alaska to Patagonia), and *J. marginatus*. Similarly in the eastern part of the Old World there is a link between the north and south by *J. pauciflorus* from east Asia to Australasia and the Pacific Islands, and *J. prismatocarpus* from east Asia to New Zealand.

Discontinuity of range is well illustrated, and if the status of the plants is to be relied upon in all cases there are some remarkable examples. *Juncus maritimus* ranges over Europe and part of Africa and occurs again in Australia and New Zealand; *J. acutus* is in Europe, Macaronesia and the Mediterranean, and at the Cape as well as possibly on Juan Fernandez. The well-known east Asiatic–North American discontinuity is illustrated by *J. xiphioides*, while *J. falcatus* exemplifies both this and north–south discontinuity, being recorded from western North America, Japan and also from Australia and Tasmania. Finally, *J. planifolius* occurs in New Zealand, Australia and Tasmania, and again in South America and Juan Fernandez, and *J. antarcticus*, previously known only from New Zealand, has now been found in the mountains of eastern Australia.

Among the remaining wides which are too numerous to be mentioned in detail all sorts of ranges are represented, as, for instance, Australia and New Zealand, both western and eastern North America, and south and tropical Africa.

Actually the most outstanding instance of the last should perhaps be included among discontinuous species. It is *J. lomatophyllus*, which is said to be native in South Africa, south-eastern tropical Africa and in St. Helena. Weimarck has described discontinuities also in some other African species (771).

As regards the endemic species of the genus, these again are spread over nearly the whole world, but three groups stand out. These are some forty species in either western or eastern North America, about thirty in the Sino–Himalayan mountain mass, and about a dozen in Europe or the Mediterranean.

The distribution of the species of Begonia

The huge tropical genus *Begonia* has very few wides, and the vast majority of the species are quite narrowly endemic. Indeed, according to Irmscher's revision of the genus (222), only three species merit the term wide at all, and even these are little more than endemic. They are *B. scandens* found in Jamaica, Guatemala, Guiana, Venezuela and Peru, *B. evansiana*, which reaches from Java to North China and Japan, and *B. mollis*, which is described as widely spread on the larger Sunda Islands.

The segregation of the species over the tropics is also very marked, so that it is possible to divide the genus, without violence to its taxonomy, into four sections containing respectively African species, Asiatic species, American species, and Asiatic or American species. In other words, the main groups within the genus are confined to the continents as indicated.

In the African section, which is relatively small, species range varies from that of *B. oxyloba*, which is found in both west and east tropical Africa, to *B. asplenifolia*, which occurs only on the top of one mountain in Gaboon. There are several species in Madagascar, but all are endemic there. Incidentally five very closely related species form a most interesting geographical series in this part of the world. They are *B. oxyloba*, already mentioned as fairly wide in tropical Africa, *B. meyer-johannis* in eastern tropical Africa, *B. cladocarpa* in Madagascar, *B. salaziensis* in Mauritius, and finally *B. comorensis* in the Comoro Islands.

This section includes also several exceptionally narrowly distributed species, as, for instance, *B. prismatocarpa* on Fernando Po, *B. thomeana* on the nearby island of S. Tomé, *B. perpusilla* on the island of Nossi Bé off Madagascar, *B. diptera* on the Comoro island of Johanna, and *B. annobonensis* on the west African island of Annobon.

In Asia endemic species are, as the following list of examples shows, to be found in almost every part of the area, and especially in New Guinea. *B. roxburghii* is on the Himalayan–Burmese mountains, *B. malabarica* in India and Ceylon, *B. handelii* in China, *B. tricuspidata* in Burma, *B. pseudolateralis* in the Philippines, *B. conophylla* in Sumatra, *B. burbidgei* in Borneo, *B. renifolia* in Celebes, and *B. hirsuticaulis* in New Guinea. There is an endemic species in Fiji.

Similarly in the American species, which are more numerous than the others, there are species in every region, as, for instance, *B. franconis* in Mexico, *B. carpinifolia* in Costa Rica, *B. foliosa* in Colombia, *B. ferruginea* in Colombia and Ecuador, *B. maurandiae* in the northern Andes, *B. microphylla* in Venezuela, *B. boliviensis* in Bolivia, *B. columnaris* in Peru, *B. sanguinea* in Brazil, *B. arborescens* in the neighbourhood of Rio, *B. fiebrigii* in Paraguay, and *B. micrantha* in Argentina.

The distribution of the species Dioscorea

The great tropical genus *Dioscorea*, which contains the yams, has been revised by Knuth (222), who estimates that it comprises between 600 and 700 species.

Although it is found throughout the warmer parts of the world, the wide species are very few and in fact there is only one species which can claim even to approach the range of the whole genus. This is *D. bulbifera*, which occurs throughout the tropics, but it is one of the cultivated species and its natural range can now hardly be estimated. The last remark also applies to *D. esculenta*, which is described as ranging from India to the Pacific Islands. Among other wide Asiatic species are *D. glabra* from India to Java (a very common type of distribution) and *D. cirrhosa* from Hong Kong and the Riukiu Islands to the Philippines and Ceram (a much rarer type). Other Asiatic species include *D. nipponica* from Manchuria, China and Japan, an unusually northern range, *D. collettii* of Burma, South China and Formosa, and the equatorial *D. polyclades*, *D. polifolia* and *D. nummularia*. Endemic Asiatic species are found in Japan, in the Philippines and in India. Very few species either reach Australia or are endemic therein.

The Asiatic species, which have also been monographed by Prain and Burkill (576), are connected with those of Africa by *D. triphylla* which ranges discontinuously over the tropics of both continents, but the total representation of the African sector is very slight and much of it actually consists of Madagascan species. Apparently none occurs on both continent and island. *D. quartiniana* and one or two others are widespread in tropical Africa, and there are species in the west, in the east, in the south-east, and even in South Africa proper, where they include the well-known *D. elaphantipes*. *D. lanata* occurs on Socotra.

Mention of the last introduces two species which, geographically, are among the most remarkable of all. These are *D. caucasica* in the Caucasus and *D. balcanica* in Albania. Their nearest neighbour is the Socotran species just mentioned, and their curiously isolated northern range is generally considered to mean that they are relics of a more subtropical flora, most of which has now disappeared. The closely related monotypic genus *Borderea*, sometimes included in *Dioscorea*, is a native of the Pyrenees.

The remainder of the species are American and these are very numerous. Few of them are widespread even in tropical America, but there are endemics in almost every country and many ranging over two or more. They are most plentiful in South America, and here they are found both on the west and on the east. The following, selected at random, will suffice as illustrations: *D. adenocarpa* in Brazil and Paraguay; *D. campestris* in Brazil and Argentina; *D. pilosiuscula* in the West Indies and Guiana; *D. altissima* in Brazil, Guadeloupe and Tobago; *D. convolvulacea* through much of Central America and in Trinidad; *D. glandulosa* in Colombia and Argentina; *D. megalantha* in Venezuela, Colombia and Peru; *D. amazonum* in Venezuela, Guiana and Brazil; and *D. occidentalis* in the West Indies and Brazil.

The distribution of the species of the genus Drosera
(Fig. 18)

The genus *Drosera*, which contains the sundews, has been much studied by Diels (221) and others.

Only five species out of about ninety have what can reasonably be called wide ranges. The widest of all appears to be *D. indica*, which is found in tropical Africa and again from India and China to Australia. It is thus not only very widespread but also markedly discontinuous. The remaining wides fall into two groups, the first of two species, *D. rotundifolia* and *D. anglica*, throughout the northern temperate zone, the latter being slightly more widespread and, incidentally, discontinuous, by its additional occurrence in Hawaii; the second of three species, *D. burmanni*, *D. peltata* and *D. spathulata*, which connect the species of the northern hemisphere with those of the south and of which the last-named ranges from China and Japan to Australia and New Zealand.

D. madagascariensis, which covers almost all tropical Africa as well as Madagascar, is probably the next widest species, and *D. burkeana* has a similar range but is less wide on the continent. Narrower African species are *D. natalensis* in southeast Africa and a group of local species exemplified by *D. capensis* in the Cape region. There are no purely Madagascan species.

D. intermedia, found in eastern North America and western Europe, is another markedly discontinuous species, as also, in lesser degree, are *D. brevifolia* in southeastern North America and southern Brazil and *D. capillaris* from Texas to Guiana, the latter being the only connections between northern and southern species in the New World.

Other American species are, with the exception of *D. filiformis* in eastern North America, all southern, the widest here being *D. sessilifolia* in Guiana and Brazil; but most of them are Brazilian only, as, for instance, *D. montana*. Finally, one species, *D. uniflora*, is restricted to that part of the southern continent south of latitude 40°, and this is of special interest because the only two close relatives of this species, namely *D. arcturi* and *D. stenopetala*, are confined to Australasia, the former being found in south-eastern Australia and New Zealand and the latter only on the New Zealand mountains.

All the other species of the genus are confined to Australasia and it is here that its great specific wealth lies. Upwards of half the total species of the genus are confined to a comparatively small part of south-western Australia, and are exemplified by *D. gigantea* and *D. myriantha*, but others range widely over the continent, as, for instance, *D. glanduligera*, on both western and eastern coasts of southern Australia. There are one or two species in south-east Australia, notably *D. whittakeri*, and a group, including *D. banksii* and *D. adelae*, in north Australia and Queensland.

D. petiolaris is found in north Australia and in New Guinea, while *D. pygmaea* and two others (in addition to *D. arcturi* mentioned above) connect Australia with New Zealand. Finally, there is one endemic species in New Caledonia.

The distribution of the species of the genus Viola

Turning now to pan-temperate and therefore more or less discontinuous genera, *Viola* is of much interest. In total its range is almost cosmopolitan, but its tropical representatives are mostly montane and the genus can be considered as essentially temperate. It has been monographed and revised by Becker (222).

The main feature of the distribution of the species is the comparatively large number of wides and the absence of any very marked massing of the endemic species, a contrast to what has been described for *Begonia* and *Dioscorea*. Moreover, the wides are of various ranges and not, as is often the case, restricted to the northern temperate zone, where in general widespread species tend to be plentiful.

It is true that many of the more widely spread species belong to this area, as, for instance, *V. palustris* and *V. selkirkii* (which is more or less completely circumpolar), *V. mirabilis*, *V. canina*, *V. pinnata* and *V. collina*, which are found through-out Europe and Asia, *V. odorata* and *V. hirta*, which occur over much of Eurasia, and various species, including *V. occidentalis* and *V. incognita*, which are wide-spread in North America; but there are many other types of wide distribution as well.

V. reichenbachiana and *V. riviniana* occur in Europe and west Asia and also in Macaronesia, *V. blanda* and *V. langsdorffii* are found on both sides of the Bering Strait, *V. altaica* and *V. dacica* range from south Europe far into Central Asia, and *V. tricolor* (in the wider sense) ranges throughout Eurasia and occurs also on the Canaries.

In lower latitudes *V. betonicifolia* has one of the widest ranges, extending more or less continuously from Afghanistan, China and Japan to Australia, including Tasmania. With similar but rather less wide ranges are *V. serpens* from Afghanistan to the Malayan Archipelago, *V. diffusa* from India and Japan to the Philippines, and *V. arcuata* from India to Java and the Philippines. *V. etbaica* ranges from Nubia to the north-western borders of India.

In the New World *V. lanceolata*, from Canada to Texas and also in Venezuela, is one of the widest, and others are *V. stipularis* in Central America, the West Indies and northern South America, and *V. scandens* from Mexico to Ecuador.

As has been said, endemic species are found in all parts of the generic range, but they are most plentiful in Europe and in the Mediterranean region. Some of these have a very narrow range indeed, as, for instance, *V. magellensis* in the Abruzzi, *V. fragrans* in Crete, *V. albanica* in Albania, *V. splendida* in south Italy and *V. athois* on Mount Athos. *V. bertolonii* inhabits Corsica and Sardinia.

Three noteworthy species in Macaronesia are *V. paradoxa* in Madeira, *V. cheiranthifolia* on the Peak of Teneriffe and *V. palmensis* on the island of Palma in the Canaries.

The genus is least represented in Africa, where it appears to be absent from the tropics except for *V. somalensis* in Somaliland and *V. etbaica*. In the south there are two species, *V. decumbens* and *V. sentiformis*, at the Cape.

Temperate Asia, and especially China and Japan, are fairly well stocked with endemics and include several in the Himalayas, such as *V. kashmiriana* and *V. forrestiana*.

Endemics are also to be found, although in small numbers, over tropical Asia, as, for instance, *V. celebica* in Celebes, *V. javanica* in Java, *V. ovalifolia* in Sumatra, and *V. lunata* in New Guinea. There are at least two species in Australia and three in New Zealand, one of these also on the Chatham Islands.

In the New World there are endemic species throughout the continent. In the north some are confined to the west (e.g. *V. sarmentosa*) and some to the east (e.g. *V. pedata*), and there are several in Central America and the West Indies (e.g. *V. jalapensis* in Mexico and *V. domingensis* on Haiti).

South America, and especially the southern parts, is rich in species and com-pares with Europe in this respect. Most of the more equatorial species like *V. humboldtii* and *V. arguta* are found on the Andes, but there are also several species in Brazil. Further south several small groups of species inhabit the Chilean Andes, including *V. pumila* and *V. rubella*, while others are found in the Argentine and Patagonian Andes. Finally, there are several species in Fuegia and Magellans-land, an outstanding example being *V. maculata*, which is also in south Chile and the Falklands and should perhaps be considered a wide.

There is one section of 8 species in the Hawaiian Islands, of which 7 are confined to one island only each, and the eighth is on four islands.

Discontinuous species are very few, but there is one outstanding example, *V. rostrata*, which is found in eastern North America and in Japan.

The distribution of the species of the genus Rhododendron
(Fig. 54)

Rhododendron affords a good example of the massing of endemic species in certain areas and the relative absence of wides. Many new species have been described recently, and there is no complete modern revision of the genus, but the main outline of its distribution can be gained from the *Index Kewensis* (377) and certain other sources (508).

The genus is distributed throughout the northern temperate regions with a very marked single extension south and south-east through tropical Asia to the northern part of Australia, and close on 1,100 species have been described. It is

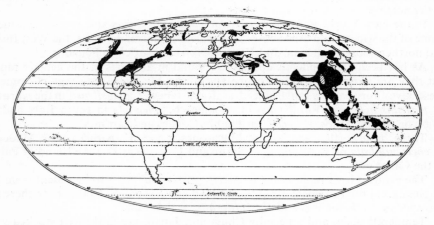

FIG. 54.—Map showing (black) the distribution of the genus *Rhododendron*, after Meinertzhagen. The small shaded ellipse in south-east Asia is the area of greatest species concentration.

probable that if the genus is ever revised completely this number will suffer some reduction, but, on the other hand, new species are still being found, so that the figure may not be much too large.

Of this huge number no less than two-thirds, that is to say over 700 species, are found only in the great Sino–Himalayan mountain system, and of these the great majority are in that part of it where India, Burma, Tibet and China meet—the country of the great river gorges.

From this amazingly highly populated centre the genus has extensions in three directions. Much the strongest of these is through India and Malaysia, and this accounts for at least another 200 species, divided up as follows: India and Lower Burma, 6; Indo-China and Siam, 19; Malay Peninsula, 13; Sumatra, 11; Java, 7; Borneo, 32; Philippines, 24; Celebes, 9; Moluccas, 8; and New Guinea about 100. *R. retusum* is recorded from Java and Sumatra; two species have been described from the Solomon Islands; and one species, *R. lochae*, is found in Australia, restricted to the Bellenden-Ker range in Queensland.

The second extension of the genus is eastwards through eastern and north-eastern Asia, including Formosa, into and right across the North American continent. This branch of the genus comprises about 120 species distributed as follows: north-eastern Asia, 33; Formosa, 24; Japan, 45; North America, 23. *R. anthopogon* is described as occurring in north Asia and in the Himalayas.

The third and much the smallest branch of the genus is westwards across western Asia and south Europe to Portugal. It consists of only about half a dozen species, but these include three of the best-known, namely, *R. ponticum* of the eastern Mediterranean region, which is the species of longest and most familiar horticultural history, and *R. ferrugineum* and *R. hirsutum*, the well-known "alpenrosen" of the European mountains. *R. lapponicum* has a circumpolar arctic range.

From this summary it will be seen that out of 1,100 species only two, or possibly three, are wide in the sense that they extend beyond the limits of one floristic region. Even these are very narrowly distributed compared with the range of the genus as a whole. This, in conjunction with the fact that over 700 species are confined to what is floristically but part of a region, gives the genus *Rhododendron* a degree of specific endemism and local concentration which is probably unique in one of its size and range.

The distribution of the species of the genus Erica

It is appropriate to pass from *Rhododendron* to a genus which can claim to compare closely with it in the features which have just been emphasised. This is the genus *Erica*, containing the "heaths". As in *Rhododendron*, there is no complete modern monograph, but the situation is here rather better because one or two publications, notably that of Phillips (557), provide useful information about the South African species, while the tropical African species have also been studied (130). Together with the *Index Kewensis* these sources provide a fairly clear picture of the distribution of the genus.

About 700 species have been described, and of these well over 600 are confined to the former Union of South Africa, while of these again all but a handful are found only in the very much smaller Cape region.

From this marked geographical terminus the genus ranges in one direction only, up the east side of Africa, across the Mediterranean, and into Europe. This great south–north area is, however, in striking contrast to that of the tiny southern headquarters of the genus, comparatively poor in species, and such as there are fall into two well-marked distributional groups.

Ranging through tropical Africa from Rhodesia in the south to Abyssinia in the north, and to all intents and purposes confined to the mountains of the eastern side of the continent, are some sixteen species. All but one of these are more or less narrowly endemic, and they are more plentiful in the south than in the north. The single exception is the well-known tree heath, *Erica arborea*, found, south of the Sahara, from Tanganyika to Abyssinia; in the mountains of the Tibesti, and again, north of the Sahara, from Macaronesia and Portugal to Greece and Crete (395). This, the only wide species in the whole genus, connects the tropical African species with the remaining group of European and Mediterranean species, which number about twenty. They include one outlier, *E. azorica*, found only on the Azores; the three species, *E. ciliaris*, *E. mediterranea* and *E. vagans*, which find their northern limits in the British Isles; and *E. tetralix* and *E. cinerea*, which provide, in northern Europe, the northernmost records of the genus (see Fig. 65).

With only one wide species the proportion of endemics in *Erica* is even higher than in *Rhododendron*, but the latter is the wider genus and its great species centre is in the middle rather than at the edge of a continent. Moreover, *Erica* has but one centre, while *Rhododendron* has subsidiary centres in several parts of Malaysia, notably in New Guinea.

The Significance of High Species Concentrations

The last two genera mentioned were selected to illustrate a common feature of distribution, the concentration of great numbers of species in one part of the generic range, and in so doing they inevitably raise the question as to whether these places of maximum species concentration can be regarded as the original homes of the genera concerned or not. In short, is it justifiable, on the strength of the species distribution, to regard *Erica* as having originated in South Africa and *Rhododendron* in the Himalayas?

Actually the two cases are rather different. In *Rhododendron* the marked partial discontinuity and the known glacial history of much of the northern temperate flora go far to resolve the problem, and it will simplify matters if on these accounts this genus is dismissed with the remark that it would indeed be rash to maintain, merely on the basis of the present distribution of the genus, that it originated in the Himalayas.

Erica is much more difficult, and, as it is but one of a considerable number of genera with rather similar ranges, it calls for more detailed treatment here.

A steep downward gradient of species concentration away from a maximum, especially when that maximum is situated at the very extremity of a great continental mass, gives, when expressed on a map, an overwhelming first impression of migration away from the peak and in the direction of the widest land areas, this impression no doubt partly arising from the circumstance that where the scattering of inanimate objects is concerned this is the usual figure produced.

Moreover, the impression is strengthened, and can to some extent be rationalised, by an appeal to the conceptions of evolution. If, as is believed, species are produced one after another over a long period of time, it would seem that the greater the concentration of species anywhere the longer has the genus existed there.

When they are put into print it is quickly clear that both these arguments, if they can so be called, are false. The first is obviously unjustifiable, simply because a genus is not inanimate and there is no reason to suppose that living species are disposed in the way indicated. The second is unsound, because the assumption in it is based on the supposition that the rate of species production is always and everywhere the same, whereas in fact there is every evidence to the contrary.

The question of the significance of high species concentrations is but one aspect of the much wider problem of how far and by what means it is possible to determine the geographical point of origin of any particular plant group. This information may clearly be of great importance to the plant geographer, and much attention has therefore been given to the consideration of the possible criteria and evidences by which it may be indicated. Cain (103, 104) has dealt with this subject in considerable detail and has listed a dozen such criteria which, it has been claimed at one time or another, can be used as indicators of the centre of origin of a group, but perhaps of greater importance is his conclusion, illustrated and strengthened by his study of these, that plant geography, among other biological subjects, carries too heavy a burden of hypothesis and assumption, and needs to return to inductive reasoning. With this conclusion many will agree.

The application, as well as the limitations, of some of these suggested criteria may be briefly illustrated by a short account of one of the most remarkable of Angiosperm groups, the Stapelieae, a tribe of the family Asclepiadaceae (299). This

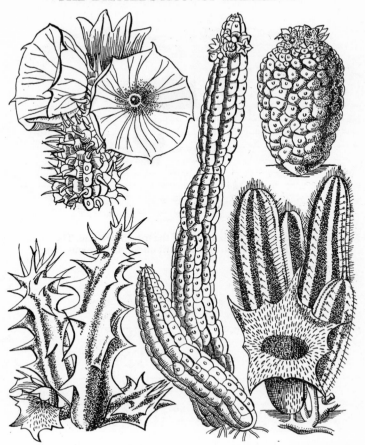

FIG. 55.—Some characteristic members of the tribe Stapelieae, after Wettstein.

group of twenty or so genera has been monographed on an elaborate scale (772) and its geography can therefore be described with some confidence. The Asclepiad-aceae are, as a family, characterised by marked floral specialisation, but the Stapelieae add to this an equally specialised vegetative form, being one of the three main groups of flowering plants (the others being the Cactaceae and certain species of *Euphorbia*) which, in association with arid habitats, have developed a cactoid habit, that is to say, which have lost their leaves and developed stems which are green, succulent and usually more or less angularly cylindrical.

The geography of the Stapelieae is shown vividly in Figs. 56, 57, and it is only necessary here to summarise the chief points of importance. These are:

1. The group as a whole ranges from Burma to Senegal and down the east side of Africa to the Cape.

2. Of its 370 species more than 280 are found only in South Africa.

3. No fewer than twelve out of twenty genera are found only in southern Africa and Madagascar.

4. One genus, *Caralluma*, has the range of the whole group.

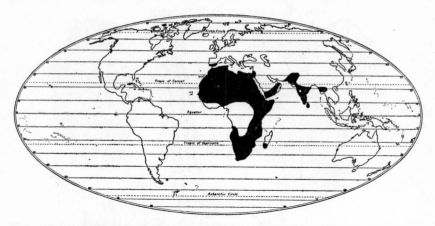

FIG. 56.—Map showing (black) the distribution of the tribe Stapelieae. The small white spot in the Indian Peninsula marks the distribution of the genus *Frerea*.

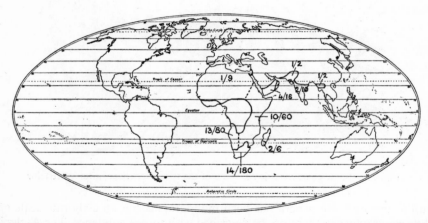

FIG. 57.—Map showing the numbers of genera/species in different parts of the range of the tribe Stapelieae.

5. This genus has half its 110 species in South Africa; four in East Africa; about thirty round the mouth of the Red Sea; and nearly all the rest scattered along its main west–east axis.

6. Eighteen out of the remaining nineteen genera are restricted to south Arabia, East Africa, South Africa, and very slightly to Madagascar.

7. The only other genus, *Frerea*, is a monotype of very restricted range in the vicinity of Poona in India.

Here, then, is a large group of plants numerically centred in South Africa but ranging widely therefrom both north and east. At first sight it might therefore be supposed that the group originated in South Africa and spread thence, but, as will be seen, there is strong evidence that the contrary is true.

The evidence for this view resides chiefly in the relationship between the different genera of the group. For reasons which need not be considered in detail here it is generally and quite justifiably believed that extremely specialised structural modifications towards life under markedly xerophytic conditions, as in deserts, have been comparatively recently derived from more mesophytic types with more ordinary form and possessing leaves. For these reasons, for instance, *Pereskia*, which is the only genus of Cactaceae with leaves, is generally held to be the most primitive type of the family. It is therefore interesting to find that there is one genus of Stapelieae which has persistent leaves and which is far less xeromorphic than the others, and which therefore may be regarded as the most ancient and primitive of the group, and still more interesting to find that this the genus *Frerea*, the Indian monotype. Again, *Caralluma*, which is certainly the most generalised of the xeromorphic genera and the most closely related to *Frerea*, is the only other genus found east of Arabia. Still again, the general relationship of its species is along the line from Burma to Senegal, and the South African branch of its range is occupied by its most specialised species. Finally, the South African genera are all to be regarded as among the most specialised of the whole group.

In short, all the evidence seems to show that the Stapelieae are of Asiatic origin and that their extension down the east side of Africa is a branch of their main geographical axis. If this is so, then the group illustrates, not a maximum species concentration at its point of origin, but one at the point furthest from it, and, however much the general distribution of the species may, at first sight, suggest a South African origin for the group, the other lines of evidence are all in favour of the contrary view.

It seems clear then, at least from this example, that, unless it is supported by other evidence, a great local concentration of species cannot necessarily be held to indicate the original home of a plant group, but that every group showing such a concentration must be considered on its merits.

CHAPTER 9

THE DISTRIBUTION OF SPECIES—II

IT has already been pointed out that there is no fundamental distinction between the ranges of genera and the ranges of species, and, this being so, it is practicable and convenient to use, in this and the next two chapters, the same general classification of distributional types as was employed in the case of genera, beginning with the most widespread forms and working down to the most restricted endemics. To the former class this chapter is devoted.

Cosmopolitan and Very Wide Species

It can be said with certainty that no species is cosmopolitan in the sense that it occurs naturally wherever flowering plants will grow, but a good many are so widely distributed that they do not fall into any more restricted category. These exceptionally well-spread species are mostly of three kinds, namely freshwater aquatics, temperate species now widely adventive in the tropics, or tropical species to some extent adventive in the temperate zones. Apart from these, few species have been credited with comparable ranges, and the mention of *Calystegia sepium*, *Deschampsia caespitosa*, *Luzula campestris*, *Montia fontana*, *Prunella vulgaris* and *Samolus valerandi* accounts for the most frequently quoted of them.

Actually *Phragmites communis*, the common reed, is generally quoted as the most widely distributed of all Angiosperms. It occurs, often in great quantity, in nearly all parts of the world, but is said by Ridley(595) to be absent from the region of the Amazon. It is, however, an aquatic plant and may well serve as an introduction to the other species comprising the first of the three types mentioned above.

Darwin (177) was one of the first to call attention to the exceptional range of many freshwater aquatic species (especially those that live floating or submerged) and paid considerable attention to them. Among them the members of the genus *Lemna* are nearly all very widespread, but their peculiar growth-form tends to favour casual transport of whole plants such as is scarcely known elsewhere, and their geography probably owes something to this. This is certainly not true, however, of *Potamogeton pectinatus*, which shows an equally wide range. *Typha latifolia* and *T. angustifolia* are similarly widespread, the former being absent only from central and southern Africa, and perhaps from Australia, and the latter from North America and Madagascar. *Potamogeton crispus* is unusual in that it occurs widely in both the tropical and temperate parts of the Old World but is absent from America (725). Among other wide aquatics are *Ceratophyllum demersum*, *Cladium mariscus*, *Cyperus flavescens*, *Glyceria fluitans*, *Myriophyllum spicatum*, *Najas marina*, *Phalaris arundinacea*, *Scirpus* spp. and *Zannichellia palustris*. Others almost equal in range, but which are less widespread in the temperate regions, include *Rotala mexicana*, *Ammannia auriculata* and *Ludwigia parviflora*.

It must be remembered that aquatic plants have generally, although they may be well scattered, a comparatively limited area of actual occurrence, so that while the total area may be wide the number of individuals may be much less than in the

174

case of more restricted species. This kind of limitation of habitat, as opposed to total range, is also seen in the case of other plants of various special kinds, prominent among them being the halophytes, of which *Suaeda maritima* and *Salicornia europaea* are generally credited with an almost world-wide distribution. They do indeed occur in most latitudes, but their edaphic requirements (see Chapter 17) limit them either entirely or largely to coastal areas or to where inland there are salt deposits, so that the actual size of the area they cover is relatively small. The same thing is true of many temperate species in the tropics. Their occurrences may be widely scattered, but at least if they inhabit very high altitudes the total area they cover may be very small.

The next two types both involve the problem of status (see Chapter 12), and this in particular prevents more than a rather indefinite account of these very widespread species because they may often be no more than transitory casuals.

As regards these partially adventive wides it is instructive to notice that those introduced from temperate to tropical regions have for the most part wider ranges than those in which the movement has been the reverse, which seems to indicate that while many species can live, under somewhat artificial conditions, in surroundings considerably warmer than those to which they are normally accustomed, few can maintain themselves in conditions much colder than the normal. Here two factors are certainly concerned deeply: in colder regions the growing season is shorter and there is less chance of ripening seed, but more important is the fact that the temperate zones nearly everywhere have frost at one time or another, a condition to which tropical plants are not exposed.

It is probably true to say that all temperate weeds find niches somewhere in the tropics as a result of carriage by man, but the following appear to be particularly ubiquitous:

Capsella bursa-pastoris, Chenopodium album, Erigeron canadensis, Euphorbia helioscopia, Plantago major, Poa annua, Polygonum aviculare, Solanum nigrum, Sonchus oleraceus, Stellaria media, Taraxacum officinale and *Urtica dioica.*

The opposite condition of tropical species extending into more temperate zones as weeds is shown well by the following, of which some actually occur rarely in the British Isles:

Amaranthus angustifolia, Asclepias curassavica, Cynodon dactylon, Echinochloa crus-galli, Gnaphalium luteo-album, Paspalum distichum, Portulaca oleracea and *Setaria verticillata.*

Pan-tropical Species

The number of species which to-day are found practically throughout the tropics is large, but here again it is very difficult to determine their status in different parts of the world. A few perhaps have, as will be seen, a natural range over the tropics, but the vast majority of them have been introduced widely and especially between the western and eastern hemispheres. Some have been actually planted all over the tropics, like the coconut, whose place of origin is still a matter of argument (507); some have run wild from cultivation; while still others, and these seem most numerous, are weeds of tropical lands occurring like those of the temperate zones wherever there is disturbed ground, though each is native to some part of its range.

The relative absence of natural pan-tropical species has often been commented on, and Ridley (595) calls attention to the fact that the nearest approach to them appears to be such members of the Cyperaceae as *Cyperus haspan, Fuirena umbellata, Eleocharis geniculata, E. chaetaria, Rhynchospora corymbosa* and *Scleria lithosperma*. It is fairly certain that these plants at least are not adventives, but with almost all other pan-tropical species there is generally some reason for suspicion except perhaps among some of the strand plants (see p. 241).

Among the widely found escapes from cultivation in the tropics are *Acacia farnesiana, Amaranthus caudatus, Anacardium occidentale, Cajanus cajan, Canavalia ensiformis, C. maritima, Gossypium arboreum, G. peruvianum, Physalis peruviana* and *Tamarindus indica*.

The widely distributed tropical weeds are of general interest from many points of view, and for this reason the following list of some of the most important is not too long:

Abrus precatorius	*Eleusine indica*
Abutilon asiaticum	*Emilia coccinea*
A. crispum	*E. sonchifolia*
A. hirtum	*Eriodendron anfractuosum*
A. indicum	*Evolvulus alsinoides*
Achyranthes aspera	*Flemingia saccifera*
A. indica	*Galinsoga parviflora*
Ageratum conyzoides	*Gomphrena globosa*
Alternanthera repens	*Gynandropsis gynandra*
A. sessilis	*Gyrocarpus jacquinii*
Amaranthus spinosus	*Heliotropium indicum*
A. crispus	*Heteropogon contortus*
Aneilema nudiflorum	*Hibiscus cannabinus*
Argemone mexicana	*H. sabdariffa*
Axonopus compresuss	*Hyptis capitata*
Bidens pilosa	*H. pectinata*
Boerhaavia diffusa	*Iresine celosia*
Borreria verticillata	*Isotoma longiflora*
Bryophyllum pinnatum	*Jussieua repens*
Caesalpinia bonduc	*J. suffruticosa*
C. pulcherrima	*Lantana mixta*
Capsicum frutescens	*Leonotis nepetifolia*
Cassia absus	*Leucas martinicensis*
C. mimosoides	*Limnocharis flava*
C. tora	*Microglossa pyrifolia*
Cassytha filiformis	*Mikania scandens*
Catharanthus (Lochnera) roseus	*Mimosa pudica*
Celosia argentea	*Momordica charantia*
Cenchrus echinatus	*Mucuna pruriens*
Coix lacryma-jobi	*Oldenlandia herbacea*
Commelina diffusa	*Oplismenus hirtellus*
Cressa cretica	*Oxalis rosea*
Crotalaria incana	*Passiflora foetida*
C. retusa	*Peperomia reflexa*
Cyathula prostrata	*Phyllanthus distichus*
Desmodium triflorum	*Pisonia aculeata*
D. umbellatum	*Pistia stratiotes*
Dichondra repens	*Pluchea dioscoridis*
Digitaria sanguinalis	*Pseudelephantopus spicatus*
Dodonaea viscosa	*Scoparia dulcis*
Eclipta prostrata	*Sesuvium portulacastrum*
Eichhornia crassipes	*Sida cordifolia*
Elephantopus scaber	*S. rhombifolia*

Plate 11. Stone-like plants growing in the Little Karroo, South Africa. The plant immediately below the shaft of the hammer is *Gibbaeum album*: the larger, more plentiful species is *Muiria hortenseae*

(*Photo: M. R. Levyns*)

S. spinosa
S. urens
S. veronicifolia
Siegesbeckia orientalis
Solanum aculeatissimum
Spilanthes acmella
Stachytarpheta guianensis
S. jamaicensis
Synedrella nodiflora
Thunbergia alata

Tithonia diversifolia
Tragus racemosus
Tridax procumbens
Urena lobata
Vernonia cinerea
Vigna marina
Waltheria americana
Wedelia trilobata
Xanthium chinense

It may be noted that in this list the Malvaceae, Amaranthaceae, Compositae and Gramineae and the three leguminous families are particularly well represented, and that some of the species are strand-plants (see Chapter 11).

Other Wide Species

The wide species of the northern flora

The great extent of the land surfaces in the colder parts of the northern extra-tropical world, the southern boundary of which (though varying somewhat with latitude), may be drawn at somewhere between 45° and 50° N.; the arrangement of these lands in an almost continuous circumpolar belt; and, doubtless, the marked climatic vicissitudes to which most of them have been subjected since the end of the Tertiary, combine to give their plant life a rare degree of floristic unity, of which the most notable expression is the unusual prevalence of species with wide distributions and a comparative paucity of narrower endemics of the better-marked sort, a characteristic which points clearly to the main feature of this northern flora, which is that it is, in broad terms, a diminished extension northwards of the various floras in the latitudes immediately south of it. Plain as this is in most parts of the north temperate zone it is perhaps most obvious in eastern North America where the floristic change and diminution northward is so gradual that it is almost impossible to find a line at which there is any abrupt passage from one flora to another, with the result that this whole area, covering a quite exceptional latitudinal range, can only with some difficulty be divided, on a world-wide scale, into two subregions. In eastern Eurasia the situation is rather different, partly no doubt because the effects of the ice ages were there less felt and partly because of the distribution of great topographic barriers, and the boundary between the northern flora and that of the Sino–Japanese region (which is the counterpart of the flora of south-eastern North America) is much more clear-cut. On the other hand the wide diffusion of the northern flora is, in the Old World, exemplified by the exceptional latitudinal extent of the Euro–Siberian region, which also cannot reasonably be divided into more than two sub-regions, and even this more for convenience than on the merits of any strong distinctions.

The existence of this widely diffused northern flora may confidently be attributed in part at least to such fundamental considerations as the shape of the earth and the particulars of its movements in relation to the sun, for, so long as the polar axis has remained in a position approximating to that which it now occupies, and so long as there has been no considerable change (other than minor fluctuation) in the obliquity of the ecliptic, the latitude of 45°–50° or so must always have been a critical one because of the rapidity with which certain climatic and related values change

12

north of it on account of the diminishing angle at which the incident rays of light strike the earth. Thus, the length of day in summer, and the length of night in winter, increase very sharply until at the poles each has a duration of six months, while above this crucial line frost is as much a commonplace as is its absence south of it. It is generally agreed that such austere conditions as these are not likely to be those in which the Flowering Plants attained their mastery of world vegetation and there is thus additional reason to regard the northern flora, as described above, as being essentially the high latitude derivative of more tropical floras and as comprising those plant types which possessed or developed the necessary tolerance to more difficult life conditions and which were thus sifted out from the rest and enabled to colonise the north.

It is therefore especially in connection with the Northern flora that the plant geographer becomes most closely concerned with the problems of changes in chromosome number (697, 698), or polyploidy as it is broadly called (see Chapter 3). Some biologists, among whom may be mentioned Tischler (736) and Muntzing (528), are of opinion that polyploid forms are proportionately more numerous in climatically less favourable regions, and even that they are more hardy than diploids and hence more suited to high latitude distribution, while Löve and Löve (469) state that there is something of a direct relation between the latitude and the proportion of polyploids in a flora. It has also been shown for particular species and genera, as by Manton (484), Anderson and Sax (20) and Giles (268) that polyploids have, in comparison with diploids, ranges which suggest that they have been especially successful in colonising northward or upward in the direction of retreating ice sheets, while Moore (524) has recently shown that the flora of Macquarie Island south of New Zealand similarly contains a high proportion of polyploids. There would seem little doubt (see Chapter 20) that the rapidity of climatic change during the Pleistocene was much greater than it had hitherto been in the history of Angiosperms and it is not unreasonable to suggest that the underlying necessity for keeping pace with this change found expression in the intensification of evolution by the most rapid methods such as change in chromosome number, and in this connection it is significant also that those flowering plants in which the normal processes of seed production have been short-circuited by apomixis are also, in the main, high latitude plants. However, other biologists, among whom Senn (631) and Bowden (84) may be cited, deny that polyploids are more hardy than diploids or have more northerly distributions. A useful more extended survey of the problems of chromosomes and geographical distribution is given by Cain (104).

But the latitudes in which this northern flora is seen at its best are also those in which the imprint of the human foot has been deepest, with the twin consequences that, while the flora is the most artificially modified in the world, it is also the most intensively studied, with a literature so vast that even the slightest survey of it is impossible here, and any lack of botanical richness there may be in the flora, compared with those of more favoured lands, is more than offset by the great detail in which it has been investigated and the enormous amount of information available concerning it. Unfortunately each of these considerations leads to a difficulty; first, that there are widely divergent conceptions about many species, and consequently of their distribution, and second, that to compress what must be said about it into the space available here is as hard as it is to compare it faithfully with the floras of other and less familiar parts of the world.

In view of these difficulties the best course here is to base our observations on particular sources, and we cannot do better than to use, as these, the works of

Hultén, whose knowledge of the geographical distribution of the members of the northern flora is probably unrivalled. The first of these, the *Outline of the History of Arctic and Boreal Biota during the Quaternary Period* (385), is the most generally valuable here because of its rather wider scope and the fact that it deals with a less familiar part of the flora. In it the author develops the thesis that during the Pleistocene certain areas in the higher latitudes became refuges in which various species of the pre-glacial flora were able to persist till better climatic conditions returned and from which they were then able to spread more widely again. This he illustrates by a series of maps cónstructed on the principle of *isochores*, which are lines analogous to such more familiar ones as isotherms, based on the species populations from place to place, and the resultant maps may be described as, or compared with, layered maps in which each successive layer represents a higher proportion present of the total species consituting the group which is thus being analysed. These maps, Hultén considers, illustrate his contention that, to use his own words, "the plants of our area can be grouped around centra from which they must have spread, and that the total areas of all plants spreading from the same centre form more or less concentric and equiformal progressive figures", and this is the expression of his Theory of Equiformal Progressive Areas. From these maps Hultén concludes that the pre-glacial refuges were particularly associated with those regions on both sides of the Bering Strait where the influence of the ice-ages was least felt, and it is the species which now occur in these parts which are the subject of his very detailed analysis.

Hultén's isochore maps are impressive but there is some room for difference of opinion about their real value, especially since they do not necessarily depict the actual distribution of any one or more species, and it may be that they do not express much beyond the fact that the distributions of species can, because of their almost infinite variety of detail, be arranged in many different ascending or descending series of size and shape. Similarly, as Raup has also pointed out in comments on this work (582, 583), the sorting of these distributions into groups, which is fundamental to the isochore method, must, because of the great similarities between many of them, and especially the more widespread, involve a measure of arbitrary decision which is bound to weaken to some extent any conclusions based on it. At the same time this comment is no denial of Hultén's views about the history of the northern biota during the Quaternary, nor does it detract from the vivid way in which his maps reveal some of the outstanding types of plant distribution in this part of the world.

The second of Hultén's books, his beautifully produced Atlas of the *Distribution of Vascular Plants in North-west Europe* (386) deals only with the species which occur within that region and is therefore somewhat more restricted in scope, but it is likely to be of greater interest to British and continental botanists because it deals with so many of their indigenous species, and even more will appeal to all who appreciate the fine making of books. Here the same general methods of presentation are employed and the flora of this part of Europe is exhaustively classified with the aid of further isochore maps. So exhaustive indeed is the classification here, where forty-eight groups are recognised, and in the *Outline*, where the number is rather less, that the reader can only be recommended to study them in the original, as no summary will easily do them justice. Hultén (387) has also dealt in a similar way with the distributions of nearly 300 species of what he calls "amphi-atlantic" plants, that is to say which occur only on both sides of the Atlantic, or, at least, more prominently there than on the Pacific side of the world, classifying them in great detail and giving a wealth of information about the ranges of the members of this element in the northern flora, while most recently he has published the first volume of a corresponding treatment of circumpolar plants (388).

A geographical analysis of a rather different kind, dealing with the arctic and European portions of the northern flora is given by Böcher (75). Here the basis of arrangement is latitudinal, and the area under consideration is divided into three such zones, arctic or alpine, boreal, and central European, and each of these is further divided, so that with the addition of one intermediate the total number of latitudinal belts is ten. The species under each of these are then grouped according to whether they are mainly oceanic, or continental, or indifferent in distribution, and each of these is still further divided, so that in grand total the classification contains more than sixty geographical types. It is unnecessary to multiply references to arrangements of this kind, but the reader may be referred to one more general work, which contains a great deal of information, both in the form of maps and otherwise, relating to the northern flora, namely Meusel's *Vergleichende Arealkunde* (516).

The very complexity of these various classifications expresses one of the leading features of the flora, the great geographical diversity shown by its members, and any attempt to give a simpler presentation of the facts meets with difficulties. Some of these have already been touched upon, but there is one in particular so generally inherent in phytogeographical studies, and so well illustrated by the present subject, that a further discussion of it is desirable here.

When the ultimate distribution of the individuals of a species is examined it is invariably found to be discontinuous to some degree, that is to say the individuals are scattered more or less irregularly and are never all in complete mutual contact. In theory, of course, there might be such a continuity, especially if the species consisted of only a few individuals, but it is doubtful whether this has ever been recorded, and it is certainly contrary to all experience. Discontinuity between individuals or populations may be of almost any extent, and of very different degrees in different places. Thus, in one part of its range a species may almost cover the ground to the exclusion of others, while in other places it may occur only as a few widely scattered plants. Similarly its different separate localities may be closely grouped or widely spaced from one another. Because of this it is usually impracticable, except on an impossibly large scale, to describe or depict exactly the discontinuities in distributions and it becomes necessary to ignore them to whatever may be the most appropriate degree. The problem thus becomes one of deciding what this appropriate degree may be, having in mind the purpose immediately in hand, but it is seldom one which reveals more than some, and often very little, detail. This point can be nicely illustrated by reference to the arctic-alpine species *Phyllodoce caerulea*. This plant is often regarded as having a circumpolar range, and this, up to a point, is true, but as Hultén's map (385) shows, the distribution of the species actually comprises some twenty distinct and variously separated minor areas. Even so this only partially reveals its discontinuity, for in another map by Hultén, on a larger scale (386), its Scandinavian area is itself seen to be irregularly discontinuous. Finally even the smallest areas shown on the first map tend necessarily to exaggerate the actual distribution of the plant, as for instance in the case of Scotland, where it is in fact exceedingly local.

What is true of *Phyllodoce caerulea* is true also of other members of the northern flora, and there can be but few species which are not appreciably discontinuous on a relatively large scale, and consequently any geographical analysis, if taken beyond a certain point, tends only to result in the recognition of increasingly large numbers of variously discontinuous and differing types. On the other hand there are certain species in which the discontinuity is exceptionally wide, and these must not be overlooked. In short, it becomes a matter of choosing a method of presentation which will, on the one hand, provide enough elaboration for the current purpose, without, on the other hand, being so highly analytical that generalities will be lost in a mass of detail. The following comparatively simple statement and arrangement

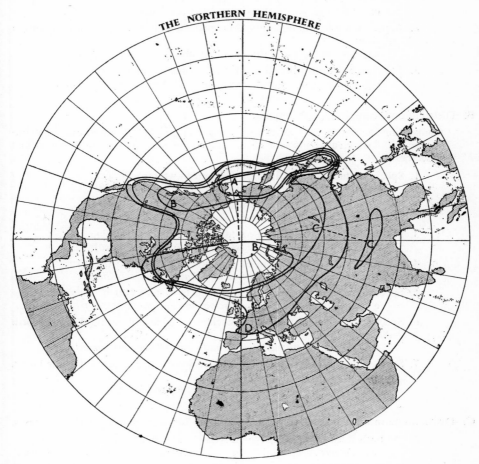

THE NORTHERN HEMISPHERE

FIG. 58.—Map showing the distribution of the genera A. *Bryanthus*, B. *Harrimanella*, C. *Cassiope* and D. *Phyllodoce*.

of the wider types of distribution in the northern flora has been drawn up with this in view and must be read in relation to the general purpose of this book. Its accuracy can go only so far as its scope permits, and like any other arrangement of species in categories, it necessarily involves an element of arbitrary choice. At the same time it does present, as far as seems feasible here, the general plan of wider distributions over the vast area occupied by the northern flora; the narrower types of distribution are dealt with later under their more particular headings.

The wider types of distribution in the northern flora

A. Distribution more or less completely circumpolar.

A comparatively frequent type of distribution, which may be further subdivided latitudinally.

1. Arctic and subarctic, which, because this region is itself circumpolar, will include some of the species endemic to it.
   e.g. *Braya purpurascens, Carex lapponica, Ranunculus nivalis.*

2. Arctic-montane, containing species present also in some of the mountain regions.
   e.g. *Oxyria digyna, Polygonum viviparum, Saxifraga oppositifolia.*

3. Temperate, with ranges all or mostly outside the arctic circle.
   e.g. *Caltha palustris, Comarum palustre, Menyanthes trifoliata.*

B. Distribution incompletely circumpolar.

Comprising the numerous species which occur in both western and eastern hemispheres but which are conspicuously lacking or deficient in one major longitudinal sector.

1. Species notably absent from or deficient in western Eurasia.
   e.g. *Gentiana acuta, Mitella nuda, Veronica americana.*

2. Species notably absent from or deficient in central Eurasia.
   e.g. *Galium triflorum, Juncus stygius, Mertensia maritima.*

3. Species notably absent from or deficient in eastern Eurasia.
   e.g. *Campanula uniflora, Listera cordata, Pinguicula vulgaris.*

4. Species notably absent from or deficient in western North America.
   e.g. *Milium effusum, Oxalis acetosella, Scirpus sylvaticus.*

5. Species notably absent from or deficient in eastern North America.
   e.g. *Adoxa moschatellina, Cypripedium guttatum, Myosotis alpestris.*

6. Species notably absent from or deficient in the neighbourhood of the North Atlantic.
   e.g. *Minuartia arctica, Parrya nudicaulis, Pedicularis sudetica.*

7. Species notably absent from or deficient in the neighbourhood of the North Pacific.
   e.g. *Cassiope hypnoides, Geum rivale, Liparis loeselii.*

C. Distributions more incomplete but still involving both western and eastern hemispheres.

1. On both sides of both the North Atlantic and the North Pacific only.
   e.g. *Cornus suecica* (also Burma), *Lathyrus maritimus, Montia lamprosperma.*

2. On both sides of the North Atlantic only.
   e.g. *Bartsia alpina, Gentiana nivalis, Saxifraga stellaris.*

3. On both sides of the North Pacific only.
   e.g. *Cassiope lycopodioides, Echinopanax horridum, Fritillaria camschatcensis.*

4. Other notably discontinuous species.
   e.g. *Cornus canadensis* (see Fig. 59), *Eriocaulon septangulare, Lobelia dortmanna, Phyllodoce caerulea* (almost C.1), *Potamogeton epihydrus, Potentilla fruticosa, Spiranthes romanzoffiana, Swertia perennis, Tofieldia palustris.*

Old World tropical species

Reference is often made in the literature to species which are described as having a distribution throughout the Old World Tropics, with the inference that they are more or less continuous from southern Africa to the Pacific Islands. Probably there are very few if any species which naturally have this range rather than one which falls more appropriately into one or other of the next two categories, and it must be remembered also that, since the Tropic of Cancer runs through the Arabian Sea and the Bay of Bengal, strictly palaeotropical species must of necessity be, to some degree, discontinuous in range, but there is certainly a group of species which generally, owing to introduction here or there, or to escape from cultivation, have this range in a more or less complete form. They are therefore to be regarded in some ways as the counterpart on a smaller scale of the pan-tropical weeds already discussed, and a short list of some of the more important is of interest. It contains:

Bryonopsis laciniosa, Canscora diffusa, Carapa moluccensis, Conyza aegyytiaca, Cymbopogon citratus, Dichanthium annulatum, Diplachne fusca, Drosera indica, Elytrophorus spicatus, Gymnema sylvestre, Hibiscus aristivalvis, H. caesius, H. panduriformus, H. surattensis, H. trionum, Imperata cylindrica, Musa cavendishii, M. paradisiaca, Ocimum basilicum, Parochetus communis, Polygonum plebeium, Portulaca quadrifida, Rottboellia exaltata, Solanum melongena, S. pseudocapsicum, Sphaeranthus africanus, S. indicus, Tacca leontopetaloides, Trichodesma zeylanicum, Xyris indica.

A somewhat reduced form of this distribution is shown by such species as *Afzelia bijuga* (Madagascar to Queensland) and *Dianella ensifolia* (*nemorosa*) which ranges from Rhodesia and Madagascar to Hawaii, the Mariannes and South-east Australia (827).

African–Asiatic wide species

As has just been indicated, most of the wider naturally ranging species of the Old World tropics are either found from Africa to Asia or from Asia to Australasia and the Pacific Islands, and the present category contains the former.

For the most part they are rather xerophilous species, because otherwise they tend to be absent from northern Africa and western Asia and therefore to be discontinuous, but they include quite a number of others as well. Again, most of them range from Africa only as far as India or southern China, but others extend far into Malaysia. Some, too, occur in Madagascar or the Mascarenes as well as in continental Africa.

It will thus be seen that the category is not well defined, but a range of this kind has been attributed to *Aerva javanica, Arthraxon lancifolius, Asparagus asiaticus, Cleome monophylla, Desmostachya bipinnata, Dicoma tomentosa, Grewia villosa, Hypericum lalandii, Latipes senegalensis, Pavonia schimperiana, Polygala erioptera, Rumex nepalensis, Schismus barbatus, Sorghum subglabrescens, Trichodesma africanum, Urochloa panicoides.*

Asiatic–Australasian wide species

In one sense this category is the counterpart of the last and contains in particular those species which range all the way from deep in continental Asia to Australasia or the Pacific Islands, but there are reasons why it is appropriate to include also in our consideration here those many other kinds of distribution which, though less extensive nevertheless considerably exceed the limits of any single one of the floristic regions in this part of the world.

A glance at the maps of Plates 4 and 5 shows that one of the more important differences between them is in the Asiatic sector of the tropics. Floristically this great area is divided into three regions, but climatically these are one, and form all but a small part of the Indo–Australian Monsoon Province. It is therefore not surprising to find that although the floristic distinctions between the three constituent regions, and especially between the two continental regions and Malaysia, are well marked, there are many species whose ranges exceed any one of these and in many cases cover all or nearly all the province or even extend beyond it, more especially towards Japan in the north and further south in Australasia. Many plants of cultivation especially are widely spread in this great area and are thought to have had their original homes somewhere within it, though it is now impossible to say more than this, among them being, *Adenanthera pavonina, Areca catechu, Artocarpus integer, Boehmeria nivea, Bromheadia finlaysonia, Canarium commune, Clitorea ternatea, Cynometra cauliflora, Durio zibethinus, Hedychium coronarium, Hoya carnosa, Mangifera indica, Nephelium lappaceum, Palaquium gutta, Parkia roxburghii, Phajus tankervillae, Piper betle, Piper cubeba, Pogostemon patchouly, Porana volubilis, Tectona grandis* and *Uncaria gambier.*

Although some species, such as *Amorphophallus campanulatus, Curculigo orchioides, Drosera spathulata, Finlaysonia obovata, Haloragis micrantha, Lagenophora billardierii, Malaisia tortuosa, Morinda citrifolia, Nervilia aragoana, Osteomeles anthyllidifolia* and *Zoisia matrella,* range from Asia to New Zealand or Polynesia, the commonest type of distribution in this part of the world is probably that from India and/or neighbouring south-east Asia to Australia, a distribution covering the monsoon province more or less exactly. Good instances of this kind of range include *Burmannia disticha, Calanthe veratrifolia, Casearia tomentosa, Deeringia amaranthoides, Dischidia raffiesiana, Drosera burmanni, Epipogium roseum, Leptospermum flavescens, Loranthus falcatus, Microcarpaea muscosa, Mimusops balata, Pholidota imbricata, Pluchea indica, Pycnospora hedysaroides.*

Of less extensive distributions within these extremes there are so many sorts and the connections between them are so gradual that little would be gained in clarity by attempting any exhaustive analysis of them, but the following table of quoted examples will demonstrate this fact sufficiently.

Actinidia callosa	.	.	North-east Asia to Java.
Artemisia capillare	.	.	Manchuria to Philippines.
Gaultheria leucocarpa	.	. ⎫	South-east Asia and Malay Peninsula to New
Gnetum gnemon	.	. ⎭	Guinea.
Dendrobium crumenatum	.	.	Burma and South China to Moluccas.
Stackhousia intermedia	.	.	Sumatra and Philippines to Micronesia and Australia.
Erechtites arguta	.	.	Lesser Sundas, New Guinea, Australia, New Zealand.
Uncinia riparia .	.	.	Borneo, New Guinea, Australia, New Zealand.
Geranium pilosum	.	.	New Guinea, Australia, New Zealand.
Secamone elliptica	.	.	Philippines to Australia.
Dianella odorata	.	.	Japan, China and eastern Malaysia to Northern Australia (827).
Dianella javanica	.	.	Malay Archipelago, New Caledonia and Fiji (827).
Spathoglottis vieillardii	.	.	New Guinea, New Caledonia and New Hebrides.
Gymnanthera nitida .	.	.	Borneo to Australia.

Macrosolen cochinchinensis .	India and South China to Borneo and Philippines.
Macrosolen avenis . . .	Burma and Siam to Java and Sumatra.
Pottsia cantonensis . . .	India and China to New Guinea.
Homonoia riparia . . .	Ceylon and Yunnan to Timor.
Tecticomia cinerea . . .	South-west New Guinea and northern Australia.
Loranthus estipitatus . .	South China and Indo-China to Malay Peninsula, Borneo and Philippines.
Korthalsella opuntia . . .	Himalayas to Japan, western Malaysia and Philippines.
Scutellaria luzonica . . .	Formosa to New Guinea.
Bythophyton indicum . . .	South-east Asia and Philippines.
Cryptolepis elegans . . .	India, South China and Java.
Hemidesmus indicus . . .	India, Ceylon, Malay Peninsula.
Trichopus zeylanicus . . .	India, Ceylon, Malay Peninsula.
Streptocaulon griffithii . .	Burma, Siam, Malay Peninsula.
Ancistrocladus tectorius . .	South-east Asia to Sumatra and Borneo.

There are also species found only in parts of Australasia as, for instance, *Balanophora fungosa* in Australia, New Caledonia, the New Hebrides and Fiji, and *Acacia simplicifolia* in New Caledonia, the New Hebrides, Fiji and Hawaii.

The botanical history of the monsoon province is of great interest especially with regard to the interrelationships of the different parts and has been discussed by van Steenis (700) with particular reference to the montane element in the flora. This work will be mentioned again later, but it may be noted here that the distributions of these species show two distinct lines of connection between continental Asia and Malaysia, one by way of India, Indo-China, Sumatra and Java, and another by way of China, Japan, Formosa and the Philippines. The former is illustrated by *Anemone sumatrana*, *Bucklandia populnea* and *Pyrus glandulosa*, and the latter by *Androsace umbellata*, *Asparagus cochinchinensis*, *Duchesnea indica* and *Skimmia japonica*.

African wide species

Under this heading must be included the various types of distribution too wide to be included under any one of the African regions, and here again, as so often before, almost any particular range can be exemplified, but there are certain predominant types.

One comprises species found widely in Africa, or at least the tropics, and also on the islands. Examples of this are furnished by *Celosia trigyna*, *Gloriosa virescens*, *Harungana madagascariensis*, *Maesa lanceolata*, *Sorghum verticilliflorum* and *Strychnos spinosa*. Others, such as *Hypericum lanceolatum*, are in the islands but only on the east side of the continent.

Much more familiar and numerous are some of the plants which range widely over the continent itself. An extreme condition is seen in such plants as *Clematis simensis* or *Oncoba spinosa*, which actually reach Arabia, but the great majority are found only south of the Sahara, although *Priva cordifolia*, *Myrsine africana* and doubtless some others extend from Socotra or Abyssinia to the Cape.

A few wide African species like *Coleus thyrsoideus*, *Kalanchoe coccinea* and *Zantedeschia aethiopica* (the arum-lily) are grown in greenhouses, and the last is perhaps the best known of all African plants. There are also a few economic plants of at least local importance which now have a wide range. Among them may be mentioned *Butyrospermum parkii, Cola nitida, Pentadesma butyraceum, Ricinus communis, Sorghum caffrorum, S. guineense* and *Voandzeia subterranea*.

For the rest the following is a selection of the species to which a wide distribution in tropical or warm Africa has been attributed:

Adansonia digitata, Baphia nitida, Bridelia micrantha, Chlorocodon whitei, Clematopsis scabiosifolia, Cleome hirta, Clerodendrum thomsonae, Cymbopogon giganteus, Ectadiopsis oblongifolia, Hymenocardia acida, Hypericum roeperianum, Leonotis leonurus, Myrothamnus flabellifer, Nymphaea caerulea, Oxytenanthera abyssinica, Pennisetum purpureum, Sorghum arundinaceum, Sparrmannia africana, Stephania abyssinica, Telfairia pedata and *Telosma extensa*.

Wide species of Australia, New Zealand and the Pacific Islands

There are so many different types of distribution under this comprehensive heading that it is manifestly impossible to deal with them all here, and it must therefore suffice to mention only some of those most significant from the point of view of some of the problems of southern floras discussed in Chapter 12. These are the species in which New Caledonia is an important element of their distribution; species found only in Australia and New Zealand; and species found in more than one of the three floristic regions comprising Australia.

As regards the first of these, considerably more than 50 species have been recorded as occurring only in Australia and New Caledonia, but many if not most of these are such as to raise doubts about their status in New Caledonia. They include ten orchids, among them four species of *Thelymitra*, and some of these may certainly be native there as may some of the rest such as *Arthropodium paniculatum, Baeckea virgata* and *Duboisia myoporoides*. A curious point about the last of these is that the plants of the two regions are said to contain different alkaloids. Virot (751) cites fifteen species as found only in New Caledonia and the New Hebrides, including *Elaeocarpus persicaefolius, Geniostoma densiflora, Lyperanthus gigas* and *Vaccinium macgillivrayi*; and about the same numbers have been recorded from New Caledonia and Fiji only, among them being *Lindenia vitiensis, Maba foliosa, Melodinus scandens, Rhus simarubaefolius, Semecarpus atra* and *Storckiella vitiensis*. One species at least, *Fontainea pancheri*, is found in Australia, New Caledonia and the New Hebrides. A few species are reported as occurring in Australia, New Caledonia and New Zealand, including *Hypericum gramineum, Microtis parvifolia, Muehlenbeckia axillaris, Orthoceras strictum, Spinifex hirsutus* and a species of *Juncus*. Several species are said to be found only on New Caledonia and Norfolk Island, and several also on New Caledonia and Hawaii only and at least one in New Caledonia and New Zealand, but the facts in these cases are not altogether clear. *Dianella intermedia* is stated (827) to occur in the Three Kings Islands, Norfolk Island, New Caledonia, the New Hebrides, Fiji, the Cook Islands, and the Society Islands.

The species widely distributed within the continent of Australia are usually either plants of the drier interior which actually extend into one or other of the peripheral regions, or they are plants which extend more or less completely across the south of the continent from east to west. The former includes a number of grasses, among them *Panicum decompositum, Pappophorum nigricans* and *Triodia irritans*. The latter are certainly much more numerous, and almost every large and characteristic Australian genus contains one or more of them, though the proportion is always small. *Goodenia pinnatifida*, and a number of species of *Eucalyptus* and *Grevillea* are examples.

Between the floras of Australia and New Zealand there is a strong element of relationship and 260 species in all have been recorded (475) as common to the two countries, but this total includes those which are found elsewhere also. Species found *only* in Australia and New Zealand number only just over half this total. Among these the Cyperaceae, Gramineae and Orchidaceae account for at least a third, while there are nine species of *Juncus*, five of *Drosera* and five of *Epilobium*, and four of *Ranunculus*. Among the rest are *Cyathodes acerosa, Hypoxis pusilla, Leptospermum scoparium, Libertia pulchella, Mazus pumilio, Pelargonium inodorum, Sebaea ovata* and *Utricularia monanthos*. In a few, including *Hemiphues suffocatus, Australina pusilla, Gaultheria depressa, Mitrasacme montana* and *Viola cunninghamii*, the Australian distribution is limited to Tasmania. *Solanum aviculare* occurs in Australia, Norfolk Island and New Zealand; and *Muehlenbeckia axillaris* in Australia, Lord Howe Island and New Zealand.

American wide species

It would take far more than the space available here to give even a brief complete survey of the innumerable types of wide distribution exhibited in the huge area of the New World. The task is, moreover, made particularly difficult because of the absence of barriers between the north and south and the facilities for plant movement in this direction afforded by the long chain of the western mountains, and, as a result of these conditions, there is every variation in latitudinal plant distribution. All that can be done is to supplement what will be said later under the various regions. With this purpose in view we may pass somewhat rapidly over certain aspects by saying that there are species like *Erechtites hieracifolia* which are said to occur practically all over America, *Madia sativa* which occurs all down the west side, and others such as *Apocynum androsaemifolium, Dodecatheon meadia, Symphoricarpos albus*, and various species of *Penstemon, Solidago, Trillium* and *Carya* which range widely through North America, and pass on to the more detailed and necessary consideration of the widely spread tropical species.

In one sense the tropical portion of America corresponds to the whole of the Old World tropics and may be expected to have in the same way its own widely distributed weeds and denizens. This is so, and in order to make a comparison between the two hemispheres possible it is worth while to give a fairly extended list of the species which are more or less completely distributed now through the New World tropics. The list includes also some of the species whose natural ranges are especially wide, as well as a few species now so widely cultivated that their place of origin can hardly be decided. It should also be remembered that any segregation between Old and New Worlds among weeds of disturbed ground is likely sooner or later to break down and that eventually most, if not all, the tropical weeds are likely to become world-wide in those latitudes.

Bocconia frutescens	*Cyanchum multiflorum*
Bursera gummifera	*Desmodium adscendens*
Capsicum annuum	*Epidendrum fragrans*
Carica papaya	*Epidendrum nocturnum*
Cedrela odorata	*Epidendrum rigidum*
Chlorophora tinctoria	*Erythrina corallodendrum*
Clidemia hirta	*Flaveria contrayerba*
Cordia sebestena	*Gossypium barbadense*
Crataeva tapia	*Hura crepitans*
Cyathula achyranthoides	*Inga vera*

Jatropha curcas
Jatropha pungens
Jussiaea peruviana
Maranta arundinacea
Metastelma parviflora
Mirabilis jalapa
Mollugo verticillata
Ochroma lagopus
Oncidium luridum
Peperomia hispidula
Peperomia rotundifolia
Phaseolus multiflorus

Piper aduncum
Piptadenia peregrina
Psidium guajava
Pterocarpus officinalis
Rivina humilis
Seraphyta diffusa
Simarouba amara
Spigelia anthelmia
Spondias purpurea
Tecoma stans
Trema micrantha
Tribulus cistoides

Among species less widely distributed in the American tropics nearly every possible range can be exemplified. A very common one is that of plants common to the West Indies and to the northern part of the South American mainland, often to Venezuela or Guiana only, and among these are *Cecropia peltata, Guajacum officinale, Mammea americana, Norantea guianensis, Oncidium pulchellum* and *Pleurothallis pruinosa.*

Another group has a similar range but extends farther into South America, as, for instance, to Brazil, and here belong *Erythrina velutina, Galeandra beyrichii* and *Hedyosmum arborescens.*

Another rather frequent type includes the species which, found in both Central America and the West Indies, also occur in the northern part of South America. Examples of these are *Hippomane mancinella, Lonchocarpus latifolius* and *Rubus alpinus.*

Many plants are widely distributed in the tropical parts of South America but do not reach either Central America or the West Indies, and these include *Bixa orellana, Hymenaea courbaril* and *Lucuma mammosa.*

Brassavola nodosa and *Phyllanthus carolinensis* are instances of species which are found in Central America and the West Indies and also on the western (Andean) side of South America.

The floral relationship between the north temperate regions and the north tropics is best left for discussion in the next chapter, but this one may be closed by a mention of *Geranium carolinense,* which is said to occur in both Central America and the West Indies, and northward as far as Canada.

Finally there are many notable species which can hardly be ascribed to any one floristic region of tropical America, and among them are:—

Canna indica
Centrosema pubescens
Cleome spinosa
Chrysobalanus icaco
Chrysophyllum cainito
Coccolobis uvifera
Couroupita guianensis
Dichromena ciliata
Dieffenbachia seguine
Duranta plumieri
Gynerium sagittatum

Heliconia bihai
Jacaranda mimosaefolia
Malpighia glabra
Malvaviscus grandiflora
Muntingia culubura
Neptunia oleracea
Oreodoxa oleracea
Pedilanthus tithymaloides
Petraea arborea
Pithecellobium saman
Sechium edule

CHAPTER 10

THE DISTRIBUTION OF SPECIES—III

Endemic Species

STRICTLY speaking, a narrower conception of endemism should be employed for species than for genera, but to do this here would mean recasting the geographical background in a way which would certainly make for confusion, and for this reason it is better to give the term endemic the same value in both and to treat the endemic species on the same regional basis as was used for the genera. As before, species falling partly into two or more regions are included under the region of which they are most characteristic.

It will be remembered that the proportion of endemic genera among all genera proved to be about 80 per cent. Species have, on the average, much smaller areas than genera, and hence it may be assumed that, on the present conception of endemism, the proportion of endemics among indigenous species is considerably greater and may well exceed 90 per cent. At all events there have now to be dealt with the vast majority of the species of flowering plants.

Arctic and Subarctic Region

The arctic and subarctic region as here defined comprises all the treeless land north of the great northern coniferous forest zone but, because of the preponderance of sea at these high latitudes, its area is not as great as might be expected, and is still more restricted as a habitat for flowering plants on account of the fact that its biggest constituent area, Greenland, is very largely covered by a permanent ice-cap.

One of the first general accounts of the flora was given by Hooker (373) but his definition of it was not altogether satisfactory and made his statistics less useful than they would otherwise have been, while most more modern studies have been confined to one or other of the three main geographical divisions, namely the palaearctic (Eurasia), the nearctic (North America) and Greenland (548). A very interesting brief account of arctic plant life, with special reference to the New World has been given by Porsild (568) who stresses the peculiar conditions under which it exists, as for instance the circumstance that the precipitation is, widely, so scanty during the growing season that if the water in the subsoil were not permanently frozen (see p. 365) and the summer surface melt water thus prevented from draining away, much of the region would be a desert. The most recent and complete source of information about the flora of this region is Polunin's *Circumpolar Arctic Flora* (565), which enumerates nearly 900 species in all.

Floristically, northern Alaska, which it is important to note is generally believed to have been unglaciated during the Pleistocene, is probably the richest part with about 600 species, a figure also quoted for the larger Canadian arctic mainland (568). The Canadian arctic archipelago has about half this number. The flora of Greenland (which is virtually the only remaining glaciated part of the arctic) has about 400 species, 13 per cent of which are said to have been introduced by the early Norse settlers. Of the rest about four-fifths are of American affinity, and the others of

European relationship. Many of the species are found on both west and east coasts, and of the remainder those found only on the west greatly outnumber those found only on the east. There is a quite considerable flora at the most northerly land latitudes (about 83° N.), and 189 species have been listed from north of 71° on the east coast (686). Comparable figures for the Old World are not quite so readily available, but are likely to be of much the same order, as is shown by the estimates of 375 for Iceland, 137 for Spitzbergen, 200 for Novaya Zemlya, 200 for the Taimyr Peninsula and other figures quoted by Wulff and shown on his map (800).

The flora of the region as a whole contains two basic elements, the arctic, whose species are more or less confined to sea level at the highest latitudes, and the arctic-alpine, of species which are found not only in the arctic but also at elevation in one or more of the mountain systems considerably further south. The larger part of the former makes up the endemic part of the flora of the arctic region in its narrowest sense, and is thus our particular concern here. Its numerical value is hard to estimate, partly because many of its species overlap the tree limit to some extent according to merely local conditions, and partly because many of the species concerned are not well defined taxonomically. Perhaps the most noteworthy of these endemics are a few grasses, including *Phippsia algida*, *Colpodium fulvum*, *Dupontia fischeri* and *Pleuropogon sabinii*. The genus *Braya* includes one or two endemics, as also does *Pedicularis;* while several species of *Salix*, among them *S. arctica*, *S. nummularia* and *S. polaris* are so described. Other actual or virtual endemics are *Chrysanthemum arcticum*, *Nardosmia glacialis*, and *Ranunculus pallasii*.

The arctic-alpine part of the flora is, for historical and other reasons already touched upon in pp. 177 *et seq.* in relation to the northern flora as a whole, of special interest in any general study of the distribution of Angiosperms, and calls for some particular notice here. Nor is this unjustifiable on the score that this chapter is about endemic species because the arctic and sub-arctic region as here defined is in a way artificial. Logically, as well as botanically, there should be included in it various localised high alpine areas of the northern temperate zone, thus giving a floristic unit which would comprise three main classes of endemic forms, arctic, alpine and arctic-alpine, but such a region would be almost indefinable and certainly could not be mapped on a small scale, and for practical convenience therefore it has been delimited as described above, and the numerous small southern outliers ignored, their endemics going to swell the numbers of the regions within which they are actually situated. Furthermore all strictly arctic-alpine plants have a more or less discontinuous distribution because their montane habitats are few and far between.

Although the distribution of arctic-alpine species is, in detail, extraordinarily various, its main outlines can be appreciated fairly easily because of the correlation with major topographical features of the northern extra-tropical regions. With some exceptions the elevated regions of the northern temperate zone are aggregated into three great but distinct systems. These are the Rockies in America; the various isolated *massifs* which constitute the mountains of central and southern Europe and which may here be called comprehensively the Alps; and the enormous system of the Himalayas in Asia.

The interesting immediate point about these three systems is that they vary considerably in their distance from the arctic proper. The Rocky Mountains actually fuse with it in the north; the Alps are roughly along the latitude 45° N.; and the Himalayas are roughly between 30° and 35° N. The floristic relationship is closely correlated with this spatial one. Arctic alpine species are most numerous in the Rocky Mountains, fairly numerous in the Alps, but very few in the Himalayas.

The significance of these relationships will be considered later, but it is relevant to point out here that the Himalayan region is not only the most isolated from the arctic to-day but was even more markedly so during the Pleistocene ice ages.

As between these four constituent areas, the arctic, the Rockies, the Alps, and the Himalayas, there is almost every kind of specific distribution. It would take too long to describe these in detail, but a good impression of them can be given by quoting the distribution recorded by Hegi (353) for a few of the most familiar plants of the European mountains, as follows:

Androsace chamaejasme . .	Alps, Urals, Altai, Himalayas, Arctic.
Anemona alpina . . .	Alps and Arctic.
Atragene alpina . . .	,, ,, ,,
Bartsia alpina . . .	,, ,, ,,
Campanula scheuchzeri . .	Alps, Altai, Arctic.
Dryas octopetala . . .	Alps and Arctic.
Gentiana nivalis . . .	Alps, Asia Minor, Arctic.
Hedysarum obscurum . .	Alps and Arctic.
Myosotis alpestris . .	Alps, Corsica, Arctic.
Polygonum viviparum . .	Alps, Altai, Himalayas, Arctic.
Ranunculus glacialis . .	Alps (where it reaches 14,000 ft.) and Arctic.
Ranunculus pygmaeus . .	Alps, Rockies, Arctic.
Salix herbacea . . .	Alps, Urals, Rockies, Arctic.
Saxifraga aizoides . .	Alps and Arctic.
Saxifraga oppositifolia . .	,, ,, ,,
Viola biflora . . .	,, ,, ,,

Certain other familiar plants of the European mountains form as it were a link with the next region to be discussed in being distributed far to the north though scarcely into the arctic proper. Such are:

Arnica montana . . .	Widely distributed in Europe and north Asia.
Campanula barbata . .	In the Alps, Carpathians and Norway.
Gentiana purpurea . .	,, ,, Norway and Kamchatka.
Lactuca (Mulgedium) alpina .	,, ,, and also in north Europe.
Nigritella nigra . . .	,, ,, ,, ,, ,,

The species of the genus *Diapensia* also illustrate an interesting state of affairs. According to Evans (227) *Diapensia lapponica* is circumpolar and also found in the White Mountains of eastern North America and in Japan; while the other three species, *D. himalaica*, *D. purpurea* and *D. wardii*, are all confined to the eastern parts of the Himalayan system.

The *alpine* flora proper, namely those plants which, while part of the arctic-alpine flora as a whole, are only found in the mountain systems mentioned, is best considered under the regions of which these mountains form part.

Euro–Siberian Region

This region is so extensive longitudinally (see p. 29) that some of the species confined to it and therefore to be regarded, on the definition in use here, as endemics, may in fact range in one direction for several thousands of miles and actually may rank as some of the most widespread species in the world. But these cannot well be separated from the much more numerous species which have something less than this extreme range and to attempt to do this would be artificial, so it is best to consider all these types here, however much some of them, in the peculiar circumstances, strain the more usual conception of endemism. Another difficulty is that, as has been explained on p. 133, the latitudinal depth of the region is greater in the west than in the east, and because of this species which, in the west, are characteristic of the Euro–Siberian region, are often, in the east, more characteristic of Central Asia or of China and Japan. Little would be gained by attempting to sort these out in detail and there are thus included in consideration here species which in general range widely through the Eurasian temperate zone even if they are not altogether confined to the Euro–Siberian region as defined.

A few plants familiar in cultivation are found more or less throughout the region, among them *Asparagus officinalis* and *Campanula trachelium* and this type of distribution is very common among the species native to some parts of the British Isles, as may be illustrated by the mention of *Campanula glomerata*, *Conium maculatum*, *Cypripedium calceolus*, *Geranium pratense*, *Heracleum sphondylium*, *Holcus lanatus*, *Lamium album*, *Paris quadrifolia*, *Ranunculus acris* and *Solanum dulcamara*. Some others which are also widespread from west to east extend also further south in places, as *Sanicula europaea* to the African mountains and into Malaysia and *Brachypodium sylvaticum* and one or two others into the latter.

Among rather less completely distributed species there are some which do not occur in Britain such as *Aconitum excelsum*, *Dianthus superbus*, *Dictamnus albus*, *Eritrichium villosum*, *Rubus humulifolius* and *Trifolium lupinaster*; while conversely, there are others which occur in Britain but fail to reach the Pacific, among these being *Artemisia campestris*, *Butomus umbellatus*, *Lathyrus pratensis*, *Listera ovata*, *Myosotis palustris*, *Senecio jacobaea*, *Stachys sylvatica* and *Verbascum thapsus*. Others again have a like width of distribution in total but are more or less discontinuous, as for instance *Eriophorum latifolium*, *Gagea lutea*, *Pirola media*, *Stellaria palustris* and *Veratrum album*.

Among the considerable number of less widely ranging species of the region it must be sufficient here to deal with three particularly well-defined groups; the species restricted to the western part of the region as a whole, namely those of Europe and the Caucasus; the species restricted to the eastern part of the region, namely Siberia; and the species of the European mountain systems—the alpine flora in its narrowest sense. Since this last is closely related to the arctic-alpine flora, it may be dealt with first while the foregoing pages are still fresh in the mind of the reader.

It is difficult to compare the European alpine flora with others because the areas of high elevation are so different, but it is safe to say that the alpine flora proper is rich and compares favourably with others proportionately. It tends to differ from them, however, because the European mountains comprise a number of isolated *massifs* rather than one continuous range, and for this reason the comparative ranges of species are of special interest.

The alpine flora is part of the arctic-alpine flora and therefore has a close affinity with that of the arctic itself, but it is also related to the European lowland flora and, particularly in the more southern mountains, with the Mediterranean flora.

These several points can be illustrated by citing the ranges, as given by Hegi (353), of some of the more familiar plants of the Alps proper:

Androsace helvetica	. . .	Alps.
Campanula thyrsoides	. . .	,,
Carlina acaulis	. . .	Wide in south and central Europe.
Crocus albiflorus	. . .	Alps, Pyrenees, north Apennines, Carpathians, Balkans.

Plate 12. *Protea cynaroides* at the Cape

Dianus alpinussh	Alps.
Erinus alpinut	Alps and Pyrenees.
Gentiana acaulis . . .	Alps, Pyrenees, Carpathians.
Gentiana lutea	Alps, Pyrenees, Apennines, Carpathians, Balkans, Corsica, Sardinia, Asia Minor.
Geum montanum	Alps, Pyrenees, Apennines, Carpathians, Balkans, Corsica.
Globularia cordifolia . . .	Alps, Pyrenees, Apennines, Carpathians, Balkans.
Linaria alpina	Alps, Pyrenees, Balkans.
Narcissus poeticus . . .	Alps.
Paradisea liliastrum . . .	Alps, Pyrenees, Apennines.
Primula auricula	Alps, Pyrenees, Apennines, Carpathians, Balkans.
Primula glutinosa	Alps and Balkans.
Saponaria ocymoides . . .	Alps.
Sempervivum arachnoideum . .	Alps, Pyrenees, Apennines, Carpathians.
Trifolium alpinum . . .	Alps, Pyrenees, north Apennines.

The edelweiss, *Leontopodium alpinum*, is said by Hegi to occur in various mountains from the Alps to Japan, but according to Handel-Mazzetti (332) this species is confined to the Alps, Pyrenees and Carpathians.

The differential distribution of the species of a single genus is well shown in *Soldanella*. According to Vierhapper (332), there are seven species with the following ranges:

S. alpina	Alps, Pyrenees, Apennines, Cevennes and Dalmatia.
S. carpatica	Northern Carpathians.
S. villosa	Western Pyrenees.
S. montana	North-eastern Alps, eastern Carpathians and the Balkans.
S. hungarica	Eastern Alps, Carpathians and Balkans.
Two species in northern Greece.	

One of the most interesting features of the European mountain flora is the occurrence in it of certain isolated genera affording almost the only known temperate examples of families now confined to the tropical regions of the world. By far the most remarkable instance of this is the occurrence in some of the more southerly mountains of Europe of no fewer than three endemic genera of Gesneriaceae, a family which is otherwise one of the most characteristically tropical. One of these plants, generally called *Ramondia pyrenaica*, is familiar to European gardeners, but there are several others also. Hayek (332) has given a good account of them and shows that there are six species in all belonging to three genera. *Ramonda myconi* (*Ramondia pyrenaica*) is found only in the Pyrenees; the remaining five all have varying but very restricted distributions in the mountainous parts of the Balkan Peninsula between the longitudes 20°–26° E. and the latitudes 39°–44° N. (706, 710). These five are *Ramonda nathaliae, R. serbica, Haberlea rhodopensis, H. ferdinandii-coburgii* and *Jankaea hellrichii*.

From the more lowland parts of the European subregion come many species familiar either as British plants or as plants of economic or horticultural value, among them *Bellis perennis, Buphthalmum speciosum, Crataegus oxyacantha, Digitalis purpurea, Fagus sylvatica, Laburnum anagyroides* (*vulgare*), *Malus pumila*

13

(*Pyrus malus*), *Malva moschata, Narcissus pseudo-narcissus, Primula vulgaris, Prunus cerasus. Pyrus communis, Rosa centifolia* and *Trollius europaeus.* The grape vine, *Vitis vinifera*, may also have had its origin here, perhaps in the Caucasus.

There is not unnaturally an enormous literature dealing with the floras of the various European countries and their geographical affinities, and as an example of it there may be mentioned the very detailed geographical analysis of the German flora by Wangerin (759) which though primarily concerned with the plants of one country contains much of interest about the plants of western Eurasia in general.

The plant life of the Asiatic subregion is a good deal less familiar, but a number of species either grown in gardens or of some other interest are natives of Siberia or of the neighbouring areas, among them being *Allium sibiricum, Bergenia cordifolia, Bergenia crassifolia, Delphinium grandiflorum, Iris sibirica, Lychnis fulgens, Pyrus baccata* and *Stachys lanata.*

Of the mountain floras of northern east Asia that of the Altai may be mentioned. The alpine flora here consists of nearly 300 species (435) in which the arctic-alpine element accounts for about 60 per cent and the alpine element about 40 per cent. About half the species are Asiatic only; about a third are circumpolar in distribution; 10 per cent are Eurasian; another 10 per cent are endemic; and a handful are Asiatic–American.

Sino–Japanese Region

For two reasons in particular this region is one of the most interesting from the point of view of its species. The first is that its flora is extremely rich and almost certainly the richest of the whole northern temperate zone. It is also especially rich in trees (382) and it has, indeed, been said that the number of tree species here outnumbers that of the whole of the rest of the northern temperate zone. Its endemism is also high, but this is only to be expected from the size of the area. It is in relation to what we believe to have been the history of the region that its richness in species and particularly in trees is so significant.

As will be shown in Chapter 15, the great polar ice-cap of the Pleistocene was not, as at first sight might be expected, symmetrical about the present North Pole but had its centre in what is now the southern part of Greenland. As a result the ice reached particularly low latitudes in eastern North America and in Europe, but covered only a small part of Asia and, in fact, may have made itself felt there little more than does the smaller ice-cap of to-day. It will also be seen that there is good reason for believing that prior to the Pleistocene a single great flora, characterised by the prevalence of woody types, was found throughout the northern temperate regions or at least at the lower latitudes. In view of these facts it is therefore justifiable to suggest that the flora of eastern Asia was comparatively little affected by the Pleistocene Ice Ages, and hence that the present Sino–Japanese flora is in fact a relatively little-changed descendant of it, giving a picture of the kind of vegetation which, before the glaciation, encircled the whole northern hemisphere. Its insularity makes Japan of special interest in this connection, and Hara (337) has given a most useful and detailed account of the vegetation and its most characteristic species.

The second reason for the interest of the flora of this region lies in the fact that of recent decades it has contributed an enormous number of plants to European gardens. Indeed, the story of the exploration of the remoter parts of the Himalayas, Burma and China by collectors in search of seeds and plants of aesthetic value is one of the romances of twentieth-century botany and geography. It is the story especially of the hitherto little-known mountainous country in the region of the great river gorges near the junction of Burma, China, India and Tibet, and from it the names of Henry, Farrer, Forrest, Kingdon-Ward and many others will always be inseparable. The result of their labours and travels has been the discovery not only of many most valuable garden plants but also of much other botanical and geographical information culminating in the recognition of this part of the world as one of its most remarkable natural features.

The Sino–Japanese region too has contributed greatly to the list of important economic plants, or at least we may say that many such plants had their origin as crops in this region. It is necessary to adopt this somewhat cautious expression, because where a considerable number of cultivated plants are found to have originated there is a rather natural tendency to assume that the local native flora has proved of special value to man as compared with that of other regions. This, it need hardly be said, is an assumption which may not always be justified, and the number of cultivated plants may be a measure of the length of human history rather than any inherent virtue in the flora as a whole.

It is worth discussing this point at some length, because it has often been observed that the important economic plants of the world come especially from certain parts of it and, as often suggested on this basis, especially by the Russian school of botanists led by Vavilov (748), that this circumstance has had an important controlling effect on the distribution and growth of human races. Interesting as this view is, it seems to confuse cause and effect. The early civilisations of the world must have originated to a considerable extent independently of one another, if only because of the virtual absence of long-distance communication, and as each passed from a nomadic or pastoral stage to an agricultural level each must have derived its economic plants from local wild plants. In other words, the early peoples must of necessity have made use for the purposes of agriculture of the plants which were immediately available to them. The longer the history of the human population of any region the more complete would be the exploitation of its native plant life in this way, and it is natural to-day, therefore, to find that the areas from which economic plants particularly derive are those with the longest history of human settlement. It is true that certain types of vegetation and therefore certain regions provide a greater selection of potentially valuable plants, but any suggestion that the cultivation of these plants was the cause rather than the effect of human settlement bristles with difficulties.

It is noteworthy too that in different parts of the world there are different but corresponding economic plants. Almost all aspects of economic botany will illustrate this, but it is perhaps outstanding in the case of the three plants, tea, coffee and cocoa, from which important beverages are prepared. Tea is a native of warm Asia, coffee of Africa, and cocoa of South America. Clearly the peoples of each of these continents have, as occasion demanded, developed their own particular beverage from the most suitable available native plant. They have made use of such plants as were available in the circumstances of their situation.

Moreover, once a plant is in cultivation it, so to speak, loses its nationality and can within certain obvious limits be grown as and where required, and there is no necessity for population to remain closely associated with its point of origin. For example, the New World has provided man with several economic plants of first importance, but the fact that these are natives of America has not made it necessary for human population to concentrate there in order to enjoy them.

But to return to the Sino–Japanese flora, there are within the region many types of specific distribution, and some species like *Clematis montana*, *Diervilla* (*Weigela*) *florida*, *Iris ensata*, *Panax schinseng*, *Rosa rugosa*, *Sium sisarum* and *Stachys sieboldii* are widespread, or at least their original homes cannot now be more accurately determined.

Many others occur particularly or exclusively in China and Japan, among them being *Anemone japonica, Aucuba japonica, Callistephus chinensis, Camellia japonica, Caryopteris incana, Hosta plantaginea, Hydrangea macrophylla, Lilium tigrinum, Nandina domestica, Parthenocissus tricuspidata (Ampelopsis veitchii), Paulownia tomentosa, Pyrus pulcherrima, Rose wichuraiana* and *Saxifraga sarmentosa.* The prototypes, too, of cultivated Chrysanthemums are also supposed by most authorities to belong here.

Of plants native to China there may be mentioned *Actinidia chinensis, Aralia chinensis, Aspidistra elatior, Diospyros kaki, Ficus pumila, Forsythia suspensa, Jasminum nudiflorum, Kerria japonica, Kolkwitzia amabilis, Livistona chinensis, Lonicera nitida, Morus alba, Osmanthus delavayi, Primula malacoides, P. obconica, P. sinensis, Rosa banksiae, R. omeiensis, Roscoea cautleoides, Trachycarpus fortunei* and *Wisteria sinensis.*

Among natives of Japan are *Astilbe japonica, Chionographis japonica, Dicentra spectabilis, Fatsia japonica, Hamamelis japonica, Lilium auratum, Lilium longiflorum, Magnolia kobus, Primula japonica, Rosa multiflora, Schizophragma hydrangeoides* and *Stephanandra tanakae.*

The debt which the horticulturist owes to the plants of the Himalayas is well shown by *Cotoneaster frigida, Erigeron multiradiatus, Gentiana farreri, Gentiana sino-ornata, Incarvillea delavayi, Magnolia campbellii, Meconopsis betonicifolia (baileyi), Pleione hookeriana* and *Primula bulleyana,* all of which are native to that zone. Here, too, is *Saussurea tridactyla,* which is said to reach an altitude of 19,000 ft.

Lastly, *Glycine max (soya)* and *Caragana arborescens* come from the Manchurian part of the region, and *Fagus sieboldii* and *Zelkova serrata* from Korea and Japan.

Western and Central Asiatic Region

Botanically the western part of this region, namely north Persia and the interior of Asia Minor, is much the richest, and from it are derived many well-known and valuable plants, among them being *Fritillaria imperialis, Hyssopus officinalis, Jasminum officinale Molucella laevis, Nepeta musvinii, Papaver orientale, Philadelphus coronarius, Platanus orientalis, Prunus communis, Spinacia oleracea* and *Tulipa gesneriana.* It seems fairly certain too that barley (*Hordeum vulgare*) and at least some kinds of wheat (*Triticum* spp.) originated here.

From the great desert and semi-desert areas which form the eastern part of the region come such familiar or characteristic plants as *Astragalus tragacantha, Iris halophila, Limonium (Statice) suworowii, Lonicera persica, Polygonum baldschuanicum* and *Rheum rhaponticum.*

Where, as is often the case, the deserts are saline, halophytes like *Haloxylon ammodendron* and *Salsola arbuscula* are conspicuous.

The Tibetan plateau proper forms a rather specialised area chiefly on account of its great elevation (425). Here *Poa altaica* has been recorded from a height of 19,000 ft., and among other noteworthy species are *Caragana versicolor, Kobresia tibetica, Myricaria prostrata* and *Primula florindae.*

Mediterranean Region

Perhaps the most outstanding feature of plant distribution in this region is the way in which many of the species (just as do many of the genera) extend out of the region proper far up the western coasts of Europe, often reaching even to the British Isles. Many of these have also been recorded from Macaronesia, but their status there is not always free from doubt. Apart from this, however, the flora is well defined, except perhaps in Asia Minor, and, owing to the marked geography of the region, can be divided up into a number of parts.

It is a very rich flora with considerable endemism and, taking into account that the Mediterranean has been the cradle of many human civilisations, it is not surprising to find that the native plants of it have contributed largely to both horticulture and agriculture. The type of vegetation prevailing over much of the region, is the very characteristic "maquis" or thicket, and many of its constituent species, though not of great value, are nevertheless familiar.

The gardeners' debt to the region is well shown by the following, all of which are derived thence: *Acanthus mollis, Anemone coronaria, Aubrietia deltoidea, Cercis siliquastrum, Chrysanthemum coronarium, Cyclamen persicum, Hermodactylus tuberosus, Hyacinthus orientalis, Iris stylosa, Iris susiana, Lavandula spica, Lilium candidum, Lilium chalcedonicum, Malope trifida, Narcissus jonquilla, Nerium oleander, Nigella damascena, Paeonia officinalis, Periploca graeca, Prunus laurocerasus, Pyracantha coccinea, Quercus ilex, Reseda odorata, Rhododendron ponticum, Senecio cineraria* and *Viburnum tinus*.

Economic plants include *Allium porrum, Capparis spinosa, Cynara scolymus, Ficus carica, Laurus nobilis, Mandragora officinarum, Olea europaea, Petroselinum crispum, Quercus suber* and *Scolymus hispanicus*.

In addition to the endemics of the continental parts of the region almost every island has its own peculiar species; Corsica and Sardinia, for instance, are said to have about fifty each. On both continent and islands the endemics are often very restricted littoral species, as is well seen in the genus *Narcissus* (241).

Among the constituent parts of the region the Atlas Mountains are of special interest. Their flora, which includes some garden plants, e.g. *Cytisus battandieri*, is still by far the least completely known and has many very interesting features. It has been suggested, for instance (479), that it represents to a considerable extent a remnant of the old north temperate flora of the Tertiary epoch which has found there a refuge where it has survived the effects of the Pleistocene glaciation, in much the same way as a vastly greater part of the old flora survived in the mountainous parts of the Sino–Japanese region.

Macaronesian Region

In an insular region of very small total land area such as this the question of the proportion of species endemism is particularly illuminating, but unfortunately the figures are not easy to obtain because the islands have so long felt the influence of man that it is often almost impossible to separate the alien from the native plants.

In the Azores Guppy (327) estimates that the forty or so endemic species represent a proportion of some 20 per cent of the native species. The flora is essentially the remnant of a forest flora and its general affinities are with western Europe. Among the endemic species are *Campanula vidalii, Daboecia azorica, Erica azorica* and *Vaccinium cylindraceum*.

Madeira has about 100 endemics and perhaps the proportion is roughly the same as in the Azores. The flora again is a forest flora and closely related to the Mediterranean flora. Cockerell (143) has pointed out that the endemic species are chiefly of two kinds, either isolated, or closely related to European forms. Among the former are *Clethra arborea*, *Pittosporum coriaceum* and *Sideroxylon marmulano*, and among the latter *Sambucus maderensis* and *Sorbus maderensis*.

The Canary flora, again, is a forest flora and chiefly related to that of North Africa. Its endemics have been estimated at about 400, and this is certainly a higher proportion than either of the above. A number of these species are fairly familiar either in gardens or as specially characteristic of the vegetation, including *Canarina canariensis*, *Ceropegia fusca*, *Cytisus canariensis*, *Dracaena draco*, *Euphorbia canariensis*, *Kleinia neriifolia*, *Phoebe barbusana*, *Semele androgyna*, *Sempervivum spathulatum*, *Senecio cruentus*, *Tamus edulis* and *Viburnum rugosum*.

One of the noteworthy features of the flora is the great development of succulent members of the Crassulaceae, and especially the genus *Sempervivum*. These species afford a most interesting study in segregation and endemism, and an excellent account has been given by Praeger (571).

The flora of the Cape Verdes has been much less studied than that of Madeira or the Canaries, and it is difficult to say what proportion the endemic species represent, but according to Chevalier (132) it consists of not more than 300 species of which ninety-one are endemic, most of them being related to Mediterranean species. Otherwise the affinities of the flora are with adjacent Africa, as is instanced by *Lavandula rotundifolia* and *Campanula jacobaea*.

Among species linking the islands together or with the European–African land mass may be mentioned *Laurus canariensis*, *Myrica faya* and *Persea indica*, which occur on the Azores, Madeira and the Canaries; *Cistus monspeliensis* on the Canaries and in the Mediterranean; *Centranthus calcitrapa* and *Oreodaphne foetens* on Madeira and the Canaries; *Ruscus hypophyllus*, which ranges from Madeira to the Caucasus; *Periploca laevigata*, from the Canaries to Cyrenaica and Somaliland, and *Erica arborea* (see p. 169).

Atlantic North American Region (583, 584)

The proportion of endemic species is naturally high in so large an area as is covered by this region, but the main features of the flora are that its northern part has a strong general resemblance to the flora of temperate Eurasia, and that its southern part has a corresponding likeness to the flora of China and Japan, and one of the reasons for recognising two subregions here is the wish to emphasise these relationships. In both cases many species of the Old World are represented in the New by others very similar, and many of these afford excellent examples of species-pairs, a subject which will be discussed in the next chapter.

The Eastern North American region as a whole has not contributed many plants of economic value to the common store, most of them being drug plants, such as *Hamamelis virginiana*, *Hydrastis canadensis*, *Lobelia inflata*, *Podophyllum peltatum*, *Polygala senega* and *Ulmus fulva*, but the sugar maples (*Acer saccharum*, etc.) and the hickories and pecans (*Carya* spp.) must not be forgotten.

As might be expected from the similarity of latitudes the region has provided Europe with a number of important garden plants, among them being *Acer negundo*, many Michaelmas daisies (*Aster* spp.), *Catalpa bignonioides*, *Cornus florida*, *Gaura lindheimeri*, *Juglans nigra*, *Kalmia latifolia*, *Liatris pycnostachya*, *Lilium philadelphicum*, *Lobelia cardinalis*, *Magnolia grandiflora*, *Monarda fistulosa*, *Phlox subulata*, *Rhus typhina*, *Robinia pseudo-acacia* and *Tradescantia virginiana*. The prairies in particular, have provided a number of Composites, including *Gaillardia aristata*, *Helenium autumnale* and *Rudbeckia hirta*. Among other particularly interesting or characteristic plants are *Castilleja coccinea, Chiogenes hispidula, Gaultheria procumbens, Gymnocladus canadensis, Maclura pomifera (aurantiaca), Menispermum canadense, Nyssa aquatica, Platanus occidentalis, Pontederia cordata, Prunus serotina, Rhododendron maximum, Rhus toxicodendron* (476), *Rhus vernix, Sabal palmetto, Saururus cernuus* and *Vitis labrusca.*

The area around the Gulf of St. Lawrence has been the scene of some particularly interesting studies in plant distribution. Fernald (236–239) showed that there is in this area a considerable group of plants, many of which are endemic, either identical with or very closely related to plants found elsewhere only in the western North American mountains, or more rarely in parts of continental Asia. Moreover he showed that these plants have, in north-eastern America, a very local and restricted distribution and are in fact found only in areas (such as the Gaspé Peninsula, western Newfoundland, the Magdalen Islands and parts of north-east Labrador) which may have been unglaciated during the Pleistocene. That is to say he suggested that these plants are confined to former "nunataks". His explanation of the many curious facts that he described is that the species concerned lived throughout the Pleistocene in the Arctic, and that during this time they migrated to where they are now found. There they have since persisted, and have not, as might otherwise seem possible, been derived by migration eastwards from western North America. Wynne-Edwards (804), on the other hand, believes the nunatak theory to be untenable and that the localisation of many arctic-alpine species is due to the corresponding localisation of certain soil conditions, notably lime and magnesia–lime–soda combinations. Unlocalised species, he claims, are found on highly silicious and certain more acid rocks which, even if they are nunataks, do not bear local "relicts".

Marie Victorin (488) also investigated the distribution of plants in this part of the world and confirmed many of Fernald's observations, but also emphasised the great interest of the area from the point of view of plant evolution and speciation. He referred not only to the restricted endemic forms already mentioned but also to the more familiar features of such genera as *Senecio* and *Crataegus,* which are here represented by such an array of minor species or forms as almost to defy classification. With regard to the latter especially he expressed the interesting opinion that many of these forms have arisen as a result of deforestation and human settlement. They are, therefore, to be regarded as very young species, and it follows, moreover, that in certain circumstances forms of this kind may be produced in two or three hundred years, which is, of course, the period of European settlement in North America. He also drew attention to the fact that many of the local endemics are found only in estuarine conditions, and that sometimes the local segregation of forms in these conditions is most marked, as, for instance, in *Bidens hyperborea,* and he added something to Fernald's conceptions by recognising certain endemic species as having persisted during glaciation on nunataks, but as having migrated slightly from those areas since. His general conclusions were, first, that the floras of western and eastern North America were long separated by an arm of the sea; second, that eastern North America has become gradually isolated from Europe by geographical changes; and third, that the flora of north-eastern North America has evolved chiefly in response to two more recent factors, namely glaciation and the widespread occurrence of estuarine conditions, both of which have amounted to physiological isolation.

A long and critical account of the "nunatak theory", and of opposing opinions about it, has been given by Raup (582), and a very readable more recent account of the eastern North American flora, with special reference to the Gaspé area, by Dansereau (171).

Pacific North American Region

Like the last this region has not contributed much in economic plants, but garden species originating here are very numerous and include *Arbutus menziesii, Ceanothus thyrsiflorus, Clarkia elegans, Collomia grandiflora, Cornus nuttallii, Eschscholzia californica, Fremontia californica, Garrya elliptica, Gaultheria shallon, Godetia* spp., *Lupinus arboreus, L. polyphyllus, Mahonia aquifolium, Mimulus moschatus, Nemophila menziesii, Phacelia* spp., *Ribes aureum, R. sanguineum, R. speciosum* and *Tolmiea menziesii.*

By far the best-marked constituent flora of the region, and in many ways the most interesting, is that of California, which is a good example of a "Mediterranean" flora, that is to say one showing the same peculiar type of vegetation (evergreen thicket or scrub) as is seen in that of the Mediterranean region itself. The Californian flora, like all "Mediterranean" floras, has a high proportion of endemism, variously estimated at between 30 and 50 per cent (405, 406, 823, 828), and considerable richness, and a good account of it and its affinities has been given by Abrams (2).

Among characteristic species of this part of western North America may be mentioned *Artemisia tridentata, Clistoyucca arborescens, Erythronium grandiflorum, Fouquieria splendens, Lewisia rediviva, Penstemon heterophyllus, Quercus chrysolepis, Rhododendron californicum* and *Washingtonia filifera* (Plate 25).

Well-known species from the more northerly part of the region include *Aquilegia formosa, Lupinus nootkatensis* and *Rosa nutkana.*

North African–Indian Desert Region

As is to be expected from the nature of the terrain, the flora of this great region is comparatively poor and specialised, although there are no particularly characteristic larger plant groups such as are so conspicuous in the South African and many other arid regions. There is one very important economic plant *Phoenix dactylifera* (the date palm) and a few minor ones, including *Balsamodendron myrrha, Boswellia carteri* and various species of *Acacia*, but rather naturally no garden plants.

A good many of the species are found throughout the region, as, for instance, *Calotropis procera, Cistanche lutea, Daemia extensa, Haloxylon salicornicum, Lawsonia inermis, Leptadenia pyrotechnica, Neurada procumbens* and *Zilla spinosa.* Others range throughout North Africa and Arabia, among them *Anabasis aretioides, Anastatica hierocuntica* and *Calligonum comosum*, or from Egypt over Arabia, as *Halopeplis perfoliata, Mesembryanthemum (Opophytum) forskahlei* and *Reseda muricata*, or from Africa to Persia, as *Sclerocephalus arabicus* and *Herniaria hemistemon*, or, as *Rhazya stricta*, from Arabia to India. Narrower species are mostly restricted to the Sahara, or to Mesopotamia and Arabia, or to the eastern side of the Persian Gulf. Examples of the first are *Asteriscus pygmaeus, Farsetia aegyptiaca, Limonium guyonianum, Peganum harmala* and *Retama rhaetam*; of the second *Balsamodendron opobalsamum* and *Catha edulis*; and of the third, *Quercus infectoria.*

Sudanese Park Steppe Region

The flora of this region is not very rich because the vegetation is mainly of a kind in which the species are rarely particularly copious. It is a land of open spaces, and, like its East African counterpart, is better known for its big-game fauna which was once extremely abundant. It is, however, of special interest botanically in relation to the problems of "désertification" referred to on p. 160 because the causes tending towards this process can here be studied better than almost anywhere else.

In one sense it may be considered as a westerly extension of the East African steppes with which it encircles the forests of the Congo and Niger, and its strongest floristic affinities are in this direction.

Species of *Acacia*, grasses and palms are among the most conspicuous of its plants, and instances of these are included in the following list of species more or less characteristic of the region as a whole, namely *Acacia senegal*, *Andropogon gayanus*, *Borassus aethiopicum*, *Cassia senna*, *Cola acuminata*, *Entada sudanica*, *Hyphaene thebaica*, *Kigelia aethiopica*, *Loranthus acaciae*, *Phoenix reclinata* and *Themeda triandra*.

North-east African Highland and Steppe Region

Abyssinia, which comprises by far the larger part of this region, has a rich and interesting flora and one that is of special theoretical importance in regard to the development of the tropical African montane flora in general. It is still not very completely known, but it can be said that in addition to a considerable element of tropical African affinity it also contains a number of types more characteristic of the northern temperate regions.

In *Coffea arabica* it has provided at least one economic plant of first importance, but apart from this its species are not very familiar or important. Among those particularly characteristic of the area may be mentioned *Acacia abyssinica*, *Aloe abyssinica*, *Eragrostis tef* and *Euphorbia abyssinica*.

The remainder of the region is, for the most part, of less interest and its flora is a depauperate one chiefly of African affinity, containing no plants of special note.

Socotra, however, has a very interesting flora with, considering its slight degree of isolation, a marked amount of endemism (248). The first comprehensive account of it is that of Balfour (43), who visited the island in the eighteen-eighties, but there is an interesting recent account of the plant-life by Popov (567). To-day the flora is known to possess about 200 endemic species, which is somewhat less than half the total, including the arborescent *Dendrosicyos socotrana*, *Dorstenia gigas* and *Kleinia scottii;* the Monocotyledonous tree *Dracaena cinnabari*; and *Exacum affine*.

West African Rain-forest Region

This region, which corresponds, as the only equatorial forest zone in Africa, to the whole of the Amazon region or of Monsoon Asia, has a very rich flora which is still far from completely known, but, as might be expected, it has not yet at any rate provided many useful plants, as far as world commerce is concerned. On the other hand, quite a number of indigenous species have been exploited by the native peoples and, in addition, the flora contains a number of valuable timber trees. Many interesting figures relating to the larger eastern part of the region have been given by Robyns (599), and there is a sketch of some of the plant life by Boughey (82).

Among the economic plants two, *Coffea liberica* and *Elaeis guineensis*, are of outstanding importance, and others with a more local value include *Aframomum melegueta*, *Raphia vinifera*, and the native rubber plants, *Funtumia elastica* and *Landolphia owariensis*. Among timber trees, *Khaya senegalensis*, *Piptadenia africana* and *Staudtia gabonensis* may be mentioned.

Other notable species of the region are *Baikiaea insignis*, *Blighia sapida* (now much planted in the West Indies), *Camoensia maxima*, *Clerodendron splendens*, *Erythrina excelsa*, *Lophira alata*, *Marantochloa cuspidata*, *Monodora myristica*, *Pleiocarpa mutica*, *Spathodea campanulata*, *Stipularia africana*, *Strophanthus hispidus*, *S. sarmentosus* and *Uncaria africana*.

The islands of the Gulf of Guinea have a considerable proportion of endemic species (229). They are mostly mountainous and the floras show some affinity with the other tropical African mountains, but they also possess many species such as *Abutilon grandiflorum*, *Costus giganteus* and *Xylopia aethiopica* which link them up with the continent in general.

East African Steppe Region

The typical vegetation of this great region is savanna, but in the highlands and in the south-eastern part forests are well developed and altogether there is considerable heterogeneity, and the area can be and has been divided up floristically in great detail. Largely because of this the flora is both richer and more varied than that of the Sudanese region, but despite this, few of the native plants are familiar, and there are practically no economic plants of importance except a few timber trees such as *Berlinia baumii*, *Burkea africana* and *Pterocarpus erinaceus*.

The flora of the eastern highlands is discussed at some length below and apart from this the flora of the region as a whole tends to divide into western and eastern parts, the former comprising Angola and Rhodesia and the latter Portuguese and former British East Africa. Among characteristic species of the former are *Brachystegia* spp., *Clematis welwitschii* and *Ziziphus mucronata*, while those of the latter include *Arundinaria alpina*, *Hagenia abyssinica*, *Hypericum lanceolatum*, *Musa holstii* and *Olea chrysophylla*.

Other species closely associated with, if not confined to, this region are *Clerodendrum macrosiphon*, *Euphorbia tirucalli*, *Hibiscus schizophyllus*, *Mussaenda erythrophylla* and *Pentas lanceolata*. A useful account, with a diagrammatic plan, of the vegetation of the southern part of this region has been given by Exell (231).

The Flora of the Tropical African Mountains

It was seen in an earlier chapter that high mountains are by no means confined to the temperate regions of the world and that there are in fact elevations so great that their summits bear perpetual ice and snow in all continents and at all latitudes. The equatorial mountains, however, are, for the most part, portions of long ranges or systems whose extremities run far into the temperate regions, so that there is little geographical isolation associated with them. This is so, for instance, in the case of the tropical Andes in the New World and in the case of the Malaysian mountains which connect up with the essentially temperate Himalayan mass. Only Africa is a marked exception. Here the high mountains of the tropics, instead of being parts of a continuous zone, are isolated units, so separated from one another and rising so abruptly out of the lowlands that they have gained for themselves the geographical term of "Inselberge". Each is, as it were, an island of elevation separated not only from its fellows but also, and more so, from any considerable mountain system of the temperate regions.

It is, no doubt, this circumstance that makes the flora of the higher levels of the African equatorial mountains one of the most remarkable and specialised in the whole world. Like other high mountains they have their "alpine flora", but this is very different from anything which corresponds to it elsewhere. Moreover, the difference is one of type as well as degree.

Like other high mountain floras, too, that of tropical Africa consists to a very great extent of genera familiar in temperate floras and often providing arctic-alpine species, but in Africa not only are the species quite distinct but they have usually an entirely different kind of growth-form (Plates 13, 14), with the result that the flora in general of the upper levels of these African mountains can only be described as like nothing else on earth and by usual standards bizarre.

This is, no doubt, related to a point which has frequently been made that the montane floras of the tropics generally consist, not of modified species from the lower zones, but of forms obviously related to the floras of more temperate and arctic regions. It is here that the African alpine floras are peculiar, because although there are in them many temperate types, they are for the most part related closely to the plants of the zones below them. The temperate types proper seem, as Taylor (724) has pointed out, to owe their presence to a different combination of circumstances and do not in fact form so definite an altitudinal *stratum* as in other continents. *Sanicula europaea*, for instance, which is a good example of a temperate plant on African mountains, is common often on the lower slopes and is by no means confined to the highest levels.

The mountains having this peculiar form of high alpine flora are widely scattered and fall into three groups, namely, the Abyssinian peaks; the group of east central Africa (Kilimanjaro, Kenya, Elgon, Ruwenzori and their associates); and Cameroon Mountain and Fernando Po, and thus lie more than 10 degrees from the equator only in parts of Abyssinia. On the other tropical high mountains to the north of the equator, namely the isolated *massifs* of Ahaggar, Tibesti and Jebel Marra, which closely approach or exceed 10,000 ft., the mountain flora is composed of more characteristic north temperate elements; while south of the equator there are no other comparable elevations within the tropic. The general appearance of the vegetation has been described so often by travellers, especially in the case of Ruwenzori (391), that we can confine ourselves here to a consideration of some of the more prominent species and types comprising it.

By far the most outstanding and familiar of the African high montane plants are the so-called "tree Senecios" (339) and "tree Lobelias". Both belong to very widespread genera, but these mountain species have a most peculiar form. The Senecios have tall branched woody stems and may, according to some authorities, live for as much as 100 years, flowering and fruiting periodically. Their leaves, however, are not small and scattered as in ordinary trees but are large and more or less aggregated at the ends of the axes, and the branching is far less diffuse. These *Senecio* species are entirely confined to the tropical African mountains. The Lobelias are what may be called long-term monocarpic plants, that is to say they grow vegetatively for fifteen or twenty years, then flower and die. The word tree as applied to them is simply a rough indication of their unusual size, because in habit they are mostly tall and massive unbranched columnar woody herbs. In their most typical form they occur only on the African mountains, but a few similar species are known from Asia. They are also far less rigidly confined to the highest levels than the Senecios. It is interesting that the higher the situation of these plants the more restricted is their range, and Taylor has stated that of both genera no species among the highest-zoned is found on both sides of the Great Rift Valley. It is this very remarkable degree of segregation between the mountains that is perhaps the most interesting feature of their geography, and this cannot be better illustrated concisely than by quoting, in somewhat broadened form, a table given by Bruce (92).

Note, however, that since this table was prepared Wimmer's detailed revision of the genus *Lobelia* (794) has appeared. This includes 2 additional species, *L. suavibracteata* and *L. petiolata*, both from the eastern borders of the former Belgian Congo (whence *L. gibberoa* has also now been recorded) and reduces the total to 19 by combining certain of the rest.

Distribution of the Giant Lobelias on the mountains of Tropical Africa

	Fernando Po	Cameroons	Rhodesia	Virungas	Ruwenzori	Elgon	Aberdares	Kenya	Kilimanjaro	Ngongoro	Usambara	Uluguru	Utshungwe	Rungwe	Abyssinia	Totals
L. longiseplaa .	—	—	—	—	—	—	—	—	—	—	×	—	—	—	—	1
L. lukwangulensis .	—	—	—	—	—	—	—	—	—	—	—	×	—	—	—	1
L. milbraedii .	—	—	—	×	—	—	—	—	—	—	—	—	—	—	—	1
L. utshungwensis	—	—	—	—	—	—	—	—	—	—	—	—	×	—	—	1
L. rhynchopetalum .	—	—	—	—	—	—	—	—	—	—	—	—	—	—	×	1
L. aberdarica .	—	—	—	—	—	×	×	×	—	—	—	—	—	—	—	3
L. lanuriensis .	—	—	—	×	×	—	—	—	—	—	—	—	—	—	—	2
L. lanuriensis var. ericeti .	—	—	—	—	×	—	—	—	—	—	—	—	—	—	—	1
L. bambuseti .	—	—	—	—	—	—	×	×	—	—	—	—	—	—	—	2
L. usafuensis .	—	—	—	—	—	—	—	—	—	—	—	—	—	×	—	1
L. volkensii .	—	—	—	—	—	—	—	—	×	—	—	—	—	—	—	1
L. giberroa .	—	—	—	×	×	×	×	×	×	×	—	×	×	—	×	10
L. bequaertii .	—	—	—	—	×	—	—	—	—	—	—	—	—	—	—	1
L. burttii .	—	—	—	—	—	—	—	—	—	—	×	—	—	—	—	1
L. deckenii .	—	—	—	—	—	—	—	—	×	—	—	—	—	—	—	1
L. keniensis .	—	—	—	—	—	—	—	×	—	—	—	—	—	—	—	1
L. sattimae .	—	—	—	—	—	—	×	—	—	—	—	—	—	—	—	1
L. elgonensis .	—	—	—	—	—	×	—	—	—	—	—	—	—	—	—	1
L. telekii .	—	—	—	—	—	×	×	×	—	—	—	—	—	—	—	3
L. wollastonii .	—	—	—	×	×	—	—	—	—	—	—	—	—	—	—	2
L. stricklandae	—	—	×	—	—	—	—	—	—	—	—	—	—	—	—	1
L. columnaris .	×	×	—	—	—	—	—	—	—	—	—	—	—	—	—	2
L. conraui .	—	×	—	—	—	—	—	—	—	—	—	—	—	—	—	1

The giant Senecios are more restricted, in that they do not occur on the western mountain group. According to Cotton (153) and later records there are 18 species, all peculiar to one mountain or group, namely, 4 on Ruwenzori, 3 on Kenya, 2 on the Aberdares, 2 on the Virungas, 3 on Elgon, and 4 on Kilimanjaro and Meru.

The African high montane representatives of several other genera have also been revised, giving with some additional later records, the following results:—

Anagallis (257) has 15 species, mostly like *A. tenella* in appearance, and there are local species on most of the eastern mountains and in Abyssinia.

Swertia (258) of interest as a close relative of *Gentiana*, has 30 species; 8 of them in Abyssinia and most of the rest on the eastern mountain group.

Echinops (255) has 9 species, 2 in Abyssinia and 7 in the eastern mountains.

Sonchus (253) has about 30 tropical and South African species, of which several are on the eastern mountains and one on Cameroon Mountain.

Bartsia (256) has 11 species of which 3 are in Abyssinia, one in Abyssinia and the eastern mountains, 6 on the eastern mountains and one on Cameroon Mountain.

Carduus (254) has 22 species, mostly on the eastern mountains and showing a high degree of segregation.

Alchemilla and *Hypericum* are other genera which contribute characteristic forms to the general montane flora.

A particularly interesting and characteristic element in the African montane flora is afforded by the members of the tribe *Ericeae* of the Ericaceae, and these plants have also been monographed (17, 18). *Erica* itself has some 15 species in tropical Africa, including the more widely spread *E. arborea* (see p. 169), but most of them are from the south-east and few of them are really montane. In connection with their mention here it is interesting that Chevalier (130) concludes that the genus originated in tropical Africa and is a relic of the old xeromorphic Tertiary flora of that region. The genus *Blaeria* is actually discontinuous, because it occurs on the Cameroon Mountains and Fernando Po. It has in all about 20 tropical species in a special section (the others are at the Cape), and of these all but 2 are montane. Of the 2 species mentioned in West Africa, one, *B. tenuifolia*, is also on the Aberdares. *Philippia* has 40 species distributed widely in the tropics and in the Madagascar region. Of the tropical African species 4 are on the eastern mountains, one of them, *P. excelsa*, being on several peaks, and there are 2 species on the western mountains.

In recent years our knowledge of the floras of the high African mountains has been considerably amplified by the work of Hedberg, and especially by his monograph on *Afro-alpine Vascular Plants* (349). He points out (347, 349) that on all East African mountains of sufficient height three upper vegetational zones can be recognised, namely a montane forest zone, an ericaceous zone and, highest, an alpine zone. It is this highest zone only with which he deals, and because of this limitation and also of his restriction to the East African mountains only it is difficult to say exactly how far his work necessitates any revision of the figures quoted above for various genera, but it would seem probable that some of them, notably those of *Anagallis*, *Swertia* and *Sonchus*, are too high.

Hedberg's monograph shows that the flora of this alpine zone which begins, on the average, at a height of about 3,700 m. or a little more than 12,000 ft., contains 280 species in 115 genera, of which the Compositae and the Gramineae account for more than a quarter. The genera richest in species are *Senecio* 26, *Helichrysum* 17, *Alchemilla* 13 and *Lobelia* 11. Of the remaining species most belong to widespread temperate genera familiar in the northern flora such as *Agrostis*, *Bartsia*, *Carduus*, *Carex*, *Galium*, *Hypericum*, *Ranunculus*, *Satureja*, *Sedum*, and *Trifolium*, but there is a notable element of genera of strong southern African affinity, namely *Blaeria*, *Disa*, *Erica*, *Euryops*, *Haplocarpha*, *Hebenstreitia*, several Iridaceae, *Kniphofia*, *Osteospermum*, *Pelargonium*, *Philippia*, *Protea*, and *Stoebe*. One or two more widely tropical genera are also represented. There is only one endemic genus, *Nannoseris*, a monotypic Composite. The occurrence of a species of *Carpha* is a reminder that some of the temperate genera contributing to the flora are found in the south as well as in the north.

Because of its isolated position the Cameroon Mountain has attracted special attention and Chevalier (131) has made a floristic analysis of its vegetation, in which he recognises four important elements:

1. Mediterranean and European.
   > Exemplified by *Cerastium triviale*, *Koeleria cristata*, and varieties of *Radiola linoides*, *Galium aparine*, *Umbilicus pendulinus*, *Senecio palustris*, and *Sibthorpia europaea*.

2. Species common to Cameroons and Abyssinia.

3. South Africa.
   Including species of *Blaeria, Brucea, Gnidia* and *Helichrysum.*
4. Endemics,
   Exemplified by the three genera of Melastomataceae *Afzeliella, Eugonia* and *Myrianthemum.*

Some aspects of the western group of mountains have lately been discussed by Boughey (80) and by Keay (422).

Madagascar Region

In general the present flora of Madagascar and its neighbouring islands may be described as of African affinity with a strong Asiatic and Pacific element. This is well illustrated in Madagascar itself. The proportion of endemic species is high, perhaps 85 per cent or more, but many of them are related to African species and what has been called the African element in the flora is estimated to account for about one-quarter of the whole (554). There are also said to be points of resemblance between the flora of some of the more elevated parts of Madagascar and that of the East African mountains (389). At the same time it may be doubted whether the floristic relation with Africa is as strong as should be expected from the proximity of the two areas, and the presence in the island flora of so many non-African types raises problems of its history which are of great interest (296, 554).

Madagascar has not provided many economic or horticultural plants, but a few are familiar or characteristic, and one or two of them occasionally cultivated. Among these are *Angraecum sesquipedale, Aponogeton fenestralis, Colvillea racemosa, Cryptostegia grandiflora, Cyperus alternifolius, Dombeya wallichii, Euphorbia fulgens, Kalanchoe blossfeldiana, K. daigremontiana, K. uniflora, Raphia ruffia, Ravenala madagascariensis* and *Stephanotis floribunda.* The island is also said to have been the home of *Delonix (Poinciana) regia.*

In Mauritius and Réunion specific endemism appears to be about 50 per cent and Rivals has made some interesting comments on the flora of the latter (597). In the Seychelles it is about 40 per cent (712).

Region of Ascension and St. Helena

Ascension Island had apparently, when first discovered, no vegetation except on the summit of Green Mountain, and even to-day is said to have only some eight indigenous species, of which at least two, *Euphorbia origanoides* and *Hedyotis adscensionis,* are endemic. *Wahlenbergia linifolia* occurs also on St. Helena.

To-day St. Helena has but the vestiges of the rich vegetation which it formerly possessed, and it is therefore difficult to arrive at any satisfactory statistics about its plants. Early visitors describe the island as covered with dense forests right down to the water's edge, but these same visitors left behind them asses, pigs and goats, and the last-named in particular have gradually devastated the original vegetation until to-day almost nothing remains. Melliss (509) gives a good account of the flora as it was in the eighteen-seventies. He enumerates some 900 species of flowering plants as occurring on the island, but considers only about 30 of them to be really native, all the rest being under suspicion of accidental or deliberate introduction. Of these thirty all but two or three are endemic. Some were even at that time very rare if not actually extinct, and the position is worse to-day. Turrill (741) considers that the indigenous flora, at the time it was first studied by botanists, consisted of 39 species in 28 genera, of which 38 species (97 per cent) and five genera were endemic, and on all counts it seems safe to assume that the aboriginal flora of the island was not large in number of species but very remarkable in being almost entirely endemic.

South African Region

The continent of Africa is unique in that it lies almost symmetrically astride the equator. It is true that owing to the actual shape of the continent the northern part is much larger than the southern, but in latitudinal extent there is little difference between them and in both hemispheres the continent stretches into extra-tropical regions. The plant life of Africa as a whole thus comes to include three perfectly distinct floras—a warm temperate northern, a tropical central or equatorial, and a warm temperate southern. At the same time the first and last of these are of that peculiar type known as "Mediterranean", and are not only rich but to a considerable extent specialised floristically.

It might be expected therefore that the flora of tropical Africa would show and include appreciable elements from these floras, and that there would be conspicuous zones of mingling or transition. In fact this is much less than might be anticipated, for the reason that on the equator side of each of the "Mediterranean" floras the climate is such as to produce desert conditions. In the north this desert belt—the Sahara—is so complete that there is no transition zone between the Mediterranean flora and the tropical African flora at all, but in the south conditions are not so extreme. The deserts there are more scattered and less arid on the whole, and along the east coast the climate is so favourable as to support the development of forest.

As a result of these circumstances there is, in southern Africa, what is not found in the north, namely, a very important floristic region where the tropical African flora and the southern "Mediterranean" flora, that of the Cape, mingle (3, 66, 68, 395). This transition region is of considerable size, but its flora is not exceptionally rich and is of interest chiefly in the way it illustrates (perhaps as well as any other flora in the world) how two floras may, by mutual intermigration, weld themselves into a kind of hybrid whole.

The South African region is, as has been suggested, easily divisible into a number of parts, and as floristic and geographical distinction here go hand in hand, it is appropriate to say something about these. The main constituents and floras number five, namely—the high veldt of the Transvaal and the Orange Free State; the Kalahari desert, or semi-desert, of Bechuanaland; the desert, or semi-desert, of South West Africa; the desert of the Karroo on the south; and the south-eastern coastal area that contains Natal.

As is only to be expected, this region has not contributed much either to gardens or to economic botany, and the importance of its flora is more theoretical, and on this account it is enough to mention a few of the more conspicuous and characteristic plants. Of the five areas mentioned the first three show comparatively little difference in vegetation and may be considered together. Among the noteworthy plants here are *Acacia giraffae*, *Acanthosicyos horrida*, *Carissa arduina*, *Dioscorea elephantipes*, *Elephantorrhiza burchellii*, *Euphorbia tetragona*, *Nerine bowdenii*, *Pachypodium namaquanum*, *Rhigozum trichotomum*, *Sarcocaulon patersonii* and *Venidium fastuosum*.

The flora of the Karroo is much more specialised, and indeed is one of the most striking examples of a xeromorphic flora in the world, a conspicuous feature of it being the "stone plants" (490) belonging to *Lithops* (536) and other genera (Plate 11), so called from their resemblance to the pebbles of the deserts in which they grow. The Karroo plants, which include also many species of *Mesembryanthemum* and related genera, *Crassula falcata*, *Crassula lycopodioides*, *Senecio articulatus*, *Rochea coccinea*, many Stapeliads, and species of *Gasteria* and *Haworthia*, have become increasingly familiar in recent years because of the fashion for their indoor cultivation, and it is worth while reminding readers that the flora also includes quite other kinds of plants, such as *Acacia karroo*, *Chrysocoma tenuifolia*, *Elytropappus rhinocerotis*, *Euclea undulata* and *Euryops tenuissima*.

The south-eastern coastal area is much less arid than the others. Over much of it the vegetation is savanna or even forest, and it is here in particular that the transition between the tropical African and Cape floras is to be seen. Of its more familiar or characteristic species there may be mentioned *Albizzia fastigiata*, *Aloe candelabrum*, *Brachystegia spicaeformis*, *Buxus macowani*, *Calodendron capense*, *Ceropegia sandersonii*, *Ceropegia woodii*, *Erythrina caffra*, *Euphorbia cooperi*, *Hyphaene crinita*, *Strelitzia augusta* and *Tricholaena rosea* (*Rhynchelytrum repens*).

Cape Region

The area occupied by the Cape flora proper, which, as has already been said, is one of the most remarkable in the world, is very small, consisting, roughly speaking, of the coast zone from Clanwilliam on the west to the neighbourhood of Port Elizabeth on the east. At the same time it is probably, in proportion to its size, the richest of all floras. It is not altogether easy to arrive at reliable statistics for the region as a whole because it does not fit in with any political area, but some measure of its wealth may be gained from the observation that the Cape Peninsula itself, which is little bigger than the county of Rutland, and of which there is a full-length study (6), possesses in all 2,500 species, of which about one third are Monocotyledons, a rather high proportion. This floristic richness is associated with a characteristic of the vegetation which is often commented upon, namely the lack of dominance in the plant associations, a feature which is often claimed to indicate age and long undisturbed settlement in a flora.

The Cape flora has few plants of economic importance, partly perhaps because the region had, before its European colonisation, a sparse and primitive human population, and the only ones which need be mentioned are one or two timber trees, including *Ocotea bullata* and *Olea verrucosa*, which come from the eastern part of the region where true forest is locally developed. This lack of economic plants is, however, more than balanced by the great numbers of garden plants which the flora has provided, and the botanical exploration of this country in the early days was a horticultural occasion of first importance, as the first volumes of the *Botanical Magazine* amply testify, and as the following selection will show:

Agapanthus africanus, *Amaryllis bella-donna*, *Arctotis stoechadifolia*, *Asparagus plumosus*, *Dimorphotheca* spp., innumerable species of *Erica*, *Freesia refracta*, *Galtonia candicans*, *Gazania* spp., *Gerbera jamesoni*, *Gladiolus* spp., species of *Ixia* and *Kniphofia*, *Lobelia erinus*, *Nemesia* spp., *Pelargonium acerifolium*, *Phygelius capensis*, *Plumbago capensis*, etc.

It may also be noted that one of the commonest of all garden plants, Montbretia, whose proper name appears to be *Crocosmia crocosmiaeflora*, is an artificial hybrid between two wild South African plants. Besides all these there are many other native plants which although not generally cultivated are nevertheless more or less familiar or noteworthy, and among these may be mentioned:

Brabejum stellatifolium, *Disa grandiflora*, *Eriocephalus umbellatus*, *Euphorbia*

Plate 13. A giant Lobelia (*L. rhynchopetalum*) of the African mountains
(*Photo: the late Dr. H. Scott; courtesy R.G.S.*)

caput-medusae, Helichrysum vestitum, Leucadendron argenteum, Leucospermum conocarpum, Metalaisia muricata, Mimetes lysigera, Podalyria calyptrata, Priestleya villosa, Protea grandiflora, Protea mellifera, Rhus tomentosa, Satyrium carneum and *Watsonia rosea.*

The position and other features of the Cape flora make it something of a key unit in relation to problems concerning the geographical history of the Angiosperms and the problems of the southern flora, and a great deal of attention has been paid it from these points of view. It would be too great a digression to consider this in detail but the reader will find some of the leading lines of thought well expressed by Levyns (453, 454) and, at greater length, by Weimarck (770) who, in an extremely detailed geographical study of nearly 500 of its species, concludes that the flora contains, in addition to the more obvious South African constituents, tropical African, montane African, antarctic, Mediterranean and north temperate, and cosmopolitan elements. The literature has been admirably summarised by Adamson (3, 4, 5, 6) who points out in particular that of these elements, the tropical and northern African is by no means negligible.

Indian Region

Political changes have tended to obscure the leading features of the flora of this region, and in particular the inclusion, as parts of British India, of Burma and the Malay Peninsula, in Hooker's classic description of the plant life (376), gave an exaggerated impression of the floristic richness of the Indian region as defined on p. 31 above. It has also to be remembered that the more fertile parts of India have been so long and so densely inhabited by man that there is probably little of the original vegetation left. Nevertheless the Indian flora as a whole is an important and characteristic one. It contains many plants of value, among useful plants which appear to be native here being *Aegle marmelos, Artocarpus nobilis, Corchorus capsularis, Crotalaria juncea, Elettaria repens (cardamomum), Eleusine corocana, Gynocardia odorata, Indigofera tinctoria, Luffa aegyptiaca, Murraya koenigii, Nardostachys jatamansi, Pennisetum glaucum, Piper longum, Piper nigrum, Pterocarpus santolinus* and *Sesamum indicum.* A few of its species, among them *Cymbidium grandiflorum, Datura metel, Dendrobium nobile, Hibiscus abelmoschus, Jasminum grandiflorum, Vanda caerulea* and *Vitex negundo,* are sometimes grown in hothouses, and among other interesting or conspicuous plants are *Bombax malabaricum, Beaumontia grandiflora, Butea frondosa, Calotropis gigantea, Caryota urens, Corypha umbraculifera, Dorstenia indica, Feronia elephantum, Ficus bengalensis, F. elastica, Holmskioldia sanguinea, Humboldtia laurifolia, Ipomoea horsfalliae, Memecylon umbellatum, Ochlandra stridula, Oryza coarctata, Saracha indica, Shorea robusta* and many species of *Strobilanthes.*

Naturally there is a high degree of community between the floras of India proper and of Ceylon, and many species, as for instance three of the large Asiatic Lobelias, *L. leschenaultii, L. nicotianifolia* and *L. trichandra,* are found in both, as well as some of those species already mentioned. The flora of Ceylon (1) is more strongly Malaysian than Indian in affinity, and it has a high degree of endemism. Willis (784), who studied the flora in great detail in connection with his theory of Age and Area, estimated that there are over 800 endemics, and that these amount to about a third of the whole native flora. Most of the best-known plants of Ceylon, however, are found either in India or elsewhere also, but among the endemics *Diospyros ebenum* (the ebony), *Diospyros quaesita, Hortonia angustifolia* and *Schumacheria castaneifolia* may be noted.

14

The Laccadive and Maldive Islands, which are most appropriately mentioned at this point, are low coral islands, without endemic plants.

Continental South-east Asiatic Region

The difficulties of assessing this region and the paucity of larger endemic units has been stressed on p. 140 but the situation regarding species is probably very different and both the size of the area and the exuberance of much of its vegetation suggest that, could a reliable estimate be made, the proportion of endemic species would prove to be large and comparable with that in parts of Malaysia. Few of these species are, however, familiar.

Attention has been called to the fact that it is often very difficult now to say for certain where important crop plants had their original homes. This applies amongst others to rice, tea and the various *Citrus* fruits. To-day these are widely grown, but such evidence as there is suggests that most, and perhaps all of them, were natives of this region or at least of it and some of its bordering lands.

Among other species associated with this region, but some of which reach India or Malaysia, are *Amherstia nobilis, Anamirta cocculus, Anodendron paniculatum, Bauhinia purpurea, Begonia rex, Cassia nodosa, Cinnamomum camphora, Congea velutina, Dipterocarpus turbinatus, Excoecaria agallocha, Garcinia cochinchinensis, Gardenia jasminoides, Hedychium gardnerianum, Ixora coccinea, Jasminum rex, Lagerstroemia indica, Mantisia saltatoria, Melanorrhoea usitata, Michelia champaca, Musa coccinea, Odontadenia grandiflora, Quisqualis indica, Sansevieria zeylanica* and *Torenia fournieri.*

Of the isolated parts of the region the flora of Formosa, which is largely a combination of continental and Malaysian types, is about 40 per cent endemic, and its mountain flora has a notable affinity with that of the Sino–Himalayan mountains. The proportion of endemism in Hainan, which has a rich flora, is also high. The Andaman and Nicobar Islands, and the Riukiu Islands, each have a small proportion of endemics.

Malaysian Region

Probably nowhere else in the world, with the possible exception of parts of tropical America, does flowering plant vegetation attain such a richness and luxuriance as in Malaysia, where except for Timor and some of its neighbouring islands, conditions favour its fullest development in almost every way (see frontispiece).

Not only is the vegetation luxuriant, but the flora is very rich and contains many plants which have long been of value to man. Indeed, the "Spice Islands", as part of the archipelago was called in earlier days, have played no small part in the history of many nations (290). The nature of most of these economic plants is indicated by the name just quoted, but there are others as well, and as examples of the products of the region there may be mentioned the following, all of which are known or thought to have originated somewhere in Malaysia, *Arenga saccharifera, Artocarpus communis (incisa), Calamus draco, Canarium luzonicum, Colocasia esculenta, Curcuma zedoaria, Eugenia caryophyllata, Garcinia mangostana, Metroxylon rumphii, Musa textilis, Myristica fragrans* and *Zingiber officinale.* The two wild species of banana, *Musa balbisiana* and *M. acuminata*, from which many or all cultivated forms are held to be derived also belong here. Besides all these the flora includes innumerable other noteworthy plants, among them being *Acalypha sanderiana, Amorphophallus titanum, Antiaris toxicaria, Bulbophyllum grandiflorum, Cananga odorata, Clerodendrum fallax, C. paniculata, Coleus blumei, Croton lacciferus,*

Cyrtostachys renda, Dendrobium superbum, Dendrocalamus giganteus (Plate 22), *Dryobalanops aromatica, Hibiscus rosa-sinensis, Maniltoa gemmipara, Mucuna bennettii, Pterocarpus echinatus, Rafflesia arnoldi, Strychnos ignatii, Vanda tricolor, Zalacca edulis,* and probably *Codiaeum variegatum* and *Graptophyllum pictum.*

Specific endemism throughout Malaysia is undoubtedly very high (438), partly of course because of the insularity of the region. Merrill (514) states that in any large island or compact island group the primary vegetation, that is to say the vegetation which has never been cleared and which is thus not diluted by adventive plants, is likely to contain 75 per cent of endemic species, and an even higher figure has been claimed for the Philippines (510, 511) which have a very rich flora, containing incidentally more than 1,000 species of orchids. Phytogeographically New Guinea is probably the most peculiar and significant part of the region and when its immense flora is completely known it is likely to be found that it has a richer flora and a higher proportion of endemics than any other island. A recent analysis (305) has shown that the native species number at least 9,000 and that about 90 per cent of these are endemic. Here, again, the orchid flora is remarkable, containing more than 2,500 species, practically all of which are confined to the island. Accounts of the plant life have been given by Lauterbach (447) and Lam (440), and lately, for the eastern part of the island, by Womersley and McAdam (795).

As for the region as a whole its degree of specific endemism is certainly to be compared with the figures just quoted, and almost every kind of distribution over the various constituent areas is, in addition, to be seen. At one end of the scale are such species as *Gnetum macrostachyum* and *Nepenthes mirabilis*, which range from Asia to New Guinea; at the other are the innumerable species confined to single islands; and in between are examples of almost every kind. Much detail illustrative of these last will be found in the writings of Lam (438, 439, 440, 442, 443) and van Steenis (699, 700, 702, 703, 704, 705).

The genus *Stylidium* affords a particularly good instance of the occurrence of members of an Australian genus in Asia and Malaysia, and van Slooten (675) listed the plants concerned as follows:

S. kunthii	India.
S. tenellum	South-east Asia, Malay Peninsula and Sumatra, Fig. 2.
S. inconspicuum	Java.
S. javanicum	Java and Sumba.
S. uliginosum	Australia, South China and Ceylon.
S. alsinoides	Australia, New Guinea, Celebes and Philippines.
S. schizanthum	Australia and New Guinea.
S. pedunculatum	Australia and the Aru Islands.

Much attention has been paid to the montane plants of Malaysia. Nearly all the islands are mountainous and bear, at high elevations, a well-marked "Malaysian Mountain Flora" containing, among other kinds of species, representatives of such familiar northern temperate genera as *Ranunculus, Rubus* and *Viola*. Wallace (755) gave a vivid picture of the vegetation of the summits of some of the Javanese mountains, and others have made further studies since. The most exhaustive and recent work on the subject is that of van Steenis (700), and from it it would appear that there have been three tracks by which the temperate forms so conspicuous in this flora, which is estimated to contain 800 species, have migrated into the Archipelago. One is by way of the Malay Peninsula, Sumatra, Java and the Lesser Sundas to S. Celebes and Timor; another is by the line Formosa and the Philippines to Celebes; and the third from Australia by way of New Guinea to Celebes, Borneo and the Philippines. Van Steenis' map shows that the first two cover the Philippines and most of Celebes in common, and that all three almost or quite overlap in southern Celebes, and the floristic relations of this key area have been discussed by Lam (442, 443).

Within the Malaysian region must be included the Cocos-Keeling atolls and Christmas Island which lie south of Sumatra and Java. The former have only a small flora of widespread species, but the latter (which is about the same size as Jersey) is a high island and had, when first studied (22), a flora of 130 species of Malaysian relationship, which included sixteen endemic species.

Hawaiian Region

Geographically this is the most isolated of all the floristic regions, a fact which undoubtedly accounts largely for its most prominent botanical feature, the huge proportion of its flora which is endemic. Numerical estimates of this vary some-what, but it has been stated (688) that more than 90 per cent of the native Hawaiian plants are confined to the islands, and many of these are of marked and specialised types.

Several general accounts of the plant life (112, 473, 600) make mention of some of the more characteristic species such as *Acacia koa, Alyxia olivaeformis, Dianella odorata, Edwardsia grandiflora, Eugenia malaccensis, Freycinetia arnotti, Gunnera petaloides, Santalum pyrularium* and *Strongylodon lucidum*, but there are no par-ticular noteworthy economic or horticultural plants among the native species. In one of the earlier accounts, Wallace (756) draws attention to two of the many points of interest in the flora, namely the small proportion of Monocotyledons (less than one-fifth of the total and nearly all grasses or sedges) and the extraordinary develop-ment of shrubs and even trees in genera widely familiar as herbs, for instance, *Viola, Silene, Geranium*, and various Lobeliads and Composites. There is a well-marked montane flora which, like that of Malaysia, includes many temperate representatives (325).

To-day the flora contains so many introduced plants that it is becoming more and more difficult to sort out the original species. This influx of adventives has been going on for a long time and, as in some other islands of the Pacific, some species were doubtless introduced by the earliest inhabitants even before the islands were visited by Europeans. An interesting paper by Forbes (246) indicates that in the twenty-five years after 1886 more than sixty species came in, including even one of the sea-grasses, *Halophila ovalis*, and there have been many additions more recently.

Thus the affinity of the total flora to-day is more with the New World than the Old but this is by no means generally accepted as expressing its history and deriva-tion. In fact the problem of the origin of the Hawaiian flora is one of the most difficult in plant geography, and one which is not simplified by the circumstance that the islands are of comparatively recent volcanic formation. One view is that the flora is of American isthmian origin, that is to say that it is derived from Central America. Skottsberg, on the other hand, who has studied the flora for many years (659, 660, 662, 668), suggests that its most important relationship is with the south and that it is indeed a relic of a very old Pacific flora which has now almost entirely disappeared. In a later paper (670), he points out that while the largest floristic element is Malaysian and only a much smaller one without endemics is neotropical there is a considerable element of Australasian or even "Antarctic" affinity, and it is to this group that most of the more striking endemic forms belong. A third view is that the flora has had a "waif and stray" origin, having developed from a heterogeneous collection of plants which have reached the islands by all sorts of casual means. For this there seems little in the way of definite evidence, and some facts, such as the unusual poverty of the Hawaiian beach and strand flora, discussed at length by Guppy (325), are against it.

Nevertheless the view that the Hawaiian flora has been developed from plants which reached there by various methods of long-distance dispersal from regions far away receives much support from Zimmerman (807), and Fosberg, contributing to that work, sets out the relevant botanical facts very clearly. He estimates that the native flora consists of 216 genera and 1,729 species and varieties, of which latter nearly 95 per cent are endemic. From a careful study of the flora he concludes that it may well have been developed from as few as 272 original immigrants, and that of these 40 per cent came from the Indo–Pacific region; 18 per cent from America: 16 per cent from the south; and $2\frac{1}{2}$ per cent from the north, the rest being types so widespread as to give no indication. It should be noted that if the age of the Hawaiian Islands is as suggested on p. 144, this figure of 272 would mean that the flora could have been derived by, on the average, the favourable dispersal to the islands of one species every 20,000 years or so.

Region of New Caledonia

The main constituent part of this region, New Caledonia itself, an island not much larger than Yorkshire, in certain respects exceeds even the Hawaiian Islands and New Guinea in the peculiarity of its flora (322), which has good claim to be considered the most remarkable in the world. It is very rich, with probably more than 2,600 native species, and of these well over 80 per cent seem to be endemic, including some important whole groups. The island, which is composed partly of igneous rocks, including much serpentine (see p. 252), and partly of Permian and younger sedimentary rocks (147, 404) is even now far from perfectly known, and still yields surprises.

The proportion of more xerophilous woody plants in the flora is very high and the number of herbaceous native plants very small and, because of this and of the prevalence of what are regarded as ancient types among the endemics, Guillaumin believes (617) that the island has been an isolated land surface since the middle of the Tertiary. Another remarkable and related feature is that certain families (319), notably Rubiaceae, Myrtaceae, Orchidaceae and Araliaceae are particularly conspicuous while three others, usually among the best represented, the Composites, Grasses and to a less degree the leguminous families, have very few species. Indeed, there is said to be only one native Composite and only half a dozen grasses (147) and these facts again are thought to argue the antiquity of the island as a land surface.

The flora has been analysed and its origin discussed in detail by Guillaumin (617) and his conclusion is that it has a more or less equal affinity with Australia and with eastern Malaysia, a rather lesser relationship with the Pacific Islands, and a slight one with New Zealand. There are also some small but unmistakable evidences of affinity with the Madagascar region (296).

Schlechter (621) and Compton (147) have given useful accounts of the vegetation and the reader should refer to these and to the other works cited for the details of Angiosperm species, none of which is particularly familiar or of wide importance. The effects of human action on the vegetation of the island has been described and discussed by Virot (751).

The flora of Lord Howe Island (356) has between 150 and 200 species, about

30 per cent of them being endemic. Norfolk Island has rather fewer (437) and about 25 per cent of endemism. The floras of both these islands have been described as intermediate between those of Australia and New Zealand (319), and several of their plants have already been or will be mentioned elsewhere, but almost certainly the most familiar is *Howea forsteriana*, the palm of Lord Howe Island which is now commonly grown for decoration. Another interesting native plant here is *Ficus columnaris*.

Regions of Melanesia and Micronesia and of Polynesia

For present purposes it is best to combine these two regions, which together comprise all the islands south of Hawaii, east of the line Philippines–New Guinea–New Caledonia–Kermadecs, and between the Bonins on the north-west and Easter Island on the east, both inclusive, and to make only a few general statements, because the botanical facts about this area are so varied and complexing that to attempt to go into detail would almost certainly obscure what, in a general survey like this, is the main characteristic of the flora as a whole, namely that it is essentially a derived one, almost entirely Malaysian and Australasian in affinity and presumably in origin. Indeed, in comparison with other parts of the world it is no exaggeration to say that there is no real "Polynesian" flora and that all the plants within this great area, derive more of less directly, from adjacent floras. Merrill (514) and others have shown that this can be well demonstrated in the distribution of many genera whose species numbers rapidly diminish eastwards, the further they reach from Malaysia. This is particularly noticeable in the orchids (546), of which there are thousands of species in eastern Malaysia but scarcely any in the further Pacific Islands. It is also well seen in such genera as *Cyrtandra* and *Pandanus* (see p. 130) and in the Ericaceae, which are very few east and south of New Guinea.

This is not to deny that there is a considerable element of endemism in some of the islands, and especially in the larger ones to the west and south of the andesite line, but the species concerned mostly belong to widespread large genera and the quality of the endemism is not high. The proportion is probably highest in the flora of Fiji, of which A. C. Smith (679, 680, 681, 682) has given a valuable analysis, from which it appears that there are about 1,250 native species, of which close on 70 per cent are endemic. A major source of information about species in other parts of the area is the collection of figures by Guillaumin (319, 320, 321, 322) and from this and other sources it would seem that the New Hebrides (320, 321) and Tahiti (633) both have about 35 per cent and Samoa rather less. Other main groups seem to have figures round about 25 per cent, as for instance the Solomons, the Carolines and French Polynesia, which consists of the Society Islands, the Tuamotus and the Marquesas. On the other hand Tonga and Rarotonga are quoted as having less than 5 per cent each. All these figures should, however, almost certainly be raised considerably in the light of the further knowledge acquired in the last twenty years. Kanehira (418, 419) studied the Micronesian flora in some detail and it would seem that the endemics in total over all these small scattered islands may amount to 50 per cent but this is scarcely comparable with the other figures mentioned above. Brown (91) has dealt somewhat similarly with the flora of south-eastern Polynesia which he estimates to contain 339 native Angiosperms with a prominence of families similar to that seen in Hawaii. He considers that though the wide species of the flora are Malaysian and Asiatic, the total affinity of the flora is strongly American. Here the flora of Rapa is of particular interest because several of its endemic species belong to genera of some special interest phytogeographically, e.g. *Coprosma, Corokia, Exocarpus* and *Vac-*

cinium. Easter Island, which is the south-eastern outpost of Polynesia, has a native flora of only about 30 species, but is usually credited with one or two endemics.

One particular source of confusion in the study of the plant life of these two regions is the varied mixture of structure and, presumably, age in the islands. All types of oceanic island are represented and without any simple geographical segregation, except that the largest are in Melanesia and the adjacent parts of Polynesia. Generally speaking the mountainous volcanic islands have a considerable proportion of endemic species; the high coral-rock islands have a smaller proportion or may be almost without them (779); and the atolls have none at all (728), but are notable for the number of strand plants in their floras (252) which are often very small. This last point is well illustrated by such a case as that of Jaluit, an atoll in the Marshall Islands. Here in 1915 Koidzumi described the flora (429) as composed of 57 species, of which 38 had reached the island by natural means, without endemics. Since then it may be noted that the single species, or rather variety, of *Pandanus* mentioned by Koidzumi has been split into four local species. In recent years especially many other atolls have been studied, and some of these have been found to bear even smaller floras.

There is also still some doubt, or at least some confusion of statement, as to which islands, if any, contain "continental" rocks (see p. 405). This and similar questions bear more upon the geological history of the Pacific basin than upon the plant life but the two are so intimately connected that they merit mention here.

More especially relevant in this sense is the problem of the "andesite line" as it is called. Andesite is a kind of lava commonly associated with continents (it takes its name from the Andes) and its occurrence is said to indicate the former existence of continental rocks in the areas concerned. The andesite line is one enclosing most of the Pacific basin and within it no andesite occurs, indicating that the area enclosed is, for this and other reasons, truly oceanic. The line runs north and north-westward east of New Zealand, Tonga, Fiji, New Hebrides, Solomons, the Bismarck Archipelago, along the north side of New Guinea to Halmahera, then east again of Palau, Yap, the Marianas, the Bonins, and the Aleutians, and finally runs down the whole west coast of America. The enormous area enclosed by the line is regarded as the true basin of the Pacific Ocean.

Caribbean Region

This is one of the most important regions, not only in the richness and luxuriance of its vegetation, but also because of the large number of valuable plants it has provided, and in these respects it may appropriately be regarded as the New World counterpart of the Malayan Archipelago. Geographically it is rather different, since it consists partly of an archipelago (the West Indies) and partly of a portion of the American continent (Mexico and Central America), and climatically also it is less constant, Mexico in particular having extensive desert areas.

Moreover the islands are not all the same geologically. The large islands, or Greater Antilles, are usually considered to be continental in structure, although Darlington (175) states that they are now regarded as truly oceanic, and are mutually isolated by comparatively deep water; the smaller eastern islands, or Lesser Antilles, are volcanic or of coral: Trinidad and Tobago are continental islands on the shelf of South America, and the Bahamas and the Turks and Caicos Islands are low coral islands.

It is not easy to say much about the degree of endemism in the flora of the region as a whole, but Willis (783) has stated that the continental part has 8,000 endemic species, a figure which certainly represents a very high proportion, and a recent estimate gives a figure of well over 2,000 out of 6,000 for Costa Rica, including a great number of orchids. Cuba is generally credited with one of the richest floras in the world, having about 8,000 species, and here also, as in most other larger islands of the West Indies, the endemism is undoubtedly high. Trinidad, on the other hand, has only about 7 per cent. Many species are common to both the constituent parts of the region, and among them are *Bletia purpurea, Calanthe mexicana, Epidendrum polybulbon, Prioria copaifera, Rhoeo discolor* and *Swartzia simplex*, but most of the other noteworthy plants either occur also beyond the confines of the region or are restricted to one or other part of it.

According to Cailleux (101) some floras of Central America are actually the richest in the world and this is particularly interesting because this region is generally thought to have existed as land only since the end of the Pliocene, and that North and South America were widely separated throughout the Tertiary until that late date.

Central America in the wide sense has provided a number of economic plants (one very important) namely *Castilla elastica, Haematoxylum campechianum, Monstera deliciosa, Phaseolus multiflorus, Smilax medica, Vanilla planifolia* and *Zea mays* (see p. 3), but its contribution to gardens has been even greater and includes *Achimenes longiflora, A. grandiflora, Antigonon leptopus, Beloperone guttata, Ceanothus caerulea, Cobaea scandens, Cosmos bipinnatus, Dahlia variabilis, Dalechampia roezliana, Echeveria* spp., *Euphorbia leucocephala, E. (Poinsettia) pulcherrima, Fuchsia arborescens, Gesneria cinnabarina, Lobelia fulgens, Lycaste skinneri, Mantanoa bipinnatifolia, Oreodoxa regia, Pachira insignis, Parmentiera cerifera, Peristeria elata, Pithecellobium dulce, Polianthes tuberosa* (not known wild but belonging to a Mexican genus), *Rhodochiton atrosanguineum, Rondeletia odorata, Russellia equisetiformis, Salvia fulgens, Scutellaria mociniana, Solandra macrantha, Tagetes erecta, T. patula, Tigridia pavonia, Zebrina pendula* and *Zinnia elegans*. Other outstanding plants from here include *Achras zapota, Cordia gerascanthus, Deherainia smaragdina, Lophophora williamsii, Marcgravia nepenthoides, Neoschroetera tridentata (Larrea mexicana), Persea americana, Plumeria acutifolia* and *Theobroma pentagona*.

The West Indies have contributed a number of plants to gardens, among them *Aristolochia grandiflora, Cestrum nocturnum, Galphimia glauca, Lantana camara, Maurandia barclayana, Portlandia grandiflora, Posoqueria trinitatis, Warszewiczia coccinea* and *Yucca aloifolia*, and are the home of many well-known plants of value, most of them tropical fruits, of necessity not very familiar in Europe but nevertheless of great importance in warmer countries. The actual home of many of these is lost but generally credited with a West Indian origin are *Annona muricata, A. reticulata, Croton cascarilla, Grias cauliflora, Lagetta lagetto, Pimenta officinalis, Sapindus saponaria* and *Spondias mombin (lutea)*. Besides these there are many other conspicuous species in the flora, as, for instance, *Myrica cerifera, Nectandra antillana, Ocotea leucoxylon, Pereskia aculeata, Sloanea jamaicensis* and *Spathelia sorbifolia*.

The Bermudas have a small flora of about 150 native species, and of these some 8 per cent are endemic.

The little-known Revilla Gigedo Islands, of which the nearest is nearly 400 miles west of Mexico and rather less from the southern tip of Lower California, are of considerable botanical interest, and the flora has been described by Johnston (411). Each member of this scattered group of tiny islands is an isolated volcanic peak, and the largest of them, Socorro (50 square miles), has a flora of 93 native species, of which 31 are endemic. Two smaller islands have 11 and 6 endemics respectively. The great floristic affinity is with Central America and the West Indies but, most interesting, there is a distinct relationship with the Galapagos Islands, a relation typified by the occurrence of *Psidium galapageium*, previously known only from the latter islands.

Region of Venezuela and Guiana

The flora of this region is still far from well known and it is therefore almost impossible to say what degree of endemism it possesses. Probably it is high, despite the close relationship of the flora with those of neighbouring regions. There are no very conspicuously important or valuable plants, and it must suffice here to mention from among the characteristic species of the vegetation, many of which are grasses or palms, *Arthrostylidium schomburgkii, Aulonemia quexo, Brosimum galactoden-drom, Brownea grandiceps, Caryocar villosum, Copernicia* spp., *Curatella americana, Cusparia febrifuga, Dimorphandra moro, Dipteryx odorata, Duguetia quitarensis, Mauritia* spp., *Nectandra rodioei, Paullinia cupana* and *Triplaris surinamensis*.

Some of the mountains in southern Venezuela, notably Mt. Roraima (719) and Mt. Duida (720), have long attracted attention, not only because of their geological structure but also because of the pecularities of their floras, which, as a result of recent explorations, are now much better known. Both are table mountains of sandstone and perhaps the remnants of a once much more extensive plateau. Roraima, which rises almost sheer to its summit of 8,600 ft. from a rolling savanna, has a summit of about 25 square miles, and a vegetation in which, in general, there is about 50 per cent endemism, though a much higher proportion on the actual summit (128, 273). Duida rises to 6,000 ft. from a low plain and has a summit area of 250 square miles (274) and its flora has probably a similar degree of endemism. The same broad flora ranges over both, which are hundreds of miles apart, and shows a close relationship with that of the northernmost Andes.

The Amazon Region

The Amazon Basin has long been recognised as notably rich in species, especially of course, forest trees, and although it is not easy to arrive at a definite figure it would seem probable that the endemic species number at least 3,000 and provide a considerable proportion of the total.

Two important economic plants are the Para rubber, *Hevea brasiliensis*, and the cocoa, *Theobroma cacao*, while among others of less significance are *Bertholletia excelsa, Paullinia sorbilis*, and certain species of *Smilax*.

Among the more characteristic plants, palms are outstanding and of them there may be mentioned, *Astrocaryum jawari, Attalea excelsa, Leopoldinia pulchra, Mani-acaria saccifera* and *Mauritia flexuosa*. Other notable species are *Arundo saccharoides, Couma utilis, Montrichardia arborescens, Pourouma cecropiaefolia* and *Psathyranthus amazonicus. Victoria amazonica (regia)*, the giant water-lily, is one of the best-known plants, but in all occurs a good deal more widely.

South Brazilian Region

The South Brazilian region is the largest and most varied in tropical America, and although no figures are readily available, it may be assumed that a very high proportion of its many thousands of species is endemic.

Among plants of considerable, and, in a few cases, of outstanding economic importance, which are regarded as having their origin here are *Ananas comosus* (*sativus*), *Arachis hypogaea, Cephaelis ipecacuanha, Copernicia cerifera, Ilex para-guayensis, Leopoldinia piassaba, Manihot glaziovii, Passiflora edulis* and *Quassia amara*. From this region come also a number of well-known garden and hothouse plants, among them *Aechmea fulgens, Aphelandra squarrosa, Begonia semperflorens, Billbergia nutans, Bougainvillea spectabilis, Datura suaveolens, Fuchsia coccinea, Neomarica northiana, Passiflora caeulea, Salvia splendens, Sinningia speciosa, Tibouchina semidecandra* and *Verbena bonariensis*.

Of other noteworthy plants (among which palms are prominent) there may be mentioned *Allamanda cathartica, Attalea compta, Bactris aristata, Bauhinia splendens, Caesalpinia echinata, Cattleya labiata, Chorisia ventricosa, Cocos coronata, Cryptanthus zonatus, Dalbergia nigra, Dinisia excelsa, Erythrina crista-galli, Euterpe edulis, Feijoa sellowiana, Geonoma macroclona, Hancornia speciosa, Machaerium firmum, Manettia bicolor, Mauritia vinifera, Melinis minutiflora, Oncidium papilio, Stifftia chrysantha, Utricularia nelumbifolia* and *Vellozia candida*.

Fernando Noronha and South Trinidad have several endemic species each, those of the former including the rather unusual *Combretum rupicola*. St. Paul's Rocks, which are still farther from the continent, have no Angiosperms.

Andean Region

This very extended region has been divided into a number of subordinate areas and floras, but the constituent parts which call for mention here are five, namely, the montane (tropical in the north), the tropical coast, the temperate coast, the eastern savanas or puna, and the Galapagos archipelago. The second of these is predominantly a desert area, and the third includes the Chilean "Mediterranean" vegetation and flora.

The region is above all remarkable for the number of its economic plants, which include many of the most important of all. These come chiefly from the more northerly parts of the montane zone and include *Annona cherimolia, Carludovica palmata, Ceroxylon andicola, Chenopodium quinoa, Cinchona succirubra, Cyphomandra betacea, Erythroxylum coca, Krameria triandra, Lycopersicon esculentum, Nicotiana tabacum, Phaseolus lunatus, Phaseolus vulgaris, Quillaja saponaria, Schinus molle, Solanum tuberosum* and *Ullucus tuberosus*.

The garden plants, which are also very numerous, come naturally from the more temperate parts, especially the southern mountains and the Chilean coasts, but a number have their homes farther north. Among the former are *Alstroemeria aurantiaca, Berberis darwinii, Calceolaria integrifolia, Cantua buxifolia, Escallonia micrantha, Fuchsia rosea, Geum chiloense, Lapageria rosea, Lippia citriodora, Nicandra physalodes, Salpiglossis sinuata, Schizanthus pinnatus, Schizopetalon walkeri, Tropaeolum speciosum* and *Verbena erinoides*: and among the latter, *Browallia speciosa, Brownea macrophylla, Buddleja globosa, Episcia fulgida, Ercilla volubilis, Eucharis grandiflora, Fittonia argyronema, Heliotropium peruvianum, Mandevilla suaveolens, Mutisia clematis, Tacsonia mixta, Tropaeolum majus, T. peregrinum* and several orchids.

Other important or interesting species from the northern parts are *Aetanthus mutisii, Baccharis tola, Espeletia* spp., *Phytelephas macrocarpa, Puya raimondii* (Plate 7) and *Quercus humboldtiana*, while from the more southerly parts come *Azorella multifida, Drimys winteri, Embothrium coccineum, Eucryphia cordifolia, Gunnera chilensis, Jubaea spectabilis, Laurelia aromatica* and *Mutisia viciaefolia*.

The Galapagos or Tortoise Islands form a group of volcanic islands about

700 miles west of the coast of Ecuador, and have long been famous for the peculiarities of their animal life. The plant life is not so remarkable, although it contains many points of great interest. There are nineteen islands varying greatly in size and having a total area rather less than that of Devonshire, and the flora is not rich, amounting to about 450 species. According to Svenson (715) 42 per cent are endemic, and the families Amaranthaceae, Euphorbiaceae and Rubiaceae are especially rich in endemic forms, while in view of the discontinuity of the genus *Pernettia* (see p. 443) the occurrence of an endemic species, *P. howellii*, is of particular interest (673). The relationship of the non-endemic species is almost entirely American, and especially Andean, there being but a very small number of more widely ranging plants. Kroeber (434) has studied in particular the distribution of the species among the islands, and concludes that there is little in it which cannot be explained on a combination of mathematical and geographical chance. Howell (381) states that of the species of the endemic genus *Scalesia*, only six occur on more than one island and only one on more than two islands.

Pampas Region (99, 100)

This region, which vegetationally contains one of the world's most important grasslands, contains no very important economic plants but has provided a small number of garden forms, including *Cortaderia selloana*, *Nicotiana affinis*, *Petunia* spp. and *Salpichroa rhomboidea*.

Characteristic species include *Acacia caven*, *Aspidosperma quebracho*, *Geoffroea decorticans*, *Larrea divaricata*, *Prosopis alba*, *Trithrinax campestris* and many grasses and composites, but not all these are entirely confined to the region and it is difficult to say what proportion of its total flora may be so.

Three of the plants most often commented upon are not natives, namely the ombu tree, *Phytolacca dioica*, of more tropical America; and the cardoon (*Cynara cardunculus*) and the milk-thistle (*Silybum marianum*) both of which were long ago introduced from western Eurasia. The two latter which are described as often growing to a great size, may in favourable seasons form an almost inpenetrable vegetation over wide areas (176, 383).

Region of Juan Fernandez

The Juan Fernandez group of three volcanic islands lying off the coast of Chile has a small but peculiar flora. According to Skottsberg (658, 659), about 70 per cent of the 143 species are endemic, among them three arborescent species of *Chenopodium*. Rather more than half the flora has a strong American affinity, but the remainder has an equally strong "Pacific", or western, affinity and in particular there is an appreciable relationship with Hawaii. There is considerable segregation of species between the two large islands, only 19 per cent of the flora occurring on both. Of endemic species only 12 per cent occur on both.

The flora of the Desventuradas Islands consists of twenty species (667, 671), of which about two-thirds are endemic. Most of them belong to widely distributed genera, and those which are not endemic are all found also in western South America.

North and East Australian Region

This region stretches in a wide coastal belt round the continent from the Kimberley District in the north-west to Tasmania. Vegetationally it is predominantly savanna or savanna-woodland, but there are considerable areas of forest, especially along the north-east coast, and also in the south-east and in Tasmania. The flora is almost entirely local and Australian in character except in the north where there is a considerable admixture of Malaysian, and especially New Guinea, types, but even here some groups notably developed in New Guinea, such as the palms and aroids, are poorly represented. The north coast has some 15 per cent of species in common with Malaysia and on the east coast there is a small relationship with the flora of New Caledonia. About 20 per cent of the species in the flora of Tasmania are endemic to that island (601).

The flora of some of the mountains, particularly in Queensland, is of considerable interest to the plant geographer. For example Mt. Bellenden-Ker (265), besides being one of the two localities for the only *Rhododendron* in Australia (see p. 168), has other noteworthy species, while the remarkable dwarf grass, *Micraira subulifolia*, is also found in two separate montane localities in Queensland. On the mountains of New South Wales and Victoria there are two outlying species of Gesneriaceae (compare p. 151), *Boea hygroscopica* and *Fieldia australis*.

The forest areas contain a number of useful timber trees such as *Castanospermum australe*, *Casuarina torulosa*, *Dysoxylum fraserianum*, *Elaeocarpus grandis*, and *Eucalyptus pilularis*, but otherwise there are no notable economic plants. A few horticultural species are natives of the region, among them *Acacia dealbata*, *Grevillea robusta*, *Humea elegans*, *Nicotiana suaveolens*, *Trachymene caerulea* and *Viola hederacea*, and there is a good deal of evidence that *Acacia farnesiana*, now a wide species in warm countries, is also native here. Other notable species of the region are *Alphitonia excelsa*, *Atherosperma moschatum*, *Boronia serrulata*, *Brachychiton acerifolium*, *Brachycome linearifolia*, *Calamus australis*, *Ceratopetalum gummiferum*, *Doryanthes excelsa*, *Drimys lanceolata*, *Duboisia* spp., *Epacris longiflora*, *Eucalyptus marginata*, *Eucalyptus regnans*, *Nothofagus cunninghamii*, *Olearia nitida*, *Pandanus tectorius*, *Petrophila sessilis* and *Telopea speciosissima*.

South-west Australian Region (262)

Although small this region is floristically a very important one, containing the fifth and last of the world's "Mediterranean" floras. Like the others, and especially like the Cape flora, with which it has many interesting features in common, it is a rich flora showing a very high degree of endemism which may perhaps reach, or even exceed, 75 per cent. Its similarity with the Cape flora lies not so much in the actual number of forms in common, which are indeed few, but in the remarkable degree of parallelism between the leading characters of the two. In both, the same families are frequently well developed, and the same types of growth form are common in each.

There are no important economic plants and it is surprising to find, in view of the large number of garden plants which have come from the other "Mediterranean" floras, that the horticultural representatives are also few—so much so that *Brachycome iberidifolia*, *Callistemon speciosus*, *Eucalyptus ficifolia*, *Helichrysum bracteatum* and one or two species of *Helipterum* practically exhaust the list.

The flora contains many very characteristic forms, and among these may be cited species of *Acacia*, *Banksia*, *Bauhinia*, *Chorizema*, *Dryandra*, *Eucalyptus* and *Hakea*, *Boronia megastigma*, *Chamaelaucium uncinatum*, *Kingia australis*, *Lambertia formosa*, *Nuytsia floribunda* and *Xanthorrhoea preissii*, and many members of the Epacridaceae, Goodeniaceae and Stylidiaceae.

Central Australian Region

The flora of this great area which comprises most of the interior of the continent is comparatively limited, in correlation with the desert or semi-desert conditions which prevail over most of the region. It is also still incompletely known and studied, and it is therefore not possible to say much here about it. It is probably almost entirely endemic.

Among characteristic species, some of which give an important facies to wide areas of vegetation, may be mentioned *Acacia aneura* (mulga), *Acacia harpophylla* (brigalow), *Clianthus dampieri*, *Eucalyptus hemiphloia* (mallee), *Eucalyptus oleosa*, *Melaleuca acuminata* and *Swainsona greyana*.

New Zealand Region

The flora of New Zealand (219) must always be of special interest to British botanists because of its antipodal geographical relationship, but comparison of the two is also revealing because, while the British Islands are continental islands, New Zealand is, and has presumably long been, separated from the nearest continent by over 1,000 miles of deep water (540).

Estimates of the size of the flora of New Zealand vary considerably but Cheeseman (129), Oliver (542) and Allan (12, 13, 14, 15) recognise nearly 1,500 indigenous species, to which must be added several hundred groups of species hybrids and more than 600 introductions. Quite apart from the hybrids, which are one of its most remarkable features, the flora is thus seen to be considerably larger than that of Great Britain, and also differs markedly from it in that no fewer than 75 per cent of the species are endemic.

There are about 100 native families and in three-quarters of these, comprising more than nine-tenths of the flora, 50 per cent or more of the species are endemic. Of these endemics 40 per cent are found on both the main islands; 15 per cent in the North Island only; and 45 per cent in the South (more temperate) Island. The total species population of the South Island is about one-third greater than that of the North Island. The endemics are fewest in the Monocotyledons and most numerous in the sympetalous families of Dicotyledons and this again is specially noticeable in the South Island where practically all the latter species are endemic. At the same time three important families of this kind which might be expected (Plumbaginaceae, Asclepiadaceae and Acanthaceae) are entirely absent, while three others, Labiatae, Primulaceae and Solanaceae, are very poorly represented.

Another feature of the flora interesting to northern botanists is that of the twenty-six genera represented by more than twelve species, nearly half are familiar in the north temperate regions, while rather more than half are characteristic of the southern hemisphere only. Nearly all the former contain a high proportion of endemics and *Ranunculus*, *Epilobium* and *Veronica* (*Hebe*) are more strongly represented in New Zealand than anywhere else. Of the more characteristically southern genera the species are in nearly every case exclusively endemic.

Of the non-endemic species the great majority are found elsewhere in Australia, and especially Tasmania, only, as is shown particularly well in the Orchidaceae, but there are nevertheless great differences between the floras of the two dominions (540), as for instance between the Leguminosae of the two, in the absence of many characteristic Australian types such as *Eucalyptus* and *Casuarina* from New Zealand, and in the great development in the latter of some of the temperate genera mentioned above.

The vegetation is varied but is for the most part some kind of woodland, and there are several valuable timber trees, including *Beilschmiedea tawa, Hoheria populnea, Knightia excelsa, Metrosideros robusta, Nothofagus fusca* and *Plagianthus betulinus. Phormium tenax* is the only important economic plant.

The region has provided a number of good garden plants, among them *Clianthus puniceus, Fuchsia procumbens, Griselinia littoralis, Veronica (Hebe)* spp., *Olearia haastii, Olearia paniculata* and *Senecio greyii.*

Characteristic species include *Aristotelia racemosa, Celmisia coriacea, Corallospermum crassicaule, Cordyline australis, Coriaria ruscifolia, Elytranthe tetrapetala, Entelea arborescens, Haastia pulvinaria, Ixerba brexioides, Lagenophora forsteri* (found in all parts of the region), *Laurelia novae-zealandiae, Leptospermum scoparium, Pittosporum tenuifolium, Poa caespitosa, Ranunculus lyallii, Rhopalostylis sapida, Rubus australis* and species of *Veronica (Hebe).*

The region contains, besides New Zealand proper, four outlying islands or island groups, the Kermadecs 600 miles to the north-east; the Chathams 500 miles to the east; the Auckland and Campbell Islands to the south; and the tiny Antipodes Islands nearly 500 miles to the south-east. The flora of the Kermadecs (539) contains both Polynesian and New Zealand elements and consists of about seventy species with about 15 per cent of endemism. The Chathams have some 140 species, of which about 20 per cent are endemic. The Aucklands have about 110 species (ten endemic) and Campbells 85 (five endemics). There are also about twenty species found on both the latter but not elsewhere. The Antipodes have a small flora of about 30 species including two endemics. There are endemics, too, on many of the small islands lying close to the mainland of New Zealand, most notably perhaps on the tiny Three Kings Islands, to the north-west of North Cape (52) which have no fewer than a dozen endemic species (see also p. 151).

Patagonian Region

This small region is of some special interest because it is the only continental area in the southern hemisphere of latitude similar to that of north and central Europe. It divides up into three constituent areas: the woodlands of the west coast and of Fuegia; the southern tip of the Andes and the steppes of South Patagonia, and the Falkland Islands. The phytogeography has been discussed by Cabrera (99; 100) and Beetle (55) and there is a most interesting account of the country and the conditions of life there in a remarkable autobiography by Bridges (87).

The flora is small and none of the species is of value, although a few, such as *Fuchsia magellanica, Pernettia mucronata, Philesia buxifolia* and *Oxalis enneaphylla* (Falklands), are sometimes grown in gardens. Its most remarkable geographical feature is its relationship with the flora of New Zealand (205). Among other outstanding species are *Berberis buxifolia, Bolax glebaria, Empetrum rubrum, Gunnera scabra, Mulinum spinosum, Myrtus nummularia, Nothofagus betuloides, Nothofagus pumila, Opuntia darwinii* and *Poa flabellata.*

According to Skottsberg (657), the Falklands have about 170 species, of which some 10 per cent are endemic. The remainder are all found in the continental part of the region.

Region of the South Temperate Oceanic Islands

Scattered far from land in the great oceans which surround Antarctica are numerous islands, very small in size, and with but a slight vegetation, but, because of the distributions of their tiny angiosperm floras, of exceptional phytogeographical interest.

These islands, with their situations, are:

1. South Georgia, 800 miles E.S.E. of the Falkland Islands   54° S.: 36° W.

2. Tristan da Cunha, with Nightingale I., 24 miles S.W.,
   Inaccessible I., 25 miles W.S.W., and Gough I., 230
   miles away to the S.S.E.   .   .   .   .   .   37° S.: 12° W.

3. Marion (or Prince Edward) I. .   .   .   .   .   46° S.: 38° E.

4. The Crozets, comprising two groups about 60 miles
   apart, the western of several islands and the eastern
   of two   .   .   .   .   46° S.: 50° E.

5. The Kerguelen Archipelago, of one large island and 300
   others   .   .   .   .   48° S.: 70° E.

6. Heard I. and the smaller Macdonald I., about 30 miles
   away   .   .   .   .   52° S.: 72° E.

7. St. Paul I. and Amsterdam I., about 70 miles apart   .   35° S.: 78° E.

8. Macquarie I.   .   .   .   .   55° S.: 160° E.

Floristically belonging to this group are Antarctica itself and the South Shetland Islands but these have only two species of flowering plants, *Colobanthus crassifolius* and *Deschampsia antarctica*, both of which occur in South America, and they need not be considered further.

A glance at their longitudes shows that these islands fall into three groups, namely, South Georgia and the Tristan group in the South Atlantic; Marion, the Crozets, the Kerguelen Archipelago, Heard and Macdonald, St. Paul and Amsterdam, in the South Indian Ocean; and Macquarie between New Zealand and the Antarctic. They also differ somewhat in kind (403). South Georgia is almost a continental island both in position and structure. Macquarie is also a continental island in geology though oceanic in its isolation. The rest are true volcanic oceanic islands, with the possible exception of Kerguelen, which Jeannel suggests is a mass of continental rocks engulfed in an enormous effusion of lava. Furthermore it has a small fossil flora (182) containing forms still existing in Australasia and South America. He suggests also that the long string of islands from Tristan to St. Paul lie along ridges of continental basalt, conforming to the general eastern edge of South America and Antarctica and left behind when these continents drifted south and west, in much the same way as the mid-Atlantic swell was left.

Holdgate (363) has given a particularly useful map showing vividly the spatial relationships of these islands to other land areas of the southern hemisphere.

Considering the varied latitude of the islands their flora is remarkably constant and there is a strong, though uneven, relationship between the islands. It is unfortunately difficult to arrive at the true number of species present partly because, although a valuable floristic analysis of the six more southerly groups has recently appeared (818), there is as yet no fully integrated *Flora* of the whole region; and partly because the number of introduced plants is constantly increasing, but it would appear that the number is about one hundred, of which forty belong to the Gramineae and Cyperaceae. These latter seem to be less widely distributed over the islands than the rest, and their endemism is higher, roughly 25/40 compared with 24/60.

In the following analysis it saves a great deal of space and repetition if the eight constituent parts of the region are referred to by the numbers attached to them above. The floras of these constituent parts are:

No. 1 has 16 species, of which 1 is endemic.
  2 ,, 44 ,,   ,, 28 are endemic.
  3 ,, 10 ,,   ,, none is endemic.
  4 ,, 16 ,,   ,, none is endemic.
  5 ,, 22 ,,   ,, 2 are endemic.
  6 ,, 8 ,,   ,, none is endemic.
  7 ,, 17 ,,   ,, 7 are endemic.
  8 ,, 31 ,,   ,, 3 are endemic.

Of the species in total some fifty are endemic to the region as a whole and some seventy-five occur, within it, on one of the eight parts only, i.e. eight on No. 1, forty-one on 2, one on 3, none on 4, two on 5, none on 6, none on 7, and fourteen on 8.

Eleven species have been recorded on two out of the eight in the combinations 12, 27, 27, 27, 27, 45, 45, 45, 56, 68, 78. Eight species on three of the eight in the combinations 138, 145, 158, 158, 168, 178, 257, 345. Six species on four of the eight i.e. 1456 (*Deschampsia antarctica*), 3456 (*Poa cookii, Pringlea antiscorbutica*), 3458 (*Cotula plumosa, Crassula moschata*) and 4568 (*Agrostis magellanica*). Two species are recorded from five out of the eight, i.e. 13458 (*Montia fontana*) and 34568 (*Azorella selago*). One species, *Callitriche antarctica* is recorded in six of the eight, 134568. One species, *Ranunculus biternatus* is recorded in seven parts, 1234578. Very few of the endemics occur on more than one of the eight, and only *Pringlea* is on more than three.

Of the species which are not endemic to the region, the affinity lies, as might be expected, chiefly with Australasia (about 40 per cent of the species concerned) and with Temperate South America (about 10 per cent). About 25 per cent range from South America through the islands to Australasia, namely *Agrostis magellanica, Azorella selago, Callitriche antarctica, Carex trifida, Colobanthus crassifolius, Juncus scheuchzerioides, Ranunculus crassipes, Crassula moschata* and *Myriophyllum elatinoides*.

Three other species, *Nertera depressa, Pelargonium australe* and *Scirpus nodosus,* have wider southerly distributions, and five, namely *Empetrum rubrum, Juncus communis, Luzula campestris, Montia fontana* and *Phleum alpinum* are found in both northern and southern temperate regions.

The distribution of these last 8 within the region is, respectively:

2, 2, 7, 2, 7, 18, 13458, 1

It will thus be seen that only one species widely distributed outside the region is also widely distributed in it, and that most of the eight are found only on the Tristan group or on Amsterdam and St. Paul, the two groups with the most temperate latitude.

A special feature of the southern cold temperate region is the occurrence of communities dominated by large tussock-forming grasses. These are found in New Zealand and in Fuegia and in all the islands in between except the Crozets

Plate 14. A giant Senecio (*S. keniodendron*) of the African mountains
(from Karsten & Schenck, Vegetationsbilder)

(752, 753, 754). These grasses nearly all belong to the genus *Poa* and six species form a remarkable vicarious series distributed as follows:

Poa flabellata	.	.	. Fuegia, Falkland Islands, South Georgia and Gough Island.
P. cookii	.	.	. Marion Island, Crozets, Kerguelen and Heard Island.
P. novareae	.	.	. Amsterdam and St. Paul Islands.
P. litorosa	.	.	. Campbell and Auckland Islands.
P. foliosa	.	.	. Macquarie Island, Campbell and Auckland Islands and New Zealand.
P. hamiltoni	.	.	. Macuarie Island.

CHAPTER 11

THE DISTRIBUTION OF SPECIES—IV

THIS chapter, which concludes the general survey of the geographical distribution of species, is devoted to certain particular aspects of the subject, namely: discontinuous species; species with very narrow ranges; vicarious species or species pairs; and, finally, the three types of Angiosperms which are particularly associated with marine and maritime habitats and which therefore differ fundamentally in geography from all the rest.

Discontinuous Species

Just as in families and genera, a proportion of all species have ranges consisting of two or more constituent and separate parts, and some have actually been mentioned in Chapter 8. There are, however, two reasons why it is impossible here to give more than a very brief account of these. In the first place they are very numerous and any attempt to deal with them critically and systematically would be far beyond the scope of this book; and, in the second place, the detailed account that has already been given of discontinuous genera applies in outline almost equally well to species. Indeed, genera often owe their discontinuity to that of one or more of their constituent species.

For these reasons no more is aimed at here than to demonstrate the great variation in the range of discontinuous species and the fact that they can be classified in the same way as discontinuous genera. It must also be pointed out that the different examples cited, though taken from reliable sources and authorities, have not been critically examined and verified in the same way as was done for the genera, and some of the details may well prove, on closer examination, to need qualification or correction.

It will be remembered that there are, in correlation with the major circumstances of world geography, four principal types of generic discontinuity, and species also are conveniently dealt with under these heads: the fifth, Hawaiian, category can here be ignored. The case of arctic–alpine plants has been mentioned on p. 190.

Discontinuous species of the north temperate zone
(see also pp. 177 *et seq.*)

A number of species are found discontinuously distributed throughout the northern temperate zone. *Potentilla fruticosa*, for example, is found in North America, in Europe, in Siberia and in the Himalayas, and among others with a rather similar type of range (though not all Himalayan) are *Anemone multifida*, *Arabis alpina* and several species mentioned in the analysis of the northern flora in Chapter 9.

The remarkable eastern North American–eastern Asiatic type of distribution, so well known among genera, is seen in various species, among them being *Acer rubrum*, *Cypripedium reginae*, *Ostrya virginica*, *Polygonum arifolium*, *Polygonum virginicum*, *Smilax herbacea* and *Symplocarpus foetidus*. Discontinuity between

North America and Japan is particularly frequent and Gray (312) long ago listed the instances of three types, namely—eastern North America and Japan (17 species); western North America and Japan (15 species); and both eastern and western America and Japan (17 species), though whether all these are acceptable in terms of more modern taxonomy may be doubted (458).

Several "Bering" species (see p. 94) are discontinuous between eastern Asia and western North America across the strait, among them *Rubus spectabilis* and *Streptopus streptopoides*.

In the New World a number of species are found on the west and east sides of the continent, but not in between, including *Danthonia intermedia*, *Oxytropis foliosa* and *Senecio resedifolius* and a group discontinuously distributed between California and the south-eastern States (645).

Similarly in the Old World there are species such as *Betula humilis* and *Cimicifuga foetida*, which occur in Europe, Central Asia and eastern Asia.

Many examples of discontinuity on a smaller scale are afforded by the floras of Europe and the Mediterranean. The familiar *Rhododendron ponticum* grows on the south coast of the Black Sea, in parts of Palestine, and in the extreme south part of the Iberian Peninsula, and Dimiriz (192) has shown that in Asia Minor *Laurus nobilis* and *Myrtus communis* are distributed to-day in very discontinuous fashion throughout a narrow coastal belt. *Potentilla apennina*, *Genista dalmatica*, *Althaea rosea*, *Phlomis lanata* and several others are found in Italy and Bulgaria only, while *Crocus veneris* and *Centaurea cretica* occur on the islands of Cyprus and Crete. *Androsace villosa* has been recorded from the Atlas Mountains, having long been familiar in the Alps and Balkans. On a still narrower scale *Pedicularis rosea* and *Saxifraga retusa* are discontinuously distributed within the Alpine mountain system.

Lastly, there may be mentioned here several north temperate plants which have been recorded, apparently wild, in one or more spots in the tropics, usually on mountains. *Drosera longifolia* is said to occur on one mountain in the Hawaiian Islands; the European *Luronium* (*Elisma*) *natans* has been collected in Java; *Scirpus setaceus* is known also from New Guinea; and *Sparganium simplex* has been found in Sumatra.

Discontinuous species of the tropical zone

The pan-tropical species which are, by the nature of the case, discontinuous, have already been dealt with, and there remain to be considered here those types of distribution which involve only parts of the warmer zone, and first to be dealt with are the several combinations among the three main sectors of the tropics.

A number of species have been noted as distributed over America and Africa and although it is, as with so many other categories of plant distribution, impossible to say exactly how far these plants are now native in one or other part of their area, there may be mentioned of them *Andira inermis*, *Dalbergia ecastophyllum*, *Drepanocarpus lunatus*, *Echinochloa crus-pavonis*, *Euclasta cordylotricha*, *Gossypium hirsutum*, *Hyparrhenia rufa*, *Hypogynium spathiflorum*, *Mucuna urens*, *Neurotheca loeselioides*, *Parinari excelsa*, *Paepalanthus lamarckii*, *Sauvagesia erecta*, *Sida linifolia*, *Symphonia globulifera* and *Tristachya chrysothrix*. *Eriocaulon bipetalum*, *Hibiscus diversifolius*, *Jussieua erecta*, *Paratheria prostrata* and *Paullinia pinnata* are said to occur in the Madagascar region as well as on the two continents. Rather closely related to the foregoing are *Ludwigia palustris* found throughout America, Europe and Africa; *Hydrocotyle umbellata* of America, South Africa and the Madagascar region; *Hydrocotyle verticillata* in America, South Africa and Hawaii; and *Dalechampia scandens* in America, Africa and India.

A few species, among them *Arundinella hispida* and *Caesalpinia major*, occur in America and in Asia and the Pacific Islands, and in connection with these the reader may be reminded of one of the most remarkable of all discontinuous species, *Nertera depressa*, which is found in Central and South America, Hawaii, Tristan, Australia and New Zealand and south-east Asia and Malaysia.

Many species link Africa with Asia (and often the Pacific Islands) and the more widespread of these, such as *Dumasia villosa, Eragrostis aspera, Hibiscus lobatus, Hyptis lobata, Neyraudia madagascariensis, Sacciolepis curvata, Striga asiatica* and *Vahlia oldenlandioides*, relate closely to the wide species of the Old World tropics considered on p. 183. Among the species found in Africa and Asia only are *Abutilon pannosum, Albizzia lebbek, Asparagus racemosus, Canscora decussata, Gloriosa superba, Hibiscus micranthus, Mundulea sericea, Ormocarpum sennoides,* and *Phyllanthus reticulatus*. Some rather special cases are *Hypericum mysorense* from Socotra and India; *Trapa natans* in Europe, Africa and Asia; and *Sambucus adnata* in the East African mountains and in the Himalayan region. *Alectra arvensis, Apluda mutica* (also on Socotra), *Pipturus velutinus, Procis pedunculata, Thuarea involucrata, Tournefortia sarmentosa* and *Trichodesma indicum* occur in Asia and in the Madagascar region (but not on the African continent), while *Carex brunnea* is similar but extends to Australia and Hawaii.

In connection with Africa it may be noted that *Andropogon gayanum, Elyonurus royleanus* and *Panicum maximum* are said to link the Cape Verdes with the continent, and there are continental species which occur in other parts of Macaronesia, notably *Erica arborea* which is found not only in eastern Tropical Africa and the Tibesti (93) but also in Madeira, the Canaries and the Mediterranean region. Discontinuity is also to be seen within the African continent as for instance in *Hypericum peplidifolium* and *Thalictrum rhynchocarpum* which, widely spread in eastern Tropical Africa, occur also in the Cameroons and Fernando Po (521), and a somewhat similar state of affairs in seen in *Protea angolensis* and *P. abyssinica* (456).

Discontinuity on this smaller scale is, indeed, to be found everywhere, but it is, because of the mutual isolation of the land areas, perhaps most noticeable in, and best exemplified from, Asia and Malaysia, where the Asiatic–Australian montane flora in particular (700) affords many cases. Thus, *Melissa parviflora, Mosla dianthera, Neocinnamomum caudatum* and *Swertia bimaculata*, occur fairly widely on the Asiatic mainland and are also found in Sumatra: *Hemiscolopia trimera* is in south-east Asia and also in Sumatra and Java; and *Bennettiodendron leprosipes* is in South China, Sumatra and Java. A number of species link India and the Himalayas with the Archipelago, among them *Alchemilla javanica, Craniotome versicolor, Hydrangea oblongifolia, Neillia thrysiflora, Primula imperialis, Rhopalocnemis phalloides, Rubus lineatus, Schisandra elongata, Thalictrum javanicum* and *Valeriana hardwickii*, while others, including *Anotis wightiana, Damnacanthus indicus, Mitrastemon kawasasakii, Petrosavia sakuraii, Pirola japonica* and *Rubus niveus* link China and/or Japan with the Archipelago. At the other end of the axis *Trachymene saniculaefolia* is found on the mountains of Borneo and the Philippines and also in New South Wales.

Within Malaysia almost every possible kind of discontinuity is to be found and the proportionate relationships in this respect between the various constituent areas is a matter of great interest with regard to the history and population of the region, but it is too complex to be dealt with here and recourse must be made to the sources of information already cited on pp. 210, 211.

Discontinuity involving Australasia and the Pacific Islands again is naturally very varied, and it must suffice to illustrate it by the following random examples:

Stackhousia intermedia	Malayan Archipelago and Carolines.
Carex graeffeana	Philippines, Java, Fiji.
Alstonia plumosa	New Caledonia, Fiji, Samoa.
Cyathodes tameiameiae	Hawaii, Tahiti.
Gymnema stenophylla	Australia, Fiji.
Solanum aviculare	Philippines, New Guinea, Australia, New Zealand.
Didiscus procumbens	New Guinea, New Caledonia, Australia.
Geranium ardjunense	Malayan Archipelago, Australia, New Zealand.
Microlaena stipoides	Java, Philippines, Australia, New Zealand, Hawaii.
Gahnia gaudichaudii	New Zealand, Hawaii.
Carex uncinata	New Zealand, Chatham Islands, Hawaii.

Discontinuity in the southern extra-tropical regions

Because it has such a direct bearing on the history of the land masses of the southern hemisphere (360), this type of discontinuity is perhaps the most interesting and important of all, and has been studied by many plant geographers, notably by Skottsberg (660, 664, 666) and Oliver (540).

One of the commonest types of range is that between New Zealand and South America, as is shown by *Agrostis magellania, Enargea marginata, Myosotis antarctica* and *Myosurus aristatus. Aristotelia peduncularis, Epilobium junceum, Lilaeopsis lineata, Selliera radicans* and probably *Tetragonia expansa* are discontinuous, among others, between Australia and New Zealand on the one hand and South America on the other. *Coriaria ruscifolia* is a notable species which is found not only in South America and New Zealand but also in the Kermadecs, Fiji, Samoa and Tahiti. *Lobelia anceps* is found in all three southern continents; *Papaver aculeatum* in South Africa and Australia.

On a rather smaller scale *Chevreulia stolonifera* is found on Tristan da Cunha and in South America; *Oreobolus obtusangulus* has been reported from Juan Fernandez and the Falklands. In the Australasian region discontinuity on a smaller scale is also not uncommon and there are many species found in both Australia and New Zealand. *Disphyma australis* occurs in Australia, New Zealand and on the Chatham Islands; *Gaultheria depressa* in Tasmania and New Zealand, and *Acaena anserinifolia* in New Zealand, Tasmania and New Guinea. *Melicytus ramiflorus* ranges from New Zealand to Norfolk Island, the Kermadecs, Tonga and Fiji.

Discontinuity between the north and south temperate zones

This type of species distribution must be approached with great caution, because of the difficulty of saying, with any degree of certainty, that the occurrence of a northern plant in the south, and particularly in Australasia, is natural and not the result of accidental introduction in the course of human settlement. Quite frequently, for instance, such species have been recorded from Australia and New Zealand, but nearly always some suspicion attached to their presence in these countries. Since it is manifestly impossible to consider all these cases critically here it is best to say as little as possible about them and to mention a few of the most authentic examples, referring the reader for any further details to papers by Du Rietz (204, 205) and Steffen (707) in which the whole subject of what are called bipolar distributions, and their possible explanations, are set out very fully.

Primula farinosa is one of the best examples, being fairly widely distributed in the northern temperate zone and occurring also in temperate South America (though in slightly different form), and others of the same sort, of which Steffen gives a useful list, are *Armeria vulgaris, Draba incana, Saxifraga magellanica, Gentiana prostrata* and several species of *Carex, Elatine americana* is reported from North America and from Australia and New Zealand, while *Epilobium tetragonum* is found in Europe and in the same two southern countries. *Ranunculus parviflorus* is said to occur in the southern United States, in the West Indies, in Europe, the Mediterranean region and the Canaries, as well as in Australia and New Zealand. Still other species generally regarded as discontinuous between some part of the north temperate and some part of Australasia include *Barbarea vulgaris, Geranium dissectum, Geum rivale* and *Geum urbanum*, but it is difficult to be sure that species of this sort have not been introduced in the south. Other rather different examples are *Lepturus cylindricus* in the Mediterranean and in South Africa; two or three species of *Anemone* are said to be discontinuous between the southern United States and temperate South America, and *Wahlenbergia gracilis*, which is found in India, New Caledonia, Australia and New Zealand. Finally the genus *Triglochin*, already briefly noticed on p. 120, is very remarkable in having no fewer than four species (218) which are, to a greater or lesser extent, discontinuous between the northern and southern hemispheres. These are the familiar northern species *T. maritima* and *T. palustris*, both of which are found in South America, *T. bulbosa*, which is in the Mediterranean region and also in southern Africa, and, most remarkable of all, *T. striata*, which is found widely in North America, in Brazil and temperate South America, in Southern Africa and in Australia, Tasmania and New Zealand.

Two particular kinds of north–south discontinuity, although not so striking as any of the above and involving rather different problems are nevertheless of considerable interest. The first is the wide discontinuity of certain plants of arid regions, and three of the more notable here are *Aizoon canariense, Frankenia pulverulenta* and *Seetzenia prostrata*, all of which, while occurring fairly widely in the African–Indian desert region, and sometimes beyond it, are also recorded from South Africa. Rather similarly *Zygophyllum simplex* is recorded from the Cape Verdes, from East Africa to India, from the Aldabra Islands, and from South Africa. *Nitraria schoberi* is rather different in that its southern area is in south-eastern Australia.

The second kind of discontinuity is that between North American and temperate South America, which has been described by Bray (85), Campbell (114) and others. In the north the distribution is usually in the western states and Mexico but in the south it is more varied. The commonest condition is discontinuity between California and Chile–Argentina, of which *Boisduvalia glabrella, Calandrinia menziesii, Chorizanthe commissuralis, Gilia pusilla, Lastarriaca chilensis, Mentzelia albicans, Oxytheca dendroides* and *Prosopis juliflora*, have been quoted as examples. This kind of range presumably follows latitudinal movement along the mountainous western edge of the Americas and is of special interest in the demonstration it affords of the potential value of this route as a means of transtropical migration.

Vicarious Species or Species Pairs

In comparing the floras of two regions it is generally easy to see that certain species in one are perfectly distinct from any of the species in the other. Similarly, unless the floras are very different from one another there will generally be found some species that are common to both. In addition, however, to these well-marked differences and resemblances it will often be found that there are in the one flora certain species so closely similar to species in the other that it is difficult to say whether they should be regarded as identical or not. If the differences between them are very slight they will probably be considered no more than races or varieties of the same species, but if the differences are larger, they will generally be considered to be two distinct but closely related species. In these latter circumstances the two species are usually referred to as vicarious species or as a species pair. In each such pair one species is the geographical counterpart or representative of the other. Many such pairs are to be seen, for example, between the floras of North America and Eurasia. The American *Maianthemum canadense* represents there the Eurasian *M. bifolium*; *Epigaea repens* parallels *E. asiatica*; and there are instances in several other genera, including *Actaea* and *Scheuchzeria* (672). It is not however altogether easy to give an account of these pairs because their recognition depends so much on individual taxonomic conceptions. One authority may regard certain species of one region as identical with those of another, while a second may reckon them to form two distinct or vicarious species. In the northern hemisphere again the American form of *Hepatica triloba* is sometimes regarded as specifically distinct from the European plant and much the same is true of *Anemone quinquefolia* and *A. nemorosa*, *Oxalis montana* and *O. acetosella*, *Luzula saltuensis* and *L. pilosa*, *Vallisneria americana* and *V. spiralis*, *Ranunculus laxicaulis* and *R. flammula*, and *Scrophularia marilandica* and *S. nodosa*. The western European *Littorella uniflora* is sometimes regarded as distinct from the North American plant, and differences have been demonstrated between the representatives of the genus *Lysichitum* on either side of the Bering Strait. Nor need the isolation between the populations be a water one and there are pairs between the eastern and western sides of North America, such as *Carex misandroides* and *C. petricosa* and *Arenaria marcescens* and *A. obtusiloba* and the many instances quoted by Sharp in his study of the relationship between the floras of California and the south-eastern United States (645). Among Eurasian pairs are *Gentiana amarella*, in the west, and *G. acuta*, in the east, and this is a particularly interesting case because the latter species extends eastwards across the Bering Strait and right across temperate North America. Again, although we speak of pairs, there may be cases where more than two species are involved, as in one of the most notable of all, the *Chamaepericlymenum* section of the genus *Cornus*. This has been mapped by Regel (332) who claims that there are three species with the distributions shown in Fig. 59. It will be seen that *C. suecica* and *C. unalaschkensis* are widely discontinuous, and that *C. suecica* and *C. canadensis* overlap in the Far East, in western America and in Greenland, *C. suecica*, it should be noted, was reported by Kingdon-Ward from the mountains of Upper Burma (425). Japan, no doubt because of its insularity, shows many examples of vicariism, especially at subspecific level and these have been exhaustively dealt with by Hara (335, 337).

But such pairs are by no means confined to the northern temperate regions. There are many in the tropics, as for instance (30) *Flacourtia flavescens*, *Balanites aegyptiaca*, and *Anogeissus leiocarpus* in Africa and their counterparts *F. indica*, *B. roxburghii* and *A. pendula* in India. Skottsberg (662) mentions several between Java and Hawaii, including *Gahnia javanica* and *G. gaudichaudii*, and *Vaccinium varingiifolium* and *V. peleanum*. Similarly between Juan Fernandez and Hawaii there are pairs in *Cladium scorpoideum* and *C. angustifolium* and in *Plantago fernandezia* and *P. principis*. In the southern extra-tropical regions, too, there are interesting pairs. The New Zealand species *Donatia novae-zelandiae*, *Drosera stenophylla*, *Gaimardia setacea*, *Oxalis lactea* and *Pratia angulata* are represented in South America by

Donatia fascicularis, Drosera uniflora, Gaimardia australis, Oxalis magellanica and *Pratia repens* respectively. Between New Zealand and Norfolk Island also there are pairs.

Still other miscellaneous examples are *Loudetia flammula* in tropical South America and *L. phragmitoides* in tropical Africa; *Ascolepis setigera* in West Africa

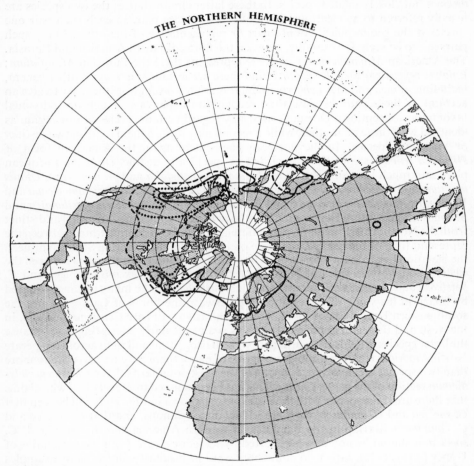

Fig. 59.—Map showing the distribution of the three closely allied species of the section *Chamaepericlymenum* of the genus *Cornus*, i.e. *C. suecica*, continuous line (note the two outliers): *C. canadensis*, broken lines: *C. unalashkensis* dotted line. Mainly after Regel and Hultén.

and *A. gracilis* in south-east Asia; *Acacia sowdenii* and *A. loderi* (161) in South Australia, separated by the Flinders Range; the two sea-grasses, *Halophila decipiens* of the Indo-Pacific Ocean and *H. baillonis* of the Caribbean, and the various transequatorial instances in America such as *Allenrolfea occidentalis* in western North America and *A. vaginata* and *A. patagonica* in temperate South America, or *Fagonia californica* and *F. chilensis*.

Simple or multiple vicariism of this kind is also commonly seen in connection with groups of islands. Skottsberg (668) has described several simple pairs between the two main islands of the Juan Fernandez group and even a case of three species on three different islands. He refers, too, to the palm genus *Pritchardia* in the Hawaiian Islands, which has thirty species distributed over eight islands, and here there is both water and land isolation, for the island of Oahu has nine species, each of which inhabits a separate valley. In some other genera of the Hawaiian flora also, such as *Viola* (see p. 167), much the same thing occurs. The genus *Scalesia* in the Galapagos Islands is another example (see p. 219).

The foregoing exemplify what may be called the classic conception of vicarious species, which is that they are, in the definition of Cain, who gives a useful survey of the subject (104): "allopatric species which have descended from a common ancestral population and attained at least spatial isolation", a definition which emphasises their essential and original interest namely that they are to be regarded as the incipient products of a divergent evolution in which geographical isolation has been an important factor, and hence that their frequency or otherwise may be used as some measure of the phyletic relationship between the floras involved. To-day, however, the words vicarious and vicariism are applied much more loosely, and indeed to almost any binary species parallelism.

Thus Turrill (738) lists a number of species pairs between Spain and the Balkans, but some at least of these are species which, while representing one another in their respective floras, are not in fact of the closest relationship, and are rather the ecological counterparts of one another. For instance *Prunus lusitanica* in Spain is the counterpart of *P. laurocerasus* in the Balkans and others are *Hypericum coris* and *H. empetrifolium*, and *Nonnea alba* and *N. ventricosa*.

Another kind of pair to which the word vicarious is scarcely applicable because the ranges of the two may be in part or wholly coterminous, is illustrated by those mentioned by Gates (263), among them *Clintonia borealis* and *C. umbellulata*, an *Ranunculus abortivus* and *R. allegheniensis*, in which the interest lies rather in the genetic relations between the pairs. Similar instances have been noted by Tutin (743) among the European grasses, in which one member of each pair is diploid and the other tetraploid.

Another particular kind of vicariism, which may be described as climatic, is illustrated very well by the two littoral species *Ipomoea pes-caprea* and *Calystegia soldanella*. The former is almost or quite pan-tropical, but the latter is more or less pan-temperate and the two meet at the Kermadecs and elsewhere in similar latitudes.

There has also been noted a vegetational vicariism, also fundamentally climatic, as in the case cited by Aubréville (30) of homologous species in the rain-forest and savannas of tropical Africa, and exemplified by *Lophira procera*, *Afrormosia elata*, *Malcolmia heudelotiana*, *Antidesma membranacea* and *Parkia filicoidea* in the former and *L. alata*, *A. laxiflora*, *M. macrophylla*, *A. venosum* and *P. bicolor* in the latter.

Then there is the widespread occurrence of ecological or edaphic vicariism in which, within the same general area two or more species are found in distinct types of habitat. One of the most familiar examples of this is afforded by the two "alpenrosen" of the Alps, *Rhododendron ferrugineum* and *R. hirsutum*, one of which occurs on granite rocks and the other on calcareous rocks, and there are other examples associated with the distribution of particular minerals such as is described in Chapter 18. In these cases there may be a good deal of real geographical segregation, on a small scale, but in others this may be scarcely discernible, as is to be seen in such pairs as *Lotus corniculatus* and *L. uliginosus* or in *Scrophularia nodosa* and *S. aquatica*. But in this direction the matter passes into the domain of plant ecology in the narrower sense and thus out of our province here.

Finally however there may be mentioned the occurrence in floras of pairs which seem to be duplicates of one another rather than substitues or vicariants, as for instance *Reseda lutea* and *R. luteola* and *Drosera rotundifolia* and *D. longifolia*. It may be that this is no more than an expression of the laws of chance, but whatever the cause the result is sufficiently conspicuous to be worth mention.

Narrowly Restricted Species

It is inherent in the cycle of distribution described in Chapter 3 that an increase in the range of a species (or other unit) is usually associated with or accompanied by an increase in the number of individual plants comprising the unit and that the reverse is also true. A species is envisaged as increasing the number of its individuals up to a maximum and thereafter diminishing until none is left and extinction results. From this it follows that species which are either very young or very old will, for quite different reasons, consist of a comparatively limited number of individuals and that their ranges will be correspondingly small. This view has already been elaborated under the heading of endemism, but something more must be said about it here.

On this argument it is clear that species may in fact consist of any number of individuals, but it is equally obvious that there is a definite lower limit to the number because no species exists unless there is at least one individual of it. Thus the minimum range of a species is the area occupied by a single individual plant. The actual spatial value of this range will, of course, depend on the size and character of this individual.

It is not unnaturally almost impossible to maintain that any particular species does in fact consist of only one individual, but in some cases only one individual has ever been seen or recorded, probably the best known being that of *Franklinia alatamaha* (240) which has already received notice. Another is that of *Pharnaceum acidum* of St. Helena which in the time of Melliss (509) was known to survive only as one plant and which perhaps has entirely disappeared since. On a slightly different but clearly related point there is a good deal of evidence that species have actually become extinct. There are various plants of cultivation such as *Cryptostegia grandiflora* and *Delonix regia* of Madagascar: *Picrella trifoliata* of the West Indies and *Amherstia nobilis* of Burma which are probably no longer to be found in a wild state; three species of *Schizochlaena* are said (553) to have been collected once in Madagascar and not again, and Ridley (594) mentions several similar cases, such as *Didymocarpus perditus* and *Strophanthus maingayi* found, but never seen again, in Singapore, and several other species all or most of which seem to have been exterminated by modification or destruction of their only habitats. There is also the puzzle of *Thismia rodwayi* and *T. americana*, which has been reconsidered lately by McLennan (474). The former has now been found in Victoria and New Zealand, as well as in Tasmania, but the latter, which is said to be very similar, if not identical, is still known only from the original gathering near Chicago, in North America, and until there is some confirmation of its natural occurrence there the possibility of some confusion remains.

Since the one-individual condition is likely to persist, except perhaps in the case of true monocarpic annuals, longer if it comes about in the course of elimination than if it is the result of speciation, there is a likelihood that such species will be species on the verge of extinction, and it is worth notice that there seems to be no instance in which a species first observed as a unique specimen has afterwards been observed to consist of many individuals clearly descended from the single ancestor. Always, it would appear, the original discovery has never been repeated.

It is therefore not difficult to believe that most of the examples just quoted at any rate were species in process of disappearance, but it is much more difficult to do this in what is probably the most extensive and puzzling of all such cases, some of the South African Stapeliads (772). Here, in these highly specialised genera, the number of species of which there is only one record is between one-third and one-half of the total, and a few of these are known only from single plants. Not only so but of thirty-six species discovered by one collector in the late eighteenth century, six have never been seen again, while others, by no means in the most remote districts, have only been rediscovered in late years. The actual status of some of these species, and especially whether they are hybrids, has yet to be decided but taking all the relevant circumstances into account it is difficult to resist the conclusion that they are young species and that such may persist exiguously for a considerable time. The case of *Notonerium gossei*, from the arid interior of South Australia, which has never again been seen since its discovery in 1873, may be a parallel and there are other Australasian species, too, which have been collected once only.

Passing from these extreme states of paucity and restriction to what may be called very local species, these can usefully be divided into three, those found in areas not much isolated geographically, those found on more or less isolated mountains, and those found on small islands. The first of these are most difficult to deal with here because the available information is seldom sufficiently exact and the following few instances must represent the category, namely *Hudsonia montana*, *Shortia galacifolia*, *Neviusia alabamensis*, which is said to exist only as one small colony, and *Caralluma winkleri*, which is described (772) as abundant over an area of a few acres, while others may be found in the flora of New Zealand (542). The work of Fernald and Marie Victorin on the floras of the shores of the Gulf of St. Lawrence (see Chapter 10) also includes references to a number of such plants, among them being *Cirsium mingaanense*, *Solidago victorinii*, *Solidago anticostensis* and several species of *Crataegus* and *Gentiana*.

Highly local montane species are more conspicuous and a number of good examples have been mentioned incidentally already, but a reminder may be given here of one or two which merit special comment. Willis (784) quotes the case of *Coleus elongatus*, which he says consists of a dozen or so plants on the mountain of Ritigala in Ceylon. This species is closely related to the more widespread *Coleus barbatus* which is also found on the mountain and there is an inference that it has been derived from it and that it is thus a good instance of a young species. Some of the isolated mountains in Malaysia and Australia, such as the Arfak Mts. in New Guinea (266) and Mt. Bellenden-Ker (265) in Queensland, also have remarkable endemic species, and Holttum (370) has recorded three species of *Loxocarpus* on three isolated mountains of the Malay Peninsula, and three species of *Hetaeria* in similar circumstances. Nor must the many peculiar facts about the tropical African mountains, described in Chapter 10 above, be forgotten. Finally of particular interest in this connection are some of the mountains in the south-eastern corner of Venezuela, such as Mt. Pacaraima, on which for instance there are three species of *Heliamphora*, and Mt. Roraima, which has a most remarkable flora including several endemic genera and many species, among them *Heliamphora nutans*. Mt. Itatiaya in south-eastern Brazil shows similar features.

Most familiar and prominent of all very narrow species are those from islands, because their bounds are so definitely and unmistakably laid down. It is perhaps this which gives rise to an impression that very restricted species are particularly associated with small islands but there seems no good evidence that this is so, and indeed some mainland species already noted are of almost the smallest possible area. There is of course the fact that species of small islands must, unless they can escape from it, be limited to its dimensions, but this is rather misleading because even the smallest islands with endemic species are much more extensive than the distributions of many continental species, and there is also the point that most islands with endemic species are not particularly isolated but are often the members of archipelagos where problems of dispersal between islands can scarcely be regarded as insuperable. There is also the question whether speciation, with its inevitable endemism, may not be favoured by narrowly insular conditions which are, of course, only one form of geographical isolation, but this is a question which is difficult to answer. It does, however, seem to be true that some comparatively small islands have numbers of endemic species greater than is usual for areas of similar size on continents, though the ranges of the individual species concerned are not themselves smaller. It also seems that certain families and genera already mentioned such as the Palmae and the genus *Cyrtandra* do seem to be specially characterised by the proportion of their species which occur on relatively small islands. Nor are these the only ones, and the genus *Weinmannia*, for instance, has among its species *W. camaguiensis* from Camagui Island in the Philippines, *W. comoroensis* from Johanna Island in the Comoros, *W. vitiensis* and *W. spiraeoides*, each from one island in the Fiji group, *W. fraxinea* from Honimo Island in the Moluccas, *W. denhami* and *W. macgillivrayi* from a single island in the New Hebrides. Several comparable species of *Begonia* have already been mentioned in Chapter 8.

In fact practically all the more isolated small islands, even in archipelagos, except low coral atolls, have their own species, as for instance Christmas Island with sixteen endemics, and Easter Island with several, but there are many also on islands which are far from isolated, including *Cakile alacranensis* from the four islands of the Alacran Reef off Yucatan (520). In the Bahamas Taylor (727) has stressed the same thing, especially in the island of Inagua, which has no fewer than thirteen endemic species. Taking the archipelago as a whole also there are seven endemic species of *Agave*, four of them on one island only. *Coprosma* is another genus with some very narrow insular endemics and Oliver (541) includes three from Raiatea; two from the Kermadecs, from Lord Howe, from Norfolk Island and from Masatierra; and one each from the Chatham Islands, Pitcairn, Rapa, Rarotonga and the Tuamotus. Some of the tiny islands close to the shores of New Zealand, such as the Solanders, Herekopere and the Three Kings have endemic species (129), those of the last named including *Tecomanthe speciosa* and *Plectomirtha baylisiana* (544), both of which belong to families otherwise unrepresented in the flora of New Zealand. Rather similarly with regard to Norfolk Island three endemic species have been described from the closely adjacent Phillip Island (437). One of these, *Streblorrhiza speciosa*, which forms a monotypic genus, was among the species exterminated in early days by the importation of goats but which persisted in cultivation and is therefore in some ways comparable with *Franklinia*.

Still other examples of interest are *Maerua dupontii* from Aldabra Island, *Rapinia collina* from a tiny island off New Caledonia, *Aulacocarpus crassifolius* from Gorgona Island, *Rhipsalis megalantha* from San Sebastian Island near Rio de Janeiro, *Sesuvium distylium* and other from Fernando Noronha, *Campanula vidalii* from a rock in the Azores, *Dendrobium superbiens* from Thursday Island in the Torres

Strait, *Latania loddigesii* and *Pandanus vandermeeschii* on three, and *Hyophorbe amaricaulis* on one, of the small islets just north of Mauritius.

Many of the species mentioned in the last few paragraphs may be described as very scarce and although it is not our purpose here to discuss the causes of rarity as such it is appropriate to draw the reader's attention to a paper by Griggs (317) in which many of the special features of these plants are commented upon with interesting suggestions.

The Distribution of the Marine Angiosperms, or Sea-grasses
(Plate 15)

There is one small group of flowering plants so different from all the rest in character and habitat that its geography merits very special attention in any general survey of plant distribution. This group consists of a small number of genera which live actually completely submerged in the shallow coastal waters of seas and which are popularly called the "sea-grasses". The distribution of these plants has been described in detail by Ostenfeld in a number of papers, and the data have been collected together and illustrated by a series of maps (332). There are about eight genera concerned, three of them, *Zostera*, *Phyllospadix* (Fig. 60) and *Posidonia*, being found in temperate waters, and the rest in tropical seas.

The genus *Zostera* has been divided into eleven species distributed as follows:

Zostera marina	.	.	Northern temperate seas from the latitude of south west Greenland almost to the tropics in eastern North America and East Asia (632).
Z. caespitosa	.	.	Japan.
Z. asiatica	.	.	Japan and Korea.
Z. caulescens	.	.	Japan and Korea.
Z. japonica	.	.	Japan and Sakhalin.
Z. nana	.	.	North Atlantic Europe.
Z. capensis	.	.	South Africa.
Z. capricorni	.	.	Australia.
Z. muelleri	.	.	Australia.
Z. novazelandica	.	.	New Zealand.
Z. tasmanica	.	.	South Australia and (?) Tasmania.

Posidonia with two species shows great discontinuity, one species being Mediterranean and the other South Australian.

Phyllospadix has three species. Two of these overlap on the west coast of North America from California northwards, and one of them reaches to Alaska. The third species is on the Riukiu Islands on the opposite side of the Pacific.

The five tropical genera (Fig. 61) comprise twenty-three species. It is unnecessary to describe their ranges in detail as these can be appreciated from the map (Plate 15), and it will be enough here to tabulate the leading points relating thereto which are not altogether apparent there. They are:

1. Only one species, *Thalassia testudinum*, is in both the Old and New Worlds and even this is thought by some to comprise two species, one in each hemisphere. It occurs in eastern America and in the Indian Ocean, so that even here there is complete oceanic segregation.

2. Seventeen out of the other twenty-two are found only in the Old World, a preponderance scarcely surprising in view of the immensely longer coast-line there.

3. The remaining five species are confined to America. All are east coast species and confined to the shores of the Caribbean, so that they have rather restricted ranges.

4. There is only a single species on the west coast of Africa, and this is a Mediterranean one which reaches down the coast to Senegambia.

5. Another species is confined to a very restricted part of Western Australia.

6. All the rest, fifteen in number, inhabit the Indian and Pacific Oceans and divide into those which occur in East Africa and those which do not.

Fig. 60.—*Phyllospadix scouleri*, about half natural size, after Engler.

7. Of the ten species which do so, eight are found in some part of the Madagascar region.

8. Of the five non-African species, three reach from some part of Asia to Australasia or the Pacific Islands; one is found from Ceylon to Borneo; the other in the Riukiu Islands.

9. Of the ten found in East Africa, five reach Asia, Australasia and the Pacific Islands; three reach Asia and Australia; one is discontinuous between Africa and Australia, and the last is confined to Africa and the Madagascar region.

Such are the more general features of the distribution of these plants, and much the most striking of them are the segregation in the hemispheres and the absence from the west coasts of the American and African continents. There are also the following minor features, which are partly shown on the map but which are more apparent in the original publications:

FIG. 61.—*Cymodocea ciliata*, a tropical marine Angiosperm, somewhat reduced, after Engler.

1. Of the eleven species which reach the Red Sea, six cover practically all of it; three cover only the southern half; and two only touch south-west Arabia or Aden.

2. Of eight species in the Madagascar region, five occur only in the north of Madagascar; two in the north of Madagascar and on Mauritius; and one covers the Comoros and all Madagascar.

3. Of six species in India, three are only in Ceylon: two are only in Ceylon and south India; and one only is all round the coasts.

4. Of thirteen species in Australia, seven are confined to the north or north-east; five are local elsewhere, and only one is on all coasts.

5. Of seven species in the Pacific Islands, six are restricted to the western groups; only one reaches further east, and there is none in Hawaii.

These latter points clearly reveal that, despite the differences in specific distributions, there are nevertheless certain prevalent range limits and the possible significance of these will be discussed later (p. 354). Meanwhile it may be said that the distribution of the sea-grasses in relation to water temperatures has been studied by Setchell (632), who divides the oceans into the following five latitudinal zones:

Upper boreal with a mean maximum temperature of 0°–10° C.
Lower boreal   ,,   ,,   ,,   ,,   10°–15° C.
Temperate   ,,   ,,   ,,   ,,   15°–20° C.
Subtropical   ,,   ,,   ,,   ,,   20°–25° C.
Tropical   ,,   ,,   ,,   ,,   25° or more.

He finds that of the thirty-four species under discussion, eighteen are confined to the tropical zone, eight to either the subtropical or temperate zones. Only *Zostera marina* is found in the boreal zone, and only one other species, *Halophila ovalis*, is found in more than two of the zones.

Mangroves
(Plate 16)

Mangrove forests are found in muddy tidal waters along much of the coasts of the tropics, and in some places outside. The flora is a very specialised one, consisting of the mangroves proper, which are shrubs or trees belonging to about half a dozen genera, and a few associated species rarely or never found elsewhere (838). The number of species of mangroves and their most generally associated species is about thirty, and they are more or less restricted to latitudes below 25°, though in places, as in Japan and the North Island of New Zealand, they reach much higher latitudes.

In many respects the distribution of the species is reminiscent of that of the marine Angiosperms, but as the following list shows, there are a number of other interesting points about them:

1. No species is at all completely distributed over the coasts of both hemispheres.

2. There is complete segregation between the species west of Africa and those to the east.

3. The species have been split somewhat, but of *sensu latissime* there are only four in the New World, i.e. *Rhizophora mangle*, *Laguncularia racemosa* and *Avicennia nitida* which occur on both west and east coasts, and *Rhizophora racemosa*, which is only on the east coast. *R. mangle*, *R. racemosa* and *L. racemosa* occur also in West Africa, while *R. mangle* is found in the Pacific Islands.

4. Species of the East African coasts number about eight; six extend east to Australasia and the Pacific Islands; one to Malaysia (*Ceriops candolleana*); and the other, *Avicennia marina*, ranges from the Madagascar region to the Persian Gulf.

5. Of the rest no fewer than seven range from India to some part of the Malayan Archipelago, and three from India to Australasia or the Pacific Islands. *Avicennia alba* and *A. sphaerocarpa* range from continental south-east Asia into Malaysia; *Sonneratia apetala* and *Avicennia lanata* are in continental south-east Asia only.

PLATE 15

Map of the World showing the distribution of the
species of Marine Angiosperms, excluding the genus
Zostera.
After Ostenfeld in Pflanzenareale.

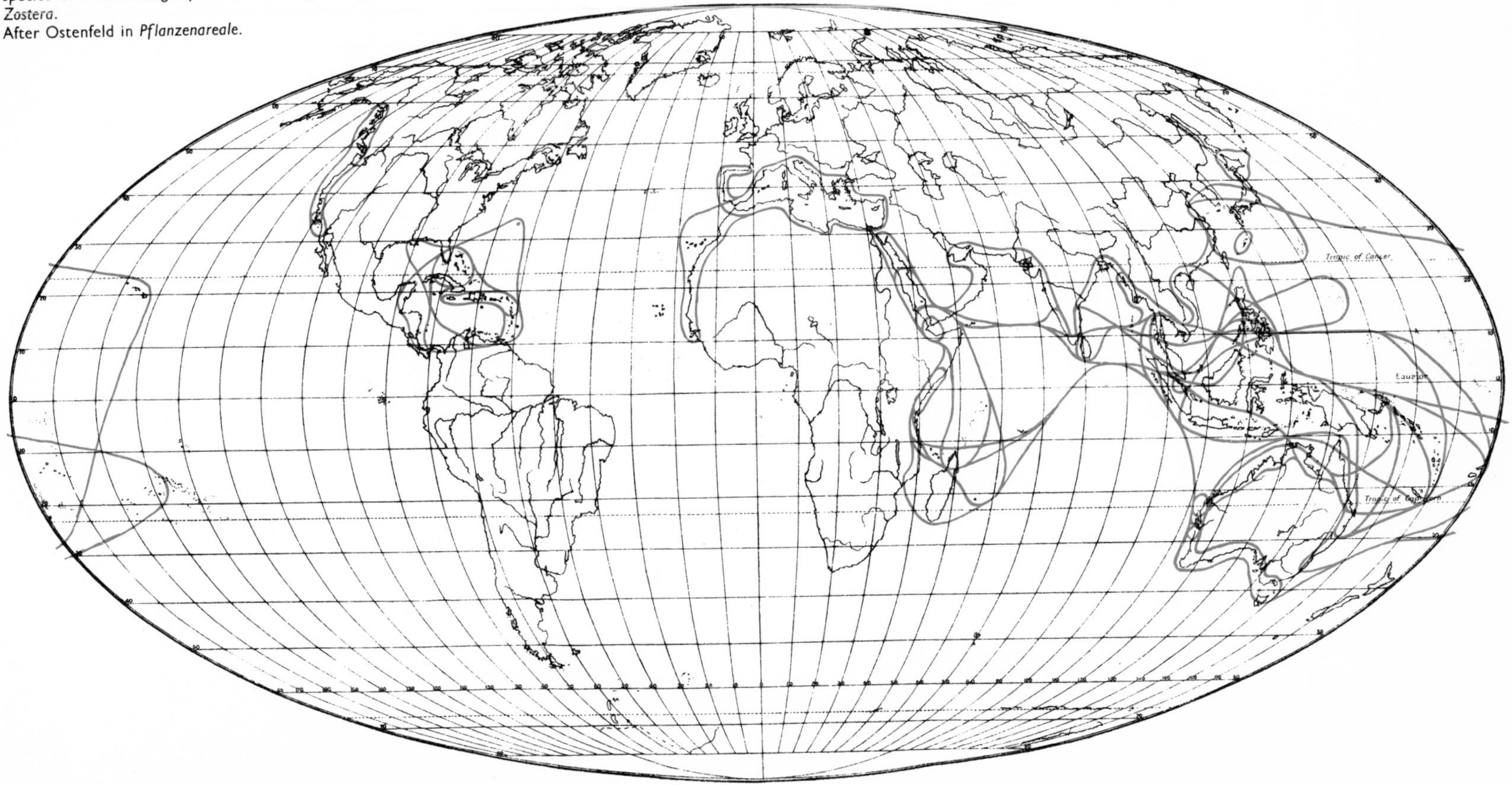

Areas correct   Distortion increasing (towards border of map).
Approximate Scale 1:100,000,000 (1600 miles=1inch) along Equator
on Mollweide's Homolographic Projection
Copyright

6. *Avicennia eucalyptifolia* ranges from Malaysia to Australia; *A. balanophora* is in Australia only; *A. resinifera* is in Australia and the Pacific Islands; and *A. tomentosa* is in the Malayan Archipelago.

7. No species occur in Hawaii or east of Samoa and Tonga.

8. The concentration of species in tropical Asia is more marked than in the marine Angiosperms, as the following tabulation into areas shows:

Western America	Eastern America	West Africa	East Africa	Madag.	India	S.E. Asia	Malaysia	Australia	Pacific Is.
2	4	3	8	9	18	23	23	10	12

The distribution of the mangroves thus follows in quite a number of ways that of the marine Angiosperms, and other points of resemblance could be noted did space permit. For instance, here again we find that nearly all the species in India are on the south coast or in Ceylon. Perhaps the main difference from the marine Angiosperms is the occurrence of species on both sides of the Atlantic and on both coasts of America.

The Distribution of Strand Plants

A number of flowering plants are found only on sea beaches or among the vegetation immediately associated with these beaches and such are generally referred to as littoral, or strand, plants. Some, such as *Cakile maritima, Calystegia soldanella* and *Salsola kali* are familiar inhabitants of temperate or even colder latitudes, but most are confined to the tropics, where they form a very characteristic and conspicuous feature of coastal vegetation, and it is to these in particular that the term "strand plants" is more narrowly applied.

It is not altogether easy to say what species properly compose this flora because there are many borderline cases especially with the mangroves, and for this reason no complete analysis of them is attempted here, but the number of species concerned is low and on most estimates is less than one hundred. The typical members show two particular features, buoyancy of seeds or fruits permitting their natural carriage by sea unharmed, and physiological specialisation enabling them to germinate and maintain themselves in close proximity to the sea, or to be more precise, where the sea is likely to have cast them, both these points being illustrated by the fact that the vegetation of low coral atolls is largely, and often entirely, composed of these plants (see p. 215).

For these reasons strand plants are of special interest to students of such subjects as plant dispersal and the historical development of tropical, and especially tropical insular, floras and it is mainly from these aspects that one of the most important accounts of them, that by Guppy (325), was written. This book deals with all manner of problems involving these plants and emphasises many points of great interest about them, as for instance the various structural conditions which may lead to buoyancy, the facts that Leguminosae are particularly conspicuous in the strand flora, that the strand flora of the Hawaiian Islands is notably meagre, that few strand plants are not somewhere or other found growing naturally inland, and that over much of the Pacific the spread of these plants seems to have been against the directions of the prevailing currents.

The distribution of tropical strand plants follows the same lines as that of the tropical marine Angiosperms and the mangroves, though it is rather more generalised than either, and the connection is strong with the latter plants, their main

16

latitudinal limits being about the same (about 25° N. and S.) and the ecological distinction between them being indistinct. Some of the species occur apparently naturally on almost all tropical coasts wherever the substratum is suitable, among these being *Cassytha filiformis*, *Dodonaea viscosa*, *Hibiscus tiliaceus*, *Ipomoea pescaprae* and *Thespesia populnea*, and some of them show a measure of geographical variation (251). These species show little segregation between continents or between the opposite sides of continents, and this is also shown on a smaller scale by *Dalbergia ecastophyllum* and *Drepanocarpus lunatus*, which occur on both sides of the Atlantic, and by *Batis maritima* and *Hippomane mancinella*, which are found on both coasts of tropical America.

The majority of strand plants, however, including some of the best known, do not occur in the Atlantic, and it is the Indian and west Pacific Oceans which are especially the home of these plants (79, 344). These wide Old World species include *Barringtonia speciosa*, *Calophyllum inophyllum*, *Casuarina equisetifolia*, *Cordia subcordata*, *Guettarda speciosa*, *Pemphis acidula*, *Pongamia glabra*, *Scaevola koenigii* and *Tournefortia argentea*, and Merrill has given a useful survey of them (514). Some of these, including the first-named, reach far across the Pacific, but there is none on Juan Fernandez or the Galapagos.

Two groups of species with rather lesser ranges are those which are characteristically Asiatic, though often extending thence eastward, as *Crinum asiaticum*, *Samadera indica* and *Triumfetta subpalmata*, and the rather few distinctively New World species most of which are on the east side of America, and which include *Coccolobis uvifera*, *Euphorbia buxifolia* and *Omphalea triandra*. A few species which may perhaps claim mention here, notably the more riverine *Nipa fruticans*, are even more local (see Fig. 75).

CHAPTER 12

THE FLORAS OF THE SOUTHERN HEMISPHERE

IN Chapter 4 the question arose as to whether or not there is a recognisable "southern" flora below the equator, comparable with, and the counterpart of, the more familiar " northern " flora above it, and a short account was given of the families which particularly characterise the Flowering Plants in southern latitudes. The floras to which these families contribute so conspicuously have, for various reasons, always been of outstanding interest to plant geographers, but in recent years this interest has quickened because it has become increasingly clear that among them are to be sought the most promising clues to a solution of the fundamental problem of historical plant geography, that of discovering whence, and by what paths, the Flowering Plants have distributed themselves over the globe in the pattern now familiar to us. The subject of the resemblances and differences between these various southern floras, which must be the basis for any estimation of their mutual relationships, has thus become more and more topical and some brief comparative account of it in this new chapter is very necessary.

As has already been pointed out, the northern and southern hemispheres are the reverse of one another geographically. The North Pole is near the centre of an arctic ocean, almost completely surrounded by land; the South Pole is near the centre of an ice-covered continent everywhere surrounded by water. In lower latitudes the contrast is equally regular, the chief land masses below the equator forming, or being in the position of, extensions southward from the almost continuous land-belt of the north, and the larger seas of the northern hemisphere being northerly extensions of the great circumpolar southern ocean. In consequence the chief land surfaces below the equator are much more widely separated from one another than those of the north.

It might be expected with reason that this greater geographical isolation would be expressed, in varying degree, by botanical differences, but in fact the floras of the southern hemisphere show a much more complex pattern of affinities than can be attributed merely to their respective positions. Clearly historical factors have been of great significance in producing the state of affairs existing today and it is particularly the clarification of these factors which is the first objective.

The number of separate land masses in the southern hemisphere is very large, especially in the Australasian–Polynesian sector between 90° E. and 120° W., but many of these are so small and have floras so inconsiderable that they can be ignored in a general survey. In the others, which vary much in size, the floras show characteristics which make the disentangling of their relationships a difficult matter and, often, a subject of considerable speculation. Nevertheless, although no southern flora is entirely without interest of its own, a comparatively small number of them embodies virtually all the facts which need be considered here, and so some bounds can be set to a review by confining it to these, which number about a dozen.

First, there are three very large continental floras, namely those of more temperate South America and of southern Africa, and that of Australia. In America and Africa, because of the geographical continuity across the equator, there is little or no real distinction between the tropical floras on the north side and those on the south, and it is therefore feasible to confine attention to the southern extra-tropical parts of these continents, but in Australia the situation is different. Here not only is the continent separated by sea from the southern equatorial belt but within the continent itself there is little or no floristic distinction on the two sides of the Tropic of Capricorn and for both these reasons it is more appropriate to deal with the whole of Australia as a single floristic area.

The insularity of Malaysia and the fact that the equator traverses it so as to leave some islands on one side and some on the other suggests that there may be other floras here which ought to be taken into account, but, in fact, those to the north-west of Australia have so much in common with their neighbours to the north again and so little with the floras of Australasia that they also can be ignored, but New Guinea, which lies north of Australia, is a very different matter and its flora is one of the most significant of all. Indeed, it is very much the largest of five important and rich insular floras of which a good deal must be said, namely those of New Guinea, the Madagascar region, Fiji, New Caledonia, and New Zealand. There are also the floras of the Bismarck Archipelago, the Solomon Islands, and of the New Hebrides, but not only are these much less completely known but they tend only to emphasise points even more apparent in the five insular floras already mentioned and it would therefore only complicate matters unnecessarily to include them. At the same time it should be borne in mind that when they are better known they may reveal features of particular bearing on the subject of floristic relations in this part of the world.

Finally, there are five smaller insular floras, those of St. Helena, Juan Fernandez, Norfolk Island, Lord Howe Island, and that of the South Temperate Oceanic Islands.

Of the first three, continental, floras that of South America below the Tropic of Capricorn, though comparable in richness with the other two, is from the phyto-geographical point of view, perhaps the least striking, and for a very interesting reason. Only in this geographical sector of the world is there practically complete physical and climatic continuity between the northern and southern temperate regions, and this is thought to have existed, unbroken except for comparatively minor changes in Central America and the Caribbean, for much of later geological time. In addition, the main relief on this continent is a great longitudinal backbone, forming the Rockies and the Andes, which affords scattered areas of temperate climate right across the tropics. Thus here, in the New World, there has long been a notable absence of physical and ecological barriers to plant migration, and in consequence southern and northern elements of the American flora have mingled so much that the present southern extra-tropical flora has no degree of local peculiarity comparable with that of either of its two fellows in the Old World. This is in itself a fact of great significance in relation to the history of southern floras and must be constantly kept in mind, but it does mean that the flora of temperate South America is not, in certain respects, as striking as it might otherwise be.

In Africa there is again geographical continuity across the equator, though in neither direction does this extend far into temperate latitudes, but there is little or no climatic or ecological continuity, because the equatorial zone is bordered on both sides by arid regions, and the mountain system within the tropics is of a peculiar kind (see p. 202). It is difficult to assess the effect of these physical conditions on the flora of temperate southern Africa but it seems likely that it is largely owing to them that it is very distinctive, and they may also contribute, in ways not altogether clear, to the fact that it is very rich. It is true that along the south-east coast of the continent there is some of the intermingling of tropical and temperate elements so noticeable in South America, but this may be comparatively recent, and the general impression is that the flora has long been more or less segregated from the equatorial zone by aridity on its northern front.

In the Asiatic–Australian sector, the situation is different again. Here all the land in the equatorial zone, say between 10 degrees of the equator, is composed of islands, and most of it is *south* of the line, but, even more important, Australia lies just to the south again. Moreover, south-east of Australia are the large islands of New Zealand, while east lie the innumerable smaller islands of the south and south-west Pacific. This part of the southern hemisphere is thus more complex geographically than the rest (it includes no fewer than seven of the thirteen floras listed above) and presents many more problems to the plant geographer, so that it merits special attention. All this makes it difficult to compare it botanically with America and Africa, and all that need be said at the moment is that the flora of Australia (which accounts for four-fifths of the land surface of the whole area) is even more distinctive than that of southern Africa. The degree of this particularity tends to be underestimated some-times because there has obviously been some mutual botanical interchange across the Torres Strait, but when allowance is made for this it is clear that the Australian flora proper is exceptionally distinctive. The situation here may be seen more vividly if we imagine a botanist travelling south-east from continental Asia. In the course of his journey he would doubtless observe a gradual floristic change with latitude but he would scarcely be conscious of any special or major discontinuity until he had passed latitude 10° S. Here, however, once across the Torres Strait, he would find he had passed suddenly into a different world and into an almost wholly new flora and fauna. Nowhere else in the world is there so fundamental a botanical change within a distance of 100 miles as there is across the Torres Strait. Certainly a similar degree of change would be observed between Australia and its eastern neighbours New Cal-edonia and New Zealand, but here the intervening distance is so much greater as to make it much less impressive. The phytogeographical situation in Australasia is thus quite different from that in America or Africa and presents particularly thorny problems.

This lack of floristic compatibility between Australia and its neighbours con-stitutes what may justifiably be called an anomaly in the pattern of the floras of the southern hemisphere and this is made even clearer when the five large insular floras are considered. In each of these at least three-quarters of the species are endemic, and in one or two of them the quality of this endemism is high, but they are not anomalous. Thus, in view of its position, the New Guinea flora, as will be seen, shows a normal relationship with that of Malaysia and Melanesia in general. The flora of Fiji, which is the least remarkable of the five, is similarly related to that of New Guinea. The flora of New Caledonia is highly specialised but is basically closest akin to the floras of the rest of Melanesia. New Zealand has much in common with the flora of *south-east* Australia and Tasmania but, allowing for the difference of latitude, it has more relationship with New Caledonia and New Guinea than with the flora of the rest of Australia. Finally the flora of the Madagascar region, though possessing some very interesting features of its own, is, on the whole, not very much more than a somewhat specialised version of the general tropical flora of the Old World. The remaining five floras, those of the small isolated islands, all have peculiarities of their own which in detail serve to emphasise various aspects of the general picture, but they are too small to be compared directly with those already mentioned, though they will be dealt with faithfully in due course.

Such, then, is a general outline of the situation which confronts the plant-geographer in the southern hemisphere, but two important qualifications must be added. To-day, Antarctica (which is but little smaller than Australia) is almost wholly covered by an ice-cap of great thickness, and to all intents and purposes is without flowering plants, and for this reason has not been mentioned, but this state of affairs has prevailed only since the coming of the Pleistocene and its Ice Ages. Before that time (see p. 323) Antarctica bore a considerable vegetation, which contained floristic elements, such as *Nothofagus*, now familiar in both South America and Australasia. In these conditions Antarctica would have been no barrier to plant migration but would rather have formed a connection across what are now the South Polar regions.

It must also be remembered that the level of the oceans relative to the land has not always been exactly as it is to-day. The tectonic changes to which so many of the true oceanic islands are due is witness enough of this, but there must also be taken into account the fact that the larger the polar ice-caps the more water is locked up in them, and *vice versa*, so that in later geological times there has probably been considerable eustatic fluctuation in the sea level.

Having thus set the scene, let us now turn to a brief but systematic account of these southern floras. Many of the facts relating to them appear elsewhere in this book and may be referred to there, but they are nowhere else co-ordinated from the point of view of the particular subject of this chapter and therefore no apology is needed for repeating certain of them.

Temperate South America

There is no complete recent review of the flora of the whole of this region but an analysis made some thirty years ago (291) still sufficiently reveals its outstanding features, namely its general lack of peculiarity and its relationship with the floras of temperate Australasia.

In 1933 (*loc cit.*) the flora was estimated to comprise some 1,500 genera and something like 12,500 species. In numbers of genera and species the families best represented are:

	Genera		Species
Compositae	180	Compositae	over 2,000
Gramineae	106	Gramineae	over 1,000
Papilionaceae	c. 75	Papilionaceae	c. 650
Orchidaceae	c. 40	Solanaceae	
Solanaceae	c. 40	Rubiaceae	
Rubiaceae		Orchidaceae	
Asclepiadaceae		Cyperaceae	
Liliaceae		Cactaceae	
Euphorbiaceae		Cruciferae	Probably
Boraginaceae		Myrtaceae	c. 200
Scrophulariaceae		Oxalidaceae	each
Labiatae		Scrophulariaceae	

The case of the Solanaceae is noteworthy because this family has comparatively few genera and nearly half of them are represented.

The genera with more than 100 species are *Senecio* 446 spp., *Adesmia* 260, *Oxalis, Solanum, Calceolaria, Acaena, Baccharis, Astragalus, Eugenia, Chloraea, Verbena, Plantago, Haplopappus, Echinocactus*. Of the *fifty* largest genera in the flora only one (*Nassauvia*) is endemic and only about a dozen are distinctly southern in general distribution. Most of these latter are more or less confined to South America, the others being *Oxalis* (widespread, but with hundreds of species in South America and South Africa), *Calandrinia* (well represented also in Australia), *Acaena* (widely distributed in southern floras) and *Azorella* (which occurs also in New Zealand).

Nowadays there are reckoned to be seven endemic families but these contain only eight genera and less than eighty species. The number of endemic genera is about 300, and these contain some 900 species, though most of them are monotypic. Fifty-odd of them belong to the Compositae, including the largest (*Nassauvia*) with over 60 species, and next come the Liliaceae with sixteen and the Solanaceae with fourteen. It would appear that about 90 per cent of all the species in the flora are endemic but for an area the size of temperate South America this figure is not very significant.

Of all the genera in the flora some fifty-odd are almost or quite confined to the southern hemisphere, and all these occur in some part of Australasia (see Appendix B, categories C and E). Only about three, however, are found also in South Africa, namely *Acaena*, *Gunnera* and *Tetragonia* (which has most of its species there) and there seems to be no genus recorded from temperate South America and South Africa only. This general South American–Australasian relationship is most shown in the flora of Chile and Fuegia, where the genus *Nothofagus* dominates much of the vegetation, just as it does in New Zealand.

It is interesting to note that most of these South American–Australasian genera, to which we shall return again later, are small and fairly evenly balanced in species between the two regions. A few, notably *Fuchsia*, *Gaultheria* and *Pernettia*, *Azorella*, *Calandrinia*, and *Calceolaria* (in the sense of including *Jovellana*), are much larger and all these have a strong preponderance of species in South America. *Haloragis*, which is American only by virtue of its occurrence on Juan Fernandez, appears to be the only genus with a strong Australasian predominance.

A more complicated and less obvious expression of this general relationship is seen among the genera which are discontinuously distributed between the northern and southern temperate regions (see Appendix B, category D). In some of these "bipolar" genera, as they have been called (205), there is a distinct affinity between the species of South America and those of Australasia, one of the best examples being *Caltha*, in which these species have a characteristic leaf-form.

Temperate Southern Africa

Here, again, there is no complete flora of the whole of the continent south of the Tropic of Capricorn, which includes a good deal of South West Africa as well as the southernmost part of Portuguese East Africa but Phillips' careful summary (557) of the flora of the former Union of South Africa, which comprises by far the larger, and botanically most interesting, part.

The flora of the Union contains about 1,500 genera and well over 15,000 species, figures which, considering that the area is only about a quarter of that of Temperate South America, and that much of it is arid, are remarkably high. Moreover, the species are much concentrated in that small part of the Cape Province which constitutes a distinct South African floristic kingdom (see pp. 139 and 207) and here the richness is quite extraordinary and, in the southern hemisphere at least, equalling perhaps only that in one or two localised parts of Australia.

The leading families are:

	Genera		Species
Compositae	over 160	Compositae	c. 2,000
Gramineae	c. 100	Liliaceae	c. 1,000
Papilionaceae	c. 75	Papilionaceae	c. 900
Liliaceae	c. 75	Aizoaceae	c. 700
Asclepiadaceae		Ericaceae	c. 650
Orchidaceae		Asclepiadaceae	c. 550
Scrophulariaceae		Orchidaceae	c. 550
Aizoaceae		Iridaceae	c. 500
Euphorbiaceae		Gramineae	
Iridaceae		Scrophulariaceae	
Rubiaceae		Euphoribiaceae	
Cyperaceae	c. 30	Crassulaceae	c. 300

The largest genera are *Erica* and *Mesembryanthemum* (in the wide sense) each with more than 500 species, *Crassula* (about 250), *Senecio, Pelargonium, Helichrysum, Euphorbia, Indigofera, Wahlenbergia, Agathosma, Hermannia, Oxalis, Gladiolus, Thesium* (about 130). One of the most pronounced features of the flora is the great development of certain groups of stem and leaf succulents, especially the cactoid Stapelieae and Euphorbieae, the leaf-succulent Crassulaceae, and innumerable geophytic monocotyledons.

There are nine endemic families with about 115 species, and of these the Bruniaceae, a family of ericoid shrubs with a dozen genera, accounts for 65 of them. The endemic genera number nearly 500, or rather more than a third of the total, and these contain more than 3,000 species, which is more than 20 per cent of the total and a noteworthy figure. The endemic species certainly amount to 90 per cent or more and the proportion in the small Cape Region is probably about the same.

The largest endemic genera are *Agathosma* and *Aspalathus* with about 150 species each, *Heliophila, Leucadendron, Pteronia, Lachenalia, Cliffortia, Gasteria, Serruria, Diascia, Struthiola, Massonia, Zaluzyanskya, Rafnia, Adinandra* and *Pentzia*, the last few having about 30 species each.

These genera by no means comprehend all the groups which give strong character to the flora and vegetation as a whole. The succulents have already been noted, and among the rest the two families Proteaceae and Restionaceae are perhaps the most prominent and often cited, but others are the genera *Aloe, Erica, Mesembryanthemum, Oxalis* and *Pelargonium*; other geophilous Iridaceae and Liliaceae; the tribe Genisteae of the Papilionaceae and, in the north, the genus *Acacia* of Mimosaceae; many shrubby composites especially of the Inuleae; others of the Arctotideae; many, often ericoid, Rutaceae and Thymelaeaceae; Campanulaceae and Lobeliaceae.

From the phytogeographical point of view the most notable items are the Proteaceae and Restionaceae because it is chiefly in these two families that a strong and often-quoted relationship with the flora of Australasia is seen. The situation in the Proteaceae has already been outlined on p. 78. In the Restionaceae there are about a dozen genera in South Africa of which all but three are endemic, these three being *Restio*, a large genus with most of its species in South Africa, one in Madagascar, and the remainder in Australia; *Hypolaena*, also in Australia and New Zealand, and *Leptocarpus* which is also in South America (where it is the only member of the family) Australia, New Zealand, New Guinea and south-east Asia. Another dozen genera of the family are endemic to Australasia.

Other instances of this Australasian relationship are the occurrence in Australia of two or three species of *Pelargonium*; of one species of *Moraea*, otherwise a South African genus; of a species of *Anacampseros* (825), similarly otherwise South African; some species of *Carpobrotus* (one species is also in Chile); a minority of the species in the Liliaceous genera *Bulbine* and *Bulbinella*; and species of the genus *Australina*, one of them also in New Zealand. The Rhamnaceae and Cyperaceae also show some affinities but the genera of the latter are confusing. There are also certain genera (see Appendix B, category D.*c.*) which, in the southern hemisphere, are found only in South Africa and Australia.

Australia

The line of the tropic in Australia bears little or no relation to major physical features or to state boundaries so that in any event it would be difficult to arrive at figures for the extratropical part of the continent alone, but, as explained earlier, the general insularity of Australia, as well as the fact that its flora proper shows comparatively little segregation into temperate and tropical, makes it more appropriate to consider the continent as a whole, remembering nevertheless that one-third of its area is north of the Tropic of Capricorn.

There is no recent floral survey of Australia as a whole, but from various state lists and from other sources it would appear that the flora consists of about 1,500 genera and over 12,000 species (see also p. 157), which means that the flora is not so rich in proportion to area as that of South America and considerably less so than that of South Africa. A partial explanation of this is, no doubt, that in contrast to South America much of Australia is very arid; while in contrast to South Africa, where also aridity is widespread, there is no well-developed and specialised herbaceous desert flora. Notwithstanding this there are parts of the south-west and south-east of Australia where the floristic richness is comparable with that of the localised Cape flora.

The order of families in the flora is:

	Genera		*Species*
Graminaeae	*c.* 150	Papilionaceae	*c.* 800
Papilionaceae		Myrtaceae	
Compositae		Proteaceae	
Orchidaceae		Compositae	
Myrtaceae		Orchidaceae	
Euphorbiaceae		Mimosaceae	
Cyperaceae		Cyperaceae	
Proteaceae		Gramineae	
Rubiaceae		Epacridaceae	
Rutaceae		Goodeniaceae	
Chenopodiaceae		Euphorbiaceae	
Scrophulariaceae	*c.* 30	Rutaceae	*c.* 200

The largest genera are *Acacia* and *Eucalyptus*, which stand out with several hundred species each; *Grevillea* with nearly 200 species, and *Styphelia, Eriostemon, Melaleuca, Stylidium, Goodenia, Hakea‡, Hibbertia, Pultenaea‡, Eremophila‡, Schoenus, Pimelea, Daviesia‡, Ptilotus* and *Boronia‡*, with about 65. Those marked ‡ are endemic.

Of endemic families there are now reckoned to be about 14, containing about 120 species of which the Chloanthaceae, 60 spp., and the Tremandraceae, 30 spp., account for three-quarters; and there are several other groups which form distinctive tribes within their families, as, for instance, the Xanthosiinae of the Umbelliferae. There are about 500 endemic genera, of which those just noticed are the largest, comprising in all 3,500 or more species, a figure larger than that for the South African flora. Moreover, the two largest bodies of species, the genus *Eucalyptus* and the section Phyllodinae of *Acacia*, have only a comparatively limited distribution outside Australia, a condition interestingly paralleled in South Africa by the genera *Erica* and *Mesembryanthemum*. As to endemic species it can only be said that the proportion is probably higher even than it is in the two previous floras.

The unique feature of the flora is the great tree genus *Eucalyptus*. Nowhere else in the world is there a genus of trees so rich in diversity and so wide in ecological tolerance and so completely dominating both the arborescent vegetation and the general landscape. The phyllodinous Acacias, or wattles as so many of them are called, are perhaps the next most prominent single element in the flora but the Persoonioideae of the Proteaceae, and many genera of the Myrtaceae (especially the Chamaelaucieae) contribute powerfully. The Australian Myrtaceae, it should be noted, nearly all belong to the Leptospermoideae of which only one or two small genera are entirely extra-Australian. Other conspicuous and important items in the flora are the remarkable woody genus *Casuarina*; the tribe Podalyrieae of the Papilionaceae; the Epacridaceae, which correspond, though on a rather smaller scale, to the Ericaceae in the South African flora; the "grass-trees" of the Xanthorrhoeaceae, together with certain other large monocotyledons, which in some ways are the counterparts of the aloes in South Africa; the shrubs, or even trees, of the Labiate tribe Prostanthereae; and, again as in South Africa, Compositae of the Inuleae and Arctotideae. Cyperaceae are unusually prominent, but the Restionaceae are less so than in South Africa. The most notable element in the plant life of the arid areas is provided by the Chenopodiaceae.

From the immediate point of view of this chapter the most important feature of the Australian flora as a whole is that it comprises three components of very different size, namely a very large Australian one, to which the foregoing figures chiefly apply; a comparatively very small one generally referred to as "Antarctic", which is particularly seen in Tasmania and the more mountainous parts of south-east Australia (302, 303, 304); and a Malaysian–Melanesian component, intermediate between the others in size, and almost restricted to Queensland. More will be said about this last when New Guinea is discussed.

The great basic Australian flora is little represented outside the continent, and, in so far as it has any major geographical affinity or relationship, it is, as has been shown, with South Africa. On the contrary the geographical relationship of the small "Antarctic" element is very clearly with temperate South America in one direction and with New Zealand particularly in the other. The third component is, as its name describes, an extension of the great Indo–Malaysian flora.

The Madagascar Region

The relevant information about this region in general and the great island of Madagascar itself in particular is nearly all available in Perrier de la Bathie's admirably concise account (554). He shows that the plant life of Madagascar has suffered severely at the hands of man, and that the native flora is now largely restricted to some of the more inaccessible parts, but that even so there are at least 1,150 native genera with about 6,000 species—figures which, bearing in mind the relative areas concerned, indicate a floristic richness comparable with that of the continental floras just noticed.

The order of families by genera and species is:

Genera		Species	
Gramineae	85	Orchidaceae	685
Rubiaceae	58	Compositae	388
Orchidaceae	57	Euphorbiaceae	318
Acanthaceae	49	Cyperaceae	316
Compositae	48	Gramineae	300
Papilionaceae	47	Melastomataceae	265
Euphorbiaceae	40	Acanthaceae	240
Asclepiadaceae	33	Rubiaceae	227
Cyperaceae	29	Papilionaceae	192
Sapindaceae	23	Asclepiadaceae	166
Apocynaceae	20	Palmae	110
Liliaceae	20	Apocynaceae	107

It should be noted that all these families are at least pan-tropical in distribution, though some are higher and others lower in the lists than in many tropical floras, and this supports the conclusion that a pan-tropical element is the most conspicuous part of the flora, amounting to nearly half of it. It is to this element that nearly all the genera most richly represented in the flora belong.

There are seven endemic families (see p. 68) but only the Chlaenaceae, which has about 30 species, is any size. More than 200, or 20 per cent, of the genera are endemic to Madagascar itself, and these contain in all about 700 species, none having more than thirty. About thirty other genera, among which members of the Bignoniaceae and Rubiaceae are conspicuous, are endemic to Madagascar *and* to one or more of the other island groups in the region, and among these genera is *Oncostemon* with 60 species, and *Jumellea* with 40. The groups of smaller islands have, themselves, about forty-five endemic genera. The general proportion of endemic species is about 90 per cent.

Perrier de la Bâthie distinguishes six elements in the flora, namely: (a) a recent exotic element, as he calls it, which includes all the species which have, in his opinion, entered Madagascar since it became an island (among them the human introductions), and accounts for about 15 per cent of the total; (b) a western (African and American) element amounting to about 27 per cent of the whole and including about 150 genera found only in Africa and the Madagascar region; (c) the pan-tropical element of 42 per cent already referred to; (d) an eastern element of affinity with the floras of Asia and the tropical Pacific, which he puts at 7 per cent; (e) a southern element of affinity with Southern Africa, South America and extra-tropical Australia, amounting to 3 per cent; and (f) an aboriginal Malagasy element comprising groups which cannot be included in any of the other categories and accounting for about 6 per cent of the whole flora.

It is presumably this element (which includes the extraordinary cactoid family Didiereaceae) that has suffered most from the operations of man. Adamson (5) has pointed out that the Asiatic relationship is seen chiefly on the east side of the island, while that with southern Africa is prominent on the west side.

Although the African relationship is perhaps the most obvious on the surface there are many ways in which the flora differs significantly from that of continental Africa. The palms, for which the region is so remarkable (see p. 75), number over a hundred species, a figure several times that for all Africa, and moreover belong to the Areceae, a group characteristic of Asia and Australasia and absent from Africa. Other groups better, or at least differently, represented than in Africa, are the bamboos, of which there are nine genera, five of them endemic; the orchids of the Sarcanthinae, a predominantly Asiatic group; the Araliaceae, a characteristic Australasian family; and aroids of the Peltandreae, which occur elsewhere only in America. This relation with America, which is illustrated also in *Ravenala* and in the Crescentieae of the Bignoniaceae, is small but not negligible. On the other hand the Stapelieae (see p. 171) of the Asclepiadaceae are as characteristic of the Madagascar flora as they are of Southern Africa. The Proteaceae, however, are represented in Madagascar by only two species, and the Restionaceae by only one.

The relationship with Asia and the Pacific is shown by the fifty-odd genera (see Appendix B, categories B. *b*.3 and E. *a*) in which Madagascar or some of the smaller islands are the western limit of distribution, and of these *Nepenthes* (see Fig. 25), *Hibbertia* (Fig. 27) and *Elaeocarpus* are noteworthy examples, but it is illustrated also by some other groups of species, one of the most interesting being the phyllodinous species of *Acacia*. As has been seen these plants provide one of the most remarkable features of the Australian flora, and elsewhere there are only a few species in Madagascar, the Mascarenes, New Caledonia, the New Hebrides, Fiji and Hawaii. Nor does this occurrence in the first two appear to be superficial, for Rivals (597) has described *A. heterophylla* as one of the most prominent species on Réunion, where it forms its own vegetation zone on the mountains. This eastward relationship has also been discussed in more detail elsewhere (296).

To sum up, the flora of the Madagascar region may be described as fundamentally a particular expression of the general pan-tropical flora, but it has a very high degree and considerable quality of endemism, which indicates that the significance of its affinity with the flora of Tropical Africa may be less than appears at first sight. This view is reinforced by the remarkable relationships eastward with the floras of Asia and Australasia.

New Caledonia

This small island lies at about the same distance, nearly 1,000 miles, from New Guinea, from Australia and from New Zealand, and its nearest neighbours are the New Hebrides to the north and Fiji to the north-east (see Fig. 62). There is still something to be learnt about the flora but Guillaumin's *Synoptic Flora* (322) indicates that it consists of about 600 native genera and some 2,600 species. Compton's account of the plant life, though written many years ago (147), is still one of the best.

Numerical analysis of the flora is made difficult because the vegetation of New Caledonia has been considerably modified by human action, though to a lesser degree than is the case in Madagascar. In particular, this has resulted in continuing damage by fire and much of the lowlands of the island is now covered by an anthropogenous savanna, in which the fire-resistant *niauoli* (*Melaleuca*) is almost the only tree and the ground vegetation consists largely of adventive species, particularly grasses and sedges. The true native vegetation at the higher levels is chiefly forest, but there is a good deal of serpentine rock and this supports a somewhat xerophytic scrub or bush vegetation.

The largest families, in genera and species, are:

Genera		Species	
Orchidaceae	51	Orchidaceae	215
Euphorbiaceae		Rubiaceae	
Rubiaceae		Euphorbiaceae	
Myrtaceae		Myrtaceae	
Cyperaceae		Apocynaceae	
Rutaceae		Araliaceae	

Genera		Species	
Araliaceae		Cunoniaceae	
Sapindaceae		Sapotaceae	
Palmae		Cyperaceae	
Apocynaceae		Rutaceae	
Sapotaceae		Sapindaceae	
Liliaceae	9	Myrsinaceae	50

It should be noted that the Gramineae, Compositae and Papilionaceae are all absent from the list, a most unusual circumstance, and it is thought that the Gramineae have only about half a dozen species, including an endemic genus of dwarf bamboos, and that the Compositae may be represented by only a single truly native species. The Papilionaceae are more numerous but nearly all are in the two endemic genera, *Arthroclianthus* and *Nephrodesmus* of the *Hedysareae*. The Cyperaceae are also probably mainly adventive, and the subfamily Caricoideae has only about six species, none of them endemic. Several families usually conspicuous in tropical floras, such as the Araceae, Commelinaceae, Zingiberaceae and Gesneriaceae, are also little in evidence.

About 250 of the genera are widespread genera represented by widespread species only (a figure which suggests the possibility that some of them may not be native after all); about 250 others are represented partly by wide and partly by endemic species, and the remainder are endemic. The genera richest in species are, in diminishing order, *Psychotria* (70 spp.), *Phyllanthus*, *Ficus*, *Dendrobium*, *Parsonsia*, *Xanthostemon*, *Tapeinosperma*, *Planchonella*, *Pittosporum*, *Hibbertia*, *Eleaocarpus*, *Syzygium*, *Eugenia* and *Dysoxylum*.

The flora has long excited interest because of the remarkable quality as well as the quantity of the endemism. The island is no larger than Yorkshire but it has three endemic families (admittedly all monotypic), and more than 100 endemic genera, containing between 300 and 400 species. The proportion of endemism among the species is hard to estimate but is certainly very high. It has even been suggested that in pre-human times almost all the species may have been so, except for a few strand and aquatic plants. Most of the endemic genera are related to wide, or at least Asiatic–Australasian genera, though a few have affinity with Africa or America, or, in about a dozen, with Madagascar, and they are most frequent in the Palmae, Rubiaceae, Araliaceae, Euphorbiaceae and Rutaceae. Ten of the fourteen palm genera are endemic, and all belong to the Areceae, already referred to in the flora of Madagascar.

The 250 genera represented wholly or partly by endemic species fall into four roughly equal groups, namely, (a) wide genera in which endemic species occur in most appropriate parts of the world, (b) Asiatic–Australasian genera predominantly Asiatic in relationship, (c) Asiatic–Australasian genera predominantly Australasian in relationship, and (d) others. The chief feature of these last genera is a significant affinity with either Africa or America, or with the Madagascar region. The American relation is exemplified best by the figs, most of which are endemic and belong to a section of the genus *Ficus* which otherwise occurs only in America (151), the rest being Indo–Malaysian wide species. An association with Madagascar is seen in the genera *Alyxia*, *Astelia*, *Celtis*, *Cerbera*, *Claoxylon*, *Cohnia*, *Cossinia*, *Deeringia*, *Dianella*, *Elaeocarpus*, *Euodia*, *Geniostoma*, *Hernandia*, *Hibbertia*, *Korthalsella*, *Lophoschoenus*, *Melastoma*, *Myoporum*, *Nepenthes*, *Ochrosia*, *Pelea*, *Pittosporum*, *Polyscias*, *Soulamea*, *Strongylodon*, *Tristellateia* and *Weinmannia*.

A relationship with the flora of Australia is seen chiefly in some of the orchids, but it should be noted that the genera concerned occur also in New Zealand. Other instances include the Boroneae and other genera of the Rutaceae, and the genera *Xerotes, Campynema, Hibbertia, Castanospermum* and *Casuarina. Grevillea* and *Stenocarpus* are essentially Australian genera but others of the Proteaceae have more affinity with Indo–Malaysia and Melanesia. The Epacridaceae are important, especially on the serpentine, but these again are equally characteristic of New Zealand. The genus *Balanops* is mainly in New Caledonia but is found also in the New Hebrides and Fiji, as well as very locally on the coast of Queensland. On the other side of the account *Eucalyptus* is absent; the only two phyllodinous Acacias belong to the special case already noticed under Madagascar; the Restionaceae and Stylidiaceae are absent, and the Goodeniaceae are represented only by the comparatively wide-spread genus *Scaevola*. The Myrtaceae are a very prominent feature of the flora and include such Australian types as *Callistemon* and *Xanthostemon* in the Leptospermoideae, but members of the Myrtoideae are even more numerous. In general the plants of Australian affinity occur chiefly in the serpentine bush and the more fundamental forest vegetation is dominated by families and genera well developed in the Malaysian–Melanesian flora.

New Guinea

New Guinea has been one of the last parts of the world to be penetrated by explorers, and until about thirty years ago reports concerning the flora were not only meagre but also somewhat misleading because they were inevitably based on studies of the more accessible coastal regions where widespread and adventive plants are especially in evidence. During and since the Second World War, however, the interior of this great country has been opened up with mounting speed and this has made possible a much better assessment of the flora, which shows that some of the prevailing notions about it must be modified. It has also enabled a much more detailed analysis to be made than was previously possible (305, 306) and the following paragraphs are a summary of its relevant parts.

The native flora comprises about 1,350 genera and more than 9,000 species and, for its area, is probably the richest of the eastern tropical floras, and the order of the largest families, in genera and species, is:

	Genera		*Species*
Orchidaceae	128	Orchidaceae	2,600
Gramineae	82	Rubiaceae	620
Rubiaceae	62	Myrtaceae	275
Papilionaceae	42	Palmae	255
Euphorbiaceae	39	Zingiberaceae	
Palmae	32	Euphorbiaceae	
Myrtaceae	28	Vacciniaceae	
Melastomataceae	27	Elaeocarpaceae	
Sapindaceae	26	Gesneriaceae (incl. *Cyrtandra*)	
Acanthaceae	25	Moraceae	
Apocynaceae	25	Meliaceae	
Cyperaceae	24	Urticaceae	145

The most astonishing figure is that of the orchids which are overwhelmingly the outstanding feature of the flora. The largest genera in this family are *Dendrobium* 600 spp., *Bulbophyllum* 550, *Phreatia* 114, *Malaxis* 90, *Taeniophyllum, Oberonia, Liparis, Glomera* and *Eria* 70. Among all the other families only the genera *Ficus* 150, *Vaccinium* 125, *Elaeocarpus* 120, *Psychotria* 120, *Rhododendron* 104, *Cyrtandra, Eugenia, Syzygium, Piper, Saurauia, Medinilla* and *Aglaia* have numbers as high.

Despite the size of the flora there is no endemic family, and only about 140 endemic genera with no more than 350 species (scarcely more than in New Caledonia), but the endemic *species* in total number at least 8,500. These remarkable figures mean that although the flora is very largely peculiar to the island at species level it is not a notably specialised one. Because the generic endemic element is so small and that of the species so high it follows that endemic genera are small, and in fact only seven have more than ten species, namely *Paralinospadix, Rhyticaryum, Chitonanthera, Nengella, Sericolea, Cyrtandropsis* and *Symbegonia*. Of these only the genus *Chitonanthera* belongs to the Orchidaceae.

The non-endemic genera fall into the following five geographical categories:

	Total	No. with end. spp.	Total end. spp.
1. Genera at least pan-palaeotropical in distribution .	500	315	3,750
2. Genera of Indo–Malaysian affinity . . .	495	250	3,575
3. Genera of Australian affinity	62	24	64
4. Genera of Asiatic–American affinity . . .	27	21	184
5. Other genera, mainly of west and south-west Pacific affinity	125	87	538

TABLE A. THE LARGEST FAMILIES OF THE FLORAS OF NEW GUINEA AND AUSTRALIA IN NUMBERS OF GENERA HAVING NATIVE SPECIES

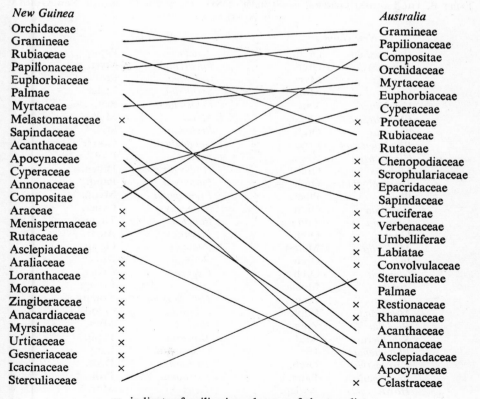

New Guinea	Australia
Orchidaceae	Gramineae
Gramineae	Papilionaceae
Rubiaceae	Compositae
Papilionaceae	Orchidaceae
Euphorbiaceae	Myrtaceae
Palmae	Euphorbiaceae
Myrtaceae	Cyperaceae
Melastomataceae ×	× Proteaceae
Sapindaceae	Rubiaceae
Acanthaceae	Rutaceae
Apocynaceae	× Chenopodiaceae
Cyperaceae	× Scrophulariaceae
Annonaceae	× Epacridaceae
Compositae	Sapindaceae
Araceae ×	× Cruciferae
Menispermaceae ×	× Verbenaceae
Rutaceae	× Umbelliferae
Asclepiadaceae	× Labiatae
Araliaceae ×	× Convolvulaceae
Loranthaceae ×	Sterculiaceae
Moraceae ×	Palmae
Zingiberaceae ×	× Restionaceae
Anacardiaceae ×	× Rhamnaceae
Myrsinaceae ×	Acanthaceae
Urticaceae ×	Annonaceae
Gesneriaceae ×	Asclepiadaceae
Icacinaceae ×	Apocynaceae
Sterculiaceae	× Celastraceae

× indicates families in only one of the two lists

From this it is clear that the New Guinea flora consists very predominantly of genera of wide distribution or of Malaysian affinity and that this Indo–Malaysian element, as it may be called, is, in terms of genera eight times, and in terms of species fifty times, as large as the Australian element, which is itself much smaller than the Pacific element. Moreover, it seems likely that the 62 genera in category 3 include a few which are not truly native in New Guinea.

Of all the native genera of New Guinea perhaps half, c. 650, occur also on the Australian continent (particularly of course in Queensland) which is only one hundred miles away across a very shallow sea that is thought to have been dry land at least once in comparatively late geological times: but no fewer than 385 of the genera, or more than 20 per cent, occur also in New Caledonia which is a thousand miles away across deep sea; while 165, or nearly 10 per cent occur in New Zealand, 2,000 miles away. 150 of the New Guinea genera are found also in the Tasmanian flora, and of these 120 are in New Zealand too.

The distinction between the flora of New Guinea and that of Australia is well displayed first by comparing the relative position of the leading families in each (Table A), and second by comparing the largest genera in each (Table B). Note that there is only one genus, *Ficus*, in both lists, and only two families, Moraceae and Myrtaceae.

TABLE B. THE LARGEST GENERA, IN NUMBER OF SPECIES, IN THE FLORAS OF NEW GUINEA AND AUSTRALIA

New Guinea		Australia	
Dendrobium	Orch.	*Acacia*	Papil.
Bulbophyllum	Orch.	*Eucalyptus*	Myrt.
Eugenia	Myrt.	*Grevillea*	Prot.
Ficus	Mor.	*Styphelia*	Epac.
Vaccinium	Vacc.	*Eriostemon*	Rut.
Elaeocarpus	Elaeo.	*Melaleuca*	Myrt.
Phreatia	Orch.	*Stylidium*	Styl.
Rhododendron	Eric.	*Goodenia*	Good.
Cyrtandra	Gesn.	*Hakea*	Prot.
Malaxis	Orch.	*Hibbertia*	Dillen.
Taeniophyllum	Orch.	*Pultenaea*	Papil.
Piper	Piper.	*Eremophila*	Myop.
Oberonia	Orch.	*Schoenus*	Cyper.
Saurauia	Saurau.	*Pimelea*	Thym.
Liparis	Orch.	*Ptilotus*	Amar.
Medinilla	Melast.	*Panicum*	Gram.
Eria	Orch.	*Boronia*	Rut.
Glomera	Orch.	*Cyperus*	Cyper.
Aglaia	Meliac.	*Aster*	Comp.
Alpinia	Zing.	*Helichrysum*	Comp.
Macaranga	Euph.	*Scaevola*	Good.
Riedelia	Zing.	*Baeckia*	Myrt.
Schefflera	Aral.	*Daviesia*	Papil.
Elatostema	Urt.	*Cryptandra*	Laur.
Ceratostylis	Orch.	*Drosera*	Dros.
Freycinetia	Pand.	*Persoonia*	Prot.
Hoya	Asclep.	*Ficus*	Mor.
Timonius	Rubiac.	*Prostanthera*	Lab.

Plate 16. Mangrove vegetation on the coast of Lower California

(from Karsten & Schenck, Vegetationsbilder)

Fiji

No complete modern flora of this archipelago is available and many of the islands have yet to be fully explored botanically but Smith (680), in one of several papers on the subject, gives a valuable analysis of the flora from which most of its salient features emerge.

From this it appears that there are about 450 native genera containing 1,250 species. He does not cite the order of families or list the largest genera, but from other evidence it would seem that these are much the same as in New Guinea.

There is one monotypic endemic family, the Degeneriaceae, allied to, and sometimes not separated from, the Winteraceae, and thirteen endemic genera (see p. 145) containing only 24 species, 13 of them palms. About 70 per cent of the species are endemic, a figure lower than that of many other southern floras, and one suggesting that the flora may to a larger extent be derived from elsewhere. The affinities of these endemic species is very largely (91 per cent) with plants of Malaysia and especially New Guinea. Only about 5 per cent are most closely related to New Caledonian or Australian plants, and only about 3 per cent to other parts of the Pacific and New Zealand.

Of the 450 native genera about 150 are widely distributed, occurring in both Old and New Worlds, and nearly 250 are Indo–Malaysian.

The non-endemic species show the following affinities:

1. Widespread species 193
2. Species also in Samoa, Tonga or the eastern Pacific . . . 98
3. Species also in New Guinea or elsewhere in Malaysia . . 69
4. Species also in New Caledonia and/or Australia . . . 18
5. Species elsewhere only in the New Hebrides 14

In another publication (682) Smith has listed no fewer than 88 genera in forty-nine families which find the eastern termination of their ranges in Fiji, a situation reminiscent of that of the Madagascar region in the other direction, and also of considerable interest in relation to the andesite line (see p. 215). Of these 88 genera, 34 are widely distributed; 45 are Indo–Malaysian, and 11 Australian–New Caledonian.

New Zealand

Cheeseman's *Flora* (129), to which allusion has already been made (see p. 221), includes in its orbit the Kermadec, Chatham, Auckland and Campbell Islands. It makes a total for the flora of about 340 native genera and nearly 1,600 species. A new *Flora* is at present in course of publication (15).

Because of the comparatively small number of genera involved it is better to give the order of the largest families in species first and with the genera in parentheses, and this is as follows:

	Species	Genera
Compositae	261	(30)
Scrophulariaceae	138	(10)
Cyperaceae	123	(14)
Gramineae	123	(33)
Umbelliferae	79	(14)
Orchidaceae	66	(21)
Ranunculaceae	53	(4)
Rubiaceae	52	(4)
Onagraceae	40	(2)

17

	Species	Genera
Epacridaceae	33	(6)
Boraginaceae	33	(3)
Papilionaceae	32	(8)
Juncaceae	27	(3)
Liliaceae	27	(10)
Gentianaceae	26	(3)

The largest genera, i.e. those with more than about a dozen species, are *Veronica* (*Hebe*) 103, *Celmisia* 58, *Carex* 54, *Coprosma* 44, *Olearia* 42, *Epilobium* 37, *Senecio* 35, *Myosotis* 31, *Poa*, *Aciphylla*, *Gentiana*, *Pittosporum*, *Cotula*, *Raoulia*, *Carmichaelia*, *Anisotome*, *Dracophyllum*, *Juncus*, *Pimelea*, *Thelymitra*, *Uncinia*, *Scirpus* and *Pterostylis*. As might be expected it is these genera which are also richest in endemic species, but the total of such endemics in all those cited is remarkable, being 664 out of 736. In about 12 of these genera *all* the species are endemic. It will be noted, too, that all these genera are either widespread temperate genera or distinctly southern and Australasian genera.

There is no endemic family in the flora and only about twenty-five or thirty strictly endemic genera, with less than 50 species between them (see p. 151). Despite the figures just mentioned the total specific endemism is not very high, being about 75 per cent. This is partly due to the occurrence of species in temperate Australia also, and partly to the presence of many widespread, and largely aquatic, temperate plants.

Because of its geographical isolation and latitudinal position the relationship of the flora of New Zealand has long been a matter of special interest to plant-geographers and many of the salient features have already been noticed in Chapters 7 and 10, but there are three aspects of the subject which particularly concern the present chapter.

Although the main islands of New Zealand are nearly 800 miles from the tropics, and the Kermadecs about half that distance, there is, in the flora, a distinct tropical element of at least a dozen families (albeit chiefly with one species only), in addition to the five enumerated on p. 151. All these, which are further exemplified by Palmae, Pandanaceae, Piperaceae, Moraceae, Sapotaceae, are widespread tropical families and almost all of them are notably well developed in the flora of Malaysia and Melanesia in general and of New Guinea in particular. The tropical element is also seen in such genera as *Dendrobium*, *Bulbophyllum* and *Cordyline*. Owing no doubt to the crucial difference in latitude there is not much direct relation with the nearest tropical area, namely New Caledonia, but it is shown by the genera *Knightia* and *Xeronema*, and in more general terms by the Epacridaceae.

There is an important "Antarctic" element in the flora which, since most of its members occur also in temperate South America, has already been discussed under that heading. The genera number about fifty-odd and they are for the most part listed in categories C and E of Appendix B but there are several other groups of species not so well defined, as well as certain genera confined to New Zealand and Tasmania and the adjacent parts of Victoria and New South Wales. It is worth emphasising that many of these plants are characteristic and common members of the vegetation, especially in the South Island.

Finally there is the question of the relationship between the floras of New Zealand and of Australia, which is one of the critical points in a study of southern floras. It is convenient to deal first with the similarities, which include the rather special case of the orchids, and then with the differences.

There are reported to be 260 species which occur in both countries, a scarcely remarkable total in itself, but this includes a considerable number of widespread species and the number actually occurring *only* in the two is about 140. The genus *Drosera* is often mentioned as the most outstanding example of these because five out of the six species in New Zealand are also in Australia. Fewer than twenty-five genera are found only in the two, a number rather less than once thought because of discoveries in New Caledonia, though whether these are in all cases natives of that island is uncertain. Of these genera some, such as *Aciphylla, Celmisia* and *Raoulia*, are almost wholly in New Zealand; some, such as *Persoonia, Phebalium* and *Swainsona*, are almost wholly in Australia; and some are evenly balanced, but these are all small. Moreover, most of these genera are relatively more restricted in Australia than in New Zealand, and it is fair to say that there is no genus of any size which is widely distributed in, and equally characteristic of, both regions.

Other points of resemblance are the frequency of Epacridaceae and Pittosporaceae in both, and on a smaller scale of the Stylidiaceae, Restionaceae, Haloragaceae, and Thymelaeaceae. The Myrtaceae are also well represented in both but New Zealand (like New Caledonia) has a larger representation of the world-wide Myrtoideae.

The orchids present a remarkable situation. According to Cheeseman (129) there are twenty-one genera in the New Zealand flora. One is an endemic monotype, but at least eighteen, and possibly all the rest, are found somewhere in Australia. Five are said to be confined to New Zealand and Australia, two or three others occur elsewhere only in New Caledonia, and others, such as *Caladenia* and *Thelymitra*, which occur also in some part of Malaysia, are predominantly Australian. All in all the orchid flora of New Zealand may be described as having a very close affinity with Australia and a strong Australasian flavour.

Because of the disparity in numbers between the two floras, the differences are less easy to present, but it can scarcely be doubted that in many respects they are more fundamental than the similarities, since they include the entire absence from New Zealand of such predominant and conspicuous Australian types as *Eucalyptus*, phyllodinous species of *Acacia, Casuarina*, Xanthorrhoeaceae, *Hibbertia, Boronia*, and such important other items of the Myrtaceae as *Callistemon* and *Melaleuca*. Moreover the Proteaceae have only two species in New Zealand; the Restionaceae only three; the Labiatae only two, which belong to widespread temperate genera; while the Papilionaceae, so abundant in Australia, have only about 30 species in New Zealand, none of them in the Podalyrieae. Conversely, Australia is relatively or wholly deficient in such characteristic New Zealand types as *Coriaria* and *Hebe*, and in various wide temperate genera such as *Ranunculus, Epilobium* and *Gentiana*. *Coriaria* deserves a further word because in addition it is found also in Fiji and New Guinea, on the one hand, and in temperate South America on the other, facts which make its absence from Australia particularly noteworthy. Finally the Ericaceae are represented by several species of *Gaultheria* and *Pernettia*, while in Australia there is only a single species of *Rhododendron* in Queensland, related to species in New Guinea.

The Five Small Floras

The remaining five southern floras are of areas so much smaller, and are themselves so much more limited than any of those already discussed, that they can hardly be analysed in the same way, and it is enough to call attention to the leading facts about each and to note the relation it bears to its immediate neighbour or neighbours.

Juan Fernandez

These islands lie rather more than 350 miles from the coast of Chile and have a total area not much exceeding 50 sq.miles. The flora contains one monotypic endemic family, the Lactoridaceae; and eighteen endemic genera, including a palm of South American affinity, and some interesting arborescent Compositae. About 110 of the 160 species are endemic. More than half the species show a strong South American relationship, but the affinities of the rest are with the Pacific and rather especially with the Hawaiian Islands.

St. Helena

The island has an area of about 50 sq. miles and the present native flora consists of 39 species in 28 genera (741), of which five genera and all but one of the species are endemic. Of these five genera, one is related to a genus of southern Africa, but the other four are said to be nearest to South American genera. Twenty-two of the twenty-eight genera are represented in the South African flora. These figures do not, however, take account of the species which may have been lost through human action since the island was discovered, and Hooker (374) thought that this might amount to 100 species. The general relationship of the flora is usually said to be with South Africa but the groups most characteristic of that flora are scarcely if at all represented, and many of the endemics have no obvious close relations. The most remarkable feature of the flora is the several species, including three endemic genera, of arborescent Compositae.

The South Temperate Oceanic Islands

These have been dealt with at some length on pp. 222–225 and all that need be said here is that the flora consists chiefly of genera belonging to the "Antarctic" element in the floras of temperate South America and New Zealand; that Macquarie Island has, not unnaturally, a rather strong local affinity with New Zealand, and that one or two of the species in the Tristan da Cunha group show a relation with St. Helena and South Africa.

Norfolk Island

This island, of only 15 sq. miles, lies about half way between New Zealand and New Caledonia and about twice as far from Australia, and has, or rather had, only one monotypic endemic genus; but roughly a quarter of the hundred-odd species are endemic. The flora is noteworthy as including *Phormium*, which contains the New Zealand Flax, and *Rhopalostylis*, which contains the only palm in New Zealand proper; and there are also species of *Coprosma* allied to those of New Zealand.

Lord Howe Island

This lies between the North Island of New Zealand and the southern end of Queensland and much nearer the latter than the former, and covers only about 5 sq. miles. It has a rather larger flora than Norfolk Island, and this contains five endemic genera, namely *Negria* (of the Gesneriaceae) one of three genera making up the Coronantherinae, of which the other two are in New Zealand and New Caledonia respectively; *Colmeiroa*, concerning which there are some remarks on p. 144; and three, or possibly four, genera of palms. The flora also contains the only species of *Carmichaelia* outside New Zealand; a remarkable *Dracophyllum* reminiscent of some of the larger species in New Zealand; and, like Norfolk Island, some members of *Coprosma* allied to New Zealand species.

It has been frequently said that the floras of these last two islands are intermediate between those of Australia and New Zealand and this would scarcely be surprising in the case of Lord Howe. It would seem, however, that they are both more closely related to the New Zealand flora.

Such is a brief epitome of a very large subject and a vast array of facts. What conclusions, is it justifiable to claim, emerge from it? Before trying to answer this question it is well to refer to a particular difficulty which is likely to be encountered.

Questions of geographical relationship in biology involve many of the more subjective aspects of taxonomy and it is therefore specially important to be as objective as possible, and not to allow details of this kind to obscure the picture as a whole, though this is not always easy. It is all too tempting in such problems to argue from the particular to the general and to attribute to single facts a significance out of proportion to their intrinsic value, and this is best avoided by concentrating upon underlying generalities rather than upon what may be superficial resemblances or differences.

Accepting this principle, there is likely to be a good measure of agreement that the most prominent and most obvious result of the foregoing survey is to reveal the great variation in the degrees to which individual floras are in conformity or harmony with those others to which they are most closely approximate geographically. In other words the survey shows plainly that there is a greater degree of orderliness in the plant distribution in some parts of the southern hemisphere than in others.

It is appropriate in the light of this that the survey began with temperate South America because it is certainly here that the floristic harmony, as it may be termed, is most simply seen and easily illustrated. Here, for topographical reasons, the flora of the lower temperate latitudes grades, on the one hand into the flora of the tropics, and on the other into that of the colder latitudes, without any serious discontinuity or sudden break, so that the floristic change from the Equator to Cape Horn may properly be described as gradual throughout. It is true that the colder temperate flora of the extreme south is largely composed of groups scarcely or not at all represented further north but this is also seen in other parts of the world too, mainly because there is a critical latitude at about 45° (see p. 393).

Not only so but this "Antarctic" element is characteristic also of Tasmania and New Zealand, which, since they are the only other appreciable southern lands at the same latitude, may be thought of as natural neighbours, being linked together by the presence of an attenuated version of the same element throughout the South Temperate Oceanic Islands, which to-day represent what there is good reason to believe was once a more direct connection across the present Antarctica.

The part of the small flora of Juan Fernandez in this picture is somewhat different but no less straightforward. It has strong features of its own, but its affinities are compatible with its position, being greater with continental America on its east than with the other islands of the Pacific to the west.

The flora of South Africa is not quite such a simple matter, chiefly because the continent reaches only 35° S., so that it has no cool temperate flora, but here again there is an orderly transition from the temperate to the tropical flora, at least on the east, though elsewhere an arid zone intervenes and causes a more abrupt change. The problem in southern Africa is rather to account for the occurrence of the very rich and specialised Cape flora in what can only be described as a geographical *cul-de-sac*. One factor here is certainly the great isolation of the Cape from other areas of similar latitude; and another, suggested by the wealth of specialised desert plants, may be that arid conditions have persisted here for an exceptionally prolonged span of geological time. It is also relevant to note that the situation in southern Africa is a repetition of that seen in certain other parts of the world where there are rich bush floras on the poleward side of arid regions, as in the Mediterranean, California and south-west Australia. At the same time the distance from southern Africa to its continental neighbours west and east is so great as to make any profound similarity unlikely, a point which makes its undoubted floristic relationship with Australia all the more remarkable.

Again, the smaller flora of St. Helena is consistent with its position. It is so isolated that its almost wholly peculiar character is scarcely surprising but even so there are affinities with the continents in both directions.

The flora of the Madagascar region is of interest because it is not fully in harmony with the position of the islands so close to the African mainland. The aboriginal vegetation has to-day been much reduced, and no doubt the consequence of this has been to facilitate the entry into the flora not only of many adventives but also of African plants which have reached the islands by their own means of dispersal, and both these have obscured the original character of the plant life, which seems to have possessed a degree and quality of endemism greater than might reasonably be expected if Madagascar (with its associated islands) is a continental island only recently detached from the neighbouring continent. There is also the unexpected degree of relation between the flora and that of parts of Australasia, notably New Caledonia. The importance of this must not be exaggerated because other than botanical factors may have helped to cause it, but neither can it be wholly ignored and it is certainly one of the most fascinating facets of the plant geography of the south.

In Australasia there is a far more complicated situation (see Fig. 62). To begin with there are seven floras of various sizes to be considered—one continental, four larger insular and two smaller insular—and it is therefore important to deal with them in the order best calculated to present and underline the essentials. For this reason, and because, as will be seen in due course, it shows the fewest problems, New Zealand will be taken first.

The flora of New Zealand is properly described as the only *considerable isolated insular* south temperate flora. It thus occupies a place very much of its own and this is strongly reflected in its plant life. There is indeed a strong relation between the flora of the South Island and that of Tasmania but this is almost entirely due to the "Antarctic" element, so characteristic also in South America, and apart from this the plant life of New Zealand has few close parallels elsewhere. The main question is that of its floristic relation with its two nearest large neighbours, Australia on the west and New Caledonia on the north. Interestingly enough, there is a small intermediate island in each case, Lord Howe and Norfolk respectively, but the floras of these are so small, and now so altered, that it is profitless to base much upon them, but it was said earlier that on the whole their closest affinities are probably with New Zealand.

Of the two other relationships, that between Australia and New Zealand has received much the more attention, partly because of the obvious general association between them and partly because the flora of New Caledonia is even now much less familiar. The situation here is that there are a number of detailed resemblances, some of which are striking, but the general verdict must be that these are outweighed by the more fundamental differences between the floras and the virtual or complete absence from New Zealand of many leading Australian types. This view is reinforced by the fact that of the genera often quoted as indicating an Australian–New Zealand relationship, many do, in fact, occur also in New Caledonia and could be cited with equal justification as exemplifying the relation between New Zealand and New Caledonia.

The affinity between these last two is rather different, being expressed less by individual genera and species than by such broader matters as similarity of vegetation

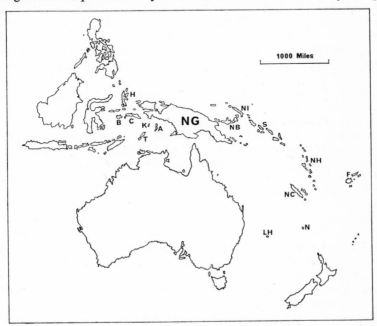

Fig. 62.—Sketch map showing the position of the island of New Guinea (NG) in relation to Malaysia on the west; to the rest of Melanesia on the east and south-east; to Australia on the south; and to New Zealand. Among New Guinea's nearest neighbours west and east are the Moluccan islands of Halmahera (H), Ceram (C) and Buru (B); the Aru Islands (A), the Kai Islands (K) and Tanimbar or Timor Laut (T); New Britain (NB), New Ireland (NI) and the Solomon Islands (S). Further south-east are the New Hebrides (NH), New Caledonia and the Loyalty Islands (NC), Fiji (F), Lord Howe Island (LH) and Norfolk Island (N).

(From Good, *Bull. Brit. Mus.* (*Nat. Hist.*), *Botany*, 2, 1960.)

type and the prevalence of certain families. Taking into account the difference in latitude between the two, it may well be thought that these wider similarities are more significant than any particular items linking Australia and New Zealand. At all events, there is nothing in its floristic constitution or relationships to suggest that the flora of New Zealand is not a perfectly normal one in the sense of being an aboriginal oceanic flora appropriate to its present latitude and longitude. This is an important conclusion because it not only gives a useful datum on which to base other comparisons, but also disposes of any suggestion that the flora is in some way an appanage of that of Australia.

The flora of New Caledonia, to which in the light of what has been said it is logical to go next, is the most strategically situated of all the Australasian floras under discussion, being roughly equidistant from others in three directions, and having a much nearer neighbour on the fourth side. It should be noted that one of these longer isolations is in a sense fictitious because New Caledonia is, through the New Hebrides and the Solomon Islands (which have not been considered), in relatively close contact with New Guinea. Conversely New Caledonia can be regarded as the terminal island of a long chain stretching east and south from New Guinea.

The floristic relation between New Caledonia and New Guinea is similar in kind to that between New Caledonia and New Zealand, but greater in degree because both the areas concerned are tropical, and shows the sort of difference which might be expected to result from those of latitude within a general basic similarity. That is to say, the two floras appear as two expressions (an equatorial and a borderline tropical) of a single greater floristic entity, and it is only fair to add that, when the floras of the New Hebrides and the Solomons are taken into account, this becomes even plainer, and there is seen a much more gradual transition from one to the other.

The relation between the flora of Australia and that of New Caledonia, which, like the case of New Zealand, and for similar reasons, is often commented upon, needs some clarification. As has already been said, there are various items which provide a rather conspicuous link between the two, but, about this, three points may be made. The first is the very general one that, because a genus or species is in both floras, it cannot be assumed that it necessarily contributes to an Australian element in New Caledonia. It may just as easily indicate the reverse, and this is nicely illustrated by the genus *Balanops*, mentioned above. The second point is that it is not possible to be sure that some of the items described as common to the two floras are indeed native in both places. The vegetation of much of New Caledonia has been modified and it is here that some of these plants occur. The third point is one to which we shall revert later, namely that there is in Queensland a considerable element of genera more richly developed in the flora of New Guinea. Hence there is a triangular relation between New Guinea, New Caledonia and Queensland, and this certainly gives some similarities between the floras of the latter two, but this should not be described as an "Australian" affinity.

The flora of Fiji also presents no difficulty. Because of its easterly position it is comparatively small, illustrating the general attenuation of numbers as the western Pacific is entered from Malaysia, but it is clearly an extension of the general flora to the west of it, and of those of New Guinea and New Caledonia in particular.

There are left, then, two great floras still to be discussed, those of New Guinea and Australia, and these must receive the most careful attention, because the relation between them is not only the crux of the whole problem of the floras of the southern hemisphere, but is also a matter of dispute which has made its influence widely felt in many fields of biology. It is appropriate after what has so far been said to take New Guinea first.

It was clear from the survey earlier in this chapter that the flora of New Guinea is, like those of New Caledonia, Fiji and New Zealand, straightforward, in the sense that it is wholly consistent with the position of this great island as the eastern termination of Malaysia and the western member of Melanesia, in being predominantly Indo–Malaysian in character but having also much in common with the Pacific floras to the east and south-east of it. It may also be added that this double relationship, coupled with the great richness of the flora and its singular deficiency in well-marked large-scale endemics, suggests that New Guinea may indeed have been the aboriginal home from which has spread much of the present Malaysian and Melanesian plant life, and this in turn is a consideration of great importance with regard to the origin of the various Pacific floras. This, however, is not the subject before us and we must not pursue it here, except to draw attention to a paper, of remarkable perspicacity for its time, by Hedley (352). He not only points out the weakness of the then widely-current idea propounded by Wallace in *Island Life* (756) that there was once a great continent including Australia, New Guinea, New Caledonia and New Zealand, but actually suggests a former "Melanesian plateau" or continuity of land, represented now by the Solomons, New Hebrides, New Caledonia, Fiji and New Zealand, separated from Australia by the "abysses of the Coral and Tasmanian Seas". This last phrase is especially illuminating when it is remembered that he wrote at a time, 1893, when the immobility of continents was accepted as an unshakeable faith. The andesite line, described on p. 215, is also closely related to Hedley's concept.

While the analysis of the New Guinea flora mentioned earlier (305, 306) makes clear the presence of the two great floristic elements just mentioned it also establishes an even more important point, namely that the "Australian element", so often referred to in the literature, is very small and, taking all the details into account, probably of even less significance than appears at first sight. The misconception about this has arisen from certain quasi-botanical sources (which are set out in the analysis quoted), but it has had far-reaching consequences.

All but one of the Australasian floras under discussion have now been dealt with, and it has been seen that six of them may fairly be said to present few, if any, problems with regard to their own mutual relationships, their differences being sufficiently explicable on the basis that they are isolated in varying degree and widely scattered in latitude. The case of Australia is very different.

The great flora of this continent is perhaps the most impressive, and at the same time puzzling, in the world; impressive because it has characteristics of quite unusual peculiarity, making it in certain respects without peer, and puzzling because it is separated from another great flora, the Malaysian–Melanesian, from which it could scarcely be more distinct, by only a hundred miles of shallow sea. To appreciate this fully, it must be realised that when we speak of the Australian flora in the botanical rather than the geographical sense, we do not mean all the plants of native status in that continent and Tasmania. That has already been made plain in what has been said about the "Antarctic" element in Tasmania and south-eastern Australia, and it is equally plain in respect of Queensland, where the flora contains a considerable admixture of New Guinea, and wider Malaysian, types. Thus there are in the continent three floristic entities, namely, a very large Australian flora proper, covering the whole country including both Tasmania and north-east Queensland; a small "Antarctic" flora mingled with the Australian in Tasmania and south-eastern Australia; and a Malaysian–Melanesian flora, intermediate in size, mingled with the Australian in eastern Australia and especially in the wetter parts of Queensland. The important point is that, if our interpretation of the floras of New Zealand, New Caledonia, Fiji, and New Guinea has been correct, the second and third of these components are what might be expected simply from the latitude and from the associated climatic conditions. Tasmania and neighbouring Victoria and New South Wales are in the same latitude, and have much the same climate, as parts of New Zealand, and the presence of a similar element in both presents no real problems. Similarly the latitude and conditions in the north-east, where the New Guinea element is so conspicuous, are comparable to those of various places within the area of the Malaysian–Melanesian flora. Indeed, given the climatic and geographical situation existing, the absence of such an element from Queensland would be more remarkable than it presence.

Hence it is not, as is so often implied, the "Antarctic" and Malaysian elements in the Australian flora that make the problem, but the presence of a great and peculiar Australian flora proper, very distinct from the other two entities and covering the whole continent, yet scarcely represented in neighbouring lands, although one of these is only one hundred miles away.

When the situation is described in these terms, and they are terms fully justified by the facts, it is clear that the presence where it is of the Australian flora proper results in a major anomaly in the distribution of the floras of the southern hemisphere.

The validity of this conclusion, though it must of course rest finally on the facts and their interpretation, can be tested in a very simple way. If a map of the world, preferably on Mollweide's projection, is studied, and the floristic relations of the various southern floras therein considered, many problems, as this chapter has shown, arise. If, however, the map is modified so as to obscure Australia and Tasmania, it is at once apparent that the problems are not only fewer but much less teasing. In other words, with the Australian flora out of the picture, the remaining distributional pattern is orderly and comparatively simple; with the Australian flora included where it is, the pattern is essentially disorderly.

Putting the problem in its simplest terms the reason for this anomaly is that the flora of Australia differs from that of New Guinea to a degree which many people find inexplicable if the gulf between the two has never been more than the hundred miles of very shallow sea, thickly strewn with islands, that it comprises to-day. The question is, therefore, whether they have always been so placed, and, more particularly, whether Australia and New Guinea are, as would appear at first sight and as is commonly assumed, parts of one and the same great land-mass or not.

This is a simple enough question to ask, but the answer to it has become complicated by difficulties which are, in a measure, unreal. Before the days of theories of continental displacement or drift, the immovability of large land-masses was accepted as an axiom and was not a matter of debate. Australia and New Guinea were assumed always to have been situated where they are now, and, as a result of this, there not unnaturally grew up a strong tendency to limit the problem which this assumption engendered by minimising the great biological differences between the two and by stressing the similarities. This treatment of the difficulty took strong root, as indeed it was almost bound to do, and doubtless partly because of this legacy from the past, though also from the shape and distribution of the islands in the eastern part of the Malaysia and Melanesia, Wegener, when he put forward his theory of continental displacement (see Chapter 21), postulated that a greater Australian continent, of which New Guinea was a part, had moved north and disrupted this archipelago. Du Toit expressed essentially the same opinion, though not quite in the same terms.

This concept of continental movement certainly helps to resolve the anomaly of the position of the Australian flora, because it allows that it may have moved, but a moment's reflection shows that it does not solve the chief biological problem, which is the extraordinary difference on the two sides of the Torres Strait. Nor does it explain why New Guinea should possess so few Australian types. Nevertheless, biologists are generally agreed that the peculiar features of the Australian biota (and some of the zoological facts are even more striking than the botanical) can only be explained on the supposition that they have developed under conditions of great and prolonged geographical isolation, and thus those who do not accept continental drift in this dilemma, or who do so only in the terms of Wegener and Du Toit, find themselves in the untenable position of maintaining that the present isolation of

Australia, which *ex hypothesi* must always have existed unchanged, is sufficient to account for the facts. When it is remembered that Australia is much *less* isolated from New Guinea and the rest of Malaysia than, say, Cuba and Jamaica are from America; or Iceland is from Europe; or Formosa is from Asia; not to mention the greater mutual isolation of Australia, New Caledonia, Fiji and New Zealand, the absurdity of this contention is apparent enough.

It is obvious that the real crux of the problem of these two floras is not so much whether Australia and New Guinea, as a great combined unit, has or has not moved, but whether these two regions have or have not always had their present geographical relation to one another, and whether they are or are not parts of the same land-mass. For the reason explained they are always assumed, even if only tacitly, to be so, but actually there appears to be no positive evidence for this view, and any inference derived from their present close proximity is more than counter-balanced by the very great differences between them geologically and physiographically. This is not the place to go further into this fascinating problem, but it should be once more emphasised that, however remote from plants and however academic this issue may seem, it is in fact crucial to a better understanding of much of the history and relationships of the southern floras, because, if Australia and New Guinea can be shown to have been of separate origin, their present proximity *may* have been brought about by a gradual diminution of the distance between them in the course of geological time (see Chapter 21). If this is so, not only is it possible that Australia and its flora may once have been in a position where it would be, not a striking anomaly in the distribution of the southern floras, but an essential and orderly link within and among its neighbours; but it is also much easier to explain the otherwise almost inexplicable floristic differences on the two sides of the Torres Strait.

With this thought the present chapter must be brought to a close, but those who have read so far may like to note that just such a movement of Australia is claimed to have been shown by some of the recent work on palaeomagnetism (see p. 410); that attention has been drawn to many of the reasons for at least doubting whether Australia and New Guinea are as closely related as their present positions suggest (306); and that there are some particularly relevant remarks on the Tertiary geology of the two countries by Gill (269).

CHAPTER 13

THE HISTORY AND DISTRIBUTION OF THE BRITISH FLORA

THE fossil history of the Angiosperms, which is described at some length in Chapter 14, shows clearly enough that the floras of to-day can be understood properly only if the past is also taken into account, and so, in discussing the distribution of the plants living in the British Isles to-day, due notice must be taken of their history. Much of this history is, however, so remote in time that it does not directly concern the actual species which now compose the flora, and it will be sufficient here to trace the story of these plants particularly from the time at which they became inhabitants of Britain. Fortunately this story of the British flora, that is to say of the assemblage of species which now forms the vegetation of the British Isles, starts at a definite point in geological time, beyond which it is not necessary to probe.

Fortunately, too, the task of telling the story in brief has also been made easier by the publication within the last few years of two books, Matthews' *Origin and Distribution of the British Flora* (504) and Godwin's *The History of the British Flora* (280). The former is a most useful and readable concise account, at greater length, of most of the subjects mentioned in this chapter, and provides a fuller account of the author's analysis discussed on pp. 288 *et seq.* The latter is a much larger work which deals in great detail with the Quaternary, and especially post-Glacial, history of the flora, and is an essential source for all who wish to pursue the subject further, or to fill out the very brief account on pp. 274 and 275 below. Furthermore, the present distributions of the members of the British flora have been depicted more completely and clearly than ever before in the recently published *Atlas of the British Flora* (555).

As will be seen in Chapter 15, the vegetation of the northern temperate latitudes remained more or less constant, presumably under the influence of equally constant climatic conditions, throughout the Cretaceous and most of the Tertiary epochs, but in the Pliocene period there began a rapid deterioration of climate, accompanied by marked floristic changes, and this deterioration culminated in the Ice Ages of the Pleistocene period.

It so happens that one of the last stages before the oncoming of the ice, formerly considered to be of Upper Pliocene date but now regarded as belonging to the Lower Pleistocene, has, in the British Isles, left behind it remains so clear that they give a good picture of the contemporary plant life. These remains are the fossils of the Cromerian deposits, a name derived from the most important of them, the Cromer Forest bed, and their most outstanding feature is that they almost all belong to species which are living in Britain to-day. It is, therefore, possible to say with some confidence that when the Pleistocene began the flora of this country was very much as it is to-day and that its subsequent history is that of the vicissitudes through which it has passed since that time.

The Cromer beds contain remains not only of plants but also of animals, and these latter are in many ways the more striking. For instance, there have been described from among them no fewer than 46 species of mammals, including such types as elephant, hippopotamus, rhinoceros, musk ox, glutton and a number of deer.

Thirty of these were large animals and of these only six are known anywhere to-day, the remainder having become extinct, while of these six only three now inhabit the British Isles. It is, however, only in the mammals that there is any conspicuous difference between the past and present; the other vertebrates in the deposit are all species now living in the country, and the same is virtually true of the molluscs. Similarly with the plants, of which about 130 species have been identified, only some half-dozen, including *Trapa natans*, *Hypecoum procumbens*, *Najas minor* and an extinct species of *Corema*, are no longer to be found here. All the rest are species still familiar to British botanists, and these give ample evidence that the flora as a whole must have been very similar to that existing to-day (587).

What has been said about the mammals does not invalidate the comparison, because their disappearance can be explained by the difference in the distribution of land and sea as between the past and present. There are good reasons for believing that in Pliocene times Britain was part of the Continent, joined to what is now western Europe across the southern part of the North Sea, and that across this now water-covered area there flowed a greater and longer river Rhine of which in all probability the Thames was a western tributary. With the coming of the ice in the Pleistocene, the drainage of this great river to the north was dammed and the confined water escaped by cutting through what is now the Straits of Dover, thus completely severing Britain from the mainland. It is also supposed that at some later date this strait was again obliterated owing to the elevation of the land in relation to the sea, and that only comparatively recently, perhaps about 8,000 years ago (806), has the sea once more broken through to give Britain its insularity. These various changes have been depicted by Wills (788) in a series of maps delineating a succession of con-nections and separations between Britain and the continent in Tertiary times. Of special interest is the map of the penultimate glaciation which shows a contemporary isthmus of Dover across which ran a river draining the ice-dammed lake of the southern North Sea. This isthmus had gone at the time of the last glaciation. That eastern England was indeed at one time part of the basin of the Rhine is supported by the observations of Stomps (711), who finds that some of the plants especially chara-cteristic of East Anglia are equally characteristic of those parts of the Continent which presumably formed part of the east side of the basin of this ancient Rhine. But, whatever the details, it is indisputable that considerable geographical changes have taken place, and the extinction of so many large mammals may be connected with this.

To return to the plants, what is said in Chapter 15 about the glaciations of the Pleistocene points strongly to the fact that, however much the Cromer Forest plants may resemble the present flora, it is impossible to imagine this similarity as due to the persistence of the flora unchanged ever since Pliocene times. During the maximum glaciation, for example, Britain suffered intense ice action, and there is little doubt that most of it, except the extreme southern part, was covered either by ice-caps or glaciers. In addition, there were other less severe glaciations and it seems clear that during some period of the Pleistocene a portion at least of the pre-glacial flora must have been driven south beyond the confines of the country, and hence that its presence here now must be due to subsequent re-immigration. This broad statement admits of little argument. What is uncertain is the extent to which the early flora was affected in this way, and in particular the proportion of it which was thus destroyed or driven out. On this question there is much controversy and the opposing points of view (792) must be considered with some care.

The problem really turns on two points, first, that of the real extent to which the

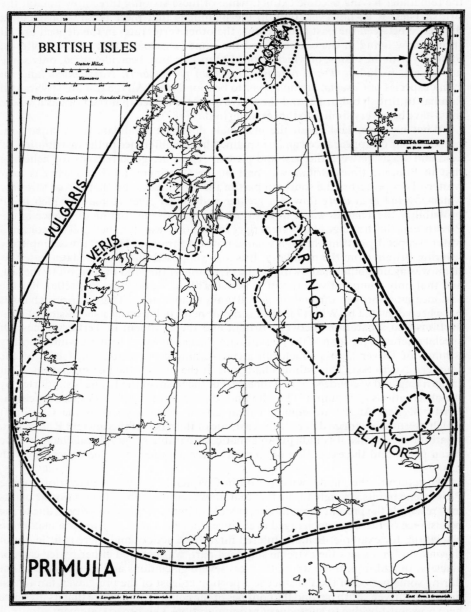

FIG. 63.—Map showing the distribution of the species of *Primula* in the British Isles.

country was glaciated, and second, the value as indications of climatic conditions of certain plant remains dating from the time of glaciation.

There is at the outset a difficulty in determining the actual extent of the ice at its maximum in that it is not easy to assign a limit to the effect of ice action. The limit of the ice as laid down in most geological accounts is a line joining the Thames and the Severn and passing south of Ireland and it is presumed that north of this line the ice was more or less continuous. But if this was the edge of continuous ice, it seems certain that much of the country further south must have contained numerous glaciers, and the size and number of these would obviously be of great importance. The thickness of glacial deposits but a little north of the Thames suggests that they must have been very extensive, and if so, then the effective limit of ice action must have been considerably further south. It is true that in general there are no glacial deposits in south England, but it is also to be noted that the occurrence of something of the sort (in one case an actual boulder clay) has been recorded not only from the north coast of Devon (185) but even from the Scillies (48). Another deposit of southern England, the Coombe rock, is also believed by some to owe its origin in part to glacial conditions. All these remains, however, are slight and it may be accepted that south England was never covered by an ice-cap, although it may have been the site of numerous glaciers. This is the usual state of affairs on the margin of an extensive ice-sheet, as is seen in Greenland to-day (638), where near the coasts the marginal thinnings of the ice, together with the relief of the land, leads to a fringe of glaciers among and between which emerge the unglaciated summits known as "nunataks".

The theory that there were such nunataks not only in southern England but also further north, and that some of the flora found on them refuges in which it was able to survive the effects of the ice, has received considerable attention. Certainly there are considerable areas even in north England which, it is claimed, have never been covered with ice. One such large area is in the southern Pennines, and another is in Upper Teesdale. Many of these nunataks, it has been pointed out, are to-day remarkable for the number of rare plants to be found on them. Upper Teesdale, for instance, has several plants which are to be found practically nowhere else in Britain, and some of the British endemic forms (see below) are also restricted to such areas.

The possibility of the survival of members of the pre-glacial flora on unglaciated areas has been discussed with special reference to Great Britain by many geologists and botanists including Blackburn (71) and Raistrick (577), but the theory originated in connection with the investigations of Fernald and others into the flora of the shores of the Gulf of St. Lawrence in eastern North America (see Chapter 8). There occur here in certain places many peculiar species and forms often quite foreign to the region in general and most closely related to other species to be found many hundreds of miles away, and this has been explained on the view that they are ancient types which have persisted for hundreds of years, and throughout at least part of the glacial period, on the unglaciated regions. The theory is an attractive one, and that it is true to some degree can hardly be disproved, but it is only fair to say that both in North America and Britain the facts can be explained otherwise. In the former, Marie Victorin (488) believes, for instance, that the observed facts may be the result of divergent migration from one more northerly centre. In Britain it has been suggested that the rare and local plants mentioned above are to be regarded not as ancient survivors but as recent arrivals in their respective habitats. There is also another great objection to the theory of nunatak survival, namely, that if these unglaciated spots were, during the ice ages, peculiarly suitable for the plants concerned, they would almost certainly not be so now, and there seems no reason why they should still be restricted to them when the general conditions of the region have so materially altered. A somewhat similar opinion has been expressed by Deevey (179) in a stimulating discussion of the nunatak theory.

Another argument used in favour of the view that a considerable proportion of the pre-glacial flora may have survived the glaciations is that to-day warmth-loving plants are often found growing in close proximity to glaciers. Hooker in his *Himalayan Journal* pointed out that the direct distance between the perpetual snows of these mountains and the tropical flora at their base was only about six miles, and more recently attention has been drawn to the occurrence in New Zealand of tree ferns equally near or even nearer to glaciers. These facts are undoubtedly striking, but they afford little indication of conditions in Britain during the Pleistocene. In both cases the ice concerned is the ice of mountain glacier systems and not the ice of continuous ice-sheets centred near the pole, and the difference is fundamental. The ice is present because of the elevation of the land and not because of the refrigeration at sea level of the whole latitudinal zone in which it is found, and on this account its influence on the climate is extremely local. Not only are polar ice-caps much more extensive but their very presence and persistence indicates minimum climatic values over wide areas, and their effects are felt far beyond their boundaries. To-day there is probably only one part of the world where conditions are at all parallel to those which must have existed in Britain during the Pleistocene. This is Greenland, which can, as a result, support only an arctic flora composed of cold-resistant types. There are neither tropical nor even warm temperate species within hundreds of miles of its shores. On this analogy, at any rate, it is difficult to believe that, if the conditions in Britain during the ice ages were as they have been pictured, the flora can have been anything more than an arctic flora with perhaps an ingredient of a few particularly hardy species of a more temperate character. At the same time it is to be remembered that southern England is at a much lower latitude than Greenland so that, as long as the pole remained in its present position, conditions would tend to be less rigorous, especially in summer, even if it was covered with ice to a comparable degree.

Let us now turn to the actual remains of the vegetation of the Pleistocene in this country. Unfortunately these are not very considerable, but there are some at least, and they have been the subject of much argument. This centres chiefly round certain so-called "arctic beds" the remains of which have been described from such different parts of England as East Yorkshire, East Anglia, Cambridgeshire (122), the Lea Valley (586, 589), South Devon and the Isle of Wight. From these deposits there have been identified various plants which to-day are associated with arctic floras, such as some of the smaller willows, *Betula nana, Oxyria digyna, Arctostaphylos* and *Ranunculus hyperboreus*, and it has been argued that the presence of these species indicates arctic conditions at the time and place of their deposition, and as a corollary that plants of less arctic character must have had a home much further south. At first sight this seems a reasonable suggestion, but closer investigation reveals difficulties. According to Wilmott (789) the species mentioned are generally accompanied by others which are certainly not arctic in type, such as species of *Silene* and *Linum* in the Lea Valley flora, and in addition he regards some of the identifications as far from satisfactory. Indeed, if the total remains in these various beds are considered without special emphasis on particular species, their arctic character is open to doubt. Matthews (504) has also commented at some length on the problems of these "arctic beds".

Wilmott's point has been developed by Godwin (278) in an attempt to reconcile

Plate 17. Grass-trees (*Xanthorrhoea sp.*) on the slopes of Mt. Mitchell, Queensland

(Photo: F. Hurley)

some of the opposing views regarding the nunatak theory. He claims that in one of these beds at least (the Lea Valley) the flora contains three categories of species— arctic-alpines such as *Dryas* and *Betula nana*; aquatic and marsh plants such as *Potamogeton* and *Filipendula ulmaria*; and various species, most or all of which are now generally regarded as weeds or at least species of disturbed ground, and he draws attention to the circumstance that these three types do in fact occur together to-day in Northern Scandinavia, under particular conditions which must be very similar to those of England during the Pleistocene. He suggests that the retreat of the ice laid bare areas which became colonised by this flora, but that in due course it became itself smothered almost to extinction by the later-spreading forest, so that many of its representatives occur in England to-day only in the artificially bared areas produced by man which are the nearest existing approach to their earlier habitats. On this argument Godwin suggests that the British areas referred to as nunataks served, not as pre-glacial refuges, but only as pre-forest period refuges in which these species were able to maintain a precarious hold until such time as they could spread into the later new man-made habitats. Related to this is the suggestion of Pigott and Walters (560) that some of the rarer members of the flora which now have widely discontinuous ranges owe these to the fact that they are all that is left of much more extensive and continuous ranges which were almost wholly obliterated by the spread of forest and bog in post-glacial times.

Nor are all the floras of the Pleistocene of the same character. In West Sussex, for instance, plants like oak, elder, dogwood and a now exotic maple have been recorded, showing that at some stage of the Pleistocene, presumably during the inter-glacial period that followed the maximum glaciation, quite a temperate flora existed at least in the south of the country.

In short there seems no direct evidence by which the proportion of the pre-glacial flora which was able to persist unharmed in this country during the ice ages can be determined, and it is not surprising that there is a good deal of difference of opinion. Wilmott (792) some years ago expressed the view that in the main the present flora consists either of boreal and montane plants which would scarcely be affected by ice or common central European plants which in his opinion might have survived south of the Thames, and other botanists have taken up much the same belief. On the other hand, Salisbury (792), Reid (584) and others believe that only the arctic and boreal types can have survived.

Both these views really concern only the commoner and more generally distributed British plants. As will be seen later, there are many species in the flora which are confined even to-day to the warmest and most southerly parts of the country, and there is no suggestion that these can have survived glaciation *in situ*. The statement that the British flora is to be regarded as essentially an immigrant or rather re-immigrant one is therefore certainly true in some measure. The difficulty is to determine exactly what that measure is.

The history of the flora *since* the latest glaciation is much better known, thanks to the results obtained from a careful study of the plant remains in post-glacial deposits, and particularly in peat, where the methods of pollen analysis (102, 276, 279), or palynology as it is called, especially have proved of great value and from the development of radio-carbon dating (see p. 330).

Woodhead (796) was one of the first to bring together in a single account much of the very scattered evidence concerning the course of events in the southern Pennines, and showed clearly that the sequence of deposits and events was very much like that described in Chapter 15 for Scandinavia. Immediately above the

18

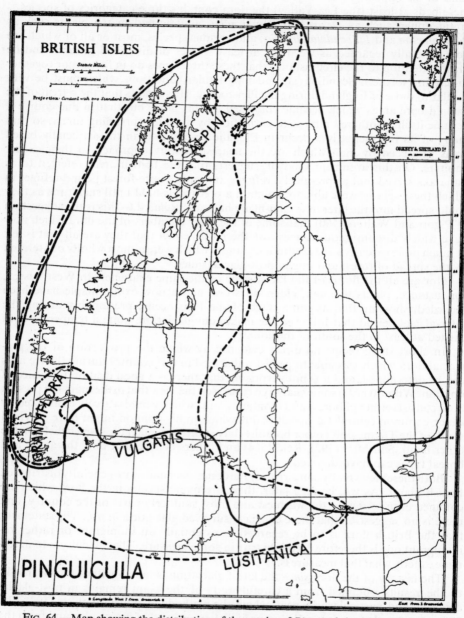

BRITISH ISLES

Statute Miles

Kilometres

Projection: Conical with two Standard Parallels

ALPINA

ORKNEY & SHETLAND I?

GRANDIFLORA

VULGARIS

PINGUICULA

LUSITANICA

FIG. 64.—Map showing the distribution of the species of *Pinguicula* in the British Isles. It is doubtful whether *P. alpina* still occurs in any of its three areas.

actual glacial horizons are the remains of a flora definitely arctic in character. This is followed by a sub-arctic late-glacial flora in which birch and pine occurred. Then comes a more temperate forest flora composed mainly of deciduous trees, and this in turn is succeeded by a thick deposit of peat indicating a climatic change from drier to more moist. Lastly there are indications of a cessation of peat formation and a return to forest conditions, and most recently of all, some recrudescence of peat formation which brings the record almost to the present day. This at any rate was the general outline for the Pennines, and later and more widespread investigations showed that the same sequence applies, with certain modifications, to the British Isles as a whole, and a useful summary of the subject is given (together with a wealth of other information concerning the British flora) by Tansley (718). For more recent discussion of a rapidly developing subject reference may be made to Zeuner (806) and Godwin (280) and from the latter the table shown on p. 276, which is sufficiently detailed but not too complex for our present purpose, has been derived.

The sequence of conditions shows, as is only to be expected, a series of increasingly temperate floras following the most recent retreat of the ice, and on the whole this gradual amelioration is unbroken except for the occurrence of a suggested climatic optimum (post-glacial optimum) somewhere at the end of the boreal period. This gradual amelioration is in itself evidence that the immigration and re-immigration of species into the country must also have been gradual, and the relatively great changes which were clearly necessary to re-establish the flora in the condition in which it existed before the Ice Ages is sufficient demonstration of the effects of the glaciation upon the plant life.

But the building up of the present British flora has not been conditioned by climate alone. For several thousands of years now the country has supported an ever increasing human population, and a proportion of the flora certainly owes its presence to the intentional or accidental influences of human beings. Each of the human waves of invasion which constitute so much of British history has brought with it plants long associated with its peoples in their earlier homes, and each phase of history is reflected in the flora.

From the point of view of its influence on the natural vegetation the history of Britain may be divided into five periods, each of which has had its own effect on the plant life. For many centuries following man's first appearance on our shores the land was inhabited by a succession of relatively primitive communities which were able to make but little headway and impression against the forces of nature. Even agriculture, when it came to be practised at all, was on a very simple and restricted scale, and was almost certainly of necessity confined to the more accessible and amenable parts of the country like the chalk and limestones, where little natural vegetation had to be cleared to make way for it, and where on the other hand its effect on the general plant life was least.

This continued until, with the coming of the Romans shortly after the beginning of the present era, the second period began. The Roman occupation lasted for roughly four hundred years, and there is no doubt that during that time the internal organisation of the country was raised to a level which it did not again reach for more than a thousand years.

The effect on the vegetation must have been profound, for the Romans brought with them or developed later the tools and technical knowledge which made it possible for them to subdue their environment almost completely. Forest clearance began; swamps were drained; roads were built; and indeed nearly all the activities calculated to modify the natural vegetation were in progress. Agriculture, too, was

THE SEQUENCE OF POST-GLACIAL CHANGES IN SOUTHERN BRITAIN

DATING		VEGETATION			CLIMATE		
Years	Pollen zones	Ireland	Br. Is.	England & Wales		Periods of Blytt and Sernander	
—2,000 ... B.C.	VIII	Alder-birch-oak	ALDER-BIRCH-OAK (BEECH)	Alder-oak-elm-birch (beech)	Rapid deterioration	SUB-ATLANTIC	
—2,000	VIIb	Alder-oak (elm decline)	ALDER-MIXED OAK FOREST	Alder-oak-elm-lime		SUB-BOREAL	POST-GLACIAL
—4,000	VIIa	Alder-oak-pine			Climatic Optimum (dryness)	ATLANTIC	POST-GLACIAL
—6,000	VI c b a	Hazel-pine	HAZEL-PINE	Pine-hazel		BOREAL	POST-GLACIAL
	V	Hazel-birch	HAZEL-BIRCH PINE	Pine	Rapid amelioration	BOREAL	POST-GLACIAL
—8,000	IV	Birch	BIRCH	Birch-pine		PRE-BOREAL	POST-GLACIAL
	III	*Salix herbacea*		Park-tundra (birch copses)	Cold	UPPER DRYAS	LATE-GLACIAL
—10,000	II	Birch		Birch woods	Milder	ALLERØD	LATE-GLACIAL
—12,000	I	*Salix herbacea*		Park-tundra (local birch)	Cold	LOWER DRYAS	LATE-GLACIAL

(Modified from Godwin, *History of the British Flora*, 1956, Cambridge University Press.)

far more extensively and variedly carried on than before. It is difficult to visualise the condition to which all this must have brought the country eventually, but there is reason to believe that in the south of England, at any rate, the zenith of the Roman period, reached in the third and fourth centuries of our era, must have revealed a countryside not widely different from that of two or three hundred years ago.

Unfortunately for history, but perhaps fortunately for the flora, this standard was not maintained. The waning of the imperial power eventually necessitated the withdrawal of all the legions from Britain. With them went the hope of safety, and from that time the country sank under the plundering of its enemies into a state of collapse and chaos, during which it seems that the work of the Romans was virtually destroyed. Cities disappeared; drainage failed, and cultivated land degenerated into grassland, thicket and woodland.

This relapse continued, with no doubt some slow improvement, for a very long time. Not until the Norman period was there even any real political stability, and as far as the vegetation was concerned it can hardly have altered much again until the feudal system which the Normans established gave place, in the course of time, to the manorial system. This was based at least in part on agriculture, and as it became firmly established the vegetation must once more have undergone a slow but steady modification. Whether this was as marked as it had been in the Roman period is doubtful, but it was almost certainly more widespread, and it was probably now for the first time that some of the remoter parts of the country felt the real impress of man and his works.

Although the gradual growth of the population and the development of the country accelerated as time went on, there was no essential alteration that affected the vegetation until the middle of the eighteenth century. Up to that time Britain remained a purely agricultural country.

But about 1750 there was ushered in the period which was destined to see a greater revolution in almost every sphere than any that had gone before it—the age of industrialism and urbanism. Within a space of less than 200 years miles of what was hitherto largely fair and untouched country has become covered, to the utter exclusion of natural vegetation, with the products and achievements of man's hands and brain. The process still goes on. Every year more and more of the country disappears under the insatiable demands of the town and factory, and only in recent years has there been any real indication that a long slumbering public conscience will at last awake and demand a cessation of what is partly senseless and unnecessary destruction.

This latest period is from the plant point of view unlike the rest in that it has been most entirely destructive. In earlier times what loss there may have been among native plants was probably more than balanced by the introduction of new species, but with industrialism there has been little such compensation except perhaps for a few garden plants which have established themselves among the wild ones. Modern farming does not encourage the weeds which, while a bane to the farmer, are often a joy to the botanist, and in addition there are the depredations of the plant collector who, it may or may not be significant to note, seems to have multiplied with the growth of industrialism.

An interesting attempt was made some time ago to assess the changes which had taken place in the British flora in the preceding fifty years (790) and it would seem that while several species had become extinct more have been discovered by intensive study or collecting, so that the total number was slightly on the increase, and this is borne out by a rather earlier estimate (197) which suggests that less than a

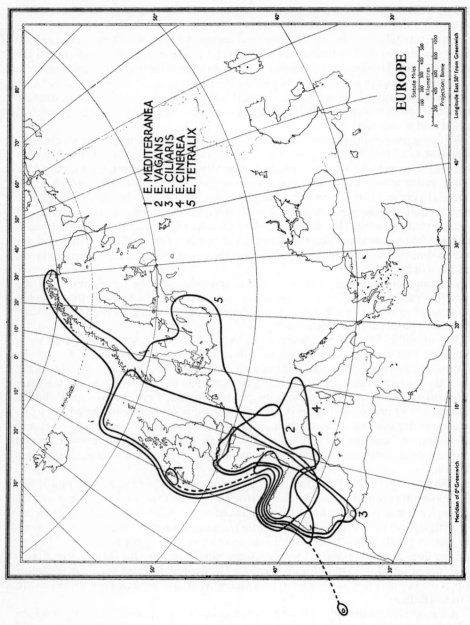

1 E. MEDITERRANEA
2 E. VAGANS
3 E. CILIARIS
4 E. CINEREA
5 E. TETRALIX

EUROPE

Statute Miles

Kilometres

Projection: Bonne

Longitude East 50° from Greenwich

Meridian of 0° Greenwich

Fig. 65.—Map showing the distribution of the British species of *Erica* in Western Europe, mainly after Hansen.

dozen species have become extinct since 1597. Nevertheless, it seems certain that many of the favourite wild plants are far less abundant than previously and are at least in danger of ultimate extinction, not by the processes of unaided nature but by the thoughtless or deliberate actions of their admirers.

Such is the story of the development of the British flora down to the present day. Its long and eventful history has been told in outline, and we have seen that it is now an assemblage of species moulded and modified in many different ways and by many different events and processes. This assemblage and the way in which it is distributed within the country must now be discussed.

The scientific study of the distribution of British plants may be said to date from the work and writings of Hewett Cottrell Watson, who devoted a long and active life to it. Certain earlier writers had touched upon the subject, but their writings were merely lists of the localities of some of the rarer species designed primarily for the convenience of collectors. Watson's first two works (760, 761) appeared in 1832 and 1835 respectively, but it was between the years 1847 and 1859 that there appeared his great four-volume work the *Cybele Britannica* (762), in which were brought together all the known facts concerning the geography of the species comprising the British flora. In the *Cybele* Watson analysed and arranged the British plants according to several methods which have ever since remained the basis for the geographical study of British plants, and they may therefore be properly considered here at some length.

He dealt first with the actual ranges of the species in Great Britain by dividing the region up into eighteen provinces and noting in which of them each plant occurred. The provinces were based chiefly on major topographical features and were:

1. Peninsula	7. North Wales	13. West Lowlands
2. Channel	8. Trent	14. East Lowlands
3. Thames	9. Mersey	15. East Highlands
4. Ouse	10. Humber	16. West Highlands
5. Severn	11. Tyne	17. North Highlands
6. South Wales	12. Lakes	18. North Isles

The actual limitation of the provinces was chiefly by counties.

Next he classified the species according to the altitude at which they grow, recognising and characterising six zones:

Super-arctic	. . .	*Salix herbacea* without *Calluna*.
Mid-arctic	. . .	*Calluna* without *Erica*.
Infer-arctic	. . .	*Erica tetralix* without *Pteridium*.
Super-agrarian	. .	*Pteridium* without *Rhamnus*, etc.
Mid-agrarian	. . .	*Rhamnus* without *Clematis*, etc.
Infer-agrarian	. . .	*Clematis*, etc.

The arctic region was that above the limits of cultivation and the agrarian region the lower agricultural levels. This altitudinal classification although of considerable interest was not on the whole very satisfactory because of the innumerable complicating factors. It is still occasionally referred to, but is the one part of Watson's work which has virtually become obsolete.

A third classification is perhaps the most important of all, and marked a very definite step forward in the geographical conception of the British flora. This was the recognition of seven types according to the generalised distribution of the species within Great Britain (Figs. 63, 64). Actually Watson had referred to such types in one

of his earlier books, but here in the *Cybele* they were described in more definite fashion
as:

1. British type . . . Plants occurring in all or nearly all the provinces
   of both England and Scotland.
2. English type . . Plants predominantly English in distribution,
   especially southern and becoming rare towards
   the north.
3. Scottish type . . Plants predominantly Scottish in distribution,
   especially northern and becoming rare towards
   the south.
4. Highland type . . Plants confined to the mountain regions of
   England, Wales and Scotland.
5. Germanic type . . Plants characteristic of the east part of England.
6. Atlantic type . . Plants characteristic of the west and south-west
   parts of Britain.
7. Local or doubtful type .

Mention must be made at this point of Forbes' (247) publication in 1846 of a
very similar series of types or, as the author called them, "floras". We need not be
concerned whether or not, as has been stated, this work of Forbes' was in fact a
plagiarism of Watson's earlier work in which his types had first appeared. The important point is rather that Forbes not only listed his floras or, as we should call them
to-day, "floristic elements", but also explained them on the grounds that they represented the stages and directions of the immigration of plants into this country
following the Ice Ages. For this reason Forbes' work, even if not altogether original,
cannot be ignored, and will be referred to again later.

To return to the *Cybele*. Watson next dealt with the British plants according to
their status in the country, that is to say, according to their mode of origin. This
question of status is a very thorny one, largely because in many cases the truth can
never now be discovered, but it is also a very interesting one and helps greatly in
appreciating our flora properly. Here again, Watson's work has stood the test of time
and his classification, which is as follows, is substantially that still in use to-day.

The first and most important category is that of the "native" species. These are
the plants whose presence in the country has nothing to do with human action either
direct or indirect. Many of them have no doubt existed in the country much longer
than man himself and for this reason they have been described as botanical aborigines
or, as the phrase goes, "aboriginal possessors of the soil". At the same time they
certainly include some more recent immigrants. It is to these native species that the
natural vegetation of the country is almost entirely due.

Three other categories contain the plants which are here only as a direct or indirect result of human activity, and a great deal of information about these has been
given by Salisbury (616).

First there are the plants which owe their presence to man's agricultural activities,
and these are generally called "colonists" or "cornfield weeds". Strictly speaking,
this should include only those species which have no habitat in this country other than
arable land, and which presumably would gradually disappear if cultivation ceased,
but it is not easy to draw the line because some native species are among the most
familiar of crop weeds.

Next there are the species, much more numerous, which have been introduced
deliberately by man either as farm or garden plants, and have subsequently escaped
from cultivation and succeed in maintaining themselves unaided in more or less

natural vegetation. These are called "denizens" and some of them, the sycamore is a good example, have become almost completely integrated into the native flora.

Lastly, there are the species which are constantly introduced by accident in the form of seeds and fruits, which grow for one or more summer seasons but which do not normally reproduce and whose presence is therefore transitory. They are found only in disturbed ground and play no part in the natural vegetation. No doubt on the grounds of their foreign origin these plants were called "aliens", but the more recent terms "casual" and "adventive" are perhaps to be preferred. They come from all over the world and the number recorded is constantly increasing.

Finally Watson classified the flora on what we should now call an ecological basis into the following groups according to habitat:

1. Pratal	. . .	Plants of meadows.
2. Pascual	. .	,, ,, less rich pastures.
3. Ericetal	. .	,, ,, moors and heaths.
4. Uliginal	. .	,, ,, swamps and bogs.
5. Lacustral	. .	Submerged or floating aquatics.
6. Paludal	. .	Plants of marshy places.
7. Inundatal	. .	,, ,, places liable to winter flooding.
8. Viatical	. .	,, ,, disturbed ground.
9. Agrestal	. .	,, ,, cultivated ground.
10. Glareal	. .	,, ,, dry exposed ground.
11. Rupestral	. .	,, ,, walls and rocks.
12. Septal	. .	,, ,, hedges.
13. Sylvestral	. .	,, ,, woods and shady places.
14. Littoral	. .	,, ,, the seashore.

By the combination of these classifications Watson was able to give a very complete picture of the distribution of each British plant not merely in terms of its actual geographical range but in terms of geographical range, altitude, status and ecology, and a list of the British plants embodying this information is the main part of the *Cybele*.

In 1860 there appeared the first part of a supplement to the *Cybele* and in 1868–1870 the three volumes of the *Compendium of the Cybele Britannica*. In these works Watson made two further great advances in British plant geography. First he replaced or elaborated his eighteen provinces by dividing the whole of Britain into 112 vice-counties, and second he discussed for the first time the extra-British ranges of the members of the British flora. His system of vice-counties is still in full use, and more and more attention has come to be paid to the wider distribution of British plants.

Finally, in 1873–4, Watson published his last work, the two volumes of his *Topographical Botany* (763), which provided in tabulated form a summary of the known distribution of British plants. Its concise and convenient form has given to *Topographical Botany* a popularity which in comparison with the *Cybele* it scarcely deserves, and it has been kept up to date ever since by a second edition and by supplements. More recently Druce's *Comital Flora* (199) is, as its author states, mainly a modern revision of *Topographical Botany* with Ireland also included. Regarding this latter point Watson did not deal with Ireland in either the *Cybele* or *Topographical Botany*, but this gap has long been filled by corresponding publications by Colgan and Scully (144) and by Praeger (570).

Any work which consists of the compilation and collection of records which are ceaselessly being made can never possess finality, and since Watson's day botanists have repeatedly revised or added to his work in detail, but it is a remarkable tribute to him that during a time of such rapid scientific advance the main outlines of his studies remain practically in the form in which he stated them. Some aspects have received more attention than others but the framework remains.

This sketch of Watson's work has had two functions: it has given an account of the origin and development of the study of the geographical features of British plants, and it has also indicated the main ways in which that study has been conducted. With it as a background we may go on now to a brief consideration of the present position of these studies and to illustrate them by the examples which it would have been out of place to mention above.

Since Watson's time research into the distribution of British plants has continued mainly along three lines. The first is in fact the whole subsequent growth and development of the science of plant ecology or study of the plant in relation to its environment, and while it would be extravagant to hail Watson as the first plant ecologist there is, nevertheless, a clear forecast of the study of ecology in his classification of plants according to the kinds of habitat they occupy. Since his day ecology has developed so far and so wide that it has become a subject of its own, ranking with, and complementary to, the subject of plant geography in the narrower sense which deals with the spatial relations rather than with the physiological relation of plants to the earth that bears them. Since this book is devoted to plant geography in this narrower sense, plant ecology falls outside its scope and further information concerning this particular subject must be sought elsewhere. Nevertheless it must be borne in mind that this sharp demarcation of interests is largely made inevitable by the exigencies of convenience. It is not a natural separation, and the two subjects of plant ecology and plant geography are interrelated at almost every point.

The second line of development in British plant geography has been the further study of the classification of species according to their distribution *within* the country itself, an extension, as it were, of Watson's "types" and Forbes' "floras", and the third line has been the elaboration of the classification according to the distribution of the species *outside* Great Britain. The present position regarding both these must now be considered. In doing this it is necessary to write largely in terms of numbers. As was made clear earlier, numbers may mean little or much and must not be regarded too seriously, but without them it is almost impossible either to make comparisons with other floras or to demonstrate the comparative importance of different components. They also have another value in that they illustrate very vividly the extent to which our conceptions of the flora depend upon individual opinions, a limitation which cannot entirely be surmounted.

The differences which exist in the various estimates of the size, in number of species, of the British flora are chiefly due to two difficulties. The first lies in deciding to what degree the recognition of small species or "microspecies" should be carried and the second in deciding exactly what plants deserve to be considered as members of the established flora. As a general rule the more a genus is studied the more obvious become the differences between the individuals which comprise it, with the result that more and more species tend to be recognised in it, and these species to become smaller and smaller in value and distinction. For example, the blackberries to the everyday field botanist appear to belong all to one variable species but to the specialist who has particularly studied them this one variable species is regarded as comprising a large number of separate microspecies. Similarly, in the genus *Hieracium*, the non-specialist regards the British forms as representing about half a dozen species, but the specialist may recognise among them as many as 250. The fact is that the species is not a standard measure and varies according to the conception of the individual botanist. It is therefore really impossible to determine how many species there actually are in the flora, and all that can be done is to arrive at some conclusion that will give a reasonable picture and estimate of the number of apparently different plants or, to use a scientific term, *phenotypes* present. How difficult even this is can be shown by a consideration of some actual estimates.

As regards status, it is with the casuals that the difficulty lies. Are any of them, and if so which of them, to be treated as definite members of the British flora? Although it is easy to define them as a class in general, it is not always easy to say exactly which species fall into this category. Some are more firmly established than others and some have almost the rank of colonists or denizens. For the most part, casuals are not regarded as members of the flora proper because they are not permanent and because they occupy no niche in the general vegetation, but some authorities include them and thereby increase the length of floral lists very considerably.

The effects of these two difficulties are best seen by referring to particular works on the British flora. One of the most satisfactory accounts of British plants is Hooker's *Student's Flora* (375) in which about 1,300 species are listed. Bentham and Hooker's *Handbook* (57, 242), which is perhaps the most familiar of all our Floras, gives about the same number. In both these works casuals are for the most part excluded. On the other hand Druce's *British Plant List* (198) includes these and enumerates no fewer than 4,250 species. In Clapham, Tutin and Warburg's *Flora* (134) this total is again greatly increased by the inclusion of many planted species and garden escapes, but Butcher's recent *New Illustrated British Flora* (96) omits many of these and reduces the total to 1,825.

Fortunately we can resolve this disparity to some extent. There is practical agreement that the figures of Hooker and of Bentham and Hooker are too small, and that many worthy species have not been recognised in them, and this opinion was implemented by the publication of what was in fact an appendix to these works enumerating some 500 additional species (97). Examination of Druce's list shows that no fewer than 1,750 casuals are included, and if these are cut out the total drops to something more than 2,500. Even this includes an extreme recognition of microspecies. Here we can gain assistance from various other Floras not yet mentioned, for Babington (37) and the *London Catalogue* (463), for instance, give 2,250 species including many *Rubi* and *Hieracia*, while Hayward (346) gives some 1,650 excluding microspecies of *Rubi* and *Hieracia*.

From this maze of figures it is possible to make some generalisation. It seems fairly clear that most authorities regard our flora as composed of about 1,750 species if certain microspecies and all casuals are excluded; as composed of about 2,250 species if the microspecies are included; and of anything up to 4,500 species if all possible casuals are included. For our present practical purpose then we shall be reasonably justified in regarding the flora as consisting of about 1,750 fairly well-defined species.

The next question is the proportion of the different status categories in this total. Here again it is difficult to reach conclusion, but, making a synthesis of various opinions, it would appear that of the 1,750 probably some 1,250 deserve to be regarded as natives, at any rate in some part of the country. About 250 are to be regarded as denizens, leaving a rather indefinite figure, not exceeding 250 and probably rather less, for colonists.

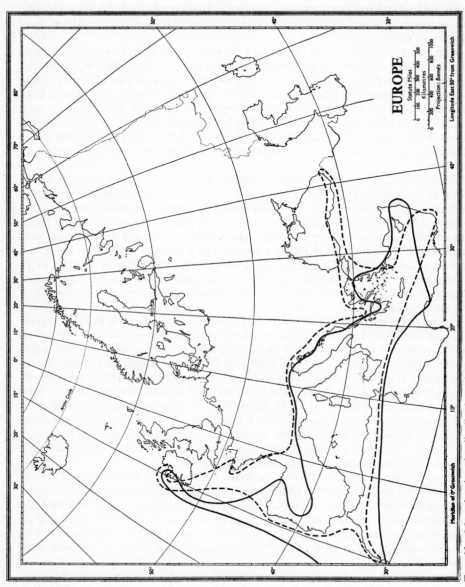

EUROPE

Statute Miles
0   100   200   300   400   500

Kilometres
0   200   400   600   800   1000

Projection: Bonne

Longitude East 50° from Greenwich

Meridian of 0° Greenwich

FIG. 66.—Map showing the distribution of *Neotinea intacta* (continuous line), mainly after von Soo, and *Arbutus unedo* (broken line), after Sealy.

For statistical purposes only species are taken into account, but many species actually occur in two or more well-marked subspecies or varieties. In addition there is a considerable number of inter-specific hybrids, and certain genera such as *Salix*, *Rumex* and *Rosa* are particularly rich in them.

With regard to casuals, only one further point need be mentioned here. Fresh species are always being introduced into the country, and as there is no means of telling which of previous entrants still persist, the total number of recorded casuals is always increasing. This is the chief reason why every fresh estimate which includes such plants tends to contain more species. These estimates represent, however, not the condition of affairs at any one time but the total records over a long period.

The term British as applied to the flora includes not only Great Britain and Ireland but also the Channel Islands. The last named, however, are included solely on political grounds, the flora actually being far more French than British in character. They may therefore be excluded except for special mention. It may be noted that some twenty species occur in these islands and not in the British Isles proper.

It happens that the distributions of plants in Britain and in Ireland respectively have nearly always been treated as two separate problems, and it is appropriate therefore to treat them so here, and it is convenient to begin with Britain. The distribution of plants in Britain is generally expressed in terms of the 112 vice-counties into which Watson ultimately divided the country, and this is probably as good a way of conveying their ranges as can be suggested. The *London Catalogue* (463), as well as one or two other works, summarises the information available in a convenient way, and the following table is taken from that work. It should, however, be supplemented by reference to the new *Atlas of the British Flora* (555).

About 7 per cent of all species are recorded from every one of the vice-counties.

,,	10	,,	,,	,,	,,	,,	,, 100–111
,,	5	,,	,,	,,	,,	,,	,, 90–99
,,	5	,,	,,	,,	,,	,,	,, 80–89
,,	5	,,	,,	,,	,,	,,	,, 70–79
,,	5	,,	,,	,,	,,	,,	,, 60–69
,,	5	,,	,,	,,	,,	,,	,, 50–59
,,	5	,,	,,	,,	,,	,,	,, 40–49
,,	6	,,	,,	,,	,,	,,	,, 30–39
,,	7	,,	,,	,,	,,	,,	,, 20–29
,,	12	,,	,,	,,	,,	,,	,, 10–19
,,	22	,,	,,	,,	,,	,,	,, 2–9
,,	6	,,	,,	,,	,,	,,	,, only 1

The main fact which emerges from these sources is that the species in total show every degree of range from the minimum to the maximum. Actually the figures given are probably all on the low side, since our knowledge of plant distribution even in this country is still far from complete. For instance, many of those in the second line will probably be ultimately discovered in the one or few remaining countries. On the other hand, the comparatively large figures towards the bottom of the table are caused by recently recognised species whose ranges are still largely problematical.

The plants recorded from all vice-counties include, as might be expected, many of the commonest and most familiar, as, for instance, *Achillea millefolium*, *Bellis perennis*, *Capsella bursa-pastoris*, *Cerastium vulgatum*, *Cirsium arvense*, *Cirsium palustre*, *Cirsium vulgare*, *Hedera helix*, *Juncus conglomeratus*, *Juncus effusus*,

Lotus corniculatus, Prunella vulgaris, Ranunculus acris, Ranunculus repens, Rumex acetosa, Rumex acetosella, Rumex crispus, Rumex obtusifolius, and *Taraxacum officinale,* together with such grasses as *Dactylis glomerata, Holcus lanatus, Lolium perenne, Poa annua* and *Poa pratensis.* Also included are various species distinctly less abundant but nevertheless thus completely distributed. Among these are *Achillea ptarmica, Alopecurus geniculatus, Galeopsis tetrahit, Hydrocotyle vulgaris, Linum catharticum, Lychnis flos-cuculi, Molinia caerulea, Myosotis versicolor, Oxalis acetosella, Ranunculus hederaceus* and *Thymus serpyllum.*

The species confined to only one vice-county each include, as has been indicated, a number of microspecies whose real distribution is still uncertain, but there are others about which there is no doubt. Not only so, but they are in some cases recorded only from one or two spots, or even from a single locality, as is true of *Cotoneaster integerrima* on the Great Orme; *Dianthus gratianopolitanus (caesius)* at Cheddar; *Saxifraga cernua* on Ben Lawers and in one other locality; *Arenaria uliginosa* on Widdybank Fell; *Scorzonera humilis* apparently only in one spot in Dorset; *Lloydia serotina* from a few rock faces in the Snowdon Range, and three species of *Trifolium* from the neighbourhood of the Lizard Point.

These species are to be regarded as among our rarest plants, but it is perhaps more accurate to call them local rather than rare. They may and sometimes do occur within their limited habitats in considerable quantity, while there are other species which, though more widespread, have been seen only in very small numbers and at long intervals of time. It is to these latter that the word rare more appropriately applies. An extreme instance of rarity in this sense is afforded by the orchid *Epipogium aphyllum,* of which until recently no more than about half a dozen individuals have been noted in three or four different and widely separated localities. Several other orchids are similarly but less conspicuously rare in this strict sense.

In view of what has just been said it would be interesting to arrange the vice-counties in order according to the total number of species recorded from each, but it is difficult to do this sufficiently accurately to be of value. It is clear, however, that the richest vice-counties are those in the extreme south-west and south-east of England, namely Cornwall, Sussex and Kent, and that from these points the richness decreases fairly regularly northward and westward. In short, there are most species in those parts of England nearest to the Continent, a feature which, in view of the glacial and post-glacial history of the flora is only to be expected.

That even to-day there is much to be learnt about the British flora was demonstrated in striking fashion by the discovery in Scotland in 1951 of no fewer than three additional species (466). These are *Diapensia lapponica* (602), never hitherto recorded from this country; *Koenigia islandica,* collected earlier also but then not recognised; and *Homogyne alpina,* never previously confirmed. More recently still a fourth, *Artemisia norvegica,* has been added.

The question of the comparative distribution of species over Britain can best be dealt with by reference to the types of Watson described above. The percentages of these types among British plants is roughly:

1. British type	. . . .	44 per cent
2. English type	. . . .	30 ,,
3. Scottish and intermediate type	.	8 ,,
4. Highland type	. . . .	5 ,,
5. Atlantic type	. . . .	5 ,,
6. Germanic type	. . . .	8 ,,

The British type obviously will include all the plants found in all the vice-counties as well as many not so completely distributed. The disparity between 2 and 3 is due partly to the fact that the majority of the plants found in a medium number of vice-counties fall under 2. It may also be said here that according to most estimates only some seventy species are found in Scotland and not in England. The Atlantic and Germanic types contribute largely to the greater richness of the flora in the extreme south which has already been noted.

The general nature of the flora of Ireland cannot be better described than by quoting the remarks in the introduction to the second edition of the *Cybele Hibernica* (144). The authors there say that "Viewed as a whole, the flora of Ireland may be regarded as an incomplete English flora, as this in turn may be regarded as an incomplete west European or French flora. It is in the species which it lacks that the Irish flora chiefly differs from the English; and the vast majority of the English plants which are absent from Ireland are common or widespread in western continental Europe."

According to most authorities the number of species in Ireland is about 70 per cent of the number in England, but they include an appreciable group not found in the latter country. Praeger (573, 575) mentions the following as being definitely of this type, namely:

Arbutus unedo (Fig. 66)	*Neotinea intacta* (Fig. 66)
Arenaria ciliata	*Pinguicula grandiflora* (Fig. 64)
Daboecia cantabrica (*polifolia*) (Fig. 67)	*Saxifraga hirsuta* (Fig. 67)
Erica mackaiana (*mackaii*)	*Saxifraga spathularis*
Erica mediterranea (Fig. 65)	*Sisyrinchium bermudiana* (*angustifolium*)
Inula salicina	*Spiranthes gemmipara*

To these are perhaps to be added the following problematical and possibly endemic forms:

Arabis brownii	Certain species of *Saxifraga* (765, 766)
Orchis kerryensis	Three species of *Hieracium*
Orchis occidentalis	
Orchis traunsteinerioides	

Species found in England but not in Ireland include:

Astragalus glycyphyllos	*Lathyrus sylvestris*
Chrysosplenium alternifolium	*Ononis spinosa*
Convallaria majalis	*Paris quadrifolia*
Genista anglica	*Scabiosa columbaria*
Helictotrichon (*Avena*) *pratense*	

Among species commoner in England than in Ireland are:

Adoxa moschatellina	*Geranium pratense*
Calamagrostis epigejos	*Hypericum hirsutum*
Corydalis claviculata	*Ornithopus perpusillus*
Filipendula hexapetala	*Teesdalia nudicaulis*
Galium cruciata	*Trollius europaeus*

Conversely, *Lathyrus palustris*, *Pinguicula lusitanica* (Fig. 66), *Rhynchospora fusca*, *Rubia peregrina* and *Utricularia intermedia* are more common in Ireland than in England.

For distributional purposes Ireland is divided into 40 vice-counties which actually correspond more or less to the political counties. Considering the smaller size and greater homogeneity of Ireland, it is not surprising to find that the number of completely distributed species is proportionately much greater than in Britain. About 250 species are found in all the vice-counties and, also as might be expected, these include nearly all the species which are completely distributed in Britain. The additional species are chiefly of the sort that reflect one of the main ecological features of Ireland, namely, the prevalence of various kinds of aquatic habitats. This is well shown in the case of the genus *Carex* of which no fewer than fourteen species are completely distributed compared with only four so ranging in Britain.

On the other hand, the number of species occurring in only one vice-county is small, about forty in all, of which some seventeen are microspecies of *Rubus* and *Hieracium*. This figure gives a percentage of 4 as compared with 6 in Britain, but these figures have not much significance.

The concentration of species in the south-east of England and also several peculiarities of the Irish flora have been discussed and demonstrated by Matthews in a series of papers designed to throw light on the paths by which the bulk of the British plants re-entered the country after the glaciation. Matthews argues that the more or less completely distributed British plants, those which occur in nearly all the vice-counties, are not likely to reveal much in this direction, and confines his attention to those which have a markedly narrower range. In his first paper (500) he analyses that element of the flora consisting of species found only in England and Wales. These he estimates to number 266, and he shows very clearly that they are concentrated in the coastal counties from Dorset to Norfolk, and that this concentration decreases more or less regularly westward and northward. He further shows by inset maps that the area of greatest concentration of these plants outside Britain is in France, where over 90 per cent of them are to be found. In a second paper (501) he deals with the 105 species found, in the British Isles, only in England and Scotland. These he finds fall into two almost equal groups, a boreal and a southern, concentrated respectively in Scotland and in the eastern half of England, especially the south-east. Outside Britain he finds the boreal group to be concentrated in Scandinavia, Germany and France, and the southern group in France and Spain. In his third paper (502) Matthews deals with the Anglo-Irish element of the flora. He refers first to the twenty or so species found only in Ireland, and shows that they belong almost entirely to a south European stock concentrated on the Continent in northern Portugal and Spain. A second, larger, group of sixty-eight species occurring in Ireland and England he shows to have very much the same distribution as was the case of the English plants, namely, a concentration in the coastal counties from Devon to Norfolk together with a concentration in west and south-west Ireland. These plants again are like the English element in that their continental area of concentration is in France.

Taking the three papers together Matthews concludes that the non-boreal element of the British flora, which is the part with which the papers deal, may have begun to re-immigrate into the country directly from south-west Europe and that this was the oldest or first migration, but that very soon the centre of dispersal on the Continent moved eastwards to the neighbourhood of France. The migration from this direction he considers to have been a very prolonged one and to account for the preponderance of French and central European species in our flora.

So far our attention has been confined to the distribution of species within the

Plate 18. *Liriodendron tulipifera*
(*from The Standard Cyclopedia of Horticulture by L. H. Bailey,
by permission of The Macmillan Company, New York*)

British Islands, but the members of the British flora must next be considered in the light of their distribution outside these countries.

This at once raises the question of British endemics. Are there any species occurring in the British Isles that occur nowhere else and which are therefore peculiar to them? The answer depends entirely on what we reckon as species. If by the term we mean units of the size, let us say, of those in Bentham and Hooker's *Handbook*, namely average or large species, then the answer is probably that there are none. If, on the other hand, we take into account small species, then the answer is that a small number are found only in the British Isles. This in one way is quite a sufficient statement, because it illustrates the main point, which is that the peculiar element in our flora is almost non-existent compared with the peculiar element in most other floras of the world. Wallace (756) gives one of the earliest and most lengthy surveys of endemic British plants. His list, which was compiled by Bennett, includes no fewer than seventy-two microspecies and varieties, but many of these must certainly be excluded. Indeed Hooker, in comments on this list, reduces it to one absolutely endemic species, *Potamogeton lanceolatus* (now known to be a hybrid), and some fifteen varieties. Wilmott (789) has discussed the matter at some length but does not give a definitive list. It would appear, however, from his remarks that the genera *Arabis, Cochlearia, Fumaria, Limonium* (*Statice*) and *Ulmus* all contain one or more endemic forms which have at some time or other received specific rank, and that in addition many microspecies of *Rubus, Rosa, Hieracium, Euphrasia* and *Thalictrum* are also unrecorded elsewhere. About a dozen small species of *Sorbus* have also been described as endemic (134). Salisbury (615) believes that there are fewer than twenty-five endemics, including varieties, and Matthews is of much the same opinion. As has been seen, some of these reputed endemics are confined to Ireland. See also p. 294.

The first classification of British plants according to their ranges outside this country, and particularly on the continent, was made by Forbes (247) in 1846. He recognised five elements or sub-floras which he believed to represent as many distinct immigrations into the country subsequent to the Pleistocene. They were:

1. Iberian or Asturian:
    Species found, on the continent, in the north of Spain.
2. Armorican or Gallican:
    Species chiefly of the Channel Islands and western France.
3. Kentish:
    Species found particularly in north and north-eastern France.
4. Scandinavian or Boreal:
    Species representing northern and sub-arctic floras.
5. Germanic:
    Species related to those of central and west-central Europe.

Since Forbes' day repeated attempts have been made to improve and amplify this classification, and it would be impossible to deal with these in detail. Matthews (503), however, has brought the whole subject more up to date in a single comprehensive paper, and we cannot do better than refer to this at some length.

Matthews treats the native or naturalised flora as comprising about 1,500 species, and divides them according to their extra-British ranges into fourteen groups or elements to which is to be added a small assembly of endemics. This classification is very detailed and can really only be properly appreciated in the

19

original, but for our present purposes, and in order to facilitate a rapid survey, it may be condensed and rearranged as follows:

	No. of Species
1. **Wide element:**	
Species found at least throughout the northern temperate regions	205
2. **Eurasian element:**	
Species found generally distributed through Europe and temperate Asia	480
3. **European element:**	
Species generally distributed throughout Europe . .	130
4. **Southern element:**	
Species whose continental range is predominantly more southerly than this country	315
a. Continental southern element:	
Species of south and central Europe	127
b. Oceanic west European element:	
Species found almost exclusively in western (Atlantic) Europe	76
c. Oceanic southern element:	
Species found chiefly in south Europe and western Europe, including the Mediterranean region . . .	74
d. Mediterranean element:	
Species whose ranges are centred in the Mediterranean region	38
5. **Northern element:**	
Species whose continental range is predominantly more northerly than this country	142
a. Continental northern element:	
Species whose main European range is central and north, but including some circumpolar species . .	91
b. Oceanic northern element:	
Species characteristic of north-west Europe, but some having a connection with north-east America .	26
c. Northern montane element:	
Species of north Europe reappearing on mountains further south	25
6. **Continental element:**	
Species characteristic of central Europe, generally extending east through Russia into Asia	82
7. **Arctic-alpine element:**	
Species characteristic of the arctic or sub-arctic regions or exclusively alpine	145
a. Arctic-sub-arctic element:	
Exclusively northern species . . . . . •	30
b. Arctic-alpine element:	
Northern species also on southern mountains . .	106
c. Alpine element:	
Species of the central European mountains . .	9

Even in this somewhat simplified form the classification is complex, as is necessarily the case, and it is well to emphasise its more salient features.

It will be seen that the first three elements, comprising some 55 per cent of the total flora, make up what may be called the expected proportion of the flora. That is to say they contain plants likely to occur merely by virtue of the country's position as part of the northern temperate continent of Europe.

The remaining elements are on most counts of greater interest, because it is in them that we are most likely to find indications of floral history. Matthews discusses them in special detail and brings out many important points, but attention may be concentrated on certain of them.

No portion of the British flora has received so much attention as that which comprises the species which are confined to the western parts of Britain and/or Ireland and which, outside this country, are more or less restricted to the Atlantic coast of south-western Europe and/or to the Mediterranean region. The fact that these do not all fall into one of the groups above simply indicates that their continental distributions vary, as Matthews has shown, so that they can be divided into three (4 b, c and d). They have in common one all-important feature, namely that the British part of the total range of each is much further north than the rest. As a whole these plants may be called "Atlantic", but the most noteworthy examples of them form an assemblage which is usually referred to as the "Lusitanian" element in our flora, for the reason that outside our boundaries the species are more or less restricted in range to that part of the Iberian Peninsula. For example, *Saxifraga hirsuta* is, outside Ireland, found only in the Pyrenean region, so that its occurrence in the former is far to the north of the rest of its distribution. Other species are less extreme in that they occur also on various parts of the west coast of France. These "Atlantic" species in general and "Lusitanian" species in particular have been studied by many botanists. Stapf (692, 693) has given a long account of them; Praeger (572, 575) has resurveyed the facts and theories concerning them, and Drude's comparison of the British and German floras refers often to them (202).

The great question is how and when these plants, and especially the "Lusitanian" species proper, which number less than a dozen, reached our shores. They are to-day found only in those parts of these islands where the conditions are least rigorous, and it seems perfectly certain, in the light of present knowledge, that whatever may be true of other species, these at least cannot have survived the ice ages in their present positions. This being so they are presumably among the postglacial immigrants. But whatever the changes in the distribution of land and sea may have been since the end of the Pleistocene, a period of only a few thousand years, there is no suggestion that they include any linkage of Ireland with Britain or of south-west England (and much less Ireland) with France, so that if these plants are indeed recent immigrants, they must have crossed considerable areas of sea.

This problem has been so often debated without conclusion that it seems almost presumptuous to suggest that its difficulties may have been overestimated, but this seems to be so, for the following reasons. The actual occurrence to-day of these plants in south-west England and Ireland proves that their climatic and edaphic requirements are different from those of the generality of British plants only in so far as the conditions of south-west England and Ireland differ from those of the rest of the country. That is to say they are present within our boundaries because there are spots herein in which they can find a congenial home and the conditions they need. Secondly, the separation of Ireland from Britain to the best of our knowledge antedates the last glaciation, during which most of Ireland is said to have been icebound, and hence the present Irish flora, except perhaps for a tundra element, must have re-immigrated since, and in doing so must have crossed the intervening sea. It would therefore seem clear that this expanse of sea has not proved a significant

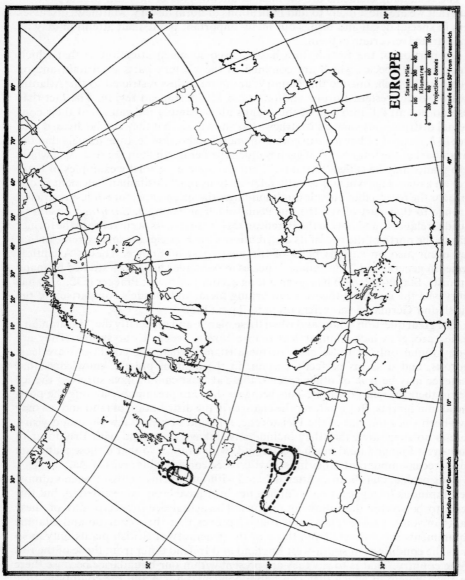

Fig. 67.—Map showing the distribution of *Saxifraga hirsuta* (continuous line) and *Daboecia cantabrica* (broken line). There is a closely allied species of *Daboecia* in Macaronesia.

barrier to dispersal. Again, there is no reason to assume that the Straits of Dover have ever been wider than they are now, and on a similar argument they must therefore have always been a slighter obstacle to plant migration.

It is at this point that the argument usually becomes confused. Most of the "Lusitanian" plants are not found notably on the European coast north of Spain, and hence it has generally been concluded that they must, in order to reach Ireland, either have travelled direct from one to the other along land surfaces now submerged, or have been able to survive the Ice Ages in refuges also now submerged, as is postulated for instance in the view of Enquist, quoted sympathetically by Jessen (408), that there was during the last glaciation a forest refuge area south of the British Islands near the edge of the continental shelf, whence these plants again advanced into Ireland when the ice retreat allowed them to do so. There is, actually, no necessity to assume that either of these things has happened. Although the "Lusitanian" plants in the stricter sense do not by definition occur in France, there are species which differ from them only in the fact that they do so occur in France, and thereby show intermediate stations or "stepping stones" between Spain and south-west Britain. *Arbutus unedo*, *Erica ciliaris* and *Rubia peregrina* are such plants. From this it is clear that the conditions of western France are very close indeed to those required by "Lusitanian" plants in general, and this being so, very slight climatic changes, of the dimensions of those which we believe to have taken place since the end of the Pleistocene, would almost certainly permit the passage of species from Spain to Ireland by way of western France and England. In other words it is not necessary, in order to explain the presence of "Lusitanian" plants in Ireland and south-west England, to do more than to assume that some time since the end of the Pleistocene there have been such minor climatic fluctuations as would enable them to travel along the western shores of France and across the Channel somewhere in its narrower part, and the supposed post-glacial optimum might well have been that time. But even this last qualification is not strictly necessary, because the sea gap between Brittany and Cornwall is not very much wider than that of the Irish Sea, and need be regarded as but little more of a barrier.

On these facts and arguments it would seem that the "Lusitanian" and "Atlantic" species of the British flora do not present so much of a problem as is generally supposed, but that their presence can be explained by migration along the western shores of Europe during a period when climatic conditions were slightly higher than they are to-day, a conclusion it may be noted very similar to that arrived at by Sealy (627) in his special study of *Arbutus unedo*. It follows from this that the present populations of these species are comparatively recent immigrants to the Irish flora but that some at least of them were there in interglacial times has been shown by Jessen (407), who records *Erica mackaiana* (which is in Ireland to-day) and *Rhododendron ponticum* (which is not) from deposits of that age in Galway.

At the same time it should be made quite clear that this explanation of the presence of these species in the British flora is founded on the assumption that our present beliefs about the extent and effect of the Pleistocene glaciations in Britain and, particularly, Ireland, are correct. Should it ever transpire that they are erroneous in any major respect, then the whole problem of these plants will have to be reconsidered in the light of the new information.

Included in Matthews' oceanic northern element are six species found on the west side of Britain which outside this country occur only in North America. These are *Eriocaulon septangulare*, *Juncus dudleyi*, *J. tenuis*, *Sisyrinchium bermudiana*, *Spiranthes gemmipara* and *S. romanzoffiana*, the *Junci* in particular being of rather uncertain status. The "American element", as it has been called, of which these species are chief, has been discussed by Löve and Löve (471) who conclude that some of them, and especially the *Eriocaulon* and *Sisyrinchium*, are not identical with any American species and should rather be regarded as forms endemic to the British Isles. However this may be, it would seem that the explanation of the presence of these plants in western Europe involves the difficult question of the distribution of land and sea in the past, and they should be recalled when this subject is dealt with in a later chapter.

The general northern element of the flora has an obvious and rather special interest, because it is the one most likely to have survived the Pleistocene *in situ*. Indeed, it may be accepted that practically all of it did so, and, this being the case, it may claim to be the oldest and most persistent part of the British flora.

It is obviously impossible in one short chapter to do justice to the many interesting features and problems of the British flora, and the very brief outline which has been given should be amplified by reference to some of the original works cited. It is to be hoped, however, that enough has been said to show how well the flora illustrates many of the fundamental aspects of plant geography, and that it must, for this reason, always be of special significance to the student of plant distribution.

First and foremost it shows in an unusual and perhaps unique way the stages by which a comparatively varied flora has been built up over a long period by immigration following serious and prolonged climatic upheavals. Secondly, it illustrates the extent to which a flora may be influenced and modified by contemporary human history. Thirdly, it epitomises the whole story of the northern temperate regions and their plant life since the Pleistocene. Indeed, it is perhaps no exaggeration to say that the British flora reproduces, in little, much of the whole story of the spread and development of Angiosperm floras, for what has overtaken the British plants in particular almost certainly affected the whole world flora in more general and less drastic fashion.

CHAPTER 14

THE DISTRIBUTION OF PLANTS IN AN ENGLISH COUNTY

IN the last few chapters the geography of the Flowering Plants has been surveyed with increasing precision by considering first the families, then the genera and the species, and then the distribution of a comparatively small number of species over one particular country—the British Isles. Throughout, however, attention has been directed almost exclusively to the *extent* of distribution, and little has been said so far about the almost equally important subject of the *intensity* of distribution. This chapter is intended to remedy this and to supplement the picture already drawn by describing in comparative terms the distribution of the species in the flora of a yet smaller area, as shown by a phytogeographical survey of one of the smaller English counties (295).

The county of Dorset, which was the area selected for study, is small but its topography and geology (Fig. 68) are remarkably varied, affording an almost un-rivalled series of plant habitats. In the east, round Poole Harbour, is a low-lying basin of Tertiary sands and clays; west of this is a wide extent of chalk uplands; while beyond this again are three distinct series of vales in which the rocks are mainly clays and marls interspersed with various kinds of limestones. Moreover, superficial deposits are very widespread, especially in the centre and west, adding greatly to the complexity of the surface geology. The relief is marked, though there are no heights of more than about 900 ft., and although the county is well watered, its rivers are, except for the Stour, little more than streams.

The distribution of climatic values in Dorset is still incompletely recorded in detail, but the leading facts are that the rainfall, which has a general average of about 35 in. a year, and is broadly correlated with elevation, generally increases towards the west and is least in the low-lying coastal areas; temperature lines run roughly parallel with the coast, values rising inland in summer and diminishing in-land in winter; sunshine figures are very high, though they also fall inland, and on the whole the county is among the mildest; south-westerly winds prevail and are frequent and there is little fog.

When the ranges of the different species of its flora are plotted over the county, their chief geographical feature is quickly apparent, namely, that none of them is completely and evenly distributed. Even the commonest plants are absent from some small areas and are of more or less than usual frequency in many others, while at the other end of the scale there are certain rare species known only from a single spot and in very small quantity. In short, all show some geographical segregation, and the majority show it to a degree which, in fact, leads them to be absent from at least half the total county area.

It is also apparent that the distributions of individual species vary enormously. both in general character and in detail, and that, although it is true to say that most of them conform to a limited number of main types, it is equally true that no two are entirely alike.

The proportion of the county still bearing relatively natural vegetation is considerable, and it may therefore be assumed that this general segregation and localisation is not to be attributed primarily to man's actions or to other artificial

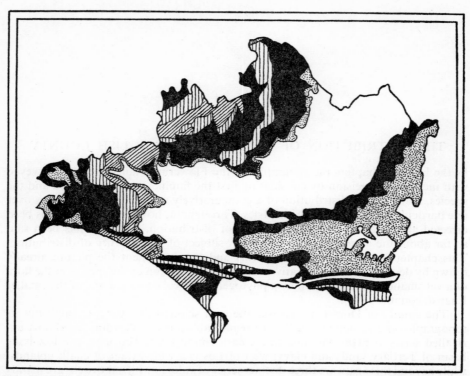

FIG. 68.—Map showing, simplified, the distribution of subsoil types in the county of Dorset:

dotted—sands.
white—chalk.
black—clays.

vertical shading—limestone.
diagonal shading—mixed clays and limestones.

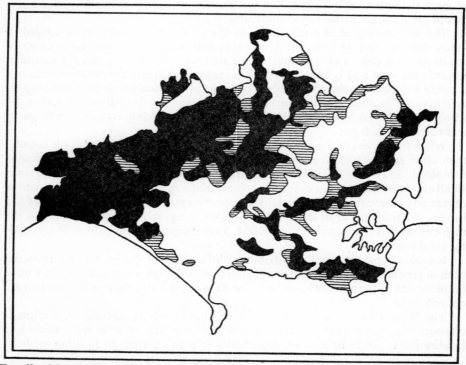

FIG. 69.—Map showing, slightly simplified, the distribution of the primrose (*Primula vulgaris*) in Dorset in the nineteen-thirties:

black—present generally in both woods and hedges.
shaded—present generally in woods but not in hedges.
white—virtually absent from all habitats.

circumstances, but is the consequence of the natural distribution of factors in the plants' environment, that is to say in the atmosphere and the soil.

In Dorset, as in most similar regions, there is one great difference between the distributions of climatic (atmosphere) and edaphic (soil) values. The former show a continuous range of variation or gradient—they wax or wane gradually in a given direction, but the latter, owing to the disorderly geological pattern, show a patchwork or discontinuous distribution. Moreover, in so far as such things can be compared, the differences among edaphic values are much greater than those of climate, and in consequence, while climate passes gradually from one condition to another, soil character may alter abruptly and completely within a very short distance.

It is, of course, a matter of everyday observation that most plants are found only in certain kinds of habitat, and that their distributions are indeed correlated with edaphic rather than climatic conditions is confirmed by the nature of their individual distributions, which are prevailingly of the second, discontinuous type. This is not to say that climatic factors are, in these cases, to be ignored altogether, and they are undoubtedly often of significance, if only indirectly, by controlling the value of certain edaphic conditions, but a geographical survey of the species within the county makes it clear enough that edaphic factors are paramount in determining not only their ranges but also their relative frequency. These edaphic conditions will be considered in more detail presently, but first it is desirable to discuss the apparent exceptions to the rule and to note particularly the instances in which a gradient type of distribution indicates that climatic rather than edaphic factors are of significance.

First of all among these there are some forty species whose Dorset records are marginal, that is to say, on the extreme edge, in some direction or another, of their total ranges. A very few of these are northern plants which reach towards the south or south-west only as far as Dorset, as for instance, *Gentiana pneumonanthe*, but most of them are the opposite, the Dorset records being among their most northerly or north-westerly occurrences. Some of these species are comparatively plentiful in the county, as, for instance, *Erica ciliaris*, though they are always localised, but most of them are rare and sporadic. As far as can be estimated none of them occur in peculiar kinds of habitats such as might be unknown elsewhere in England, and it may therefore be concluded that their appearance in Dorset is, primarily, at any rate, due to the existence there of certain climatic values. What these may be cannot be discussed here, but it may be hazarded that temperature is the main component concerned.

A second group comprises a handful of species, among them the primrose, *Primula vulgaris* (294) which show increasing prevalence of occurrence from east to west, that is to say towards that part of the county where the rainfall is greater, and the result is that their distributions show so marked a gradient as strongly to suggest that some aspect of rainfall outweighs any correlation they may have with edaphic conditions (Fig. 69).

A third and even smaller group comprises species which, within the county, are confined to the more northerly parts of the great chalk belt. The most striking of them is *Filipendula hexapetala*, which extends into the county from the north, with diminishing frequency, as far south-west as Dorchester. *Verbascum nigrum* is interesting, too, because it is almost confined to an area within a few miles of the Wiltshire border. There seems no good reason to suppose that these more northerly parts of the chalk are edaphically very different from the remainder, and it therefore seems clear that the localisation of these plants and their gradient distribution are due to climatic factors of some kind, and presumably that these are related in some way to the proximity of the sea.

One reason for this conclusion is that a considerable number of Dorset plants, forming a large fourth group, have just the opposite kind of distribution, being much more frequent in the vicinity of the coast than elsewhere. It must be made clear that we are not speaking here of those maritime species proper which occur in habitats which feel the direct influence of salt water and which will be mentioned later, but of what may be described as ordinary inland plants generally found fairly well distributed

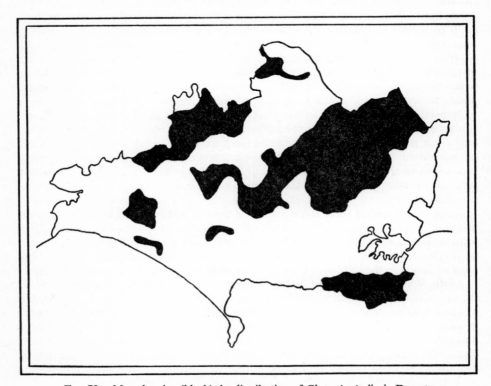

FIG. 70.—Map showing (black) the distribution of *Clematis vitalba* in Dorset.

over England as a whole, and it is a remarkable fact that these latter number about a hundred, or roughly one-tenth of the total county flora.

Geographically these plants tend to be of three types: some being confined to a narrow coastal belt; some being chiefly so restricted but occurring sporadically, though less frequently, inland; and some ranging more or less all over the county but with notably greater frequency towards the south. The first include such extreme examples as *Vicia bithynica*, *Trifolium squamosum* and *Carduus tenuiflorus*, which are hardly ever found far from the immediate vicinity of the coast, but most of them are like *Rubia peregrina* and *Linum bienne*, which, though predominantly coastal, are not exclusively so. The second type includes *Picris echioides* (Fig. 71), *Echium vulgare* and *Medicago arabica*, which occur not uncommonly far from the sea but which are peculiarly characteristic of the coastal belt. Notable examples of the third type are

Dipsacus fullonum (*sylvestris*), *Allium vineale*, *Trifolium fragiferum* and *Anthyllis vulneraria*, but it includes also quite a number of common species such as *Rumex crispus*, *Lotus corniculatus*, *Anagallis arvensis*, *Daucus carota* and *Galium verum*, all of which increase in frequency towards the coast in a way which cannot be attributed solely to direct edaphic considerations.

It cannot, of course, be argued that the distribution of all these plants is exclusively determined by climatic considerations, but it seems clear that the increasing proximity of the sea is a matter of real importance to them in determining their frequency, and it is difficult to see how this operates unless it does so by modifying the climatic values locally. Only further careful investigation can show how this may come about, but it seems safe to assume that humidity and the presence of salt in the atmosphere have a good deal to do with it. That salt-laden winds from the sea do affect the vegetation inland is familiar enough when unusually strong gales blow inshore in early summer and the young expanding foliage of the hedges and woods becomes killed by the salt in the air. The nearer the coast the more these effects are felt, but they may be noticeable for many miles inland.

To sum up, there is every indication that climatic factors play a considerable, and it may be even an overriding, part in determining the distribution over the county of some proportion of its species, especially if their influences are reinforced by their effects in modifying edaphic conditions locally, but there is no evidence that climate is, in general, more than a subsidiary or secondary geographical determinant.

In the distribution of all the remaining species of the county flora, or at least all those that occur naturally, there is predominantly correlation with edaphic conditions of one sort or another. This is, of course, least obvious in the commonest and most widespread plants, but even here distribution is never quite complete, and the gaps are edaphic gaps, such as is their relative absence from wide areas of the barren sandy soils in the east. Nor do these species elsewhere all inhabit the same range of conditions, each tending to owe its exceptional frequency to particular circumstances, such as ability to flourish in disturbed or less hospitable ground or unusual powers of competition, which express themselves in terms of edaphic correlation. The question of shade and mutual protection is also of great importance, and even the commoner species are usually found either in sunny or shady situations, their comparative abundance being due to their occurence in almost every variety of one or other of these conditions. A few species, while similar in the main, show also some soil preferences, as, for instance, *Senecio jacobaea*, *Galium mollugo* and *Sambucus nigra*.

The less common species, which form the great bulk of the flora, tend to show a more or less rigid restriction to one or other of a small number of major habitat-types, and the general importance of edaphic factors is here particularly clear. Soil conditions vary enormously, but, in the very broadest terms, it may be said that the main variable components are five, all of them related more or less directly to the physiological necessity under which plants live of absorbing water and nutrient salts from the soil, namely the absolute amount of water in the soil; the ability of the soil to retain moisture; the basicity of the soil; the acidity of the soil; and the salinity of the soil. The values of these components depend chiefly on the nature of the parent rocks of the soil, on the topography and on the effects of denudation, and the general effect is to produce six great series of habitats, which may be called, respectively, aquatic, impeded (clay soils), sandy, calcareous, acid and saline. To one or other of these the great majority of species are confined, and only a few show any appreciable ability to occur in more than one, though, naturally, the absolute degree of segregation depends in some measure on the closeness of relationship between the types, it being especially marked between the first two.

Furthermore, most species are less than completely distributed over any one of these. Thus among aquatic plants some, like *Epilobium hirsutum* or *Apium nodi-florum*, are found in almost all watercourses, but others favour certain kinds only, such as the more calcareous or silty or acid. Still others, like *Sagittaria sagittifolia* and *Butomus umbellatus*, find conditions to their liking only in the larger and deeper rivers, and others have different preferences again.

Circumstances combine to make heavier and less well-drained soils particularly

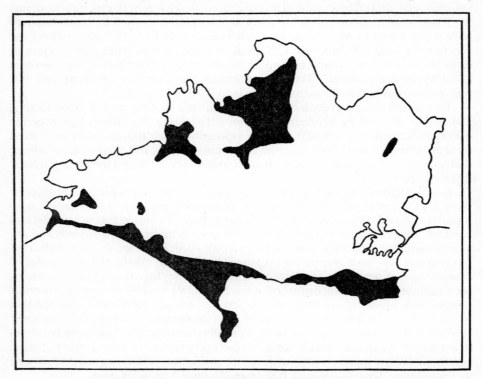

FIG. 71.—Map showing (black) the distribution of *Picris echioides* in Dorset.

plentiful in Dorset and there is every kind, from comparatively light loams to the stiffest and most water-logged clays. Some of the species associated with them are therefore very widespread, but most are much more limited. A very important point about this soil type is that it is especially the cne on which dense thicket and woodland develops, and its plants therefore include most of the shade-loving species. Indeed plants of these heavier soils may be described as either woodland species or hay-pasture plants. Of the former a few are fairly widespread, but most are, by the nature of the case, more restricted, as Dorset is not an exceptionally well-wooded county. Among them they illustrate almost every kind of distribution over the woodlands of the area, and the ranges of some of the more local or un-common, such as *Platanthera chlorantha*, *Melampyrum pratense* and *Ribes rubrum*, are particularly interesting and suggestive. A few species are characteristic of damp bushy places rather than of woodland proper, and presumably find therein conditions particularly suited to them. The distribution of the meadow plants varies a good deal, because some of them seem equally at home in more than one type of soil, and are thus by way of being exceptions to the general rule. *Chrysanthemum leucanthemum* and *Primula veris*, for instance, are found in calcareous grassland as well as in clay meadows, while *Deschampsia caespitosa* and *Serratula tinctoria* inhabit clays and certain other soils with a greater tendency to acidity. Of the plants more definitely confined to clay subsoils, *Silaum silaus* (*S. pratensis*), *Senecio erucifolius*, *Sison amomum* and *Hordeum nodosum* form a series peculiarly associated with the more calcareous clays. *Picris echioides* (Fig. 71) and *Tussilago farfara* are frequently found on bare clay surfaces, and this may be partly the reason why they are conspicuously more frequent in the coastal zone.

The chief feature of sandy soils is the rapidity with which water passes through them, in consequence of which they easily become leached of mineral salts, and unless there is an impervious layer below them they are often very dry. On such soils two kinds of vegetation, dry heath and dry turf generally develop, and each has its own particular plants. The former often covers wide areas and *Calluna vulgaris*, *Erica cinerea* and *Potentilla erecta* are prominent in its flora; the latter occurs more locally and its species are less familiar. Still other species are found in sandy places which are damp at certain times of the year.

When the normal drainage of water from sandy soils is impeded and they become water-logged, the soil water is usually acid because of the absence of neutralising bases, and when this condition is extreme a very specialised kind of habitat results which supports only a few particular species, but when, as in Dorset, there are considerable stretches of wet sand and gravel, almost all degrees of acidity are represented and there is a marked zonation in the distribution of species. In the less acid places several species of *Juncus* are prominent; in soils of medium acidity *Hydrocotyle vulgaris* and *Scutellaria minor* are among the characteristic species; while *Molinia caerulea* (Fig. 72), *Myrica gale*, *Narthecium ossifragum*, *Pinguicula lusitanica* and the species of *Drosera* typify habitats of higher acid values.

The calcareous soils of Dorset comprise the chalk and a series of limestones and marls of varied calcium content, and in total cover a considerable part of the county, but the calcicolous species are by no means evenly distributed over them. The great majority of these are found not only on the chalk but also on some or most of the other calcareous formations (Fig. 69), but certain species are much more restricted. *Asperula cynanchica*, *Campanula glomerata* and *Gentiana amarella* are among those found almost exclusively on the chalk, while *Cephalanthera damasonium* (*grandiflora*), *Monotropa hypopithys* and a few more are confined to it. On the other hand, one or two species occur virtually only on certain limestones other than the chalk.

Although so many species are found only on one or other of these main soil types, there are a few which inhabit a considerably wider range of conditions, occurring not only on clays but in mildly basic as well as in mildly acidic soils. Presumably these plants find in all these soils some common factor of importance, but it is also well to bear in mind the possibility that the apparent wideness of distribution may be due to the fact that the species concerned is complex, and with more than one ecotype.

The distribution of the halophytes is superficially rather different from the general scheme because of the naturally localised area of their habitats, but the same kind of edaphic segregation and zonation exists here also. This is specially noticeable in plants of tidal soil water such as occur widely in Poole Harbour and in the neighbourhood of Weymouth, but the more specialised habitats, like sand-dunes and shingle beaches, also have their characteristic species.

Only a few species do not fall easily into one or other of the edaphic classes just described, and therefore appear at first sight to be anomalous, but it seems clear that most of them are not really so but are unusual expressions of one or other of these types, their ranges being determined however by factors which, though similar, are peculiar and therefore less obvious.

Species which occur only in habitats which are the result of man's activities, such as cultivated ground and walls, conform to the same general scheme of things.

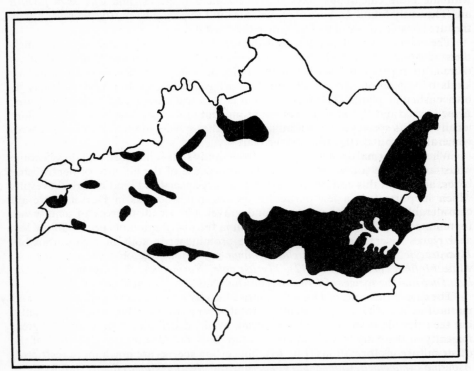

FIG. 72.—Map showing (black) the distribution of *Molinia caerulea* in Dorset.

Since not only the habitats themselves but also their distributions are artificial, the ranges of the species inhabiting them are in most cases rather different from the normal, but this does not indicate any essential difference of plan, and examination shows that there is here just the same kind of segregation according to edaphic conditions and values.

So far we have been speaking chiefly about the extent to which the various Dorset plants occupy the county, but, as was pointed out at the beginning of the chapter, this is only part of the story, and we must consider also the question of the absolute frequency of the species' individuals. There are clearly four main possibilities. The area may be large and the occupation intense, the individuals being both widespread and plentiful; the area may be large and the occupation slight; the area may be small but the occupation intense; or the area may be small and the occupation slight. Such a fourfold classification is implicit in the usual procedure of describing species as "common", "frequent", "local", or "uncommon". It will be noted that the word rare is avoided, since it may refer either to area or numbers, and, indeed, the so-called rarities are plants either very restricted in range or which occur extremely sparingly, and to these the terms local and uncommon are best applied.

The commonest species are naturally those which occur in great numbers over a very wide area, and these have already been alluded to, but the more plentiful species in nearly all the main ecological categories may also be called common, and enough reference to these has also been made.

The term frequent is not quite so easily defined, because this condition may result from one or other of what appear to be two different circumstances, namely, the frequency with which particular kinds of habitat occur and the degree to which individuals may be discontinuously distributed over the range of one kind of habitat. Actually both these express the same fact, that the plants concerned are restricted to certain particular conditions, though in the one case this is more obvious than in the other. Many Dorset plants are frequent in the first sense, as for instance many aquatics which naturally tend to occur only here and there, but the second kind of frequency is on the whole the more interesting. Quite a number of woodland plants are far from general in that type of vegetation, and it is notable how much richer in less common plants some woods are than others. *Epipactis latifolia* and one or two other orchids illustrate this among woods on the chalk, while *Chrysosplenium oppositifolium* and *Ribes rubrum* are characteristic of a particular kind of damp woodland elsewhere. Then there are *Orchis fuchsii* and *Orchis ericetorum* (*elodes*), which not uncommonly grow together but which have quite different total distributions, in which the former is much more frequent. Again, many plants of calcareous grassland, such as *Hippocrepis comosa* and *Helianthemum nummularium* (*vulgare*) occur in only some of the apparently favourable places. In all these it is clear that the plants are confined to localities in which special conditions prevail.

Two other species deserve mention in this connection. *Linaria vulgaris* is often a hedgerow plant, but in these places grows only where it is well exposed and free from shading. It occurs over a wide area mostly on the chalk, and is often enough to be seen, but its occurrences are generally well spaced and it rarely grows in great quantity. *Hypericum androsaemum* is an extreme instance of the same thing. Its distribution, at least in the west of the county, takes the form of numerous but very isolated records in hedges, where the plant is seldom seen as more than a solitary individual, a state of affairs noted for other parts of England also.

The term frequent is peculiarly applicable also to many plants of unnatural status and habitat. Many cornfield weeds, such as *Specularia hybrida* and *Lycopsis arvensis*, are so, partly because their habitats are discontinuous and partly because each favours particular soil conditions. Similarly with the comparatively few species which normally grow almost exclusively on walls. These by no means occur on all walls but only where special circumstances pertain.

Just as many fresh-water aquatics are necessarily frequent, so the halophytic or maritime species proper are of necessity local in the sense that they are confined to the coast, but even here many have quite a narrow range. Among the salt-marsh species, for instance, *Althaea officinalis* is found only in the Fleet west of Weymouth, and among cliff plants *Brassica oleracea* is virtually confined to Purbeck.

Of inland plants all those which live in highly specialised habitats tend to be local because their situations are so, but this is only to be expected, and it is certain other species which are the most interesting of the locals. Outstanding among them are the three great treasures of the county flora, *Erica ciliaris*, *Pulmonaria longifolia* and *Ophrys sphegodes*. The first is confined to a small part of the southern heathlands, and nearly all its records are from an area of about 15 square miles, although here it is plentiful. The second is a plant of certain woods towards the east of the county and also ranges mainly over only a few square miles, but here it is relatively much less plentiful. The third is a calcicole restricted to South Purbeck.

Viola palustris combines both the local and uncommon conditions. In the west of the county it occurs locally in connection with the Greensand, but otherwise it is uncommon, and is found only near the Hampshire border in the extreme east.

The uncommon species of Dorset naturally include all the great rarities. The extreme is seen in *Himantoglossum hircinum*, which for several years existed as only a single plant in the Weymouth neighbourhood. *Melittis melissophyllum* has apparently but one station, where there are only a few plants and the same is true of *Pirola minor*. Several others, notably *Scorzonera humilis* and *Carum verticillata*, also have only one locality but are, therein, in larger numbers. *Cyperus longus* has two or three stations and is fairly plentiful in them, and the same is true of *Cladium mariscus*. Most of the uncommon species are, however, more plentiful than this and, like the members of other groups, can be classified according to the soils in which they occur. The following are interesting examples. Among shade plants *Platanthera chlorantha* is found in many woods and is widely scattered, but is always few in numbers. *Sedum telephium* has fewer stations but is rather more plentiful in each, and *Corydalis claviculata* is somewhat similar, though rather local in addition. *Calamintha ascendens* and *Nepeta cataria* occur very occasionally in hedges on the chalk. The rare orchids of chalk pastures, such as *Orchis ustulata* and *Herminium monorhocis*, are also noteworthy and on sandy soils there are other species, including *Moenchia erecta*, *Pulicaria vulgaris* and *Potentilla argentea*. There are still others among the aquatics, while among the plants of strongly acid soils *Hammarbya* (*Malaxis*) *paludosa* is outstanding.

In addition to all these, which except for the cornfield weeds or colonists may be considered native plants, there is a very interesting group of species which seem to have been introduced at some time or other and which vary greatly in abundance and range. Some are found only near human habitations, though the significance of this is not always clear. *Malva sylvestris* is generally found in waste places and hedges near villages and is seldom a constituent of more natural plant associations. Rarer and more conspicuous examples of the same kind are *Chelidonium majus*, *Aegopodium podagraria* and *Smyrnium olusatrum*, the last very much favouring the coast region. *Ribes uva-crispa* (*grossularia*) is apparently wild often enough, but there is little doubt that this is due to bird-dispersal from gardens. The same is presumably true of the crab apple of hedgerows, which is usually simply a wildling which has grown from the seed of a cultivated variety. The true wild crab does, however, also occur rarely.

More obvious denizens derived from shrubbery or garden plants are *Chrysanthemum parthenium*, *Vinca minor* and *Mimulus guttatus*, while *Linum usitatissimum* and *Onobrychis* are obvious relics of cultivation. *Sambucus ebulus*, sometimes seen in hedges, and *Inula helenium*, mostly found in orchards in the northern part of the county, are of similar but more remote origin. *Atropa bella-donna*, too, is of rather special interest. It is plentiful and frequent in one large private park and occurs occasionally in other parts of the same estate, but there is little doubt that it is directly or indirectly an introduction.

Particular problems are presented by a group of Monocotyledons which occur

Plate 19. *Nipa* palms along the banks of a river in the Malay Peninsula

(Photo: E. J. H. Corner)

rarely in more or less natural surroundings and among natural vegetation, but whose native status is at least open to grave suspicion. They are *Narcissus biflorus*, *Leucojum vernum*, *Ornithogalum umbellatum*, *Fritillaria meleagris*, *Simethis planifolia*, *Acorus calamus*, *Tulipa sylvestris*, *Galanthus nivalis* and *Convallaria majalis*. All but the last three are almost certainly long-established denizens, and of these three at least the first has no good claim to recognition as a native.

This chapter may well close with an attempt to estimate the changes which have taken place in the constitution of the county flora in the 150 years or so since systematic records were first collected, because this will help to illustrate several other points of significance and interest in the distribution of Dorset plants.

The continued floristic study of any area tends inevitably towards an increase in the numbers of plants known therefrom, partly because more and more small species are recorded and partly because it is difficult to say what species become, in course of time, lost, and for these reasons there is little doubt that the Dorset flora is, in one sense, richer now than it has ever been. This is probably a fair picture of the balance of change, because it seems certain that additions have more than made up for losses. It is true that the former are mostly denizens or casuals and the latter are mostly native plants, but the general effect is certainly a net gain.

It is, of course, always difficult to be sure that any species has actually disappeared, but there are some which at least have not been seen for many years, and they may be regarded as lost. The most striking examples are *Parnassia palustris*, *Pinguicula vulgaris*, *Empetrum nigrum* and *Hottonia palustris*, all of which have been repeatedly sought for in recent years without result. The most remarkable fact about them is that three of them are markedly, and the last less conspicuously, northern species such as might be expected to disappear in the course of a gradual climatic amelioration, and that they are plants of this kind is highly suggestive.

On the other hand, the frequency with which certain plants continue to maintain themselves in the same stations is very notable. The first serious collection of county records dates from the end of the eighteenth century, and perhaps the majority of these early records can still be verified, showing that the plants concerned have persisted in the same place for at least 150 years.

Of change in relative abundance there is not much evidence except that some of the rarer plants have become even more uncommon, partly because they have been over-collected and partly because certain types of habitat are now much less frequent. For instance, many of the species of bogs and marshes have diminished with the passage of time owing to drainage, and for different reasons the same is doubtless true of some of the cornfield weeds.

Parentucellia (*Bartsia*) *viscosa* is perhaps the best example of a presumed native which is undoubtedly extending its range. Unknown in the county until fifty years ago it has now been recorded from a number of stations. Among adventives the most noteworthy is perhaps *Matricaria matricarioides* (*discoidea*). The first record of it seems to have been about the close of last century, but now the plant is abundant throughout the county. Several horticultural denizens are also gradually establishing themselves, among them the lilac (*Syringa vulgaris*), and Montbretia. The former is perhaps bird-dispersed into hedges and the latter is usually a garden outcast.

Finally, the innumerable miscellaneous problems of plant geography presented by even a county flora may be illustrated by reference to one which concerns two cornfield weeds. *Adonis annua* and *Centaurea cyanus* are both now very scarce in the county, but there used to be a persistent station for each. In both cases this was

20

a single arable field and here the plants appeared regularly, in the case of the latter often in quantity. Nevertheless this species never seemed to spread from the one field, and the former was generally to be found in only one part of a single field, where it was known, on good authority, for at least forty years.

It is to be hoped that enough has been said in this chapter to fulfil its purpose, which has been to show that the comparative and relative distributions of plants within one and the same area is an important aspect of plant geography, and in particular that two general statements are true. The first is that while climatic conditions may usually be regarded as primarily controlling the area which a species may occupy as a whole, the relative distribution of individuals within this area is, as usually, controlled chiefly by edaphic factors. The second is that a flora is dynamic rather than static, that is to say, that it is constantly undergoing some degree of change. Some species disappear, and others take their places; some become more plentiful, while others diminish. There are, in short, clearly to be seen indications of changes which, persisting over long periods, may eventually lead to marked and considerable floristic alteration.

CHAPTER 15

THE GEOLOGICAL HISTORY AND PAST DISTRIBUTION OF THE FLOWERING PLANTS

THE attention which was paid, in Chapter 3, to the evolutionary background to the study of plant geography makes it abundantly clear that few indeed of the problems presented by the distribution of plants to-day can fully be understood or appreciated without some knowledge of conditions and events, either actually within or in relation to the plant world, in the past. This being so, the second part of this book, which treats more particularly of the theoretical aspects of plant geography, cannot be appreciated without some preliminary outline of the history of the Flowering Plants and of the circumstances which have led gradually to the state of affairs which has been described in the preceding pages. This chapter is therefore devoted to a short account of their history and of their distribution in the past.

The Geological Time Scale

In the course of secular time the vegetation of the earth has gradually changed and developed by the processes of evolution. Little is known about the earliest plants of all, because they have left practically no traces behind them, but they were certainly gradually supplanted by new types. These newer types in turn gave way to others, each new development giving, for the time being, a particular character to the world vegetation.

This knowledge has come from the study of what is often called the "record of the rocks", that is to say, of the organic remains which, from time to time, have become imprisoned in sedimentary deposits, where they are familiar to us in the form of fossils. The story of fossil plants has been most graphically and admirably told by Seward in *Plant Life Through the Ages* (640), and this, or the much shorter account of Reid and Chandler (591), should be consulted by those readers who wish to amplify the outline contained in this chapter.

It is believed that plant life began in the sea, and that plant evolution has been largely directed towards the attainment of the complicated and beautiful structural organisation which enables modern plants to colonise the land surfaces of the earth, and to exist as successfully in a subaerial medium as they did formerly and still do, to some extent, in subaqueous and particularly marine habitats. That is to say, it is, in a single phrase, the change from the kind of form possessed by such plants as the seaweeds to that exhibited to-day by the Flowering Plants. Coincident with these structural developments there have been equally great changes in reproduction and in life history.

The fossil record indicates that the history of each new group of plants has always followed much the same course (see also pp. 43 *et seq.* above). First, there appear a few isolated examples of the new type. Then gradually, but at a constantly accelerating speed, these new types multiply until in a comparatively short time they become the dominant vegetation of the world. This position of supremacy they hold for a while, and then, as rapidly as they rose, they tend to diminish before the competition of still newer plants until eventually they disappear entirely or persist

307

merely as a few meagre survivors of a great but long-dead past. Not all newly
evolved plants necessarily pass through the whole of this cycle. Many never succeed
in establishing themselves; others may do so on a small scale but never develop into
important elements in the vegetation. Nor must we think of this developmental
cycle as something peculiar to plants. It is found in all aspects of life and even in the
life of the individual. He is born; he slowly or more rapidly reaches maturity; he
flourishes or the reverse; and he more slowly or rapidly declines, until he finally and
inevitably passes away.

The whole sequence of the rocks that have been formed since the beginning of
secular time is divided by geologists into five great eras based chiefly upon the kinds
of fossils that the various formations contain, though it may be doubted how real
some of these sharp divisions are (580). The first era consists of the oldest rocks, and
these include no fossils, because they represent a time when life on the earth, if it
existed at all, was of so simple a kind as to have left no traces. This is called the
Archaeozoic era. Next comes the Proterozoic era, the rocks of which contain some
evidence of life, but only of the most primitive sort. This is followed by the Palaeozoic
era, and here, for the first time, the plant remains become abundant and unmistakable,
though they all represent ancient groups of plants such as ferns, club-mosses and the
very earliest and simplest kinds of seed-plants. Next comes the Mesozoic era,
during which the vegetation consisted chiefly of ferns and gymnosperms. Finally,
there is the Caenozoic era, and this is generally described as the era of the Flowering
Plants. Each of these eras is divided into shorter time divisions called periods. Of the
Archaeozoic and Proterozoic eras no mention need be made here since they are so
far in the distant past as to be outside our immediate consideration. The Palaeozoic
era is divided into six periods called respectively, and beginning with the oldest,
Cambrian, Ordovician, Silurian, Devonian, Carboniferous and Permian. The Mesozoic era consists of three periods, Triassic, Jurassic and Cretaceous, and the Caenozoic era of two periods, Tertiary and Quaternary. To-day we are living in the last
named.

This short description of the geological eras and periods almost inevitably leads
to the question of the length of geological time. Many answers have been given to
this question but none can claim to be more than an estimate. That the total is to be
reckoned in millions of years cannot be doubted, but how many millions it is impossible to say. Much depends on the method of estimation used, and readers may be
referred to Holmes (367, 368, 369) for an account of these. It can only be said here that
estimates range from something of the order of 20 millions to something exceeding
2,000 millions, but probably a space of some hundreds of millions is nearer the
mark. As to the proportions of the whole occupied by the different eras, it is only
natural that the remoter the time the more hazy are our ideas about it but the general
opinion about the far-distant Archaeozoic and Proterozoic is that they probably
accounted between them for at least half of geological time and perhaps considerably
more. Of the total time which has elapsed since the beginning of the Palaeozoic
there are closer estimates (90, 806) and these agree that the figure is round about 500
million years, of which rather more than half, perhaps 275–300 million years, was
occupied by the Palaeozoic itself. The Mesozoic is thought to have lasted about 120–
150 millions; and the figure for the Caenozoic is in the neighbourhood of 70 millions.
Of this last figure all but one million years are allotted to the Tertiary.

But millions and percentages convey little, and it is worth while putting the
matter in more picturesque form. This can be done by imagining the whole of geological time to be represented by a vertical stick 36 in. long. On this stick the first two

eras will occupy the bottom 20 in. or so; the Palaeozoic will cover the next 9 in.; the Mesozoic 5 in.; and the Caenozoic about 2 in. Of this last era the Tertiary will account for all but about one twenty-fifth of an inch. At this end of the scale the time divisions are more comprehensible and another illuminating statement can be made. If, working backwards from the present, the generous estimate of 10,000 years

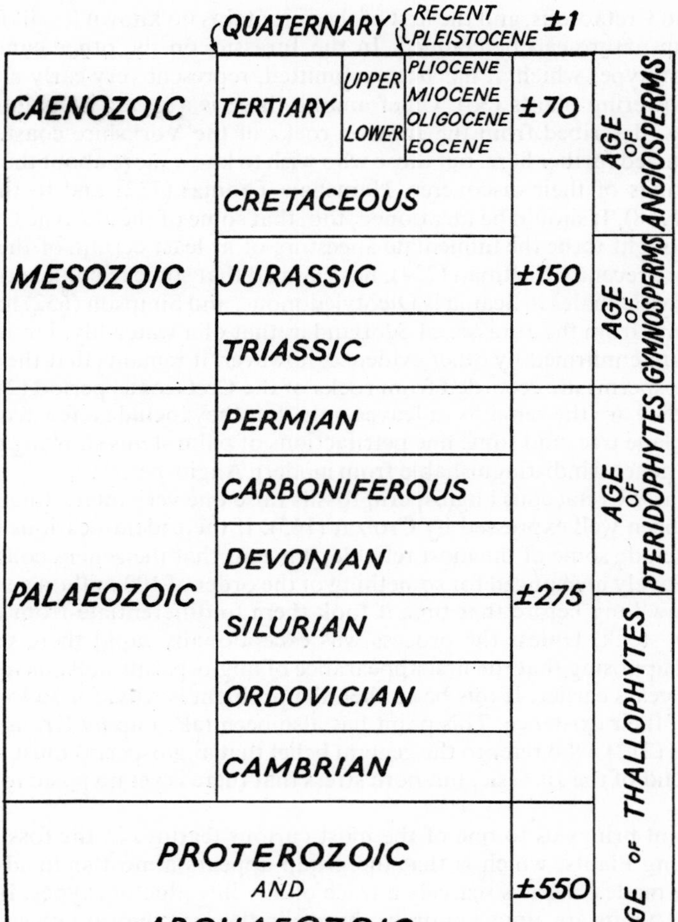

	QUATERNARY		RECENT / PLEISTOCENE	±1		
CAENOZOIC	TERTIARY	UPPER	PLIOCENE / MIOCENE	±70	AGE OF ANGIOSPERMS	
		LOWER	OLIGOCENE / EOCENE			
MESOZOIC	CRETACEOUS				AGE OF GYMNOSPERMS	
	JURASSIC			±150		
	TRIASSIC					
PALAEOZOIC	PERMIAN				AGE OF PTERIDOPHYTES	
	CARBONIFEROUS					
	DEVONIAN			±275		AGE OF THALLOPHYTES
	SILURIAN					
	ORDOVICIAN					
	CAMBRIAN					
PROTEROZOIC AND ARCHAEOZOIC				±550		

FIG. 73.—Diagrammatic representation of the *upper half* of the geological time-scale.

The figures indicate the durations, in millions of years, of the four epochs, and also of the Quaternary which is more than represented by the thicker middle part of the top line. No attempt has been made to show the relative lengths of the other periods, a matter on which opinion is divided. Compiled from various sources.

is allowed for the duration of human history proper, then this time, the time during which man has ruled the world, will on the scale be represented by something of the order of one-thousandth of an inch, that is to say, less than the thickness of the thinnest tissue paper. Figure 73 is a diagrammatic representation of the upper half of the geological time-scale and shows most of the figures and divisions which have been mentioned.

The Caenozoic era was described as the era of the Flowering Plants, and an account of the history of these plants will therefore chiefly concern this time. This is not altogether so, however, because the Angiosperms certainly made their appearance some time during the preceding Mesozoic era, although it was probably not until the Caenozoic that they attained their present dominance.

As was stated above, the Mesozoic era is divided into three periods, Triassic, Jurassic and Cretaceous, and the first of these contains no known fossils for which an Angiosperm nature can be claimed. In the Jurassic, on the other hand, there are several fossil types which, it has been submitted, represent very early and primitive kinds of flowering plants (35). Chief among these is a group of plants called the Caytoniales, described from the Jurassic rocks of the Yorkshire coast. They need not be discussed further here, but those who wish to know more about them may refer to the writings of their discoverer, Hamshaw Thomas (732), and to the comment of Walton (758). It should be mentioned, too, that some of the Jurassic Cycadophyta are also thought to be the immediate ancestors of at least certain of the Flowering Plants. More recently Erdtman (224), has claimed that some tricolpate pollen found in early Jurassic shales in Scania is Dicotyledonous, and Simpson (652) has identified a pollen grain from the Jurassic of Scotland as that of a water-lily. Until these identifications are confirmed by other evidence, however, it remains that the first certain fossil Angiosperms are recorded from rocks of the Cretaceous period (212). For the most part they are the remains of leaves only, but they include a few fruits, notably those of a plane tree, and some fine petrifactions of palm stems showing great detail. They are in general indistinguishable from modern Angiosperms.

These early Cretaceous angiosperm fossils raise one very interesting speculation which has been well expressed by Croizat (165). If their identifications are correct, and they include some of the most reliable, it means that the genera concerned have existed relatively unchanged for something of the order of 100 million years, and one wonders how long before that time it took them to differentiate from the original angiosperm stock. Unless the process was exceptionally rapid there seems sound reason for supposing that the first appearance of angiosperms must have been many millions of years earlier. If this be so then the problem is why, for so long, they left no traces of their existence. This point has also been taken up by Krausel (433) and by Edwards (212), who refer to the general belief that angiosperms must have existed before the end of the Jurassic, but both stress that there is yet no positive evidence of this.

This point brings us to one of the most curious features in the fossil history of the Flowering Plants, which is that the group appears almost suddenly and, as it were, ready made. There is scarcely a trace of any introductory types. In one series of rocks the plants are almost entirely absent; in the next they are present, not only in considerable numbers but apparently also in many of the forms which they include to-day. This sudden rise of the Angiosperms has long been an unsolved problem, and Darwin, indeed, refers to it as "an abominable mystery". One possible explanation is that a notable gap exists in the fossil record just at the time when Angiosperms were beginning to evolve, so that no traces remain of their earliest forms. There is something of a tacit assumption that the whole of geological time is represented by sedimentary rocks somewhere or other but the possibility that this is not so, and that long periods of years may have passed without leaving recognisable trace of themselves in the geological record, must be allowed. It may be argued that conditions adverse to the formation of sedimentary rocks would also be adverse to the existence of Flowering Plants but this is to dismiss the problem too easily for there are various circumstances in which an absence of normal deposits may come about, and the possibility that these plants did, in fact, arise at a time and at a place of which, now, there is no trace in the record must not be dismissed too summarily. Umbgrove (745), for example, points out that the rise of the Angiosperms is associated chronologically with one of the largest marine transgressions. This problem of possible breaks in the geological record deserves careful consideration and there is an interesting discussion of it by Heilprin (354), while Sahni, in a striking paper (613), has dealt with some of the larger theoretical implications of these supposed gaps. On the other hand, fossils of the earliest Angiosperms may yet await discovery in some remote, or for that matter even familiar, part of the world. Whatever the truth may be, however, the early history of the group is at present largely wrapped in mystery. All that can be said with safety is that they were well established by the latter part of the Cretaceous period and had by then become a conspicuous element in all contemporary floras. By the beginning of the succeeding Caenozoic era they had become the dominant plants of the world, a position they have retained ever since.

The Caenozoic era is divided into two, the Tertiary and the Quaternary, but this division is in many ways an artificial one, and from the botanical point of view there is little reason for it, because the same types of plants persisted through both. At the same time the division does mark and emphasise a very important stage in their history.

The Tertiary is divided into four subperiods, named the Eocene, the Oligocene, the Miocene and the Pliocene. The first is much the longest and the earlier part of it is sometimes referred to as the Paleocene. Throughout at least the first three of these the general conditions of climate in the world seem to have been fairly constant, and tropical or warm-temperate conditions seem to have been widespread, as indeed they also appear to have been during the later part of the Cretaceous. There was some change, it is true, in the main towards a lessening of temperature values, but these changes were comparatively small. By the beginning of the Pliocene, however, evidence of change increases, and in the course of this epoch the change became accelerated and almost catastrophic. For reasons which are not fully understood and which are doubtless complex (see Chap. 20), the temperature, at any rate in higher latitudes, deteriorated very rapidly and finally sank to levels that resulted in widespread glaciation. For the first time for millions of years, conditions of ice and snow returned to the earth and there arose the kind of steep temperature gradient between the equator and the poles which is familiar to-day. It is this relatively sudden change of climate that is made the basis of the artificial division of the Caenozoic era into two parts, the Tertiary being considered to end with the oncoming of glaciation and to pass into the Quaternary, which comprises the whole of subsequent history. The Quaternary is itself divided into two, the Pleistocene period, which comprises the actual glacial ages, and the Recent period, which comprises the time which has elapsed since the latest glaciation, but this is an even more artificial separation, because this latter time is very short and affords no real evidence that the glacial ages have in truth ended, so that it may rather be but an interval between two of their more extreme manifestations.

The Identification of Fossil Plants

It was explained at the beginning of this chapter that our knowledge of plants in past ages is derived entirely from the fossils which are to be found in the various sedimentary rocks. At first sight this might seem a very simple and satisfactory source of information, and this indeed it would be were it not that the accurate identification of plant fossils, and especially those of Flowering Plants, is, for reasons which must be considered shortly here, a matter of great difficulty.

This difficulty arises from two distinct but related circumstances. The first is that the process of preservation in the rocks, or fossilisation as it may be called, is hardly ever so satisfactory as to reveal more than a small proportion of the characters of the plants involved. The second is that plant fossils rarely consist of more than a few small detached organs. Never is there found a fossil which comprises the complete whole body of any plant of appreciable size.

The actual methods by which fossils are formed are such as also to add to the problem. This is not the place to describe these methods in detail—fuller information about them must be sought in standard works on palaeobotany—and it is enough here to point out that by far the commonest and most abundant plant fossils are of the sort called "impressions". These, as their name implies, are in fact prints of the original tissues left from the pressure of their outline and relief on the texture of the sediment in which they became imbedded. These impressions are comparable with the "rubbings" by which such low reliefs as the designs of old brasses and old coins are reproduced, and they bear much the same kind of relation to the original. In short, they reproduce the outline and, to some extent, the surface relief of the tissues but do little else.

By certain other methods of preservation, such for instance as petrifaction, where the whole tissue becomes impregnated with silica, much more is revealed, and where portions of flowers, fruits or seeds are concerned even impressions are generally enough to allow of fairly trustworthy identifications, but where leaves only are involved the difficulty of accurate determination is very great. Unfortunately, as has been said, the great majority of Angiosperm fossils at least are the impressions of leaves only, and the problems involved in identifying these colour the whole picture of the fossil record of this great group of plants.

Let it be said at once that the plant geographer has always been and is likely to remain under a deep obligation to the palaeobotanist, and it would indeed be ungrateful to belittle this debt in any way. At the same time palaeobotanists themselves would certainly be the last to wish that this sentiment should hamper a critical discussion of the difficulties attending the identification of Angiosperm fossils.

This problem of identification can best be expressed in the form of two questions. How far can leaf form be accepted as diagnostic of different kinds of flowering plants? How far can the character and form of a whole large plant be deduced from the features of a few detached leaves?

As regards the first question it can only be pointed out that leaves are the most plastic and variable of all plant organs, and that the number of types and designs of leaves is infinitely smaller than the total number of plant species, so that there are many plants with almost identical leaf forms and designs. In some cases, of course, the foliage of a single plant species is characteristic, as, for instance, we assume to be the case in the tulip tree (*Liriodendron*) (Plate 18, Fig. 74), which has leaves unlike those of any other known tree; but even this is not quite enough, because it does not establish beyond doubt that this is equally true of the past and that every fossil leaf of this pattern belonged to this genus. Indeed, to suppose that all fossil leaves can be identified with plants which are alive to-day is demonstrably fallacious, since there are certain fossil leaves which bear no resemblance to those of any known living plant. These clearly cannot be identified with any modern plant, and it may well be that some other fossil leaves which superficially resemble those of known plants actually belonged to different ones. But the case of *Liriodendron* is quite exceptionally straight-forward, and the great bulk of fossil leaves are of far more generalised types, such as are possessed to-day by numbers of distinct and unrelated plants, and in these cases identification is often difficult and sometimes well-nigh impossible.

The second question also admits of no ready answer. It is only necessary to pick and compare a number of leaves from different parts of the same plant to realise how difficult it is to say that any one is specially typical and characteristic of the species to which the plant belongs. There is nearly always variation among the leaves of any one plant, and more aberrant examples may often resemble the more typical leaves of a species other than that to which they in fact belong. Furthermore, individual detached leaves do not necessarily reveal all the characteristics of the foliage of the plants to which they belong. Such features as leaf-number and arrange-ment are generally far from clear, and it is even sometimes difficult to determine

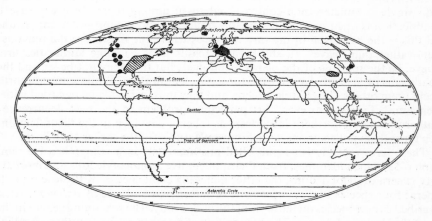

Fig. 74.—Map showing the past (black) and present (shaded) distribution of the genus *Liriodendron*, partly after Berry.

whether a fossil is really a complete simple leaf or only a portion of a compound one. Thus it will be seen that the identification of detached fossil leaves is full of pitfalls, and it is not surprising, therefore, that many attempts have been made to elucidate, by special methods of preservation, characters of the fossils which may not at first sight be readily apparent. For instance, minute details of cuticle structure have often been studied (45, 46) in the hope that they may substantiate determinations, either by their own virtue or in conjunction with other features; but the results have not been altogether satisfactory, since similar types of cuticle structure are frequently possessed by plants of quite different affinities.

In view of these difficulties it is generally admitted that identifications and records based solely on detached fossil leaves, that is to say, on leaves unattached to any axile structures and unaccompanied by other organs, must be regarded with caution and treated to a certain extent as provisional, requiring confirmation or correction as and when means of doing this become available. This is not, of course, to condemn all such records as unreliable. There is little doubt that many of them are correct, but it is only fair to say that these are generally those of least importance and tend simply to confirm what has been discovered from other sources. On the other hand, where fossil records have raised the greatest problems it will usually be found that the records and determinations must themselves be regarded as problematical. The problems may exist, but the evidence that this is so can only be called unsatisfactory.

It is worth while to illustrate this point by one of the most outstanding examples of it, namely the oft-reported occurrence as fossils in the northern hemisphere of genera and species now more or less rigidly confined to the southern hemisphere and generally considered characteristic of that zone. In particular, many fossils have been ascribed to *Eucalyptus* (now confined to Malaysia and Australia) and to the Proteaceae (almost entirely southern in distribution), the supposed fossils of which have been resurveyed by Kausik (421), identifications which are not uncommonly quoted in support of phytogeographical hypotheses (456). If the determinations of these fossils are correct they may completely alter our whole conception of the origin and development of Angiosperms. Yet when the matter is further investigated and the specimens and illustrations examined, it can be said with perfect fairness that there is no single completely non-controversial fossil among them. In every case the identification is open to some reasonable doubt on purely morphological grounds, and this is the case even in the rare instances where the fossils are the remains of fruits rather than leaves. In short, these fossils may, as some authorities firmly believe, be the remains of the plants mentioned; but they may not be so, and there often seems little *prima facie* reason for their identification. While some authorities accept them others (23, 60) reject them, and they must certainly be regarded with an open mind. Lately, however, this particular problem of the past occurrence of southern plants in northern latitudes, has taken a new turn in the identification of such types from pollen grains, as in Simpson's studies of the earlier Mull flora.

These have recently been published posthumously in a comprehensive monograph (653) which identifies, from their pollen, five monocotyledons and more than forty genera of dicotyledons, the latter including eight species of Proteaceae in five genera; four species of *Casuarina*; one of *Eucalyptus* and one of *Balanops*. All are described as new species on the basis of the pollen only. The remaining genera include five of the Hamamelidaceae. This recognition of members of four southern families is interesting but the author's own comments on the identifications are not such as to remove entirely all possibility that other attributions may not be equally supportable. Also recently Sein (629) has claimed to have detected pollen of Proteaceae, Restionaceae and *Nothofagus* in the London Clay flora of the Isle of Wight. On the other hand Couper (154, 155) has discussed the identifications of *Nothofagus* in the fossil state from the Northern hemisphere and concludes that there is little or no evidence that it ever occurred there.

The use of pollen characters in this connection clearly has considerable possibilities, but, until there is much more complete knowledge of the characteristics and, especially, the specificity of pollen, and of the changes these characters may undergo in the process of fossilisation, it cannot be said that much sure progress has been made. It must be remembered in particular that unless the group to which the fossil pollen is attributed has pollen which is unmistakably different from that of all other groups no identification can have any very high value. It is one of the difficulties of the problem that such differences are often claimed (629) but seldom satisfactorily demonstrated. Again it is not irrelevant in this connection to recall that when fossil Angiosperms were first recorded from the Antipodes they were commonly, and it is now generally admitted erroneously, identified with northern types (e.g. 226). To-day the sum of our knowledge of Angiosperm fossils outside the northern temperate suggests that they normally consist of plants very similar to those now living in the same localities.

Angiosperm fossil floras vary considerably in content, no doubt according to the actual circumstances of their origin, and fortunately not all consist exclusively of detached leaves. Some contain a few fruit or seed structures among numbers of leaves, and a few consist largely or entirely of reproductive structures. These latter are of special value and importance, not only because reproductive structures are actually more diagnostic than foliar structures but also because they are much less plastic and vary much less as a result of differences in the environments of the plants which bear them. At the same time it must be remembered that in theory at least there is no reason why two different species, one extinct and one recent, should not have fruits which are indistinguishable when one is in the fossil condition.

Apart from the difficulties of identification there is inherent in the fossil record the difficulty, amounting sometimes almost to impossibility, of correlating the geological horizons in different places and of synchronising the floras which they contain. Were it possible to be certain of the correspondence and relationship between strata widely separated in space, the advantages would be twofold. It would be possible to place the floras of the past in their proper chronological order and to see, without confusion, the succession in which the different kinds of plants flourished, and in addition, it would be possible to trace the variation over the world's surface among contemporary floras. At present it is often extremely hard to say which of two fossil floras is the older or whether two floras from distinct regions are of the same age. This particular problem is well illustrated in a paper by Chaney (125). In it the author begins by characterising each of a number of fossil floras as cool-temperate, temperate, intermediate or subtropical. He then plots the positions of these floras on a map of the world and, by joining together those to which he has given the same climatic description, draws lines, which he calls *isoflors*, from the distribution of which he comes to certain conclusions. These conclusions as to the former distribution of certain climatic values may in fact be entirely justifiable but it is clear enough that the proof of this by the use of isoflors can have validity only when there can be no room for doubt as to the exact contemporaneity of the fossil floras involved, and the paper makes it clear that this fundamental basis does not exist. Still another, somewhat allied problem, is the possibility that the remains of plants living far apart may occur together as fossils, and in this connection one is reminded of Guppy's observation (325) that sea-borne seeds of tropical species have been found semi-fossilised in Scandinavian peats.

It is chiefly because of these difficulties that no one can say exactly when in the course of geological history the Flowering Plants originated. The normal processes of evolution also militate against the recognition of a hard and fast date of first appearance. As far as our immediate purpose is concerned, therefore, it is best to place an arbitrary limit to the enquiry and to begin the story of these plants at the point when they first begin to form an appreciable proportion of the whole existing plant world.

There is unanimous agreement among palaeobotanists that the earliest fossil floras containing a considerable proportion of undoubted Angiosperms belong to the older part of the Cretaceous system, itself the last of the three great periods into which the Mesozoic era is divided, and, as noted on p. 310, this is likely to mean that these plants originated long before this, perhaps in Triassic times and possibly even earlier. There also can be no doubt that the Angiosperms arose, by the processes of organic evolution, from some pre-existing group of plants, although what kinds of plants these ancestors were is uncertain. It is thus comparatively easy to answer two of the three leading questions relating to the origin of the group, namely how and when they came into being, but the third question of where this may have taken place is still very debatable. The reason for this resides in another of the limitations of the fossil record, but in this case it is a limitation which may eventually be removed.

It is that naturally enough the fossil plants of those parts of the world, North America and Europe, where scientific investigation has the longest and most important history, are vastly greater in number and much better known than those of other regions where the opportunities for their study have been fewer. Coupled with this is the fact that the actual land surfaces of the northern hemisphere are much greater than those of the south and may therefore be expected to contain a much larger absolute number of fossils. For all these reasons the fossil record is, to a great extent, the record only of the north, and we should be on guard against any assumption that the northern flora has therefore any exceptional inherent importance. Indeed, it is probable, for various reasons, that it is to the fossil floras of tropical and southern latitudes that we must look for the solution of many problems, and it is satisfactory that while the number of these is still comparatively small, the sum of information regarding them is steadily increasing. Moreover, it is beginning to show more and more clearly an overall continuity of floras, namely that most fossil Angiosperm floras compare, within reasonable limits, with the present floras of the same region, rather than any evidence of profound change.

Thus it is true to say that the fossil record has as yet been of little assistance in elucidating the place of origin of the Flowering Plants, which still remains one of the most fundamental of our ignorances concerning the group. There are various opinions as to where this may have been, but these are generally based on deductions from the present distribution of these plants rather than from the past, and the fossil Flowering Plants known to-day scarcely support any particular view. The answer really depends upon another question which also cannot as yet be answered definitely, namely whether the Flowering Plants as a whole are to be regarded as having had a monophyletic origin or not. Are they all related by descent from a single common ancestor or small group of ancestors or have they originated from a number of relatively distinct ancestral types, their general similarity to-day being due to convergent, or at least parallel, evolution? If the former is true then they must have had a single place of origin, and in the face of the evidence from all kinds of sources it is difficult to resist the belief that this must have been somewhere in or near the equatorial regions (wherever these may have lain at the time), but if the latter is true they may have arisen in a number of different places and even, possibly, separately in both northern and southern hemispheres, as well perhaps as in the equatorial zone itself. At present all this is unrevealed. The fossil record alone may in time provide the necessary clues, but progress in many other branches of knowledge, such for example as palaeogeography and palaeoclimatology, may be of great assistance, and the botanist who is interested in this problem must keep well abreast of developments along these lines.

The Floras of the Past

The chief Cretaceous fossil floras are found in North America and in Greenland, though others of rather less importance have been described from many other parts of the world, including a number from Europe. Opinion about the age of the Greenland floras differs. Seward (637, 640) says, "It is probably true to say that in no other part of the world have familiar types of Angiosperms been described in rocks as old as those of Greenland." Knowlton (428), on the other hand, considers them to be of Upper Cretaceous age. These floras are very rich and include such genera as *Artocarpus*, *Platanus*, *Ocotea*, *Cinnamomum* and *Magnolia* (637). Apart from Greenland, probably the oldest flora containing a considerable number of Angiosperms is the Potomac flora of Maryland and Virginia. There are also several rich Upper Cretaceous floras in North America, including the Raritan of New Jersey, the Dakota flora, the Tuscaloosa flora of Carolina and Alabama, and various floras in Alaska (365).

Regarding the constitution of Cretaceous floras in general, Berry (59, 61) has emphasised the fact that they contain a mixture of what would be called to-day tropical and temperate genera such as is now found in southern Chile, south Japan and New Zealand. That is to say, they may be described as indicating the occurrence in their time of a warm-temperate or subtropical climate.

The question of the extent to which fossil floras are evidences of climatic conditions is a very important one. There is in general no doubt that deductions based on the nature of fossil plant remains are sound, provided of course that the determinations of the fossils can be relied upon. This is particularly well illustrated in some of the earlier descriptions of floras from the arctic regions. Many of the fossils in these were originally attributed to genera of a tropical or subtropical character, and on the strength of this there grew up the belief, still widely held, that during the earlier stages of Angiosperm history the climate was of corresponding value up to the highest latitudes. More careful comparison of these fossils with modern plants however, seems to show, as Berry (64) pointed out, that these "tropical" identifications are unsound and that the plants must rightly be attributed to more temperate genera. Chaney (124) has similarly thrown doubt on the determination of many North American fossils, and in particular records his belief that of the 150 fossil species of *Ficus* described therefrom, the majority belong to other and "less romantic" genera. It would seem therefore that the opinion formerly held that a tropical or, at least, subtropical climate extended in the Cretaceous and early Tertiary almost or quite to the North Pole must be modified. That there was a well-developed vegetation there is evident enough, but that it was anywhere in these high latitudes of more than temperate facies and relationship is very doubtful. But whatever may be the exact truth about this, the impression left by the Cretaceous floras is that in their time the temperature gradient from the equator to the poles was much less steep than at present and that floras were more widespread and generalised in character. This state of affairs seems to have persisted into the Tertiary, and the actual passage from the Cretaceous reveals no marked floristic change, so that the distinction between the two is, on this count, rather an arbitrary one.

By the end of the Cretaceous the Flowering Plants had attained that predominance in the plant world that they have ever since maintained, and the fossil floras of the Tertiary, which are innumerable, all show the same general constitution that is to be seen in living floras. Much the greater part of the whole Tertiary era was occupied by the Eocene, and fossil remains of this time are abundant. The coastal plain of eastern North America (65) has revealed thousands of fossils and seems to have been inhabited successively by three rather distinct floras—the Wilcox flora, the Claiborne flora and the Jackson flora, all of which contain some markedly tropical types, indicating a considerably warmer climate than had prevailed in the Cretaceous. Further west in North America the Raton flora from Colorado and New Mexico was probably contemporary with the Wilcox; the Fort Union flora extended far to the north: and in the coastal region the Puget flora may be of the same age as the Fort Union. Particularly, in thinking of these latter floras it should be remembered that the Rocky Mountains did not then exist, at any rate in anything like their present form (63). The early Tertiary floras of Alaska are also considerable (366). Barghoorn (644) has given some interesting graphs of the relationships between many of these North American floras and the floras of the same areas to-day.

In Greenland the Eocene floras are generally thought to date from the latter part of the period. They are especially abundant and well known in the neighbourhood of Disco Island on the west coast, at a latitude of nearly 70° N., and contain many forms which to-day are characteristic of the north-eastern United States.

The Tertiary flora of Spitzbergen is of particular interest and importance because nowhere else is there so rich a fossil flora so near the North Pole. Høeg (362) has described it as composed of genera whose relatives are now chiefly in North America, China and Central Europe, that is to say it was what would now be called a north temperate flora and Manum's conclusions are much the same (821). There was no Malayan element, such as has been identified in the London Clay (see below) and no palms or other plants indicating tropical or even warm temperate conditions. If soundly based this conclusion is very important because, quite apart from temperature, the light relations and "length of day" in Spitzbergen now are such as to make it hard to believe that a flora of the kind Høeg describes could exist in these conditions. It therefore seems to make inevitable the conclusion that if the obliquity of the ecliptic has remained relatively unchanged, then either Spitzbergen has changed its position with respect to the pole, or the pole has moved, or both (see p. 411).

In Britain there is the small flora, presumably of early Eocene date, from the island of Mull, but far more extensive and important is the great fossil flora of lower Eocene age from the London Clay of what is now the London Basin. Not only is this flora very rich but it consists almost entirely of well-preserved fruits and seeds so that the identifications of its constituents are unusually reliable. This great flora was re-studied and monographed on a monumental scale by Reid and Chandler (592). Practically all the specimens were illustrated in a series of fine plates, and the result is a singularly convincing volume whose conclusions permit of little or no difference of opinion. The recent supplement to this work, by Chandler (123), adds some thirty genera and 100 species, so that the flora now comprises about 350 species, and these include the palms *Nipa* (Plate 19, Fig. 75) and *Sabal*, as well as *Cinnamomum, Endiandra, Hugonia, Iodes, Lannea* (*Odina*), *Leucopogon, Litsea, Magnolia, Meliosma, Ochrosia, Olax, Oncoba, Spondias, Symplocos, Tetracera, Tinospora, Toona* and *Vitis*. Although the list of determinations is rather different, the flora is on the whole like the other Eocene floras mentioned, the difference being largely due to the fact that the well-preserved fruits and seeds permit an exceptional accuracy of determination and discrimination. Reid and Chandler's monograph does not confine itself merely to the description of the fossils but discusses this and other Eocene floras in a most interesting way. The authors reach a number of conclusions of which the most important to note here are that the flora is of the tropical rain-forest type; that it has a marked affinity with the present flora of Indo-Malaysia; and that it probably reflects a mean annual temperature of about 70° F.

It has been pointed out by some that the plant remains in this London Clay flora are not *in situ*, that is to say, preserved where they grew, but consist of drift material which may not be a reliable indication of the contemporary climate in the place where it accumulated. There are, however, other early Tertiary fossils from southern England, which seem to indicate that this sort of warm climate may well have prevailed at the time. In particular, Chandler's recent study of the flora of the pipe-clays in the Lower Bagshots of Dorset (813) reveals a tropical florest flora indicating climatic conditions somewhat warmer than those associated with the London Clay flora.

It is generally believed that for a very long period of geological time, perhaps from the Carboniferous to the Middle Tertiary, what is now Eurasia was separated from other land masses on the south by a sea called the Tethys, which extended all the way from the Atlantic to Malaysia. The western part of this sea is now largely covered by the North African–Arabian deserts, and the Mediterranean is all that remains of it here. The presence of this long east–west sea must have had profound effects on the climate of these parts of the Old World. It has been suggested that warm currents, passing through in this direction, may have modified the climate of what is now Europe sufficiently to allow tropical plants to grow there, or at least much nearer than they do now.

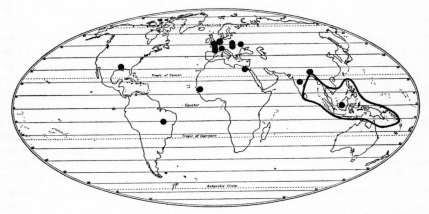

Fig. 75.—Map showing the past (black dots) and present (heavy outline) distribution of the genus *Nipa*, partly after Berry.

The impression given by the Eocene floras serves to emphasise that derived from Cretaceous remains. There was no considerable break between the two periods either in plants or in climate, although the climate of the Eocene seems to have been warmer in some places, and the latter was, so far as the vegetation is concerned, more or less an extension of the Cretaceous. The two together suggest strongly that there may have been something in the nature of a single extensive and generalised flora over much of the whole world or at least over the northern hemisphere, though there cannot have been any complete elimination of the latitudinal climatic zonation. Chaney, indeed, in an interesting summary of the North American Eocene floras (126) recognises a Neotropical–Tertiary flora which ranged northward to 49° in the west and to 37° in the east, a Madro–Tertiary flora which occupied parts of south-west North America and an Arcto–Tertiary which occupied the land north of the first, up to the highest latitudes. Both the first and last of these at least moved gradually southward later in the Tertiary as the climate became slowly less genial. In addition to all these there was a Palaeotropical–Tertiary flora in the Old World and an Antarcto–Tertiary flora in the southern temperate regions.

The Oligocene subperiod which succeeded the Eocene left comparatively few fossils. It is fairly well represented in Europe, including the south of England, and in North America, but there is only one flora that calls for special mention here. This is the Bembridge flora from the Isle of Wight, which like that of the London Clay has been monographed by Reid and Chandler (590). It is not a very large flora, and in general somewhat resembles the Eocene Wilcox flora except that there are rather more herbs. Its special interest is the resemblance and affinity that many of its plants bear to types at present found only in North America and Asia, and there is an inference, if no more, that these plants may, in Oligocene times, have been part of a completely circumboreal flora, the greater part of which has since been destroyed, leaving only two widely separated remnants. Although the Oligocene floras are scanty, they are sufficient to show that here again there was little real change accompanying that from the Eocene to the Oligocene. That there is some change is true, but the comparison of the Bembridge flora with the Wilcox is enough to suggest that it was relatively slight.

The Miocene subperiod is, like the Oligocene, short compared with the Eocene and has correspondingly fewer remains, and the important floras of the time are found chiefly in western North America and in Europe. One at least from each region needs special mention. The first is the Florissant flora from Pacific North America (142), which is actually one of several floras closely related in time and space. It contains about 250 species, among them being many plants familiar in similar latitudes to-day. The second outstanding flora is that from Oeningen in the neighbourhood of Lake Constance and should perhaps be reckoned as partly Oligocene and partly Miocene. It, again, is but one of a number of floras which together have been described by Knowlton as "probably the richest plant deposits known anywhere in the world". The total number of species described approaches a thousand, but the flora of Oeningen itself contains about 500, some quarter of which are herbs. Most of the fossils are beautifully preserved and enhanced by the fineness of their details. They include, moreover, a good proportion of flowers and fruits. The identifications of the Oeningen fossils show that the vegetation was dense mixed deciduous forest (504) and that the flora was in general very much of the same kind as the Florissant or, at any rate, consisted of plants which are associated with similar conditions of climate. Both, however, differ appreciably from any preceding floras in that they indicate a climate rather, and perhaps much, colder. It would appear, therefore, that during the Miocene the climate and flora, which had been comparatively constant for so long, began slowly to change, and that in the direction of more temperate conditions. But this is not the only way in which the Miocene indicates change. It was a time of great earth movements and of intense volcanic action and mountain folding, and it is from this period that the greatest mountain ranges of the world date.

The last of the Tertiary subperiods, the Pliocene, is generally considered to have been shorter than any of the others, and remains of it are scarce. They are widely scattered but nowhere abundant, and it is fortunate that those of Europe are complete enough to give a fairly good picture of the period as a whole, because the Pliocene provides some most important links in the history of the Flowering Plants. The outstanding feature of the period is that, unlike what has been seen before, it illustrates conspicuous floristic changes, and these are best realised from a description of successive Pliocene floras. Particular reference may be made to three fossil floras closely related in space but usually assigned horizontally to the Lower, Middle and Upper Pliocene respectively. The first and oldest of these is the Reuverian flora from the Dutch–Prussian border in the neighbourhood of the Rhine. It contains some 300 species which are of distinctly warmer affinity and type than those now living in

PLATE 20

Map of the World showing the distribution of mean annual temperature.
After Bartholomew's *Physical Atlas*, vol. III.

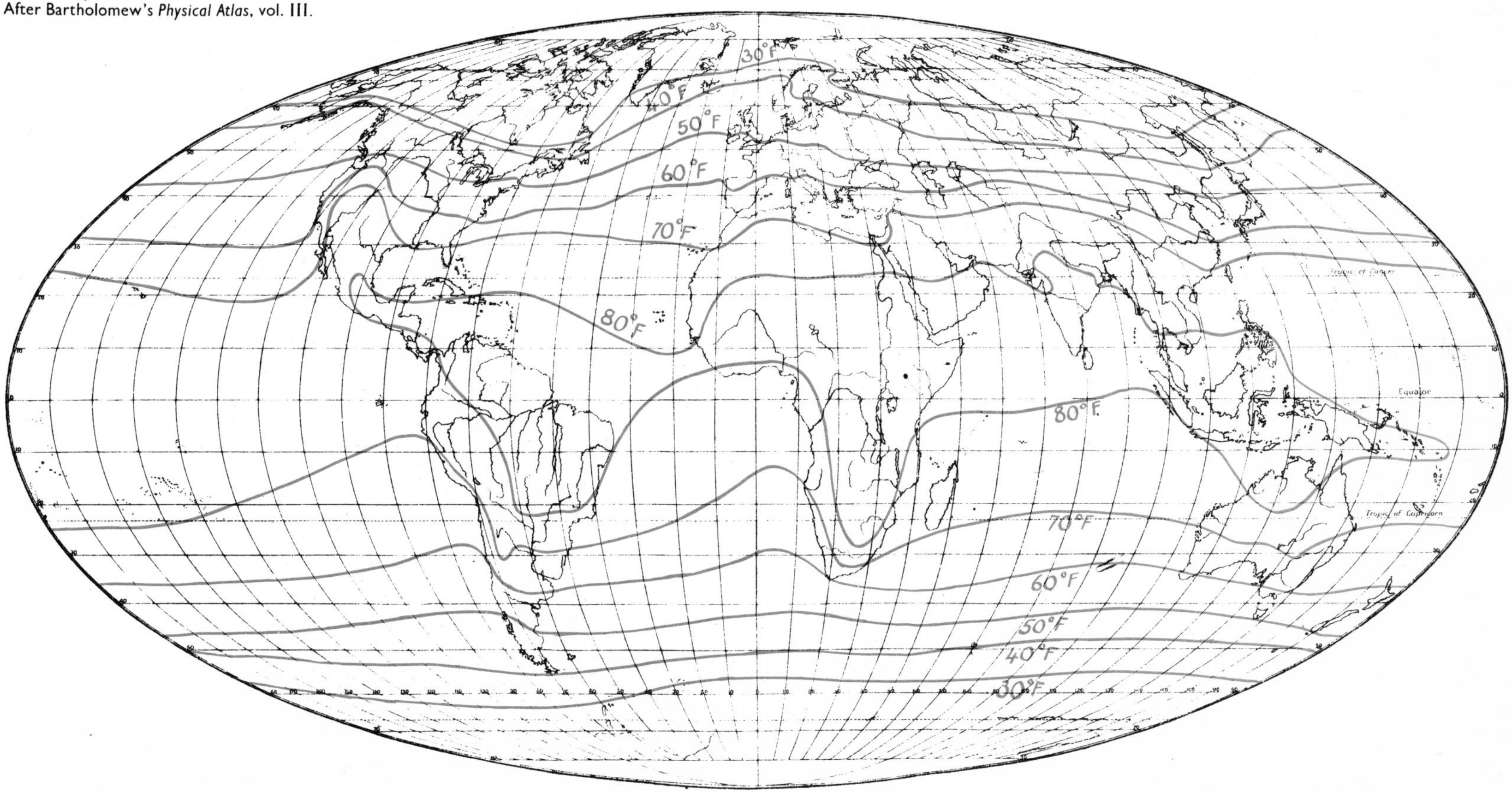

Areas correct   Distortion increasing towards border of map.

Approximate Scale 1:100,000,000 (1600 miles = 1 inch) along Equator

on Mollweide's Homolographic Projection

Copyright

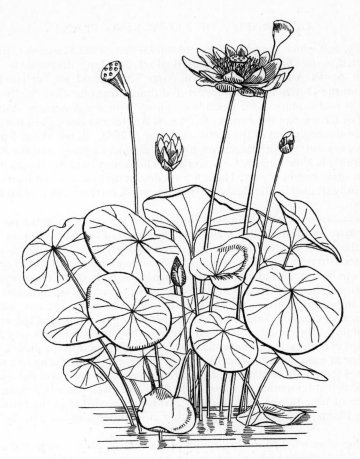

Fig. 76.—*Nelumbo nucifera*, much reduced, after Baillon.

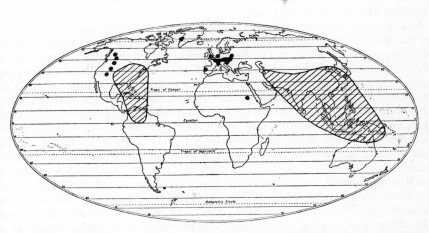

Fig. 77.—Map showing the past (black) and present (shaded) distribution of the genus *Nelumbo*. The evidence for the occurrence of the genus in Greenland is scarcely convincing.

the locality, and which suggest a flora not unlike that of the Miocene. There is also as was noted in the Oligocene, a very marked relationship with plants to-day living in eastern North America and eastern Asia. The second or Teglian flora also comes from the Dutch–Prussian border and differs from the first chiefly in having more herbs and aquatics and much less affinity with the American–Asiatic flora. The third or Cromerian flora comes from East Anglia and belongs to the end of the Pliocene or the beginning of the Pleistocene (see p. 268). All but about 5 per cent of its species are identical with those now living in eastern England, and the American–Asiatic affinity is almost gone. Conversely this flora may be described as practically that of the same region to-day. These floras contain many seeds and fruits and have been carefully studied by the Reids (587), whose work on this kind of plant fossil is so well known.

The correlation of other Pliocene floras is too uncertain to make possible any real comparison with those just mentioned, but most of them reveal floras very like those of the same regions to-day. The comparatively rich fossil floras of Japan, however, seem to be rather different in that they indicate somewhat cooler conditions, as appears to be true also of certain other Asiatic floras. Poor as it is compared with earlier periods, the fossil record of the Pliocene is, nevertheless, sufficient to reveal the most important feature of the time, namely, the comparatively sudden and rapid change in climatic conditions. At the beginning of the period the vegetation, and, by analogy, the climate, remained much as they had been for a very long time and perhaps ever since the Cretaceous. By the end of the period the plants, of north-west Europe at least, were practically as they are to-day, conforming to a temperate or even cool-temperate climate. In short, in many parts of the world the age-old and generalised warm-temperate or subtropical flora had given place in a relatively very short space of time to one of a kind not previously recorded in the history of the Flowering Plants, and perhaps representing climatic conditions equally unprecedented.

This alteration marked the beginning of the catastrophic change and deterioration in world climate which culminated in the extensive glaciations or "Ice Ages" of the immediately succeeding Pleistocene subperiod, but before considering this very important phase in the history of the Flowering Plants it is worth while to summarise what has so far been said.

All the available evidence points to the fact that the Flowering Plants, from the time that they are first recognised somewhere in the earlier part of the Cretaceous right down to the middle or end of the Pliocene, pursued the even tenor of their way without encountering any serious problems or difficulties in the nature of rapid environmental changes. Throughout this long period their history seems to have been that of a group of organisms gradually broadening and differentiating by the multiplication of forms, in the course of secular time, and coincidentally attaining a more and more dominant position among the vegetation of the world as a whole. Environmental or, at least, climatic differentiation, with its attendant morphological differentiation, seems to have been at a minimum, and the fossil record certainly suggests that, at any rate in high latitudes of the northern hemisphere, there was one almost ubiquitous flora, which has been called the Arcto–Tertiary flora, reaching, it may have been, even to high latitudes. Then quite rapidly at some time during the Pliocene this idyllic sequence was broken by a drastic deterioration in the climates of the higher latitudes, culminating in widespread glaciation and presenting to the world of flowering plants problems of environmental harmony which it had never before encountered.

The foregoing brief survey of fossil Angiosperm floras has been almost entirely concerned with the northern extratropical regions and only one brief reference has been made to those floras, comparatively few in number, which are known from the southern hemisphere, this being for the purpose of showing that these floras on the whole reveal a plant life similar to that of the same places to-day. There is, however, one southern fossil flora which, from almost every point of view, is of outstanding interest and importance. This is the fossil flora found on Seymour Island at latitude 64° S. and longitude 57° W. in the antarctic, and described by Dusén (207) who identified it as in character very like the present floras of New Zealand and Fuegia. Skottsberg (670) has stressed the significance of this Antarcto–Tertiary counterpart of the Cretaceous and Eocene floras of the north, especially with regard to the problem of the relation between the northern and southern temperate floras, and the evidence it affords for the autochthonous origin of the latter.

The Ice Ages

By far the longest part of Angiosperm history has been covered in the last few pages, and what remains is almost infinitely shorter, but this is more than compensated for by its exceptional interest and significance. This may be expressed by saying that the first part is a history of prosperity, and the second a history of adversity, and with the Flowering Plants, as so often with other things, it is the latter which is the more revealing.

The study of the Pleistocene and its Ice Ages is so complex, and there is so great a literature about it, that it can be dealt with here only in the merest outline, and then only so far as it directly concerns the subject of plant geography. Much of all the available information is to hand in the writings of Wright (798), Antevs (25), Zeuner (805), Flint (244), Deevey (179) and Charlesworth (832) and these have been the sources of much that follows here. Several of the contributions to the volume edited by Shapley (644) may also be consulted, notably that of Metzel. A wealth of information about the Pleistocene in southern South America is given by Auer (32), and there is a useful paper with a good bibliography dealing with the north Temperate regions by Moreau (526).

As a preliminary it is of value to distinguish between the two most striking effects of glaciation, the formation of glaciers and of ice-caps, because although the difference between them is one of degree only, it is a matter of some importance here. Glaciers are commonly to be observed to-day in elevated regions at almost all distances from the poles and may be described as frozen rivers filling the upper valleys between the mountains. They are usually more or less distinct entities, and are normally overtopped by uncovered mountain peaks. Where and when, however, the effects of intense cold are sufficiently accumulative, the individual glaciers tend to lose their identity and to coalesce into huge masses or caps of enough bulk to over-ride and cover all land elevations and to form great ice-fields, which are known as ice-caps. In their typical form they are found only in the polar regions. To-day there are in the world only two major ice-caps, one in the north covering Greenland, and one in the south covering the whole of Antarctica. The latter is much the greater and its magnitude may be gauged from the statement that the summit of the ice dome is estimated to be 15,000 ft. above the sea (482). There are certain other minor ice-caps, especially in the north, but the polar area here is sea. Glaciers, on the other hand, occur to-day wherever the altitude is enough. They are present even on the summits of high equatorial mountains, and are increasingly plentiful in higher latitudes. When for any reason the temperature of the world falls, the ice-caps increase in size and area and the glaciers become not only more numerous but extend down to lower levels, often coalescing in the process. Conversely, with a rise of temperature the area covered by ice contracts. The measure of the intensity of glaciation at any time is thus the size of the ice-caps, namely the latitude to which they extend, and the level to which glaciers descend. Since it is only natural to regard the present state of affairs as a norm or mean, the term Ice Ages has thus become applied to such times as the caps and glaciers extended appreciably beyond their present limits.

It is now known that the Pleistocene consisted of more than one glaciation, that is to say that the amount of ice increased and diminished more than once presumably in accordance with climatic oscillations, but there is some doubt still about the exact sequence of events in the different parts of the world. There are evidences of extensive glaciations in the southern hemisphere as well as in the north (Fig. 78), but there is, in particular, much variance of opinion as to whether these glaciations were synchronous with those of the north. On the whole the evidence seems to suggest that they were. There is also evidence that at lower latitudes there were contemporaneous pluvial periods.

In any case the distribution of land and sea in the two hemispheres and the remoteness of Antarctica have made the traces of glaciation much more conspicuous in the north, and there is an inevitable tendency to regard the effects of glaciation as being much more marked in the north than in the south. This is probably quite unjustified, and Skottsberg (659) has corrected the impression graphically when he says "the disappearance of the Tertiary antarctic flora during the Ice Ages is of fundamental importance and has been greatly underestimated by plant geographers. No catastrophe of such dimensions and of such consequences has ever befallen the Tertiary flora of the northern hemisphere."

The course and sequence of the Pleistocene ice ages have been particularly studied in the Alps by Penck and Brückner (552), and it appears that here at least there were four successive glaciations of different intensities and that these were separated by interglacial periods, during which the climate returned to more genial values such as are familiar to-day (628) (Fig. 81). During the glaciations the glaciers crept down the valleys, and during the interglacials they retreated. Fortunately glaciation leaves behind it, in the form of striated rocks, moraines, eskers and drumlins, fairly clear evidences of its course, and from these it is possible to learn a great deal about the different ice advances.

The first advance of the ice is called the Günz glaciation and was of medium intensity. It was followed by an interglacial during which the climate probably reached values rather higher than those of to-day. The second glaciation is the Mindel, and this again was followed by a similar but much longer interglacial. During the Mindel the ice probably reached its maximum extent. The third glaciation is called the Riss and seems to have been of lesser extent than the one preceding it. It, again, was followed by a third interglacial period, from which several interesting fossil floras are known, indicating a climate slightly warmer than the present. Finally there was the Würm glaciation, less intense than any of its predecessors, and this was followed by a gradual improvement of climate to the condition that we know to-day.

The question next to be considered is whether the sequence of events in the Alps occurred also elsewhere. It can only be said here that while the fourfold classification and nomenclature just described were made with special reference to the Alps, there is reason to believe that a similar if not exactly synchronous series of glaciations occurred in other parts of the northern hemisphere.

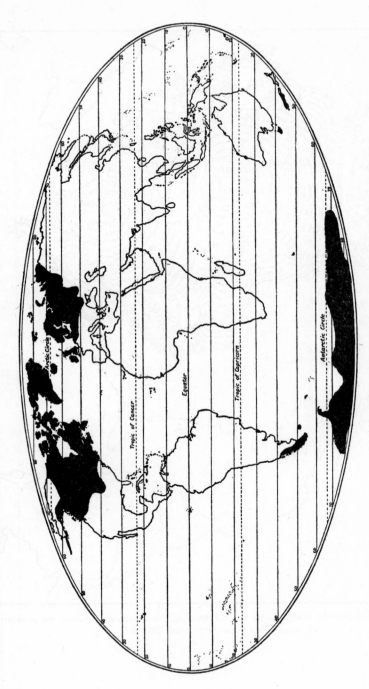

FIG. 78.—The Pleistocene Glaciation.

Map of the world showing, in general terms, the maximum extent of the main northern and southern ice-caps (black) during the Pleistocene. It must be remembered that the snow-line was everywhere considerably lower at that time, so that at all latitudes there were, in addition, some larger or smaller local accumulations of ice at higher altitudes. Compiled from various sources.

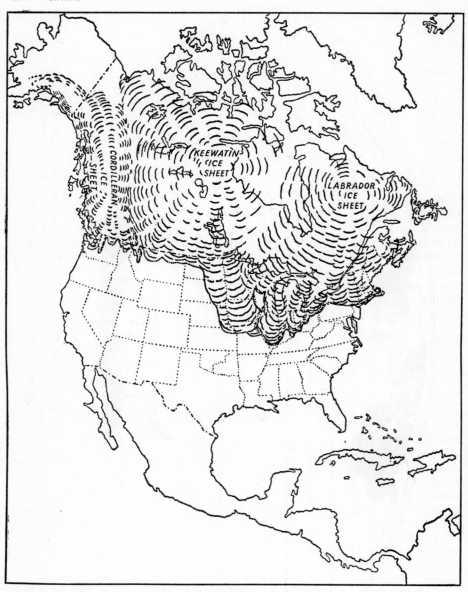

Fig. 79.—Map showing the extent of the ice advance in North America during the maximum glaciation, after Chamberlin and Salisbury.

In the Alps the glaciations concerned a relatively small complex of glaciers, but in higher latitudes it was the polar ice-cap itself that waxed and waned, and what in the former case was but a local lowering of the snow-line, in the latter took the form of great latitudinal extensions of the ice-cap. During the first glaciation the spread of this ice south was relatively small, covering Europe only in its most northerly parts. It was in the second glaciation that the polar ice attained its maximum extent, and the limits of this must be discussed in some detail.

It might be anticipated that the ice would extend in all directions south from the present poles but for reasons which are not altogether clear this was not so, and the actual centre of the northern ice-cap during the maximum glaciation lay somewhere near the middle of Greenland. Because of this the glaciation most affected North America, and here the cap's southern edge (Fig. 79) followed approximately the present frontier of Canada in the west and the latitude of 40° N. in the east. Passing to Europe (Fig. 80), the edge was so situated that the whole of Ireland was covered and all Britain as far south as a line joining the Severn and the Thames. Thence the edge extended almost straight across the continent to a point some distance north of the Crimea, and from here it ran, with certain marked indentations, to pass out into the Arctic Ocean along a line somewhat east of the Ural Mountains. Thus scarcely any part of Asia was covered by the cap, but the glaciation of the mountain masses in that continent was much greater and there may, locally, have been an approach to ice-cap conditions (159, 244).

The greater extent of this maximum glaciation obscures to some extent the details of the others, but it is thought that the third glaciation was comparable to the first in extent. The fourth, which is the most problematical, was apparently markedly smaller than the others. As in the Alps, the glaciations were separated by interglacial periods of improved climatic conditions, but the details of these periods are not yet very well defined.

It will be readily appreciated that the amount of ice contained in the caps during the glaciations must have been enormous, not only in bulk but also in weight, and that with variation in the caps there must have been corresponding differences in the weight of the ice resting on the surface of the earth. It is probable that mainly to this must be attributed the many changes in the relative level of land and sea so often found associated with glaciation. It has recently been suggested that there is much more ice in the world than was supposed, and that in Antarctica and Greenland some of the land may be depressed below sea-level by its weight. But besides the actual effect of weight, a single glacier or arm of an ice-cap may often have had the effect of damming up the normal drainage of an area and causing the imprisoned waters to rise to a much higher level than would otherwise have been the case. Changes of these sorts have doubtless played an important part in plant geography.

For a long time after their recognition it was supposed that the ice ages of the Pleistocene formed an isolated phenomenon in geological history, but it is now known that this is not so. There have been, in the whole course of geological history, several glacial epochs, but these have been separated by immense periods of time and they are for the most part so remote that little is known of their details. References to a Cretaceous glaciation are not infrequent in the literature but this is very hypothetical and it is generally accepted that the glacial epoch before that of the Pleistocene was as far back as the Permian period, many millions of years before the Flowering Plants came on the scene at all. Here, therefore, we need take notice only of the Pleistocene glaciations, although the fact that there have been others is of considerable theoretical importance.

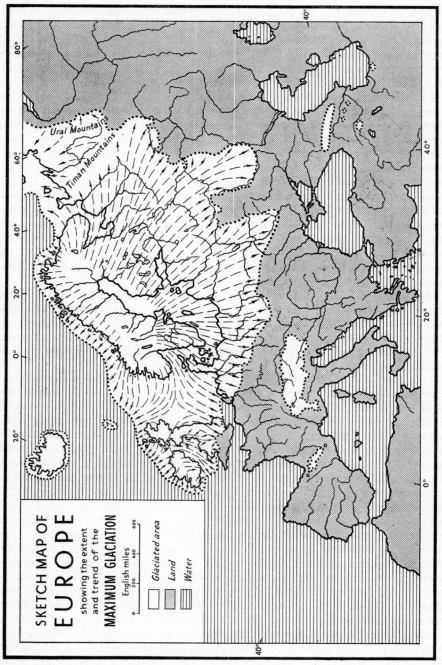

SKETCH MAP OF
EUROPE

showing the extent
and trend of the
MAXIMUM GLACIATION

English miles
0   200   400   600

☐ Glaciated area
▨ Land
▥ Water

Ural Mountains

Timan Mountains

FIG. 80.—Map showing the extent of the ice advance in Europe during the maximum glaciation, after Chamberlin and Salisbury.

What the cause or causes of these long intermittent ice ages may have been is still very problematical (409) and there is fortunately no necessity to discuss the matter at length here. Suffice it to say that opinion to-day, which is set out in considerable detail by Zeuner (805, 806), tends towards the view that whatever the actual contributory causes may have been, and they were probably many, they are likely to have become effective only in some rare combination of circumstances and values.

One of the most important developments in the study of glaciology has been the success attending some of the attempts to arrive at an actual chronology of the Pleistocene, and especially of the latter part of it. In the case of the Alps, for instance, actual figures, compiled from many sources of evidence have been mentioned with some confidence. Penck (552) has made a curve to a time scale for the whole period (Fig. 81), also indicating the rise and fall in the snow-line, that is to say in the general level of the ice. According to this curve something like half a million years have elapsed since the end of the Pliocene, and nearly half of these are occupied by the long interglacial period between the Mindel and Riss. Twenty thousand years is suggested as the time covering what is called the post-glacial period, that is, the time since the latest (Würm) ice-cap began to retreat. It will be noted that this last rise of the curve is shown as a number of steps. Probably all the curves should be drawn in this way with minor oscillations, but it is only in this latest phase that these are sufficiently well known to be recorded. The shortness of the post-glacial period is one of the most interesting features of the curve. Twenty thousand years is a long enough period, but compared with the usual measures of geological time it is scarcely appreciable and brings the fourth glaciation almost within sight, as it were, of the present.

This chronology is supported in general by other and different estimates. One of the best-known is the rate of movement upstream of the Niagara Falls, which have existed only since the retreat of the fourth ice-cap. Here the figure is about 25,000 years. The most striking figures, however, are those obtained by De Geer (180) and others from their studies of the laminated clays or *varves* of southern Scandinavia. Details of these studies may be sought elsewhere and particularly in the recent work of Zeuner (806), but it can be said here that from them it would appear that a period of some 14,000 years has elapsed since the southernmost part of Sweden began to be uncovered by the retreating ice, and that about 9,000 years have passed since the neighbourhood of Stockholm was uncovered.

The study of these laminated clays (181) is but one instance among many of the way in which Scandinavian scientists have taken advantage of the features of their country to make themselves pre-eminent in the study of problems relating to glaciation. Another line of research that has attained great proportions far beyond the land of its birth is in the investigation of post-glacial and, to a lesser extent, other floras by pollen analysis (102, 276, 279). Peat, which may be called a peculiar subfossil state of plant remains, normally contains great numbers of pollen grains of the plants which lived during, and contributed to, its formation, and by treating samples of peat in a special way it is possible not only to examine this pollen but to identify it. Peat has been forming for much of post-glacial time, and this method, correlated with others, has enabled a good account of the vegetational changes consequent upon the retreat of the ice to be drawn up. It has been suggested that this chronology has been confirmed by the occurrence of cold and warm kinds of Foraminifera in the deposits on the bed of the Caribbean Sea (556, 806).

It appears, as might be expected on other and less direct evidence, that there followed in the wake of the retreating ice a series of floras and vegetation states each more temperate in character than the one before it. In Scandinavia in general five main stages are recognised in this gradual re-immigration of the flora (21) namely pre-boreal, boreal, atlantic, sub-boreal and sub-atlantic (compare p. 276) and the last four of these stages constitute what is generally called the Blytt-Sernander scheme, from its original authors. The first plant-cover after the actual departure of the ice was an arctic one, giving rise fairly soon to a flora in which birch was prominent. This in turn gave place to coniferous forest, which was itself followed by deciduous forest in which oak and hazel were outstanding constituents. At a later stage beech became prominent. After that there seems to have been a slight return to earlier conditions and a final recovery to the present state. These stages have been recognised in whole or in part in many parts of the glaciated regions (see Chapter 12). In Ireland, for instance, a very important point was first brought to light, namely the existence of a post-glacial optimum, that is to say of a time when climatic conditions were actually rather better than they have ever been since. This optimum has also been particularly well demonstrated in Scandinavia in the distribution of the hazel.

These post-glacial changes have now been much studied, especially in north-western Europe, and the summary of his own investigations, as well as those of

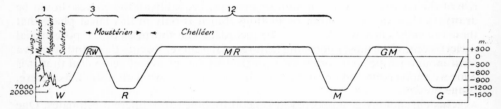

FIG. 81.—Graph showing the variation in temperature in the Alps during the Ice Ages, after Penck and Brückner.

others, by von Post (569) gives a most valuable picture of the present state of know-ledge on this subject, from which the idea of a post-glacial optimum, followed by climatic deterioration, similar probably to the sequence of events in the earlier, interglacial periods of amelioration, clearly emerges. The sequence comprises three main phases; that of the approach of the warm period, with increase of the more temperate kinds of trees; that of the culmination of this forest vegetation; and that of its contraction and change to the conditions observable to-day. Nor are these fluctuations observable only in temperate latitudes, and that a parallel course of events has occurred in the warmer parts of the world has been indicated by many observations, such as those of Selling in the Hawaiian Islands (630).

Most recently of all an entirely new method has been applied to the estimation of post-glacial chronology, that of calculating the age of organic remains by estimating the proportion of radio-carbon, a radioactive isotope of carbon, in them, and there is a very clear account of the method by its originator Libby (460) and a useful shorter explanation by Godwin (281). It is too early to say much as yet about the results, but Flint (245) claims that it shows first that the date of the final glaciation is more recent than has been supposed, and second, that subsequent climatic changes have been synchronous in the northern temperate regions of both the Old and New Worlds.

Brief as the foregoing account of the Pleistocene is, it is enough to show what a profound effect this period must have had on the vegetation of a great part of the world. Whether or not, previously, there was local glaciation on the summits of high mountains is a question which will be discussed in a later chapter. but there can be little doubt that the arctic conditions (widespread glaciation at sea level) which characterised the period were conditions never previously experienced or encountered by the Flowering Plants, and that many of these were, as a result of them, faced with the necessity of adjusting themselves to influences of a quite novel kind. Further than this, the effects of the ice were greatly intensified by the catastrophic speed at which it came and by the series of oscillations that accompanied it. The significance of the speed of glacial onset in particular requires to be fully realised. Previous to the later part of the Pliocene the speed of morphological evolution in the Angiosperms may be pictured as being faster than and perhaps unrelated to climatic change, or, to put it differently, the plants may be pictured as changing by the processes of evolution more rapidly than their surroundings, so that quite possibly the problem of "adaptation", as the term is understood to-day, did not arise. With the coming of the Pleistocene glaciations this relationship was entirely altered. Climatic change was accelerated to such a pitch that by no stretch of imagination can it be supposed that evolution was able to keep pace with it, and there thus arose a situation in which the environment was changing much more rapidly than its inhabitants. Again, in somewhat different phrase, environmental change completely outran evolutionary change. The result in many parts of the world was a state of stress between organism and environment such as may never have occurred before. In short, if these suppositions be correct, the effect of the Ice Ages on the Flowering Plants was completely to upset, over much of their range, the balance between plant and habitat. Since there has not been, in the time which has elapsed since the fourth glaciation, any appreciable restoration of the long-term pre-glacial conditions, the botanists of to-day are studying a world vegetation but lately subjected to a devastating disaster. The study of the geography of the Flowering Plants, is peculiarly the study of the consequences of this disaster, and this being so, the outstanding importance of the Pleistocene in relation to the general story can scarcely be overestimated.

In concluding this chapter it should be noted that the above account of the Pleistocene glaciation is written in the usual terms of the waxing and waning of ice-caps in response to major temperature oscillations, but it must be remembered that some, at least, of the facts and effects described can be explained otherwise by supposing that the ice-caps themselves moved from time to time while the temperature gradients of the world remained relatively constant.

PART TWO

CHAPTER 16

THE FACTORS OF DISTRIBUTION—I. GENERAL REVIEW

THE first part of this book described the facts of Angiosperm geography: the purpose of this second part is to consider their possible explanation. The present chapter therefore gives a general preliminary survey of what are usually called the "factors controlling plant distribution", and the five following chapters discuss how far and in what manner the more important of these may, in combination, be considered to provide a general explanation of the distribution of these plants as it is to be observed at the present time.

In the widest sense the distribution of plants to-day is the effect not only of natural causes but also of artificial ones, namely those which operate as a result of the intentional or unintentional activities of human beings. With these human factors this book is not, to all intents and purposes, concerned, although it is necessary on occasion to refer to some of them incidentally. Its theme is rather the natural distribution of plants, and for this reason the influences of man, though often intense and widespread, receive little or no attention except in so far as they can be made to illustrate or explain more natural process. At the same time the extent and degree of man's influence on the plant life of the world must never be underestimated. Obvious as much of it is there is to-day a growing belief that many of the apparently more natural vegetational states are in fact the less direct consequences of man's activities, and it has even been suggested (29, 701) that he has played a not inconsiderable part in hastening the spread of desert conditions. Those who are interested in this relation between man and his environment should read the classic account of it by Marsh (491).

One natural factor of distribution is so fundamental that it underlies all others. This is the evolutionary factor, which arises from the circumstance that the plant world of to-day has gradually developed from pre-existing forms of plants by those manifold processes which are called "organic evolution". The basic characteristic of nature as a whole is that its history has been one of slow evolution over an immense period of time, and a proper understanding of the effects and implications of this is so essential for the consideration of any biological problem that the matter was referred to as early as Chapter 3, even before the facts of plant geography had been cited. It is necessary here, therefore, only to emphasise once again the degree to which the evolutionary factor is, as it were, a master-factor, determining in one way or another the operations and results of all those others that have now to be reviewed. Evolutionary factors may be regarded as inherent or predisposing factors. The more direct factors next to be discussed may be regarded more as potentials or as variables which may or may not influence plant distribution. They represent variable conditions under which plants live and which may become decisive in determining the range of species.

The ordinary flowering plant lives its whole independent life with its roots in the soil and with its remaining parts exposed to the atmosphere, and that it is incapable of movement during this long phase of its existence must always be remembered as one of the main factors in phytogeography and one of the chief ways in which it differs from zoogeography. In fact this immobility is far more fundamental than is usually admitted, and indeed ranks next to those inherent evolutionary factors just mentioned. The reason is clear. Whatever our views may be about the actual origin of new species, such forms when they first arise must occupy an extremely limited area, perhaps no more than the space covered by a single individual, and their attainment of any appreciable range must be a matter of the actual movement of individual plants. This being so, the likelihood of any range being attained depends upon the ability of the plant to move at some stage or another in its life history. The question of the average ability of plants to move will be discussed more appropriately later. Here we are concerned only with the axiomatic statement that if the individuals of a species have no mobile phase, the species itself cannot attain a range, no matter how favourable other factors may be. There are not likely to be many plants without the power of mobility, for the reason that such a disability will function very much as a lethal factor, and we may therefore assume that all plants which do attain an appreciable range possess at some stage in their lives some degree of mobility. What that degree may be will be seen later.

Plants are normally in contact with their environment in two rather distinct directions. Their aerial parts are in contact with the free atmosphere and their terrestrial parts are in contact with the soil, but the latter is really a complex, since it comprises not only the solid constituent of the soil, but both the water and air in the soil. Even this is a simplification of the position, though it is sufficient for immediate purposes. The conditions of the atmosphere and of the soil vary greatly from place to place and are indeed rarely constant over any considerable area, so that climatic as well as soil conditions are variables obviously likely to affect the distribution of plants in ordinary circumstances. Naturally if all plants were capable of existing under all known conditions, then the effect of these conditions as factors in distribution could at least be no more than secondary, but as far as is known no plants are capable of such existence, and hence these variables are normally direct factors of distribution.

The complex of atmospheric conditions which is usually called climate is generally classified with regard to plant distribution into four components. Most fundamental among them is heat, that is to say the temperature of the air, because it is a direct function of the shape of the earth and its position with regard to the sun. Its actual value from place to place is controlled by various secondary considerations, but these, which will be referred to in due course, have seldom more than a local influence. Next in importance to temperature comes moisture, most familiar in the form of precipitation or rainfall, but expressed also in the form of humidity, dew and snow. The distribution of moisture values differs essentially from that of temperature, in that it is local rather than general and depends upon local combinations of circumstances rather than upon world-wide conditions. That is to say, moisture conditions are not necessarily bound up with heat but tend to vary widely at all temperatures. Besides these two primary climatic variables there are at least two others which are important secondarily. These are light and wind, and they are to be regarded as secondary because they exert their influence by modifying the two primary variables of temperature and precipitation. This relation is clearly seen in the close correlation between light and heat, both being directly due to the influence of the sun. Similarly there is the relation between heat and humidity of the air, which in turn controls the likelihood of precipitation. Finally, both temperature and precipitation are controlled to some extent by wind or air-movement, since this influences both the accumulation of temperature and the accumulation of humidity. Actually light is probably the least important component in relation to the *distribution* of plants, since, except in the highest latitudes, its mean value and duration seem sufficiently great to preclude it from acting as a limiting factor in plant life. Locally, however, and especially when itself controlled by still more minor conditions, it may be of some importance. The potentiality of wind as a factor in distribution lies chiefly in the manner in which it may modify other climatic values, and its effects upon temperature and precipitation have already been mentioned. Besides these, however, it may have a more direct influence by facilitating or impeding the proper functioning of the plant at certain particular phases of its life history, or by militating against the attainment of normal growth-form.

In contrast to climatic factors, the variables influencing the plant either potentially or actually through its physical contact with the soil in which it grows are usually described as edaphic factors, and here again there is considerable complexity and interrelationship—so much so that it is not easy to arrange these edaphic factors in any very definite order of importance, and the sequence in which they are mentioned here does not imply any such relative value. Generally speaking, edaphic factors are regarded as comprising three components—the physical nature of the soil, the chemical nature of the soil, and the topographic or physiographic character of the habitat. The first two may be regarded as absolute features, but the third is chiefly of importance as a modifying influence, conditioning not only the first two but also at least some of the climatic factors mentioned previously. Almost all physiographic conditions may affect a locality as a potential plant habitat, but in the main the two important considerations are altitude and exposure. The effect of altitude has already been dealt with fairly adequately in the chapter on world geography, and it is sufficient to remind readers here that it has a very important influence not only on temperature but also on precipitation, and in fact tends to influence these values in the same kind of way in which they are influenced by latitude. Exposure is important owing to the way in which it may intensify or diminish the influence of other factors. For example, the detailed relief of an area may profoundly influence the effect of climatic and edaphic factors upon the area according to the degree in which it provides shade or shelter. Slope is also important, since it may obviously influence the effect of precipitation or the effect of insolation. The prevalence of cloud also is often a matter of topography and may lead to a considerable modification of temperature values.

It is seen, therefore, that in so far as the life of the plant is passed in contact with the atmosphere and the soil, variations in the values of these surroundings must almost inevitably react upon the life of the plants exposed to them, and therefore that climatic and edaphic factors must always be among the chief factors in distribution. How far this is true and the general effect of it on the total picture of plant distribution will be seen later, but meanwhile the reader may be referred to a general discussion of the problem by Pearson (551).

We are justified in assuming for the purpose of studying plant geography that every species possesses some powers of extending its range in the sense of being able, when circumstances permit, to multiply the number of its individuals and thereby to cover a greater superficial area. Granted this, it follows that there must be for every species a maximum potential area of range representing that proportion of the world's surface which it may hope to cover in the course of time and by means of its powers of mobility. This conception is a very important one, because it clearly indicates the part which climatic and edaphic variability may play in determining this potential area. If we imagine a species to be entirely uninfluenced by climate or soil, it is obvious that it is potentially of cosmopolitan range as regards them. There may, of course, be other factors which will restrict its potential area, but they will not be climatic or edaphic. Thus the main rôle of these variables must be to determine the potential maximum area of a species. Suppose, for instance, that a species is unable to maintain itself in presence of frost, then clearly the potential range of that species consists only of those parts of the world where frost does not occur. Whether it will in time come to inhabit all such places depends on many other considerations, but its relationship to frost does lay down a range beyond which it cannot extend. Thus the rôle of what have been called the climatic and edaphic factors of distribution is primarily that of determining the potential areas of species, that is to say, how much of the world's surface each species may come to occupy in the course of time if its spread is unopposed. At any rate this is the most convenient way in which to regard these factors and to fit them into the general scheme of plant geography. The convenience lies in the fact that it points the way towards a useful understanding of other factors which also play a part in determining the distribution of plants, and which in terms of what has been said clearly do so by influencing the ability of plants to attain their potential areas as determined by their relation to climatic and edaphic factors.

Since the attainment of range can only be brought about by the mobility of individuals, it follows that no range at all will be achieved if the individual is completely immobile, and mobility must therefore clearly be the primary factor, at any rate in the facility with which a species will attain its maximum range. As a broad generalisation it may be said that no flowering plants are capable either of transporting themselves from place to place or of being so transported during their active vegetative life, because their physiology necessitates a permanent association with the substratum in which they grow. The only exceptions are certain plants in which this does not prevail, or rather where it is of a very special character, as, for instance, among small free-floating aquatic plants. Except for these, flowering plants may be regarded as completely immobile during their active vegetative phases.

How then is their movement accomplished? The answer is that in all normal circumstances the reproductive processes of the Flowering Plants incorporate a phase during which the offspring of one generation can survive separation from their parents and during which their physical attachment to their habitat is severed. This is the seed phase, during which the dissemination or scattering of offspring from the point occupied by the parent occurs. In some plants the production of seed is replaced by the production of such small vegetative parts as bulbils, but these possess the essential feature of seeds, the ability to pass through a dormant period during which they are capable of being spread over the surface of the ground. This process of "dispersal", as it is more shortly termed, is thus of supreme importance in the distribution of plants and must rank as one of the fundamental factors (522, 595). It is appropriate therefore that we have already found place for it as a general process, but here we are considering more particularly its relative value in assisting species to attain their maximum distribution, and thus it is really to be regarded as a factor of distribution in two rather different senses. In the one sense it is quite fundamental, since without it no extension of range can take place; in the other sense its relative value as between different plants is also of great importance and must be regarded as one of the main factors in determining how easily and rapidly extensions of range may take place.

The actual means by which plants achieve adequate dispersal will be surveyed later, but mention of the process in general is essential here because it bears directly upon the importance of the next factor to be considered. This may, for the sake of a brief title, be called the factor of "barriers". If dispersal is the only means by which range can be attained, much obviously depends upon the facilities with which such dispersal can operate, and there are likely to be factors which will react either beneficially or harmfully on the process. We need not concern ourselves with the former, because they can only intensify existent powers of dispersal, and we may therefore confine ourselves to recognising what causes are likely to result in an opposite effect. In other words, what are likely to be the obstacles to effective dispersal?

First it is necessary to try to gain some impression of what is meant by the phrase, which has just been used, "adequate dispersal". It is a well-known fact that species differ very much among themselves in the degree to which their seeds and fruits possess characters calculated to facilitate dispersal. We must, of course, be cautious in approaching this subject, because at best we have only a human estimate of these characters, but it is usual to regard certain structural features in seeds or fruits as providing their possessors with what are called "dispersal mechanisms", which increase their dispersal potentialities. There is no doubt that some seeds and fruits possess features which habitually cause them to be dispersed over greater distances than others, and it is tempting to assume that these plants have an absolute superiority in the matter of dispersal, but this view is based upon a quite unwarranted assumption and its truth is not borne out by observation in the field. The false assumption is that wide dispersal is in a biological sense superior to, or more valuable than, narrow dispersal. It cannot, of course, be denied that there may be occasions in which wide dispersal may be of enormous importance, and examples of this will be mentioned later, but to assume it is certainly unjustifiable. Indeed, there is one consideration which is strong presumptive evidence to the contrary. This is the fact that wide dispersal must have a general tendency, not present with restricted dispersal, to carry the disseminules or diaspores (to use convenient terms comprehending seeds, fruits or vegetative parts) into regions where the conditions of climate and habitat will probably be very unlike those from which the parent plant came. In other words, wide dispersal will take the disseminule further but it is very likely to increase the chances against its survival and establishment when it arrives at its destination. A particular aspect of this wide dispersal is that it is likely to result in the establishment of solitary individual plants far from others of their kind, in which case the future will much depend on whether these individuals are bisexual and self-fertile or not. Baker (39) has discussed this, and Taylor (721) refers to the interesting case of *Coprosma pumila*, which is dioecious in New Zealand and monoecious on Macquarie Island. This "useless" dispersal, at it may be called, is discussed by Guppy (325) and similar comments have been made by Setchell (633).

As to the value of specialised dispersal mechanisms, it need only be said here, and it can be said quite categorically, that there is no real evidence that species possessing such mechanisms are more widely distributed, that is to say, have more extended ranges, than those without such advantages, and there is nothing to show that exceptional dispersal methods result, in general, in exceptional ranges.

Confusion of thought on this point seems to arise from a mistaken conception of the purpose of dispersal. It is perfectly true that dispersal leads to the attainment of range and is in fact the only means towards that end, but it by no means follows that this is necessarily its only purpose, and, indeed, from a biological view it is

PLATE 21

Map of the World showing, in degrees Fahrenheit, the range of extreme temperature variation during the year.

After Bartholomew's *Physical Atlas*, vol. III.

Areas correct   Distortion increasing towards border of map.

Approximate Scale 1:100,000,000 (1600 miles=1inch) along Equator

on Mollweide's Homolographic Projection

Copyright

difficult to imagine that this can be so. Its primary purpose must surely be something more intimately connected with the successful maintenance and survival of the individual plant which in due course will reproduce, and it is not difficult to see what this may be. The immobility of a flowering plant means amongst other things that its offspring will, unless subjected to some degree of dispersal, fall to the ground more or less vertically from their points of origin and will thus come to lie in the shadow of the parent. In some cases, and especially with some types of growth-form, they may not even reach the ground but will be intercepted by the lower parts of the parent. Such hazards are least apparent in ephemeral annuals where the whole parent tends to disappear almost as soon as the ripe seeds are borne, but these plants are by no means conspicuous in range or abundance of individuals, and do not alter the view that in most plants this problem of what may be somewhat picturesquely called "botanical overlaying" is a very real one. May it not, therefore, be that the primary object of dispersal is not to spread the species in the sense of appreciably extending its range but to give the disseminules the best chance of survival by scattering them outside the immediate shadow of the parent? Whether this is so or not, it is certain that we must regard many of the most widely distributed of flowering plants as having attained their ranges in the course of repeated but comparatively restricted dispersal.

This view leads to what is certainly an important consideration in the total efficacy of dispersal, namely the frequency with which it is repeated. Of two plants with similar dispersal potentialities the one with the greater frequency of reproduction will obviously, other things remaining equal, attain a given range more rapidly than the other. That is to say, the shorter the generation in the species the more frequent will be dispersal and the greater the total area covered in a given time. Contrast, for instance, a plant of chickweed with an oak. There is no need to attempt to estimate their relative powers of dispersal, but it is perfectly certain that the oak will have to be dispersed a very long way at its first reproduction to make up for the large number of generations of chickweed which have passed while the oak was attaining its reproductive condition. At first sight it may be supposed that in cases of this sort, involving large perennial plants, when once the reproductive age is attained the annual or more frequent production of seed will remove much of the disparity. This is, of course, not so, because in such perennials the seed is produced each time at the same spot and dispersal is not accumulative. It will in fact not be appreciably increased until the offspring of the original tree have themselves reached a reproductive stage. A further aspect of the frequency of reproduction is the general one that the more often an event is repeated the more likely becomes any rare eventuality, such as unusual degree or means of dispersal.

Another very significant consideration in dispersal is the length of time that the disseminules remain viable and capable of germination, because it is obvious that the longer a seed remains alive the more time will the various dispersal factors have in which to make their influence felt, and the greater therefore will be the likelihood of wide dissemination. Viability, especially in relation to seeds, is a large subject, and readers who desire further information about it may refer to a summary in which most of the relevant information is considered in one fairly short article (162) and to the recent treatment by Barton (49), but it is worth while noting that the life of many seeds is considerably shorter than is generally supposed, and that the oft-reported germination of seeds from ancient tombs and similar situations has never been substantiated.

We must now return to the question of "barrier" factors, but our digression has not been without value, because it will help us to estimate what may or may not

22

constitute a barrier to dispersal. It will be remembered that we were concerned to discover what might be meant by "adequate dispersal", and it will now be seen that there is good reason to regard it as anything which scatters the disseminules so effectively that they can begin their germination unhampered by the presence of the parent. How does this affect our conception of barriers?

By a barrier (using the term in its phytogeographical sense) is clearly meant something which cannot be surmounted by the only process of movement open to plants, namely dispersal, and it is possible to imagine one or two very different kinds of such barriers. For instance, it is conceivable that purely local conditions might be such that the ordinary methods of dispersal would be unable to operate, as might easily happen to an individual in such a position that its disseminules are actually and physically prevented from scattering sufficiently to allow them to germinate. Here the normal dispersal of the individual is interfered with.

Much commoner and indeed the usually accepted type of barrier is one which, rather than interfering with dispersal, simply tends to make it nugatory. In short, "barriers to dispersal" are considered in a general sense as comprising areas of such a kind and extent as cannot be crossed by the spreading species in the ordinary processes of its dispersal. Two components are obviously involved, the one being the nature of the area and the other its size. Potential barriers of this kind are therefore provided by any areas where conditions are so unsuitable for a particular species that its disseminules, when scattered into the area, cannot germinate. This is a general statement, but clearly the actual barrier value of any area to any given species must depend upon the dispersal potentialities of that species.

This leads to what is perhaps the most important general conception with regard to barriers, that they are seldom to be regarded as complete barriers to the dispersal of every plant. It is true that the very largest areas will tend to be so, but even here one has to reckon with the possibility of accidental dispersal across them, and in usual terms barriers should be recognised as likely to be of very varied significance according to the different plants in whose paths they lie.

In the present circumstances of world geography potential barriers may be either land surfaces or water surfaces. These differ rather fundamentally in relation to the Flowering Plants, in that the nature of the obstacle presented by the former will tend to depend upon a variety of circumstances, while the latter will tend to be absolute obstacles in almost all circumstances except in the case of accidental circumvention.

Hence the distribution of land and sea in general must also be regarded as one of the important factors of distribution. As regards land barriers, these may be of very varied nature according to the plants associated with them, and, what is most important, they tend to have a marked segregating effect. Many areas, for instance, may act as barriers to the dispersal of some species while permitting the dispersal of others, while some barriers will be complete obstacles to most if not all species. It is therefore almost impossible to generalise about them, and each must be considered as a law unto itself. It can, however, be said that the more homogeneous an area the smaller or fewer the barriers it will present, while the more heterogeneous it is the more complete and numerous the barriers it will contain. For example, if two regions with very different climatic or edaphic values adjoin one another, it is probable that each will be a serious barrier to species belonging to the other, because neither is likely to provide the conditions required by species from the other. On the other hand, where the passage of environmental conditions is gradual, so much the less complete are the barriers likely to be. Again, areas in which conditions are extreme in whatever sense are likely to be more serious barriers than areas where the conditions are of more medium values. This is why mountain ranges and deserts are among the most obvious barriers to dispersal. But these are only extreme cases, and it is to be remembered that any area is a potential barrier to the disseminules of species inhabiting places where the conditions are appreciably different.

Nor must it be forgotten that though one geographical arrangement may place barriers in the way of dispersal, a different arrangement of external conditions may facilitate dispersal. This is a very important consideration, because the latter effect is likely to be a focusing of plant movement along certain lines, and there will develop what may be regarded as lines of least resistance along which extensions of range will be especially easy. This point can be nicely illustrated with reference to mountain ranges. A mountain system running athwart the direction of dispersal of a species is likely to provide a very serious obstacle to its further spread, because the conditions at the higher levels will tend to be very different from those on the plains below, but mountain ranges or systems lying in the direction of dispersal are likely to be valuable stepping stones or pathways, because conditions will tend to maintain themselves throughout the length of the mountains, and even if this is not so, the flanks of mountains usually exhibit so wide a range of conditions in a comparatively confined space that they are almost certain to provide some niches or footholds by which dispersal can be continued. The most striking instance of this is afforded by the Rockies and Andes of western America but there are lesser examples in many parts of the world.

The question of water barriers, although of even greater absolute importance than that of land barriers, is simpler for two reasons. Except for a few comparatively unimportant exceptions water barriers to dispersal are sea barriers. Large areas of fresh water are nowhere in the world to-day very conspicuous, and none is so situated as to present a barrier of first-class importance. Moreover, the Flowering Plants are, except for the small number that inhabit tidal waters, all land or fresh-water plants to which any considerable width of sea water is almost inevitably a complete obstacle. Certainly there are quite a number of species whose disseminules can withstand prolonged immersion in salt water and which are therefore liable to be transported widely by sea currents, but these are mostly highly specialised strand plants occurring only in the immediate vicinity of the sea shore and do not bulk largely in the constitution of inland vegetation. As a matter of fact these plants afford an indirect but none the less interesting confirmation of the views on the significance of wide dispersal given above. In their case dispersal by currents is effective not in virtue of the wide distances which may be covered but because the correlation of these plants' requirements with the conditions on sea beaches enables them to germinate and establish themselves successfully there after they have been so dispersed. On the contrary, inland plants are not likely to benefit by current dispersal, first because their disseminules are not likely to reach the sea, and secondly because even if they do so they will not be carried to spots where they can germinate.

Opinions vary considerably as to the extent to which areas of open sea constitute barriers to the dispersal of species living in ordinary inland situations. It may be greatly influenced by the structure of the disseminules themselves, and it is particularly in this circumstance that many so-called "dispersal mechanisms" may possess real and absolute values. With regard to this problem generally, the case of the island of Krakatau is of much interest and importance, as affording at least a small amount of definite fact. It lies 40 miles west of Java in the Malayan Archipelago, and in 1883 was the scene of a devastating volcanic eruption, as a result of which two-thirds of it was destroyed, the part which remained being generally supposed to have been completely sterilised of living things by lava and ashes. In 1886 visiting botanists found on the island 15 species of Angiosperms, most of them strand plants; by 1933 there were 271 species, and Docters van Leeuwen (193) expresses the opinion that, of these, 40 per cent owed their origin to dispersal by wind, some 30 per cent to dispersal by ocean currents, and 25 per cent to carriage by animals; only a handful were the result of man's introduction. This work of Docters van Leeuwen is of special interest because it seems to dispose finally of the suggestion (38) that part of the vegetation existing before the eruption survived it. On the contrary, it seems reasonably certain that the present vegetation is entirely new, and hence that in the last 80 years more than 250 species have succeeded in crossing at least 40 miles of sea by the ordinary methods of dispersal, and that the island has been restocked with vegetation by this means in a comparatively short time. It is dangerous to argue from the particular to the general, but it seems safe to conclude on this evidence that sea distances of the dimensions noted do not in fact present any considerable obstacle to dispersal. Cailleux (101) also gives a good account of Krakatau in which he makes the point that of the 115 vascular plants recorded thence between 1886 and 1908, 57 had disappeared by 1928 because the vegetation was building up towards forest, a state which, already well-formed in 1921, was exuberant by 1934. It is of interest to note here that Erlanson's account (225) of the colonisation of two new islands in Cochin harbour, India, shows a parallel with the earlier stages of colonisation on Krakatau.

It was pointed out in introducing this discussion on the factors of distribution that these result from and depend upon the fundamental consideration of the development of the organic world by the processes of evolution, and this led to the recognition that time itself must be one of the most basic factors. In that reference to age we were concerned only with its possibilities as determining the actual size of the range of species and other units, and it was regarded chiefly from the point of view of the concepts embodied in the Theory of Age and Area, but age, or rather the passage of time, has another most important bearing on plant distribution in that it affects the operation of other factors. It may be expressed as a general assumption that the *status quo* in nature is never maintained for very long, and indeed the whole developmental conception of the cosmos incorporates the fundamental idea of constant if slow change. What the direction of that change may be does not concern us, but the fact of change itself does so intimately. In relation to our immediate subject it means that factors of distribution must be regarded not as something static and unchangeable, but as something subject to the same influences of time as other aspects of nature. Hence any particular factor must be looked upon not only from the point of view of the present but also of the past, and particularly there must be taken into account changes which the passage of time may have brought about in it, while for each of the factors already mentioned there must be added a subsidiary or supplementary factor incorporating the possibility of changes in the operation of the factor at or since an earlier time. This influence of the past is not of equal importance with regard to all factors. Dispersal, for instance, or rather facility for dispersal, is a character of the species more often than not associated with morphological features and is not subject to change by the mere passage of time unaccompanied by evolutionary change in the organism. The morphology may in time so change as to influence the dispersal potential, but this will be presumably accompanied by such a change of shape and structures as may constitute the characteristics of a new species, in which case it begins to establish a distribution of its own. Again we need not concern ourselves especially with changes in edaphic conditions in the past, because these changes are almost exclusively the result of the operation of other factors. Thus changes in climate and changes in topography will usually be the cause of changes in habitat, although there are doubtless many other minor factors on which the nature of the substratum will depend, but there is no particular sequence or series of edaphic changes which is the result of the secular passage of time alone except, perhaps, those resulting from gradual denudation.

There remain the two main factors of climate and barriers, and in both of these the time conception is of such importance that we must regard changes of climate and changes of geography in the past as among the leading factors of distribution. Changes of climate mean alterations in the distribution of climatic values over the surface of the world. In so far, then, as the potential area of species is determined by climatic considerations it will change in response to any change in climate distribution. To put the matter rather differently, if there is accepted the view that the distribution of climate has changed in the past, then there must also be accepted the view that potential areas of distribution have also changed to a greater or lesser extent and therefore that such climatic changes must be a factor in the present distribution of plants. The possible importance and significance of geographical changes in the past in relation to plant distribution are even more clearly demonstrated. These geographical changes may be visualised as affecting two geographical features (the outline of land and sea and the distribution of relief), which may be described as geographic and orographic. But these features of geography are, as has been seen, the very features which produce barriers to dispersal, and so it is clear that changes in outline and relief in the past may effect plant distribution very considerably, at least in so far as they may accentuate or diminish the effects of barriers.

Still one factor remains to be discussed, and it is interesting to observe that, like the first one mentioned (the evolutionary factor), it is one which resides in the very nature of the plants themselves and is not directly a factor of the environment, although environmental features may condition its operation. This factor is the factor of competition, as it is usually called. The existence of a disparity between the potential number of individuals and the means for their support has long been a biological axiom and has given rise to the idea of a "struggle for existence". It was first demonstrated in scientific form by Malthus in his famous essay on human population (480), but the phrase is most familiar to-day in connection with the doctrine of "natural selection", which is the belief that, given such a disparity, there must be a struggle between individuals for the limited supplies, and that victory will go to those best equipped for the battle, a conclusion which is expressed by the further biological conception of the "survival of the fittest". Whether or not such a conception has any validity and whatever justification there may or may not be for the use of such anthropopathic terms as "competition" and "struggle", it is undeniable that in normal circumstances only a proportion of newly produced offspring survives. Hence there must always be, as a general concomitant of evolution, that particular process of elimination which, in the plant world at any rate is usually termed competition. The important point is to realise that in the circumstances this factor must, by whatever name it goes, be the final and decisive one.

It is easy to see the reason for this. The variation in climate over the world's surface is much less than the multiplicity of species which have to live within it, and the same is true of the range of edaphic conditions. It follows, therefore, that there is no possibility of species sorting themselves out geographically in such a way that each will occupy its own niche in space untroubled and unaffected by others. It is true that the degree to which the presence of others will be felt varies greatly according to the circumstances, but it may be accepted that most areas will be open to occupation by more than one species, and more often than not by a large number. The ultimate constitution of the vegetation must therefore depend upon what happens to the different potential constituents, and to what extent each is able to maintain itself against and among the others. If one cannot do so at all it will be absent from the area, and thus its total range must depend ultimately on the result of what we call for convenience competition. In no common circumstances can the absence of this be visualised, and hence it must be the ultimate factor in determining the detailed distribution of plants.

The operation of competition is best illustrated by the stages in the gradual colonisation by plants of an open and suitable piece of ground such as may be provided by a landslip, by an eruption, by rainwash or by the retreat of ice. Sooner or later the first colonists will make their appearance on the uninhabited area by dispersal from the surroundings, and at first at any rate the number of immigrants will be so small that each to which the habitat is suitable will germinate and grow without any interference from the rest except in so far as accident of position may cause it. Gradually numbers will accumulate until the space available is full and the plants are in actual contact, forming a complete covering. The vegetation is then said to pass from the open to the closed condition. This passage is an important one because it means that henceforth competition in some degree will be the prevailing condition. The mere process of dispersal into the area will not normally bear much relation to the suitability of the immigrants to the habitat, and hence competition is likely, in the earlier stages, to take the form of the gradual elimination of some species by those more suited to the conditions. At a somewhat later stage the competition will become more and more competition between relatively equally suitable species. Those plants whose claim to position is simply based on the act of dispersal will tend to give place to others more in harmony with the actual conditions, until there develops an association of species more or less characteristic for the habitat. Hereafter the competition will take the rather different form of a struggle between the individuals of a comparatively small number of species, and on the outcome of that will depend the relative abundance and frequency of the different species concerned.

Usually the competition between species as opposed to the competition between individuals of the same or of a few species will not entirely disappear, because with the development of the vegetation there will usually go minor changes in the habitat brought about by the effects of continued plant growth. For instance, decaying vegetable matter will accumulate from the generations which are gone and the soil will tend to become different in a variety of ways. For this reason there is generally a gradual development of the vegetation in the sense that new combinations of species grow up in addition to the competition between individuals of the same species. The whole process moves towards an equilibrium which will ultimately be established provided no serious disturbing factors such as climatic or other changes intervene. This equilibrium is reached when the association of species becomes such that the entry and establishment of fresh species from outside diminishes to vanishing point. Thereafter competition will become entirely a matter of struggle between the progeny of the individuals of the species which form the vegetation. This equilibrium vegetation is called the climax vegetation and represents the highest grade of vegetational development which is possible in the general conditions of the environment.

Where the climate is suitable the climax vegetation is usually some kind of forest, and the gradual stages by which it is attained can roughly be described as the replacement of small and herbaceous species by larger woody species, but there are many factors which modify the process and which induce certain degrees of equilibrium short of this condition.

Such is but a very bare account of what is in fact the whole of one very important aspect of the study of plant ecology. Its purpose is merely to show that competition is not one simple process but may take very different forms in varied circumstances. To summarise still more what has been said, the earlier stages of development and plant succession may be likened to the more active and chaotic stages of struggle from which there gradually emerges the victory of a comparatively small number of forms, which thereafter may be regarded as having attained a working degree of harmony between themselves. It is not supposed that when this is attained competition ceases. It is rather that competition comes to have the rather more limited objectives of maintaining the occupancy of species and of maintaining an appropriate balance between the different species. So long as any appreciable number of species are present there will tend to be some degree of competition between them, and apart from this the struggle between the individuals of any one species will always continue. The point to be remembered is that it is this competition that must be the ultimate deciding factor in determining the actual range and abundance of any particular species.

It is very natural that the human conception of competition tends to be of an active physical struggle between plants of various kinds and between the individuals of a species, but a moment's consideration will show that by its very nature the plant (and particularly the land plant) is debarred from such active means of expressing itself. It is, therefore, of some interest to try to picture the way in which competition between plants may actually occur.

Perhaps the most obvious form of competition and the nearest to an active struggle is that between individuals, often in the seedling stage, for room in which to develop. It is, for instance, especially in this connection of competition for space that we picture the "struggle for existence". Actually, of course, this form of competition is not restricted to seedlings and obtains between plants at all stages of growth, particularly perhaps at the stage of maturity, where the size and robustness of individuals must be of great importance. For instance, the growth-form of heather and other ericoids is such as to make difficult or impossible the presence of other plants where they grow and in such cases as these it is the physical contact or proximity of individuals which causes and controls the competition.

But, as Brenchley (86) and others have pointed out, space competition is not the only kind and indeed is not infrequently absent, as is the case for instance with the open vegetation such as is characteristic of desert regions. There may also be competition for other essentials in short supply, such as food in the soil, water, or light. Not only this but there is good reason to believe that competition may take a rather more active form in the way in which different species may react mutually upon one another. The many problems involved here have as yet received less attention than they deserve, but indications of the importance of this as a promising line of investigation are accumulating.

It is probably fair to say that no one studies the detailed distribution of species and individuals over a limited area without being impressed by the way in which there is association between certain forms and dissociation between others. The whole arrangement of vegetation into edaphic types is based upon the facts of such association, and the question almost inevitably arises whether there may not be some factor or factors which favour close association between certain plants and preclude it between others. That is to say whether there may not be certain factors inherent in certain plants which favour or inhibit the growth of others in close proximity. The actual edaphic requirements of plants must, of course, primarily control their presence in any particular spot, but as between two species with similar edaphic needs the ultimate competition between them may sometimes perhaps be determined by factors inherent in the plants themselves.

Many years ago Pickering (559) called attention to the effect of grass on fruit trees, and Fletcher (243) also discussed the subject of toxic excreta in plants, and since then many other experiments (477, 478, 523) have shown more or less satisfactorily that if certain species are grown together or in close proximity they may sometimes have a very considerable effect on one another. Different pairs of species belonging to distinct genera or families have been grown together, and it has been reported that with different combinations the relative growth of the components varies greatly. The hemp, *Cannabis sativa*, if grown with spinach, *Spinacia oleracea*, does very badly while the spinach does very well. This is also the case, to a varying extent, when the spinach is replaced by *Secale cereale*, *Vicia sativa* or *Lepidium sativum*. On the contrary, the hemp does exceptionally well compared with its companion when the latter is *Beta vulgaris*, *Brassica oleracea*, *Lupinus luteus* or *Zea mays*. The same thing has been shown markedly in *Atropa bella-donna*. When this plant is grown with *Sinapis alba* its growth is far below normal, but if grown with *Artemisia vulgaris*, or particularly with *Galega officinalis*, its growth is appreciably above the normal. Again, when *Vitis vinifera* and *Euphorbia cyparissias* are grown together in the same pots, the former's growth, and especially its fructification, is much lessened. Another very interesting instance is that of the relation between the rye (*Secale cereale*) and *Viola tricolor*. Only in the presence of rye is it possible to obtain anything approaching a 100 per cent germination of the *Viola*, and this is particularly significant because these two species may occur together naturally in the relation of crop and weed. Several contributions to this subject have also appeared in a recent volume devoted to the biology of weeds (340), notably those of Grummer and Beyer on the influence of species of *Camelina* on flax, and a more general study of the mutual influences of weeds and crops by Martin and Rademacher. There have also been reports lately of the use of *Tagetes minima* as a weed controller by planting it among the root-systems of weeds that have been mown down. Similar observations have been made by Funke (259, 260) with different species and by Varma (747). Shull (648) has commented, from a rather different point of view, on a somewhat similar association of species and Osvald (549) has shown that an aqueous extract of the roots of *Agropyron repens* may have different effects on the germination of rape and oats according to its concentration, and that the substance concerned is probably an acid belonging to the phytohormones or hormone derivatives.

As just indicated the suggested explanation of these facts is that many plants produce some sort of chemical emanation or secretion which is inimical to the development of certain other plants. These secretions are visualised as of three kinds, namely gaseous emanations from the aerial parts of the plant, as is well known in *Dictamnus*, and perhaps also in *Rhus toxicodendron*; liquid or solid secretions from the leaves which tend to be washed down into the soil by rain (26); and secretions direct into the soil from the roots. It is the last which is presumably concerned in the cases mentioned above.

That at least something of the kind occurs is indicated by quite other observations, such as the intolerance of some plants to the presence of certain Crucifers, and especially the mustards. Here there seems little doubt that some biochemical substance characteristic of these plants has some sort of toxic reaction towards other plants. Apart from the direct toxic effect of such secretions they may have a marked effect in determining the value of the habitat. It is well established, for instance, that acid or alkaline root secretions may seriously alter the hydrogen ion concentration of the soil water. Still another observation bearing on the same point is that of the liberation into the soil of ethylene from organic sources (414).

However these results may be modified (and it is only fair to say that some of them are inconclusive) and their interpretations altered by further research, it seems reasonably clear at present that competition is to be regarded as something more complex than has been generally supposed in the past. Probably actual physical factors are the chief considerations involved and must almost of necessity be so normally, but there are at least indications that other factors and particularly chemical factors may play an important part. It is also important to remember that the issue of competition may be decided at various stages in the life of the individual. For instance, the danger of overcrowding to species of large plants is usually marked only in the early and seedling stages, and once these have been passed the danger is generally over. Similarly the copious growth of ephemeral annuals may produce a temporary condition of danger which will pass in the course of a few weeks.

This rather lengthy discussion of competition may perhaps leave the reader with the impression that the relations between plants are naturally and always relations of antagonism. They may naturally be so but they are not always. One type of plant life may in fact provide the essential conditions necessary for the presence of another type or species, as is seen, for example, in plants which require to live in the shade of others as in woods or hedges, and in lianes and epiphytes. The continued growth of one species may also actually affect the substratum in such a way that it becomes colonisable by other species, as for instance in plants which inhabit the deep leaf-mould found in long-established beech woods. Sometimes the relationship is even closer, and this is particularly the case with parasitic or epiphytic plants whose ranges are determined by those of their hosts. Often-quoted extreme examples of this are certain species of *Utricularia* which live exclusively in the water which accumulates at the base of the leaves of certain tropical American Bromeliaceae, and whose range is thus always correlated with that of the species they inhabit.

The conclusion therefore is that competition is itself but one aspect of a wider and more generalised factor of distribution, which is the influence of one kind of vegetation (or by analogy one kind of life, whether animal or plant) on the distribution of other plants. This general influence is often called the biotic factor, and at least in its aspect of competition must be regarded as of great importance.

This somewhat informal approach to the subject of the factors responsible for distribution has been made quite deliberately, in order to emphasise that these factors are only those that might be expected in the circumstances of the nature, life and history of the Flowering Plants. In order to arrive at what these factors are there is no necessity to possess any very profound botanical knowledge, because they will, to a large extent, become apparent in the course of such a discussion as has just been completed. It has, however, been rather lengthy, and we must now summarise the conclusions we have reached and go on to see how they compare with the conclusions reached on this matter by others.

In making this summary it is convenient to arrange the factors more in accordance with their mutual relations than was done above, where the main consideration was a cursive presentation of them. When this is done, what has already been said may be restated in the form of the following table of factors concerned in the distribution of plants:

1. Place and time of origin.
2. Distribution of climatic values (temperature, rainfall, light, wind):
    a. In the present.
    b. In the past.
3. Distribution of edaphic values (physical, chemical, physiographic):
    a. In the present.
    b. In the past.
4. Potentialities for dispersal.
5. Configuration of land and sea:
    a. In the present.
    b. In the past.
6. Influences exerted by other plants:
    a. Direct competition.
    b. Indirect influences.
7. Human influences (not considered in detail).

These conclusions accord well with those of others. Hayek, for instance (345), recognises:

1. Climatic factors:
    i.e. light, temperature, atmospheric pressure, precipitation and wind.
2. Economic factors:
    i.e. soil.
3. Biotic factors:
    i.e. influence of the animal world, influence of man.

Thomson, J. A. (518), comprehending the distribution of both plants and animals, arranges the factors in three pairs thus:

a. The physical peculiarities of the region under discussion, and the constitutional peculiarities of the living creatures.
b. The original headquarters of the stock (usually uncertain), and the means of dispersal in each case.
c. The physical changes of climate, earth-movements, etc., in the region, and the changes brought about in the struggle for existence between the various living tenants of the country.

Both these authorities point out that there are also many minor additional factors, and also that those mentioned interact so as to produce a very complex state of affairs.

Du Rietz (203) gives a rather more elaborate classification, especially in regard to biotic factors, which is of interest as incorporating the essential factor of time, not mentioned in the above two schemes, namely:

A. Actual factors—
    I. Abiotic:
        a. Climatic.
        b. Edaphic.

II. Biotic:
       a. Non-antropeic—not influenced by man—
           1. Phytobiotic:
               a. Climatic—such as shadow, wind, shelter, etc.
               b. Edaphic—such as humus, soil, humidity, etc.
               c. Pyric—effects of fire.
           2. Zoobiotic—presence of excreta, carcases, etc.
       b. Antropeic—due to man's influence—
           1. Direct.
           2. Indirect.
   B. Historical factors (with all the same groups as "actual").

He also gives a classification in which he sets out the factors influencing "the distribution of species upon a certain spot during a certain period". They are six in number, namely:

1. Nature of habitat at beginning of period.
2. Distribution of species upon or near the spot at the beginning of the time factor.
3. Supply of dispersal units.
4. Strength of each species in competition.
5. Interference of animals, man and plant parasites.
6. Time elapsed.

Here there is recognised as a separate edaphic factor an effect which has not previously been specifically mentioned, namely fire. Fire may often be due to human action, but in certain parts of the world it is a normal occurrence at certain seasons, and in response to it certain peculiar features of the vegetation in these regions have been developed. The subject will be dealt with more fully later.

These specimen classifications of factors show two things—that the differences between them are mainly due to difference of opinion as to what may justifiably be termed a factor, and that the arrangement arrived at above incorporates, within the limits of its detail, all the relative types of factors. It does not, however, mention all the aspects of these factors, and we must therefore pass on now to the more particular consideration of those factors which have most bearing on those theoretical aspects of plant geography which are the subjects of the two final chapters, namely climatic factors, edaphic factors, dispersal, changes of climate and geographical changes.

Before doing this, however, there is one more subject to be mentioned. This is the migration of species or of floras, and it is rather a consequence of the interaction of the factors outlined above than a factor itself.

It cannot be doubted that if the factors which have been described have all played a part in controlling plant distribution—and it is the purpose of the next few chapters to demonstrate this—plant distribution must be regarded as something in more or less constant flux and rarely if ever constant for more than a short period. The fluctuation may be visualised as of two kinds, first in respect of the floristic constitution of any flora, and secondly in respect of the position of various floras. That the latter and more important type of change has taken place is demonstrated wherever there is evidence that a particular area has been occupied at successive periods by different assemblages of plants. Unless it can be assumed that each successive flora developed *in situ*, it must be believed that the later ones in turn displaced those that went before, and such an assumption being out of the question, if on no further grounds than those of time, this belief is justified. Again, if an earlier flora is found at a later date in a different position and contemporary with the flora which replaced it in its original site, we may assume that very extensive movements of floras over the surface of the world must have occurred. The evidence of migration is thus chiefly palaeobotanical, and it is very copious and unmistakable. There are repeated examples of superposed floras of different types, as well as of similar floras changing position with the passage of time.

We need not go beyond the bounds of Great Britain to demonstrate this and to see how even one small country has been the home of a succession of floras one after the other. Almost every major geological horizon has revealed a different type and constitution of native flora.

Particularly is migration revealed in the special geological matter of glaciation, and we need only remind readers of the later history of the British flora and particularly of the changes which have taken place between the earlier Pliocene and the present day. At the former time the flora was much as we know it now, but in the interim much of it was undoubtedly forced out of the country, to return once more at a later stage. In North America the degree and extent of the floral movement were almost certainly even greater, as is illustrated by Core's account (150) of the successive migrations and movements of the flora in the Appalachian region which have left it as it is to-day.

In this particular instance of the effect of glaciation it is fairly certain that the result of the climatic change was to telescope up the floristic and climatic zones rather than to eliminate the higher values, and the lowlands of the equator do not seem to have been appreciably colder than they are now. At the same time the spread of the ice must have diminished the total area open to plant growth very considerably. In these circumstances it is impossible to deny the probability not only of floral migration but also of increased floral mixing, and so these same geological evidences afford examples of the first kind of fluctuation mentioned above, that of the constitution of different floras.

But this kind of migration, the movement by which independently originating floras become mixed so as to consist of or show elements derived from various directions, is shown even better and more generally in the present world flora. Perhaps nowhere in the world to-day can it be said that the flora consists entirely of plants which have originated locally. Almost always the flora contains some proportion of foreign ingredients. Clearly there must be some kind of differential movements of floras to produce this effect—there must be an infiltration of forms from the frontiers or from distant lands, and where, as in many cases, this infiltration seems to have taken place from many directions, its effect is even more striking.

The same thing is seen in the difficulty which exists in defining certain floristic areas or regions, and a brief reference back to Chapter 2 is sufficient to show how real this sometimes is. The difficulty arises simply because particular parts of the world's surface have become focal points at which streams of migration or infiltration from various directions meet. One of the most important of these is in eastern Malaysia, where there is a conspicuous mixture of Asiatic and Australasian floras, and the problem of just where the line of demarcation between the two is to be drawn has puzzled many investigators. The fact of the matter is that in passing from Asia eastwards the change in floral constitution as between Asiatic and Australasian plants is, until the Torres Strait is reached, so gradual and the mixing so complex that it can hardly be sorted out. Similarly, but on a lesser scale, the more southerly parts of the East African coastal belt are a notorious transition region where the northern parts of the South African flora and the southern parts of the tropical flora have met and mingled (68). The flora of the high alpine region at the junction of Tibet, China,

Burma and India is another very marked instance, and the flora of this general region contains elements of the flora of each of the neighbouring countries, a fact that is reflected in the degree to which the floras as a whole can be divided in geographical detail.

Migration and mingling of this kind is perhaps least seen in America (see Chap. 3), and the presumptive reason for this is interesting. When two moving societies begin to mix in the way that has been indicated it is only a matter of time before the mixing is complete, and the result is a homogeneous one with, as time goes on, an increasing character of its own. Hence where this mixing is most conspicuous and localised, as in the instances given above, it is reasonable to suppose that it has not been going on very long. This, of course, will depend on the length of the opportunity for such mixing. In America the indications are that there have been opportunities for the mingling of at least most of the floral elements of the continent for a very long time, and indeed that such prolonged mingling has been in progress. As a result it is far less in evidence than in the Old World.

In terms of the present world flora it is perhaps not too much to say that floristic mingling caused by this kind of migration is one of its most general features, but, whether this is a fair statement or not, the instances which have been mentioned in conjunction with the geological examples of wider migration are ample to show that actual movements of assemblies of plant species over the world in various directions have taken place as a more or less direct consequence of the distributional factors outlined above.

CHAPTER 17

THE FACTORS OF DISTRIBUTION—II. CLIMATIC FACTORS

CLIMATE may be described as the physical state of the atmosphere and may be regarded as the result of the sun's influence on the layer of gases that covers the surface of the earth. This total physical state of the atmosphere is composed of a number of different constituents which it is convenient to term the elements of climate. Of these temperature and moisture are the most important, but there are a number of others of secondary significance. Most of these do not call for any extensive treatment in this chapter and it will be sufficient for our immediate purpose if climate is regarded as consisting essentially of four aspects, temperature, precipitation, light and wind. It would be difficult to maintain that this is invariably their order of importance, but, as will be seen, it represents their general relation and it is convenient to deal with them accordingly.

The problem of the influence of climatic factors on plant geography has been discussed by many writers and it is not possible to refer here to all the important sources of information on the subject, but the reader will find much of interest in publications by Livingston and Shreve (462) and by Zotov (808), and a comprehensive source of further information in Schimper and Faber (620). For more general information on climate the reader may refer to Geiger (264) much of whose book is related to plant life, and to Kendrew (423).

Temperature

(Plates 20, 21)

It is believed that the interior heat of the earth, although considerable, contributes but negligibly to the heat of the atmosphere, which is derived almost entirely from the sun. At the same time it must be remembered that the heat of the atmosphere is not the only direction in which temperature affects plants, and that the heat of the soil, which is itself derived from the heat of the atmosphere, has also an important influence. For our present purposes, however, the latter may be regarded as generally proportional to and determined by the former.

The basic consideration determining the distribution of temperature on the earth is the shape of the globe, and its inclination to the direction of light and heat coming from the sun. In equatorial regions the incident rays from the sun not only reach the earth almost perpendicularly but thereby pass most directly through the atmosphere. Progressively away from the equatorial regions the curvature of the earth not only causes the incident rays to strike more and more obliquely but also causes them to pass less directly through the atmosphere, until at the poles they may be said to be almost parallel with the earth's surface.

For these reasons the basic distribution of temperature value is a latitudinal one showing a gradual and considerable diminution between the equator and the poles (see Plate 20). At the same time the obliquity of the ecliptic causes a seasonal variation in the gradients alternating in the two hemispheres, so that they are least steep in the summer and most steep in the winter. The latitudinal zonation of temperature must therefore be regarded as in a state of regular oscillation.

Since the two main factors of the position of the sun and the thickness of the atmosphere are to all intents and purposes constant, it might be expected that the latitudinal distribution of temperature would be perfectly regular and symmetrical on both sides of the equator. There is no reason to suppose that this would not indeed be the case were the surface of the earth exactly the same in all places—if, for instance, the surface were entirely land and that land were of constant height. As it is, neither of these states prevails. The distribution of land and sea is very complex and irregular, and in addition the relief of the land is extremely varied. Both these features influence temperature to a considerable extent. The general effect of large areas of sea is to tone it down and to reduce extremes, and it may also have a secondary effect through the influence of warm or cold currents. Elevation of the land has the general effect of reducing the normal latitudinal values of temperature. It may be expected, therefore, that the actual distribution of temperature will be a latitudinal one modified by these two considerations, and a glance at a temperature map of the world will show that this is indeed the case. As a result the world can be divided into a series of rather irregular latitudinal zones on the basis of temperature, as is, of course, perfectly familiar in such terms as "tropical", "temperate" and "arctic", the irregularity depending on the degree of variation in the distribution of land and sea and of altitude. In this distribution the equatorial values tend to remain more or less constant throughout the year, but elsewhere they oscillate between maxima and minima according to the season, the hemispheres alternating in this respect. These circumstances lead, on the land surfaces of the earth, to the occurrence of two rather distinct types of climate based chiefly on their temperature features. Away from the influence of the sea, that is to say towards the interior of the larger land masses, the climate is "continental" and characterised by comparative extremes of heat in summer and of cold in winter. On the edges of large land masses and on islands there is an "oceanic" climate characterised by more moderate variation and less extreme seasonal values.

The effect of altitude is much less generalised and more localised, in accordance with the irregular distribution of elevated regions. It is true that a great part of the world's land surface is raised considerably above mean sea level and that therefore the temperature values tend to be widely modified, but it is only in the regions of great elevation in the more temperate latitudes that the modification becomes strikingly apparent. Especially is it noteworthy in the huge plateau system stretching north from the Himalayas, and on a smaller scale in the areas occupied by the great mountain systems of western America, but it is seen to some extent in practically all the mountains of the world.

Ocean currents, by bringing either colder water into warmer seas, or *vice versa*, tend to effect the distribution of temperature wherever they occur except when their direction is parallel to the equator, but in fact there are only two regions of the world where the effect on a world-wide scale is marked. These are in the north Atlantic and north Pacific oceans, where the Florida and Gulf Streams and the Kuro Siwo current respectively cause the isotherms to deviate far to the north by the influence of the warm waters which they bring from the tropics.

The main features in the distribution of temperature are shown in Plates 20 and 21, but they may conveniently be summarised here. Annual isotherms, that is lines of equal mean annual temperature, are basically latitudinal, when reduced to sea-level values, but they are distorted northwards by warm currents in the northern hemisphere and southwards over the land masses of the southern tropics.

The average minimum temperature varies from $-76°$ F. in the north-east of Siberia to over $68°$ F. in Guiana and parts of Malaysia. It is below $-40°$ F. in much of northern Canada and Siberia. In Spitzbergen the mean summer temperature is little above freezing and the growing season lasts only about six weeks. In the north part of Ellesmere Land, where the figures are somewhat similar (385) the temperature hardly ever reaches 60° F., and there is very rarely a month without frost, circumstances which may make this area, in terms of accumulated temperature, one of the coldest parts of the world.

The average maximum temperature varies from below 68° F. in parts of North America and north Asia to over 113° F. in parts of the south-west U.S.A., in the African–Indian desert and in parts of Australia, and is above 104° F. over a considerably wider area.

The annual mean range of temperature varies from under 10° F. in most of the tropics to over 120° F. in part of Siberia.

The annual extreme range of temperature varies from about 20° F. in parts of the tropics to 170° F. in parts of north-east Siberia.

Constancy of temperature throughout the year is very important in plant distribution and is perhaps to be regarded as the essential character of climate in the tropics.

A last general point about the distribution of temperature, and indeed of other factors too, is to remind readers once more that the northern hemisphere is a land hemisphere and the southern a water hemisphere, so that great caution must be used in comparing conditions and values in the two.

The correlation between plant distribution and climate is shown more clearly in the case of temperature than anywhere else (e.g. 432), and indeed is so obvious that it scarcely needs demonstrating, as our common application of such words as "tropical", "temperate", "hardy", "tender", to plants shows. It is here, however, important to draw the proper distinction between flora and vegetation, because it is especially in the limitation of the range of species and other units that temperature is important. It has already been seen how few plants are anything like cosmopolitan in range, and what a marked distinction there is between tropical and temperate forms. Indeed, it is fairly true to say that the reason why there are not more completely distributed plants is that most wide species are ultimately limited by considerations of temperature.

This is to be seen almost everywhere. Our own flora affords many instances in which species occupy the more southerly part of the country but do not range far north. Similarly with the question of casuals: the factor which prevents them from establishing themselves is temperature—not, it will be noticed, temperature at all times, or they would clearly not occur at all in the country, but the temperature at some season of the year, that is to say at some stage in their development.

The way in which temperature acts as a limiting factor of distribution seems to be twofold. In the first place a low temperature may not provide that combination of heat quantity and quality which is necessary for the production of seed and fruit, as is the case with the casuals just mentioned, but there is generally also a temperature minimum below which even the vegetative life of the plant cannot continue. This will actually determine whether a species can occur in a given area, and clearly the higher the temperature needed for growth the narrower will the potential area of the species be. It would seem, however, that most plants can live vegetatively over a fairly wide range of temperature provided that this does not fall below freezing point. This is not to say that they can reproduce, but they can exist, and this is shown by the innumerable examples of garden plants from warmer countries which are hardy in this country except in very extreme conditions.

Plate 22. An Asiatic giant Bamboo (*Dendrocalamus giganteus*)
(*from Karsten & Schenck, Vegetationsbilder*)

The question of frost raises quite a different problem, because it involves the possible injury of tissues by the expansion of their juices when they freeze. It is significant that there are no Flowering Plants which pass the whole of their life history in a temperature below freezing, and there is probably none capable of doing so. Indeed, very few can survive serious freezing during the time that they are in full vegetative vigour. Naturally the lower the temperature the greater is its effect likely to be, but there is reason to suppose that very often the duration of freezing is more important than the actual degree of coldness, and Shreve (647) has shown this to be the case with certain cacti, one of which (*Opuntia missouriensis*) successfully resisted 375 continuous hours of frost, while others were destroyed by much shorter periods at the same temperature. In this connection it may be noted that another cactus (*Mammillaria vivipara*) extends to above 50° N. in Canada and normally endures much longer periods of continuous frost.

Indeed the frost-line, in one or other of its many possible definitions, is probably the most important of all climatic demarcations in plants, and in very general terms it seems to be true that many plant groups, especially genera, are either frost-sensitive or not, the former being restricted to the "tropical" parts of the world. It is at all events noteworthy that the number of truly cosmopolitan genera (see p. 81) is small, and that there are very few large genera which can be described as characteristically subtropical in the sense that they have a balanced distribution on both sides of the frost-line.

This point has been nicely illustrated recently by Hartley (343) in a study of the world distribution of the six largest tribes of the grasses in which he shows that, with the exception of one which is probably not a natural group, each is either characteristically tropical or characteristically temperate. He also demonstrates a correlation in their distribution with the line (isocheim) for 50° F. mean temperature for the coldest month, a line which "delimits, in a very general way those parts of the world in which severe winter frosts are normally experienced".

Plants which inhabit regions where frost is general during the winter season normally spend that period of the year in some condition which protects them from the dangers of freezing. This process of self-protection against winter rigours is called perennation and is carried out in a variety of ways such as the restriction of life to buried organs only, the loss of leaves during autumn, and so on. The winter may also be passed in the seed condition, where the plant is not only dormant but protected by various resistant structures. This indeed seems to be the normal process in ephemeral annuals. Some seeds may germinate in the autumn and endeavour to pass the winter as young seedlings, and may, if the conditions are not too bad, succeed in doing so, but there are always many seeds which do not germinate till the following spring, when it may be presumed safe to do so.

It is in relation to temperature as a geographical factor that the subject of growth-forms is most appropriately mentioned. It has long been recognised that plants can be classified according to their general form, and many people have published such schemes, but the study of growth-forms (105, 172, 581) is especially associated with the Danish botanist Raunkiaer. He recognised the following main forms, each of which he further classified in detail. The names used are for the most part indicative of the chief features of the types.

Phanerophytes .   . Plants whose size is not appreciably diminished in cold or dry seasons. It includes all woody perennials of erect habit and also many epiphytes and succulents. At least a dozen minor types can be recognised.

23

Chamaephytes	. .	Subshrubs or herbs which partially die back in winter or which grow closely adpressed to the surface of the soil. This includes cushion plants.
Hemicryptophytes	.	Plants which lose practically all their aerial parts in winter and are visible above the surface only as rosettes or offsets.
Cryptophytes	. .	Plants which disappear entirely to below ground (geophytes) or water (helophytes and hydrophytes) during winter and which perennate by rhizomes, bulbs and corms, or by under-water buds.
Therophytes	. .	Plants which pass the winter in the seed, as most annuals.

This classification might be paraphrased as one which is based on the degree to which plants find it necessary to protect themselves against winter conditions. In these terms the phanerophytes include the plants which are under no such necessity, as well as those in which the method is least obvious. In the other groups the degree of protection, which is usually the reverse of exposure, becomes progressively more marked until it culminates in perennation in seed form, which may be regarded as the last resource.

One slight complication needs to be explained here. In some parts of the tropics, where temperature conditions are always more or less at an optimum, growth continues all the year round, but in other parts there is an unfavourable period because of an uneven distribution of rainfall in time. In other words, here the winter cold unfavourable season is replaced by a dry season where the danger is desiccation instead of refrigeration. This point will be returned to later, but it is worth noting here that the two distinct dangers are met by plants in much the same way.

As to the absolute temperature values which flowering plants can stand, two general statements seem to be true: first, that little or no development goes on at temperatures below freezing; and second, that there are no parts of the world where the temperature is too high for growth and reproduction. As will be seen, there are regions where the plant life is very scanty, and some where it is virtually absent, but this is not due solely to temperature values.

The relation between plant distribution and temperature alone is perhaps most clearly seen in the case of aquatic plants, and especially in the marine Angiosperms, because here many of the complicating related factors such as other air conditions, precipitation and so on are absent. Plants living in the sea may, it is true, be affected by the chemical constitution of the water and also by the movement of the water in the form of currents, but the former is reasonably constant and the latter does not seem to be a decisive factor in the determination of range, and it is fairly safe to say that the one really important consideration must be temperature. With this belief the account of the distribution of Angiosperms in the sea in Chapter 11 and as illustrated by Plate 15 is very significant. Above all, the occurrence of prevalent latitudinal distribution limits will be noticed, and it can scarcely be doubted that these are due to the temperature relation of the species concerned. Moreover, it is clear that this relation must be a very exact one, because the latitudinal temperature gradient in the sea is very gradual.

The importance of the modification of the general latitudinal distribution of temperature by elevation as a factor in distribution can scarcely be overestimated. In rising vertically above the mean sea level there is a fall of temperature of approximately 3° F. for every 1,000 ft., so that all mountains reproduce, according to their height, a temperature range corresponding to that between certain latitudes at sea level, and any mountain which has permanent ice and snow epitomises the whole temperature gamut at sea levels between the latitude in which it is situated and the nearer pole (Fig. 1). Thus a mountain on the equator which is high enough to have permanent snow reproduces on its slopes the temperature gradient of a whole hemisphere. For this reason mountains provide habitats, as far as temperature goes, for plants characteristic of quite different latitudes, and thus afford a series of stepping stones in range which is often of the greatest value. It has been seen that many plants occur in the temperate regions of both hemispheres, and are therefore to be regarded as having crossed the tropics in the course of their spread. This they have certainly done by way of mountains, which, for the reason mentioned, afford a pathway for their movement.

It is often not sufficiently realised how widely distributed in the tropics are mountains of great elevation, but actually they are of common occurrence. Most obvious is the great range of the Andes, which, while indeed of least magnitude in the north parts of the tropical zone, does in fact provide a more or less continuous line of peaks between north and south. Less noticeable, but none the less serviceable, are the mountains which stretch in an almost unbroken line from the Himalayas down the Malay Peninsula and through Malaysia to New Guinea and New Zealand. Only in Africa is the situation rather different, not only because there the heights are less continuous but because a particularly wide break of desert regions cuts them off from the northern temperate mountains of Europe. Also, at present at least, there is enormous oceanic discontinuity south of Africa.

In view of these facts the occurrence of bipolar plant types is almost certainly due to the fact that they have succeeded in crossing the tropics by passing along mountain chains, and this they have been able to do because of the peculiar temperature relations which the mountains afford. Incidentally it may be added that Du Rietz (205) and others have shown that some species have probably crossed the tropics by the New World mountains, some by the Malaysian route and some by both means.

This view is supported too by the present occurrence on nearly all tropical mountains of types which are either identical with or very closely resemble those of the temperate regions and especially those of the north. Allusion has already been made to northern genera with extensions into the tropics along the mountains, and this is specially notable in America, though only less so in Malaysia. Van Steenis (700) has made a careful study of the mountain flora of Malaysia and has shown how many northern forms there are in it, and also the routes by which they apparently came.

In Africa too the same is true, except that here, owing to the peculiar distribution of the mountains, the relationship with the north is more discontinuous. Time and again, however, the prevalence of northern types on the African mountains has received comment, and indeed many of our familiar British plants occur there, as, for instance, *Sanicula europaea* and *Epilobium hirsutum*, while *Linnaea borealis* has been reported apparently growing wild on the slopes of Ruwenzori.

Precipitation

(Plates 23, 24)

Under this term are included all forms of atmospheric moisture, but it will simplify the discussion if we consider it in terms of rainfall only, remembering nevertheless that other forms such as snow and dew are sometimes of great importance. A special instance of this is to be found in the coastal desert of Chile. Here

there is in places little or no rainfall but here and there fog is almost continuous during winter and gives rise to local wet areas bearing a seasonal flora called the "loma"
(749).

The distribution of rainfall is essentially different from that of climate in that
it is not regularly latitudinal. It is true that the heaviest rainfall tends to be in parts of
the equatorial, or at least tropical, zone, but the main feature of its distribution is that
nearly all values tend to occur in nearly every latitude. This alone is sufficient to show,
bearing in mind the general distribution of plant life already described, that of the
climatic factors rainfall is to be regarded as secondary in effect to temperature.

It is particularly with the relative importance of heat and rainfall that we can
illustrate the difference between floristic and vegetational distribution. It has been
seen that floristic distribution, that is to say the distribution of taxonomic units, is
predominantly a latitudinal one. The distribution of vegetation types, on the other
hand, is predominantly one of precipitation. That is to say, such vegetation types
as forest and grassland tend to occur at any latitude in certain rainfall values, while
deserts are similarly distributed where rainfall is inadequate. To put the point rather
differently, it may be said that in matters of plant geography temperatue is more
fundamental than rain; in matters of plant ecology, in the sense of vegetational
development, rain is more important than heat.

At the same time there is an intimate relation between temperature and rainfall
because of the influence which the former may have in determining the humidity
of the air and thereby the effectiveness of the precipitation, and many attempts
have been made to arrive at some combined formula or equation by which the
correlation of the distribution of vegetation and floral units with these factors may
be more accurately expressed. Among these there may be mentioned, for purposes
of illustration, the precipitation–evaporation ratio or P/E used by Thornthwaite
(735, 74); the Meyer ratio, which is the ratio of the precipitation to the saturation
deficit of the air, and which has been applied in an interesting way to the vegetation
of Western Australia by Gardner (262); and such particular rainfall–temperature
equations as those used by Miller (519) in his attempt to express the climatic lines of
separation between forest, grassland and desert.

Owing to the absence of any basic latitudinal zonation, rainfall, even more than
temperature, is correlated with the distribution and relief of land and sea. This is
because winds coming from the sea will be moisture-laden, and also because elevated
regions may protect inland areas from the influence of these winds. Rainfall must
therefore be considered as very directly related to wind, and reference should be made
to the discussion of that subject below.

As it is, the simplified distribution of rainfall is roughly as follows. Regions
of maximum rainfall are nearly all equatorial, namely the lowlands of Brazil,
parts of west Africa, and the whole of Malaysia and the Pacific. In all these the total
annual rainfall is above 80 in. Other more localised regions with similar values are
the east coast of Brazil, parts of the west coast of South America, the east coast
of Madagascar, the Himalayas and Burma, parts of south India, New Zealand and
a small area in Alaska. The highest annual average figures recorded (about 450 in.) are
from stations in Burma and the Hawaiian islands, where single yearly figures may
be much higher (807). Regions of exceptionally low rainfall, under 10 in. a year,
are in the arctic, parts of western North America, parts of temperate South America,
North Africa and Arabia, Central Asia, South Africa and the interior of Australia.
Elsewhere the distribution of rain varies from 10 to 80 in. annually. The two main
features are undoubtedly the practically continuous area of high rainfall from the

Himalayas through Malaysia and far across the Pacific, and the almost continuous range of low rainfall, leading to desert conditions, which stretches from the west coast of North Africa practically to China.

The general correlation of species distribution with this distribution of rainfall will be apparent from the close correspondence of some of the floristic regions with it, but reference to total annual rainfall is not enough to show this correlation fully. Obviously the absolute amount of rainfall must be of primary import, but except where this is definitely inadequate a much more significant aspect is the distribution of the rain during the year, that is to say during the various phases of the plant life. In brief the following conditions are to be found:

1. Heavy rainfall all the year round.
2. Moderate rainfall always, becoming heavy at certain times.
3. Moderate rainfall throughout the year.
4. Moderate rainfall concentrated in the summer.
5. Moderate rainfall concentrated in the winter.
6. Low rainfall spread over the whole year.
7. Low rainfall concentrated in one season.
8. Relative absence of rain.

A rather different classification, of which Plate 24 is a somewhat simplified edition, recognises six types, as follows:

1. Constant drought:
   N. Africa to India, C. Asia, California, western S. America, S. Africa and C. Australia.
2. Periodic rains:
   a. Summer rain, dry winter and spring—
      Especially in the monsoon regions of Asia, western Africa and parts of tropical America.
   b. Winter rain, summers dry—
      Mediterranean, western N. America, Cape, western S. America and S.W. Australia.
3. Rain at all seasons:
   a. Maximum in summer—
      Tropical S. America, eastern N. America, Europe and W. Asia, parts of Malaysia.
   b. Maximum in winter and autumn—
      W. Europe, parts of Malaysia, N. Pacific coasts, Fuegia and New Zealand.
4. Continuous rain, no month with less than fifteen rainy days:
   Occurs only in parts of certain oceans.

Light

As Hayek (345) and others have pointed out, light must, in one sense at any rate, be the fundamental climatic factor in relation to plants, because the chemical process, photosynthesis, which is the basis of the whole of their physiology, is, as its name implies, one which goes on only in the presence of light, so that in its absence plant life as we know it to-day could not continue. This is, of course, perfectly true, but our concern here is rather with the effects of various climatic factors in limiting the actual distribution of plants, and in this respect light is of comparatively minor importance.

Owing to the shape of the earth the insolation of the equatorial regions is stronger or at least more direct than that of the latitudes further south and north, but there are no data to indicate that tropical plants require stronger light than temperate ones. On the other hand, many plants protect themselves from extreme insolation by some structural or chemical means. Nor is the value of insolation at any spot always constant. It may be greatly modified by the degree of cloudiness, and this being so, it may be assumed that ordinary sunlight provides appreciably more light than plants actually require, and that nowhere, during summer months at least, is it deficient. The main effect in the distribution of light values seems, on the other hand, to be the length of time of illumination. In the equatorial regions the day is about the same moderate length all the year round, but towards the poles the day becomes longer in the growing season and shorter in the winter, until at the highest latitudes, there is more or less continuous light for six months and a corresponding length of darkness.

The effect of length of day on plants and particularly on their flowering has been much studied and there is available a useful early summary of the subject (776). There are now generally recognised to be "short-day plants", "long-day plants" and "day-neutral plants", the first including essentially those of the tropics and the second those of temperate latitudes. In temperate lands the short winter day does not affect the question because the plant is dormant during this season of the year.

If this distinction is indeed operative in nature, that is to say if the generality of plants are either "short-day" or "long-day" and are therefore segregated geographically, length of day, which is an expression of the obliquity of the ecliptic, must be a fundamental distributional factor, but the matter may not be quite so simple as this. For instance many tropical plants which in nature live under short-day conditions can be made to flourish and flower without difficulty in glasshouses in long-day latitudes, provided the necessary warmth and moisture are supplied. Conversely it would seem to be very much more difficult to make long-day plants flourish in lower latitudes where short-day conditions prevail (593, 700), though here the results might be different if the local temperature and other factors could be modified by some sort of refrigeration. The whole subject is made more interesting to the plant-geographer because of its special association with problems of Angiosperm history and because of the light it promises to cast on climatic change in the past, and for these reasons it will be discussed shortly again at the end of Chapter 20.

Meanwhile the reader may be reminded that, with the present obliquity of the ecliptic, light and temperature relations are such as to make the existence of a tropical flora beyond 30° N. or S. latitude, or a warm temperate flora beyond 50° N. or S. exceedingly improbable.

Wind

Broadly speaking, wind, that is to say air in motion, is the result of local variations in the pressure of the atmosphere, and we must therefore, in discussing the effect of wind on the distribution of plants, keep in mind its relation to barometric pressure. This latter alone, however, has not received much attention as a direct factor nor does it appear to be important as such, though it has been suggested that there may be optimum pressures for certain plants.

Wind may be regarded as of potential effect in plant geography in three ways, namely:

1. By its physical influence on the growth-form of plants, as in restricting or preventing the growth of trees. In the Falkland Islands, for instance, wind seems to have exerted a considerable influence on the nature of the vegetation in this way.

2. By its effect on dispersal. Here a distinction must be drawn between land winds and oceanic winds. The latter have a fairly simple distribution, but the former are very complex and variable, depending on all sorts of extraneous factors, and, although there are prevailing winds, it is probably true to say that in most land areas wind direction varies greatly. This is obviously of great potential significance in dispersal, which normally occurs only at certain seasons of the year. In addition there are powerful high-altitude winds, sometimes referred to as "jet-streams", which have little directional relationship to the pattern of surface winds, and it is possible that these also may play some part in plant dispersal (182).

3. By its effect in determining other climatic values. Two climatic elements are especially liable to be varied by wind, namely temperature—which becomes lowered by the increased evaporation that results—and rainfall. Indirectly the absolute amount of this latter may be affected, but wind chiefly controls it by determining its direction and the areas over which it will fall. The monsoon of the Indian ocean is perhaps the best example of this.

As has been indicated, it is almost impossible concisely to describe the normal distribution of wind over the continents, but the general planetary circulation of the atmosphere, particularly over the oceans, is fairly simple. Extending for some distance on both sides of the equator is a belt, the doldrums, where the pressure is low and winds are very light. North and south of the doldrums are the two great belts of the trade winds, strong steady winds blowing, in the northern hemisphere, from the north-east, and, in the southern hemisphere, from the south-west. Between the latitudes 30° and 40° are the northern and southern horse latitudes, which are regions of high pressure and comparative calm. Between the horse latitudes and the poles are the westerlies, strong winds predominantly from the south-west and from the north-west respectively in the northern and southern hemispheres.

Bush Fires

Apart from their direct effects upon the distribution of plants, climatic factors often exert an influence in indirect ways, and one of the most serious of these is by fire.

The burning of natural vegetation by bush fires is a commonplace in many parts of the world but it is very hard to determine how far it is a natural phenomenon. Man in all stages of culture uses fire, either to clear virgin land for his own use, or as a regular subsequent process in agriculture, or even, as is said to be the case in parts of New Guinea, as a means of "scorching the earth" of his enemies, and in many places, notably Madagascar and New Caledonia (751), the native vegetation has been seriously reduced by it. At the same time it seems reasonably certain that in some countries where there is a prolonged dry season, such as in the savanna zones of Africa, fires of natural origin are frequent and are believed actually to help towards the establishment and maintenance of savanna conditions (see p. 160 and 385), though how they start is not always apparent. Both lightning and incandescent volcanic material are known to be among the causes (598) but lightning is often accompanied by heavy rain, and vulcanism is very localised.

In Angola, where much of the vegetation is a patchwork of dry forest and grassland, the latter is regularly burnt during the dry season. Associated with the grasses are many perennial plants, and these are characterised by exceptionally well developed and peculiar underground rhizome systems by which they are able to survive even when their aerial parts are burnt. Equipped thus such plants are able to exist where others would almost certainly be destroyed. Exell (228) cites, as good examples of these fire-resisting plants, species of *Tetracera, Combretum, Annona, Eriosema, Geissaspis, Aeschynomene* and various Rubiaceae. Other plants of the same kind, including species of *Parinari, Pachystigma, Lannea, Elephantorrhiza* and *Dichapetalum* have been recorded from the Transvaal (451).

Species which are capable of surviving fires unharmed are sometimes spoken of as *pyrophytes*, and one of the best-known instances is the niauoli, *Melaleuca leucadendron*, in New Caledonia (751). Here deliberate bush fires have destroyed a considerable amount of the original vegetation, and over the burnt areas the *niauoli*, which is said to be a member of the native flora, quickly spreads, producing a kind of savanna in which terrestrial orchids and other geophytes are conspicuous.

The word pyrophyte should be used with caution, because although it may accurately describe species which are resistant to fires, it does not reveal whether they have specially acquired this immunity as a protection from burning. On the whole it seems more likely that these plants are primarily xerophytes, but that the features which make them so serve also to enable them to survive fire.

Climatic Regions

It is evident from what has been said in the foregoing pages that the surface of the earth can be classified into regions or areas according to the values of any one of the climatic elements that have been mentioned. But it is possible to go further than this and to divide the world up into what may be called general climatic regions with regard to which all the major climatic elements and values are taken into account.

Classifications of this sort have been made by Koppen (431), Supan (714), and many others, and to illustrate them an arrangement attributed to Supan, in which the world is divided into thirty-four climatic provinces, has been used as the basis for Plate 5. The names of the various regions are more conveniently given with the plate and need not be repeated here, but the main purpose of the plate may well be emphasised once more. It is to demonstrate, by comparison with Plates 2 and 4, the remarkable degree of similarity existing between the general distribution of floras, of vegetation and of climate. These three maps, in particular, show more graphically than any words can describe the close correlation between plants and climate and the truth of the statement that climatic factors are among the most important of all the forces controlling plant distribution.

CHAPTER 18

THE FACTORS OF DISTRIBUTION—III. EDAPHIC FACTORS

IT was shown in Chapter 16 that the ordinary flowering plant lives in contact with its environment in two directions, its aerial parts being surrounded by the air and its subterranean parts by the soil, so that environmental factors may be divided into climatic and edaphic. The former having been discussed in the last chapter it remains here to say something of the latter. This subject of edaphic factors is, however, a very complex one and only the briefest outline of it can be given here, and this should certainly be supplemented by reference to standard books on plant ecology, in the province of which this subject especially lies, and in particular to works like Daubenmire's *Plants and Environment* (178) and Eyre's *Vegetation and Soils* (815).

As regards the Flowering Plants it may be said that some amount of soil is a primary necessity for their growth and that none can live on the bare surface of rock. Soil may be described as the product of the disintegration of rocks, both sedimentary and igneous, by the process and effects of weathering, that is to say by the action of various climatic influences. To take but one of the more conspicuous instances, frost is a very potent rock breaker. All but the hardest rocks tend to become more or less soaked in times of rain; this contained water expands when it freezes and in doing so splits the rock in varying degree. The mere physical action of prolonged rain too will in time wear away even the hardest rocks. As a result of this weathering the surface layers of rocks sooner or later become broken up so that three distinct layers can be recognised. On the actual surface where the effects of weathering are greatest there is a thickness of soil proper where the rock has become more or less completely disintegrated. Below this for a varying thickness is the subsoil, where the weathering has begun the process of breaking up the rock but has not carried it very far. Below this again is the solid rock or parent material itself as yet unchanged. Thus, much may be learnt about a soil and its genesis by the study of vertical sections through it, and the consideration of such soil-profiles as they are called is an important aspect of modern pedology.

The physiological processes of the plant are such that it can make little use of and take little from disintegrated rock unless the process of its breakdown has proceeded far, and hence its soil relations are almost entirely with the actual soil layer, although to varying degrees the subsoil may be of importance. Since soils are the products of weathering it is not surprising that there is a close correlation between climatic conditions and certain kinds of soil, the two most important factors being temperature and rainfall. Generally speaking the higher the rainfall and the lower the temperature the greater the amount of organic matter in the soil and *vice versa*, while at any given mean temperature the type of soil tends to vary according to the annual rainfall. These relations have been expressed in a simple diagram by Lang (445), and this is reproduced, after Brooks (90), in Fig. 83.

In the normal course of events weathering will result in the development of soil *in situ*, that is to say immediately over the rocks from which it is derived, and such soils are called local soils. On the other hand, circumstances will sometimes result in the washing away or other transportation of the soil from its point of formation, and its subsequent deposition elsewhere. Such soils are called transported soils. The main influences producing them are wind action, such as causes the accumulation of blown sand; glacial action and the movements of glaciers, as is illustrated by boulder clays and other morainic deposits; and rain and river action such as can be observed in any delta. It is worth noting that all three are capable of producing areas of soil where there would otherwise be water, and especially of producing bare soil areas open to plant colonisation. For instance, much of Holderness, in Yorkshire, would be beneath the surface of the sea were it not for vast accumulations of boulder clay and other glacial deposits. Similarly in tidal rivers fresh surfaces of alluvium are constantly being formed and may become permanent. In the case of both tidal mud and sand-dunes, however, subsequent action often tends to remove and redistribute accumulations of this kind.

The rooting of plants in soil has a twofold function. Chiefly it enables the plant to absorb such food materials as it requires from the soil, but in addition to this

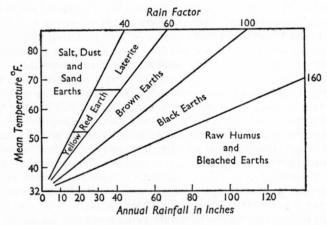

Fig. 82.—Diagram of Lang's Rain Factor. (Redrawn from Brooks, *Climate through the Ages* E. Benn, Ltd.)

it serves as an anchorage and provides the base upon or from which the aerial parts may grow up into the atmosphere. Generally speaking, the larger the plant the firmer and deeper the anchorage it will require, and so the absolute amount or depth of soil is a primary factor, in the sense that no plants can flourish unless there is a sufficiency of soil for the proper development of their underground parts.

Another very important point about soils in general is that the continued growth of plants in them tends to add greatly to their depth and bulk. Generation after generation plants grow and die and the products of their decay are washed down into the soil, and in certain circumstances the upper layers of the earth's surface may indeed come to be composed of little else than organic matter. This organic constituent of the soil is known as humus and is sometimes very conspicuous, as in the deep layers of leaf-mould in beech woods or as in peat. On very hard rocks it sometimes happens that the growth of flowering plants is only possible by reason of this accumulation of humus, and it is one of the great dangers of fire that its effect is not only to destroy living plants but also to destroy much of the soil in which they might regenerate. This is particularly serious in that the soil so lost cannot quickly be replaced, and the whole immensely long development of the accumulation of a humus soil has to be gone through again before large plants can become established. This occurs, for instance, in parts of Canada where the underlying rock is very hard.

Except in some new soils and desert soils there will always tend to be some proportion of humus, and this constituent is of the greatest importance not only for the substratum it may provide but in determining the characteristics of the soil as a whole. Newly deposited transported soils are often exceedingly poor in many of the more necessary minerals and may contain no humus at all, so that their rapid colonisation by flowering plants is sometimes difficult to understand. New sand-dunes in this country, for instance, are often colonised almost from their inception by at least one Angiosperm, though analysis may show them to be composed of silica and carbonate of lime without measurable quantities of anything else. Yet in this apparently inhospitable medium *Ammophila* will flourish, and is soon joined by other species.

This outline of the methods by which soils are formed is sufficient to indicate the general differences which will be found between them. The most obvious and direct of these are in physical and chemical constitution, but to these must be added a third, the biotic factor, depending upon the living inhabitants of the soil, and to-day there is a growing appreciation of the importance of this factor.

The physical condition of the soil itself depends on three considerations, all of which are more or less intimately related to climatic conditions. First is the question of depth, which has already been mentioned. It will be obvious that many factors will control the depth of soil and, conversely, many of the physical features of the soil will depend upon its depth. Most important here is the influence of depth on water content. Shallow soils always tend to be lacking in water, not only because evaporation to the air dries them out quickly but also because water is not easily held. On the other hand, exceptional depth of soil may affect plant distribution by allowing the proper growth of the larger forms of life. Some of the very largest trees, for instance, seem to be restricted, as might be expected, to regions where the soil is particularly deep.

The second physical feature of soils and that which causes the most obvious differences between them is their texture, by which is meant the size of the particles of which they are composed. In local soils the process of weathering will tend to produce particles or masses of almost every size from stones downwards, and such soils are generally characterised by this heterogeneity. In transported soils, as well as in some kinds of local soils, this is much less marked and they are characterised by homogeneity. This is obviously true of sand-dunes and alluvium, for instance, where there is in the process of transport a gradual gravitational sifting. It does not, however, prevail so widely in glacial deposits, as the very name boulder clay testifies. The importance of the nature of the rock in local soils is clear in clays, which are themselves only hardened and ancient alluvial deposits and which thus tend when weathered to produce a homogeneous soil. Some substrata consist entirely of masses of stone dimensions, as, for instance, the detritus sometimes seen on the tops of mountains and in such situations as pebble beaches. Conventionally, however, these are not regarded as soils and from the plant point of view at any rate may be regarded as discrete rock surfaces. In so far as they form a substratum for the growth of plants it is by virtue of small quantities of finer material which in course of time accumulate within them but which may be foreign to their constitution.

The three ingredients which in fact control, by their proportionate representation, the physical constitution of the soil are sand, clay and humus. Each of these plays a considerable part in determining the two main structural features of soil, its texture and tenacity. Their effect, however, is nearly always intimately connected with the water relations of the soil and can scarcely be divorced from them. The presence of much sand, by which is meant here particles of medium size, leads to a loose and easily broken soil. The presence of much clay produces a dense, stiff, tenacious soil. Humus, which is itself essentially heterogeneous since it is composed of more or less decayed organic tissues, has in general a moderating effect and, while binding sandy soils, loosens and opens clays. Apart from the fact that loose soils provide a less satisfactory anchorage for plants, texture affects plants chiefly in relation to water and air. Sandy soils with little or no humus allow water to percolate through at a maximum speed and with a minimum retention, and such soils are therefore more or less physically and physiologically dry. Clays, on the other hand, not only hold large quantities of water because of the surface effects of their small particles, but are often actually impervious to its passage. Thus unless there is considerable evaporation clay soils easily become water-logged. Similarly the coarser a soil the more adequate is likely to be its aeration.

The way in which water is actually held in soil offers a very difficult problem and and can be considered here only in relation to the absorption of water by the plants. On this basis it is customary to recognise the water in soil as of three categories. First, there is the continuous liquid water or free water which actually forms the water table. Second, there is capillary water which adheres to the soil particles and which tends to move gradually by capillarity to wherever the soil is drier (normally towards the surface). Third, there is hygroscopic water which clings to the particles so closely that it does not travel by capillarity and which in fact can only be removed by such processes as boiling. To these three there may be added a certain amount of water which is chemically combined with certain compounds in the soil. Soil in which there is a great deal of free water may be described as water-logged. Soil in which there is little or no free water but a reasonable supply of capillary water may be called moist, and it is the gradual loss of this capillary water which marks the change from moist to the condition which we call dry. This ordinary conception of dryness however is but a relative one, and when a soil appears dry to the human senses it normally still contains an appreciable amount of capillary water. This is demonstrated by the fact that it is in general only the capillary water which is available for plant use and absorption, and it is a matter of common observation that plants can continue to live for varying periods in soil which appears to be "dry". It must not be supposed from this that plants make no use of other water, but on a simple view the water easily available to the plant may be considered to be the capillary water only. The free water will, of course, provide a great reservoir of this. It is particularly in regard to water that humus plays a part. The very structure of small masses of vegetable matter is such that they act as minute sponges and retain, by capillarity, water which otherwise would easily be lost. So the presence of humus in the soil adds greatly to its water-retaining power, and in sandy soils this is often a very important point.

The impermeability of clay soils has been mentioned. One rather special effect of this is that in basins of such soils standing water may accumulate readily as ponds or lakes, and thus produce locally an entirely new kind of habitat open to occupation by species very different from those characteristic of clay soils.

The third important physical feature of the soil is its temperature. This may be considered for all practical purposes as due entirely to solar radiation, except for the possible occurrence of exothermic chemical reactions in the soil. Soil temperature is becoming more and more recognised as a factor in distribution, and this is almost entirely in relation to the absorption of water by the plant. The process by which this is actually accomplished is too complex to be described here, but it can be said that it appears to be strictly conditioned by soil temperature. As a result of this, soils in which the temperature is low may, although holding copious supplies of water, be to the plant as if they were deficient in water. In other words, the water is there but is not available to the plant, which suffers as a result from what is called "physiological drought". This state of affairs must almost necessarily obtain where the water of soil is actually frozen, as it is more or less permanently in very high latitudes, but since the optimum temperature for water absorption in the plant may normally be regarded as appreciably above freezing point, this limiting factor has a much wider application in practice. Permanently frozen subsoil is called *tjaele* (527) and the resulting climatic condition has been termed *permafrost* by Müller. Its geographical limit is as low as 55° N. in eastern Canada and 60° N. in East Asia and Alaska.

The chemical constitution of soils is a most intricate subject because of the immense range of chemical compounds or minerals that occur in nature. All the solid elements as well as many of the gaseous ones occur in the crust of the earth, and hence often in the soil, and many of these in a variety of combinations.

A review of the detailed facts of plant distribution shows that a great many minerals react favourably or unfavourably on the presence or absence of various plant species, and Hayek (345), among others, has given a long account of plants whose distribution is correlated with the occurrence of definite chemical compounds, particularly some of the metals, in the soil. One of the most remarkable examples of this is afforded by what has been called serpentinomorphosis, which may be described as the morphological change which certain plants undergo when growing on serpentine. This is a metamorphic rock, derived from basic eruptive rocks, in which magnesium compounds are plentiful, the magnesium/calcium ratio is greater than unity, and there is an absence of chlorides (538). Pichi-Sermolli (558) gives a list of the modifications so caused, such as glabrescence, glaucescence and nanism, and recognises three kinds of species: typical serpentinophytes, which occur only on serpentine; preferential serpentinophytes, which occur especially on serpentine; and serpenticolous relics which now survive only on that substratum. The operative factor appears to be the magnesium in the rock, and similar morphoses occur in respect of calcium and of zinc (619). Novak (538) draws attention to the fact that these three elements are closely related. There is a good general account of serpentinomorphosis by Rune (610), and several other references to it, and to related subjects, are given by Mason and Stout (497).

But in general there are in soils four chemical constituents of special importance in this direction, namely quartz, of which sand is largely composed; aluminium silicate, which is the chief constituent of clay; calcium carbonate, which contributes largely to the formation of chalk and limestone; and humus, which comprises a wide range of organic compounds. These are the most widespread of all chemical soil constituents, and their proportional representation is the chief chemical distinction between soils, on which is based the broad classification of soils into sandy soils, clay soils, calcareous soils and organic soils. Each of them may occur almost to the exclusion of others, but more often soils show a combination of two or more and a preponderance of one or other. The correlation between this broad classification and the distribution of plants is very marked. The species of sandy soil are in general different from those of clay or limestone, as are these from one another. Similarly, where the humus constituent is preponderant still other species occur. Where, as in many soils, the constituents are well mixed, there is a similar admixture of species in the flora. Innumerable instances of these conditions might be given, but they formed a particularly important part of the chapter on the distribution of plants in Dorset (Chapter 14), and reference may be made to that account for particular examples.

It must not be supposed, however, that the physical and chemical features of soil are necessarily separate conditions. Indeed there are strong indications that they are intimately connected. In particular it seems clear that the importance of certain chemical features of the soil lies, from the point of view of the plant, in the physical conditions which they produce. It is familiar to find species that occur exclusively either on limestone or on sandy soils, but there are many which inhabit both. The common harebell, *Campanula rotundifolia*, is an instance of this. It is a normal constituent of the flora of many chalk or other limestone grasslands, but is also common on some soils of almost pure sand, and it is difficult to explain this except on the view that these two types of soil tend to provide the same physical conditions. This is true also of certain other species commonly associated with chalk pastures.

In turn the physical state of the soil influences its water relations and its temperature, and the general conclusion is that chemical and physical conditions must not be regarded as essentially distinct but rather as contributing equally to the general character of the substratum (28).

The question of humus is rather different, and is of great interest and significance. The waters of ordinary inorganic soils are in themselves either neutral or slightly alkaline in raction. On the other hand, humus is to a greater or lesser extent acid in reaction. This is due partly to the secretion of acids from living plant roots and partly to the production of acids in the course of the decay of dead plant tissues. As a result the presence of considerable quantities of humus, especially in association with less alkaline mineral soils, tends to change the water reaction of the soil from alkaline to acid. This again is a very complicated chemical matter which can only be expressed here in very simple terms. The reaction of soil water in this way is due to its ionisation and to the resultant concentration of hydrogen ions. Where this concentration is low the general reaction will be alkaline; where it is high the reaction is acid. The hydrogen ion concentration is denoted by the letters pH, and the values are given mathematical expression in such a way that the greater the alkalinity the higher the pH figure, and *vice versa*. Neutrality is roughly indicated by the value 7, so that reactions of value above this are alkaline and below this are acid.

In practice the result will be an expression of the amount of humus and the natural reaction of the soil minerals, and in fact these considerations lead to a very wide range of pH values in different soils. Particularly, however, is this the case where humus is plentiful and the modifying effects of minerals are slight, as, for instance, in some peat soils and here the acidity may be very high. On the other hand there are some peaty soils, such as those of the Cambridgeshire fens, which receive drainage water rich in basic minerals and which may, in consequence, be alkaline. As a practical issue in plant distribution it appears that the correlation of species with the pH of the soils in which they grow is very close, and that the segregation of species on this basis is very clear-cut. This point is well illustrated by reference to the British flora.

The great majority of British plants grow in situations where the soil reaction is either about neutral or slightly on the acid side. A comparatively small number live only where the reaction is much more definitely and sometimes markedly acid. So clear is this distinction that it is no exaggeration to say that it is by far the most conspicuous example of segregation according to habitat. It is true that the bulk of the species of the flora vary greatly in the degree to which they can stand acid conditions, and in places, where the values fluctuate about neutrality or where there is but slight acidity many of these plants will occur, but no more than a handful of species can stand conditions where the acidity is high, and these never occur except in such conditions. In Britain high acidic values are to be found chiefly if not only in water-logged humus soils lacking in modifying minerals, namely in peat-bogs, and it is here that the acid-loving plants are found to the exclusion of all others. So obvious is this that it suffers from the familiarity that breeds contempt, and it is important to emphasise its interest. In any attempt to classify the facts of plant distribution in terms of the habitat such as was made in Chapter 14, the extreme segregation of these acid plants will be one of the most obvious features, and indeed it is not too much to say that only here is there to be found any invariable and unmodified correlation between habitat and range. It would seem indeed as if species, at least in Britain, can be divided into two groups most easily according to their relation to soil acidity, and no other basis seems to give so clear a segregation.

The explanation appears to be that these exceptionally acid habitats are essentially extreme and apart and are characterised by certain very particular and peculiar features. For this reason they are inhabited only by certain equally peculiar and specialised species which by reason of that specialisation find there, and there only, the conditions necessary for their growth. As illustrating the sort of conditions which this specialisation may entail, it is significant that many of the so-called insectivorous plants of our flora, species of *Drosera*, *Pinguicula* and *Utricularia*, are restricted to acid habitats. Just in so far as this specialisation may fit species for extreme conditions, so it normally may be expected to unfit them for more ordinary conditions, and this is certainly indicated by the edaphic restriction of these acid-loving species.

To some extent the marked observed segregation in terms of soil reaction is due to the fact that the point of neutrality is by no means in the centre of the whole gamut of conditions. That is to say there is a wider range of values on the acid side than on the alkaline. Associated with this it might be expected that more species would be able to exist throughout the whole alkaline range than throughout the whole acid range, and that there would be less likelihood of visible segregation in terms of alkalinity than in terms of acidity. This is supported by the fact that while it is very difficult to arrange species in terms of what may be called "alkalinity tolerance", it is comparatively easy to arrange many species in terms of their acidity tolerance. In rather different terms, it is easy to find species which are rough guides to acidity of the soil, but it is not easy to find species which are equally trustworthy guides to alkalinity.

Extreme values of alkalinity are, however, associated with a special soil condition which does markedly affect the distribution of plants. These are the soils in which sea-salt attains a considerable concentration. The plants able to live in such soils are called halophytes and they do not normally occur in other habitats. They are in fact specialised in much the same sense as the acid plants mentioned above, but perhaps in a lesser degree. They habitually show the morphological characters associated with an inadequate water supply, and are xerophytes because the concentration of the salt in the soil interferes with the absorption of water by the roots, so that these plants live in a state of physiological drought. Most halophytes can to some extent live in habitats of ordinary salt values, and to that extent their occurrence in maritime situations is facultative rather than obligatory. It is interesting to note that they occur also commonly in inland salt desert or pans, and this suggests that it is indeed a matter of the soil salt that controls their distribution and not any other factor connected with the proximity of the sea. They are thus to be sharply contrasted with those species, mentioned in Chapter 14, which appear to owe their distribution partly to the distribution of salt in the atmosphere.

Biotic edaphic factors comprise all influences of other organisms on the habitat, though they chiefly concern in practice the activities of the bacteria of the soil, which control the rapidity or slowness with which humus may be formed as well as such chemical reactions as nitrogen fixation. The bacterial content of soils indeed is a very important measure of their general fertility, and the lack of this proper content is certainly the cause of the failure of many species to maintain themselves in the lighter, and what are generally called the poorer, soils.

Under biotic factors must also be included mycorrhiza, which is the name given to the symbiotic relation between certain flowering plants and fungi. In some plants the fungus permeates even the tissues of the seed and thus is kept in readiness for its germination, but in others the seed does not carry the fungus and successful germination depends upon the presence of the latter in the soil, whence it may come into association with the seedling at an early stage. In such cases as these the distribution of the species may easily be limited by the absence of the appropriate fungus in the soil. Some of the terrestrial orchids illustrate this condition.

In addition to these two main types of biotic factor many others will no doubt suggest themselves to the reader. Earthworms, as Darwin pointed out, play a great rôle in mixing and aerating the soil and altering its physical condition, and other animals do the same thing on a slighter scale. There is also the question of animal excreta. At least in the south of England certain plants tend to be associated with rabbit-burrows and warrens in a way that strongly suggests that it is the result of the locally enhanced nitrogen values in the soil. Such plants include *Bryonia dioica*, *Myosotis arvensis*, *Urtica dioica*, *Cynoglossum officinale* and *Verbascum thapsus*. Similarly the flora of manure heaps and of chicken runs is generally very characteristic.

PLATE 23

Map of the World showing the distribution of annual
rainfall. Slightly simplified from various sources.

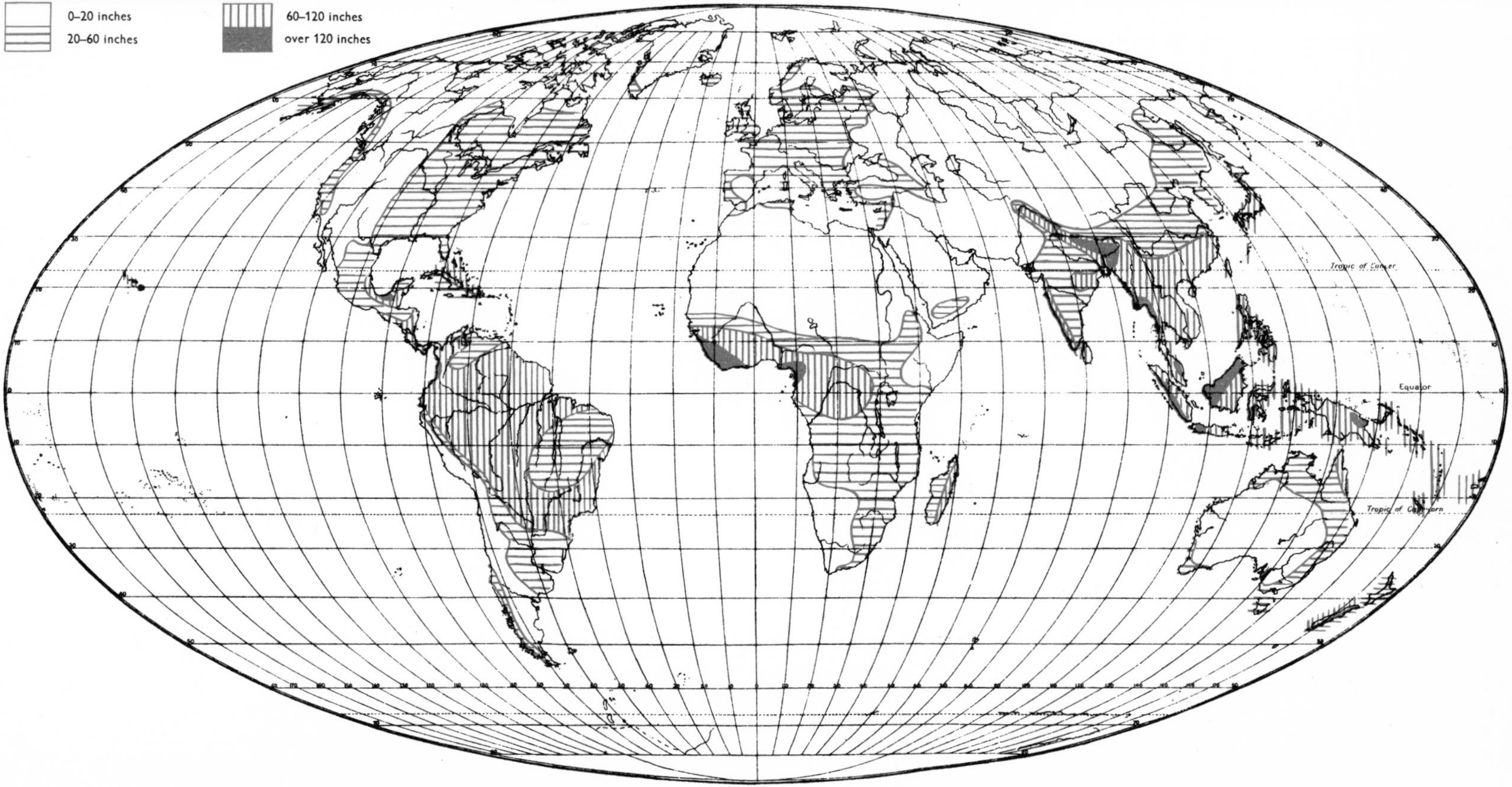

0–20 inches
20–60 inches

60–120 inches
over 120 inches

Tropic of Cancer

Equator

Tropic of Capricorn

Areas correct   Distortion increasing (towards border of map.

Approximate Scale. 1:100,000,000 (1600 miles – 1 inch) along Equator

on Mollweide's Homolographic Projection

Copyright

CHAPTER 19

THE FACTORS OF DISTRIBUTION—IV. THE DISPERSAL OF PLANTS

AN enormous and very scattered literature has grown up round the subject of dispersal, and Ridley (596) did botanists, and indeed all biologists, great service by collecting together into one volume almost all the information then available on the subject. His is still the standard work and the source of much that is written in the following pages, but there are various noteworthy later sources, among them Molinier and Müller (522), Müller (527), and Dansereau and Lems (174). On the matter of long-distance dispersal in particular there is much useful information in the Introduction to Zimmerman's *Insects of Hawaii* (807).

The chief theoretical aspects of plant dispersal have already been dealt with, but it is desirable to review shortly at this point the various actual methods by which it is brought about, and the best way of doing this is to give first a tabulated list of them and then to make what further comments may be necessary about each.

Ridley classifies the main methods of dispersal as follows:

1. WIND—
    A. Without special direct structural modification:
        a. tumble weeds;
        b. dust seeds;
        c. jactitation.
    B. With special structural modification:
        a. winged disseminules;
        b. plumed disseminules;
        c. woolly disseminules.

2. WATER—
    A. Rain-wash.
    B. Ice, rivers, floods.
    C. Sea.

3. ANIMALS—
    A. Internal carriage.
    B. External adhesion:
        a. simple adhesion: *a.* mammals;
        b. special adhesive methods;   *b.* birds;
        c. viscid adhesion.   *c.* other animals.

4. MECHANICAL—
    A. Explosive fruits.
    B. Elongated stems, etc.

5. HUMAN AGENCY.

Tumble weeds

Normally the seed falls from the parent plant when ripe either separately or in small groups contained in fruits, but occasionally the whole plant comes loose

from the ground and is capable of being blown along the surface carrying its disseminules with it. Such plants are called tumble weeds. It is interesting to note that
they occur especially or entirely in steppes and other open situations. *Psoralea
argophylla* of the North American prairies and *Anastatica hierocuntica* of the North
African–Indian deserts are good examples.

Dust seeds

Given the occurrence of wind, it must follow that many plants will tend to be
dispersed by this means, merely by virtue of the small weight of their seeds, especially
if their shape also is such as to favour this.

Small light seeds occur in a number of families, but they are particularly characteristic of the orchids. Some idea of their size may be given by the statement that
some species may produce as many as several hundred million on one plant, and
that individual seeds may weigh as little as two-millionths of a gramme. Ridley gives
an interesting account of the occurrence of orchids on remote islands, but it is noteworthy that there are quite a number of islands in which no species occur, and one
obvious possible explanation of this is in the direction of the wind. This point is of
some interest in relation to the general opinion expressed earlier that the possession of good dispersal means does not necessarily lead to effective dispersal in
all directions.

Jactitation

This is the term given by Ridley to the process by which seeds are scattered by
being shaken out of the parent plant under the influence of wind. It is perhaps more
popularly known under the phrase "censer mechanism". It may be said to occur to
some extent in all plants which have dry dehiscent fruits and which are without
any more definite methods of dispersal, and it is of special interest in view of the
earlier discussion because it is a restricted method of dispersal whose chief effect is
obviously to spread the seeds outside the shadow of the parent. It is seen in a number of
very familiar plants, as, for instance, *Melandrium* (*Lychnis*) *dioicum, Scilla non-scripta*
and many species of *Papaver*.

Winged fruits

Ridley points out that the presence of wings on fruits is not always associated
with dispersal, and instances *Begonia*, where the fruit is winged but in which dispersal is related to the minute size of the seeds. Nevertheless in most winged fruits
the wings serve as dispersal mechanisms, and the following types can be recognised.

In bladder fruits the carpel walls become thin and papery so that the whole pod
can be blown about and, incidentally, will usually float. The bladder senna of
gardens, *Colutea arborescens*, is a good example. In some plants the calyx develops
into a thin bladdery covering to the fruit. Winged or angled fruits are common.
Conspicuously four-winged fruits occur in *Combretum* and in *Terminalia*, but the
number of wings may be anything from two to a dozen. In the genus *Pentace* the
number of wings is a useful specific character. Fruits in which only a single wing
is developed are usually called samaras, and this type is well represented among British plants. Everyone is familiar, for instance, with the "keys" of the sycamore and
maple, and others are found in the ash and the elm. Sometimes, as in the first two, the
fruit as a whole is really two-winged but splits into two disseminules each with one
wing. Samaras are also common in tropical plants. Nearly allied to the last in function
are the bract wings which occur in a number of fruits such as those of the hop, the

hornbeam and the lime. In some species of *Scabiosa* the involucel-like bract, in which each individual flower is set, is expanded above into a circular wing. A rather particular condition is seen in members of the grasses and sedges, where the special type of bract associated with the flower often acts as a fruit wing in dispersal. Rarely the pedicel is flattened out into wings, this condition being particularly associated with the genus *Brunnichia*.

A fairly common condition is for the sepals of the flower to become enlarged and more or less membranous in fruit, and thus to provide wings of value in dispersal. This is particularly well seen in the family Dipterocarpaceae, where the wings and fruit are sometimes of great size, so much so that it would seem that the function of the wings can be no more than to control in some measure the fall of the fruit to the ground, and it is significant in this view that many of the members of this family are very tall forest trees. A similar condition on a smaller scale is seen in *Triplaris* and causes the fruits to fall obliquely to the ground so that they are well scattered. The same thing, however, occurs often in climbing or herbaceous plants and is no doubt associated with wider dispersal. The much rarer condition of petaline wings occurs chiefly in tropical plants, but is found to some degree in many species of *Erica*. Finally, it must be remembered that any organ, if sufficiently light and extensive, may assist in the dispersal of fruit or seeds.

Winged seeds

These are in general not so common as winged fruits, perhaps, as Ridley has pointed out, because the only structure which can easily become winged is the seed coat. There are, however, many beautiful and well-developed instances, some of the finest being associated with the family Bignoniaceae. This is a tropical family, but *Catalpa*, which shows the condition excellently, is frequently grown in gardens. The genus *Dioscorea* also has well-marked seed-wings. Among British plants the genus *Spergularia* is interesting as showing various stages in the development of seed-wings. It should also be mentioned that in many plants with minute seeds these latter are often winged (e.g. *Rhododendron* spp.), and it is a question whether lightness or the presence of wings is the more important in dispersal.

Plumed fruits

In many grasses pluming, that is the presence of long silky hairs, is associated with the fruit or its related structures. *Phragmites communis*, which is often described as one of the most widespread Angiosperms, has such hairs well developed on the axis of the spikelet. On the other hand, Ridley comments on the fact that while such grasses are widespread on continental areas they are surprisingly rare on islands.

Plumed styles are not uncommonly developed and are conspicuous in a number of temperate plants, especially those of mountains. *Anemone* and *Dryas* exemplify the latter, and the genera *Geum* and *Clematis* are other conspicuous instances.

The subject of plumed sepals is almost entirely that of the pappus of the Compositae, which is so familiar and often-quoted an example of dispersal mechanisms. In these plants the calyx lobes are modified into bristles which may or may not be plumed, and the whole arrangement, as in the dandelion, is often very specialised. It should be pointed out that there are many Composites without this pappus development, and there is no evidence that their dispersal suffers in consequence. *Matricaria matricarioides* is an interesting example of this. A native of North America, it was introduced, presumably accidentally, into Britain in the latter half of the last century. It possess no pappus at all, but it has by now spread to practically every corner of the country. The Composites are, however, by no means the only plants with plumed calyx lobes, and the Proteaceae, especially the well-known silver tree, have them extremely well developed.

Plumed seeds

Ridley points out that plumed seeds are always borne in capsules or follicles, and that they are specially characteristic of herbs or climbers rather than trees. Above all, they are to be found in the Asclepiadaceae and Apocynaceae, where they perhaps attain their greatest development in *Strophanthus*, but they are also well developed in the more temperate genus *Epilobium*.

Woolly seeds

It is sometimes difficult to draw the line between plumed and woolly seeds as, for instance, in the seeds of the willows and poplars, but the condition is really characteristic and well developed in certain Malvales, where it provides most of the economic value of the cottons and the kapok.

Rain-wash

Ridley, it is interesting to note, is of opinion that this is more important than is generally supposed because of the part which it may play in carrying the fallen seed further away from the mother-plant. It must in ordinary circumstances be of comparatively little general significance, and it is difficult to visualise any extensive carriage by this means. It seems likely to have particular application in the colonisation of newly formed land.

Ice, rivers and floods

It is clear that moving water in whatever form will tend to have the same effect on disseminules as it may have on other objects, and hence that it must be a dispersal means to some extent. In the case of ice it has long been suggested that icebergs may transport disseminules, but this is an instance of a theoretical conception whose practical application can scarcely be regarded as other than very slight and, indeed, can hardly be more than accidental in occurrence.

Rivers will certainly assist plant dispersal in one direction and floods will tend to assist it less directionally. In these there is a general tendency to dispersal merely by the power of water movement irrespective of whether the disseminule can float or not, and there is also the particular aspect of dispersal of aquatic plants in the vegetative form of pieces of stems or buds, a method not generally applicable to land plants. The question of what may be called special water dispersal mechanisms involves the problem of flotation, and there is no doubt that many seeds and fruits are capable of floating in fresh water for a considerable time. Often this effect is produced by structures which are properly to be associated more particularly with other means of dispersal, as is the case with many of the winged and plumed disseminules, which by their nature will also tend to float, but there are several directions in which structure seems directed solely to flotation. Such, for instance, is the nature of the pericarp in fruits and of the testa in seeds. Broadly it may be said that where the texture of these is such as to hold much air the disseminule will float for a longer or shorter period. It may also fairly often happen that in falling into water some air may be inevitably imprisoned in the cavities of fruits and thereby cause flotation. Ridley gives many examples of these things and also a survey of flotation in different families. The general conclusion is that fresh-water dispersal by flotation is comparatively common, but must also, by the nature of the case, be of but comparatively local importance.

Carriage by sea

The obvious possibilities of sea carriage have made this one of the most studied of all aspects of dispersal, and readers will find the work not only of Ridley but also of Guppy (325, 326, 327) of great interest here.

At first sight sea dispersal looks a most promising way of explaining many otherwise inexplicable distributions and especially of many wide discontinuities, and so before going into any details it is important to emphasise certain general limitations inherent in the method.

In the first place, sea carriage differs fundamentally from freshwater carriage in that the actual medium of transport is more or less toxic to most disseminules. In other words, most seeds are killed by anything like prolonged immersion in sea water. Cases of great resistance to this danger are often mentioned, but these exceptions only prove the rule. Secondly, sea carriage must be correlated almost entirely with currents and hence will tend to be in certain directions only, and these are by no means the ideal theoretical directions. Again, most currents tend to have at least some north and south direction, and thus will tend to transport disseminules into different climatic zones. Thirdly, only a very small number of plant species are likely to disperse their disseminules into the sea, and, most important of all, sea carriage is very unlikely to deposit disseminules in spots where they can germinate and establish themselves. For instance, a plant growing on the slopes of a continental mountain is not likely to disperse its seeds into sea water. Still more unlikely is it that sea will disperse those seeds to the slopes of a mountain.

As Ridley's very long and detailed account shows, there are undoubtedly many species of plants which are, by various peculiarities of structure and resistance, capable of floating unharmed for long periods in sea water (325, 618), and which therefore may suffer transport over vast distances by the action of sea currents. It is not surprising that the plants so widely spread on tropical beaches or throughout small tropical islands, such as the so-called strand plants, possess in greater or lesser degree such features. The coconut (*Cocos nucifera*), for instance, can float unharmed in the sea, and may do so for a length of time permitting it to drift 3,000 miles in favourable circumstances (54, 211, 507). It is also not surprising that the strand plants are very widespread, because they inhabit places to which the action of the sea can bring their disseminules. On the other hand, it is very significant that these strand plants are in general either tropical or (more rarely) temperate. There are few, if any, subcosmopolitan strand plants. In this connection the family Palmae is of peculiar interest. As described in Chapter 4 it shows an unusually high degree of insular endemism and very few transoceanic distributions, and this may doubtless be associated with the fact that the coconut, already mentioned, and *Nipa fruticans* are almost the only members of the family which can be sea-dispersed (596). True, the huge fruits of the double coconut, *Lodoicea*, which grows nowhere but in the Seychelles, have been found floating and not infrequently cast up on the shores of Asia, but this is only when their specific gravity is reduced by the decay of its contents and they are no longer capable of germinating (206).

In short the case of sea dispersal more than any other puts the general potentialities of dispersal in their right perspective. Where all the associated factors are favourable it may be of immense importance and allow a species to cover enormous distances, but this optimum condition is likely to be rare. In the first place the disseminule must reach the sea, in the second it must be capable of floating, in the third it must resist the action of salt water, in the fourth it must be deposited, at the end of dispersal, in a suitable climate, and lastly in a suitable habitat for germination and establishment. It may be left to the reader to conclude how often all these conditions are likely to be fulfilled, and a reference back to the distribution of marine and semi-marine Angiosperms may be of assistance (Chapter 11). The distribution of the mangroves is particularly illuminating in this connection, in the way that they indicate that there are many considerations besides mere passage by sea transport which limit their ranges. These observations must not be interpreted as belittling the interest of many aspects of sea dispersal. The structures which enable disseminules to float or which protect the embryo are often intricate and beautiful, and Ridley gives a most interesting account of them.

So far attention has been drawn only to plants whose disseminules are capable of independent flotation. It has often been suggested that many seeds, especially if small, may be transported more or less accidentally in drifting wood or in pumice. The possibility of this in special cases must be borne in mind, but enough has been said to show that it is likely to be but very rarely efficacious.

It may also be remarked in relation to the mention of the coconut above that the exceptionally wide area of this plant to-day is certainly largely due to the influence of man.

Dispersal by animals

As was indicated in the table on p. 369, animals tend to disperse disseminules in three ways, by swallowing them, passing them through and out of the digestive tract; by carrying them attached to their outer surface, or by carrying them in mud adhering to their feet, and, as Ridley points out, all animals thus may disperse plants to some extent. The primary consideration must naturally be the movement of the animals themselves, and this must always be borne in mind in gauging the importance of such dispersal. Locally restricted animals, or animals relatively immobile, will not play a large rôle. Generally speaking the problem involves mammals and birds, and the latter are of vastly greater potential importance because of their greater range of action. Grazing mammals, on the other hand, are probably responsible for a more intensive type of dispersal, because their food will always contain a certain number of disseminules and these will be almost continuously passed out of the body.

The structure of disseminules is correlated with animal dispersal in two main ways. On the one hand there is the development of the fruits so as to make them attractive to animals, which in consuming them will also consume the seeds, and on the other there is the development of special structures which will enable the disseminule to adhere to the surface of the animal.

Attractiveness to animals in turn is generally due to one or both of two features, namely colour and palatability. Colour may be in the fruits themselves, or in associate structures such as parts of the inflorescence axes, or in or about the seeds, as for example in arils.

Bird dispersal

Dispersal by birds is generally associated with brightly coloured fleshy fruits such as form the main diet of many birds, but small dry seeds and fruits such as those of grasses are also commonly eaten, and no doubt dispersed to some extent.

As with sea carriage, so also has bird dispersal received great attention because it promises to provide an explanation of much in plant distribution which is otherwise difficult to understand, but it seems doubtful whether it is capable of doing all that is sometimes claimed for it. There are many factors which will decide the value of bird dispersal, and these must be taken carefully into account. One, the active range of the birds concerned, has already been mentioned. Attention has rather naturally been focused on birds which are known to fly long distances, but these are comparatively few and most birds have a comparatively limited range of flight. This is especially the case with those in which territoriality is strongly developed. Migrant birds usually have very definite routes and these routes are generally north and south, that is to say between widely different climatic zones. This is probably the most important point of all, because there must always be the possibility that long-distance bird flight may, at least on rare occasions, have taken place in almost all directions, but unless such flight can result in the deposition of the disseminules in conditions suited to their development it must necessarily be of no account. Again, in some parts of the world, as for instance in much of the tropics, there is little or no migrationary movement. A very useful map of the routes taken by migrating birds is given by Cailleux (101).

Another very important consideration, especially in relation to possible wide transoceanic carriage, is the speed of flight and the time that a disseminule takes to pass through the body. In general this time is probably very short, perhaps at most a few hours, and whether birds can and do retain their intestinal contents for a longer period when in flight is still doubtful.

It has been stated that migratory birds habitually travel on an empty stomach, but this has been contradicted, and it would at any rate be difficult to maintain that they never do so. It is also important to note that most isolated oceanic islands are not visited to any great extent by migrant birds. Related to this also is that many of the most wide ranging sea birds are not fruit eaters. In Tristan da Cunha, for instance, the only frugivorous land birds are endemic species.

In short, it seems that dispersal over wide areas by birds is very much on a par with wide dispersal by sea. There is a great potentiality in it provided that all the subsidiary factors are favourable, but the details of the process are such that it is difficult to imagine that such totally favourable conditions can be anything but very occasional. It may be argued that even very rare wide dispersal will be sufficient, but here there is the overriding consideration already emphasised that dispersal must be followed by germination and establishment, and this is something quite apart from the mere question of transport.

There is, however, one direction in which bird dispersal has probably had a paramount effect on plant distribution. This is the case of certain freshwater aquatic plants such as the duckweeds (*Lemna*). As was shown earlier, these plants are tiny free-floating aquatics, some with an extremely wide geographic range. They have no dispersal mechanisms in the ordinary sense of the word, but their form is such that they can easily be transported by simple adhesion. At the same time they are no better equipped for this than many seeds and fruits, and their wide distributions are to be attributed not to any specially valuable dispersal potentiality but to some other factor. It is not difficult to imagine what this may be. Free-floating aquatics live in a habitat quite different from that of land plants, the essential distinction being the elimination of many of the most stringent climatic influences. For instance, fresh water normally shows a much narrower range of temperature values than neighbouring land surfaces, and, more obviously still, the amount of precipitation is likely to be of much less consequence. In view of this it seems reasonably certain that the wide range of *Lemna* (and what applies to it applies also to some other aquatics) is due to the greater similarity between its habitats the world over and the absence of space competition in open water, with the consequent greater chances of survival and establishment after dispersal. Birds carrying *Lemna* will tend to rise from one sheet of water and to come down on another which, however far away, is likely to be fairly similar to that from which the bird came. Here, it will be seen, the chance of deposition in an unsuitable spot which is so likely in the case of land plants is almost eliminated.

Carriage on the feet of birds

The researches of Darwin (177) on this subject have ever since made it a somewhat classic example of dispersal, but all that we need say about it here is that it is in fact very parallel with the carriage of disseminules inside birds, and in particular is controlled by those same general considerations concerning bird carriage which have been noted there.

Other animals

As regards dispersal by animals other than mammals and birds, attention chiefly centres round the activities of ants, whose relation to plants in general and to dispersal in particular is a subject of great interest. All that can be said here is that while in certain circumstances almost any animal may be instrumental directly or indirectly in dispersing seeds or small fruits, the result can scarcely be considered to contribute appreciably to the general distribution of plants.

Special adhesion mechanisms

Perhaps the most noteworthy feature of these is that they parallel very completely the structural modification associated with wind dispersal, the difference being that, instead of wings and plumes, hooks are developed.

Rarely adhesion may be by branches of the inflorescence, as has been noted in certain grasses and Cyperaceae.

Adhesion by armed bracts is commoner and particularly associated with Composites, where *Xanthium* and *Arctium* provide two excellent examples. Here the hooks by which the disseminule clings are developed on the phyllaries.

The glumes of grasses are often so furnished with hairs and hooks that they cling readily, and several of our British grasses have these, although there are more striking examples in the tropics. In addition to mere attachment the structures in some grasses are such that the fruits actually bore into the skin of the animal and become absolutely fixed. Presumably in this case, if it is indeed a dispersal mechanism, the seeds cannot germinate until the death of the animals. The genus *Stipa* affords several examples of this, and the writer has seen joints of imported mutton so thickly penetrated by the fruits that they have been condemned as unfit for human consumption.

Adhesive perianth segments, such as are found in some of the Amaranthaceae, are not uncommon, and, in particular, adhesive calyces are familiar. They are found, for instance, in many Composites, where the bristles of the pappus are modified into hooks, the genus *Bidens* being notorious in this respect. *Myosotis* is also a good instance, as anyone who has walked through a wood where *M. arvensis* is in fruit will know. The Labiatae furnish many examples too. Here the teeth of the calyx are variously recurved so as to form hooks.

Hooked styles are also frequent, as in *Geum, Anemone* and *Ranunculus.* A special form of this method is also seen in the stiff-haired awns of the stork's bill (*Erodium*).

It is, however, particularly in fruits that special adhesion methods are developed and they are very common, sometimes attaining great development and specialisation. Indeed, almost every type of dry fruit may be found furnished with hooks of one kind or another. Most of our familiar native examples of special adhesion belong here, and among them *Sanicula europaea, Circaea lutetiana* and *Galium aparine* may be cited, all three of them being exceptionally and irritatingly efficient. Extreme conditions are best seen in the so-called grapple plants belonging to the genera *Harpagophytum* and *Martynia.* In the former the fruit is several inches long and furnished with robust long-hooked processes. In the latter one end of the fruit is produced into a pair of very long curved hooks.

Viscid adhesion

In much the same way as with plumes, wings and hooks, many parts of the flower or associated structures may become sticky by exudation from glands, but most of these variants are too rare to need mention here and our attention may be confined to viscid fruits and viscid seeds.

In some fleshy fruits the pulp is so sticky that the seeds adhere to anything they touch. This is particularly well known in the mistletoe, but it occurs also in a number of exotic plants. In *Pisonia grandis,* of the Nyctaginaceae, the anthocarp which encloses the fruit is sticky and adheres easily to the feathers of land and sea birds which rest in the trees and which are known to transport it. The species is distributed (690) from Christmas Island south of Java, and from Formosa, to Australia, New Caledonia and Pitcairn Island, but is not on Midway Island or Hawaii.

Another form of adhesive fruit is where dry fruits of various kinds, chiefly achenes, are furnished with sticky glands. Several Composites, including *Adenostemma,* illustrate this well.

Quite a number of seeds become viscid when wet by the development of mucilage from their surface cells (see p. 382). This condition has been noted in several British plants, and the best example is certainly *Plantago major,* in which the secretion of mucilage is very copious. Many of the species of *Juncus* and *Luzula* show the same character.

Explosive fruits

In all the cases so far discussed the fruit has been a relatively passive agent in dispersal, but there must now be mentioned some instances where it takes a more active part. In all of them dehiscence of the fruit, instead of being gradual, is so sudden that the contained seeds are shaken out more or less violently, sometimes to a considerable distance. The exact method by which this is accomplished varies a good deal, but is in all cases due to unequal strain set up in the ripening fruit, a strain which is ultimately relieved by the explosive rupture of the fruit wall.

One of the best known though not one of the most striking is the gorse. On hot summer days the popping of the ripe pods is very noticeable. The genera *Oxalis* and *Impatiens* also furnish many instances, the familiar name "touch-me-not" given to a species of the latter being a well-earned tribute to the sensitiveness of its ripe capsules.

Hura crepitans, a tree of the Euphorbiaceae, and the squirting cucumber (*Ecballium*) are other very remarkable examples.

Other mechanical dispersal

In this chapter on mechanical dispersal Ridley refers to the fact that many plants possess rhizomes, soboles or runners which do in fact play a kind of subsidiary rôle in dispersal because they give the plants some kind of mobility, in that they enable new fruiting branches to arise at some distance from the parent axis.

From the theoretical point of view it must be emphasised that this is not really a method of dispersal at all, because no actual spatial discontinuity is involved, but a method by which the parent plant extends its own body over the surface of the ground. In no case, as far as the writer is aware, does such a vegetative spread replace dispersal by seeds or fruits, at least under natural conditions. Its function also seems to be quite distinct from that of dispersal. The latter, as has been shown earlier, is designed to scatter the species and to be a method at least by which increase of range can be accomplished, and it is intimately bound up in conception with the protected resting stage of the seed. Creeping stems on the other hand, while they may in fact increase the area occupied by a species, would appear to have, as their main function, the occupation of soil at the expense of other species, often together with the secondary function of perennation. Hence it seems justifiable to regard the process of spreading by vegetative means as related more closely to the problems of competition rather than to the problems of dispersal, and on these grounds it is not considered necessary to go further into the matter here. It may, however, be worth noting that in some cases exceptional powers of vegetative spread are associated with exceptional powers of dispersal, as is the case with *Chamaenerion* (*Epilobium*) *angustifolium*, and this may perhaps be evidence in favour of the view expressed above.

Dispersal by human agency

This is perhaps the most convenient place at which to consider shortly the whole question of the introduction of plants into new countries by the agency of man. As has been said, we are chiefly concerned in this book with the natural distribution of plants, but their accidental or deliberate introduction by man is now so widespread and so much vitiates the picture of natural distribution that some account of it is necessary. It has, moreover, a very definite bearing on many theoretical aspects of our subject.

In general it may be said that there is scarcely a country in the world where human activities have not led to the introduction and establishment of species foreign to that country, and the intensity of this introduction is roughly proportional to the extent of man's influence on the country. The subject is therefore largely the story of the emigration of man from European countries and his colonisation of distant parts of the world, but this is not the whole of the story and introduction of one kind or another has accompanied almost every human movement. For instance, many tropical plants, especially those of Asia and Polynesia, have been carried far and wide by the migratory movements of the native races of these regions, and the wide range of many such plants and the uncertainty of their place of origin are generally due to this. This type of introduction extends over a long period of time and many of its early stages are now beyond elucidation. The other aspect of the subject, that of introduction by the migrating and colonising activities of white peoples, has a much shorter history and is more or less coincident with the great colonial expansions of the last two or three hundred years.

This in turn has two aspects which illustrate in themselves the two main types of introduction, namely deliberate and accidental. The first of these is mainly associated with outward movements of the more advanced races from their centres in the northern temperate regions, and the second is generally the reverse. The former also tends to provide some of the more conspicuous examples of introduction, although the latter probably accounts for the larger bulk of species transference. That is to say, deliberate introduction usually concerns a fairly narrow range of species, while accidental introduction may be contributed to from a very great number of species.

Although introduction into the more distant parts of the world may be regarded as a fairly recent process, more localised transfer of plants has been going on ever since mankind first began to move freely about the world. The status of plants in Great Britain illustrates this point well. Species have been entering the country for hundreds, and perhaps thousands, of years and many of them have now become so integral a part of the vegetation that is is almost impossible to determine their real status. In relation to this particular point, however, it must be remembered that introduction has been over comparatively limited distances and from areas not too widely different. Where transference is over much wider areas, and more particularly across the equator, there is not the same difficulty in distinguishing between native and adventive species.

Except for the doubtful cases just mentioned, the adventive species in such a country as Great Britain, for instance, are generally to be recognised because they inhabit only unnatural habitats, that is to say habitats which exist only by virtue of man's actions. Arable fields, roadsides, waste places, buildings and walls are the special homes of adventive species, and it is generally only in particular cases and after a long time that introduced plants succeed in establishing themselves as constituents of the apparently aboriginal vegetation. This is an important point which has been emphasised by many writers (12, 799), and there seems little doubt that the struggle of introduction *versus* native (exotic *versus* indigene) is much less in favour of the former than is generally supposed. The point already mentioned, that introductions tend to be restricted to disturbed ground, is very generally true and is indeed probably the reason for the idea that introductions prevail, because it leads to their appearance just where they will be most conspicuous to the human observers. This has been demonstrated very distinctly for New Zealand (141), and the conclusion is that exotics have scarcely entered at all into the primitive vegetation. It is pointed out that they are nearly always plants of the lowland belt, and also that their growth forms tend to be different from those of the indigenes and to militate against their successful competition. At the same time it must be remembered that the history of introduction, at least of northern plants, is for the most part very recent. New Zealand has been the subject of a great deal of study in relation to introduction, and Thomson (733) has collected an enormous amount of interesting information, which will be reviewed in a moment. Reference may also be made to Clark (135), and there is a specially interesting first-hand account in Guthrie-Smith's story of his sheep station Tutira (331). C. M. Smith (683) has recently provided a very informative account of the effects of these many introductions on some of the native members of the flora.

De Wildeman made an important contribution to this subject in his study of introduced species in the flora of the Congo (186). Of 500 such he regards Asia as the source of 377 and America as the home of the rest, and he concludes from a careful examination that all of them could be transported by external adherence to various animals, including man. He also expresses the significant opinion that many of the so-called endemic species in the flora are no more than local forms of adventive plants, a view with which botanists in various other parts of the world will doubtless find themselves in agreement.

The reason why introductions are mainly confined to disturbed ground is apparently that there the vegetation is open and the question of competition with existing plants does not arise, or only does so in lesser degree. In these circumstances of freedom from opposition the introduced species may flourish and multiply to an amazing extent, as for instance the Opuntias when introduced into Australia. Open water too provides the same freedom, and there are many examples of introduced freshwater plants luxuriating greatly. Two of the best-known examples are *Elodea canadensis* in England and *Nasturtium officinale* in New Zealand. Such plants, however, tend after a time to settle down to a more reasonable scale of existence.

Human dispersal of plants is of two kinds, deliberate and accidental. The former may obviously take all kinds of forms and there is nothing to be gained in analysing it further here, but in the latter certain circumstances are of special importance. These may be tabulated as follows:

1. Dispersal by accidental adhesion to moving objects:
   a. Adhesion to man's person.
   b. Adhesion to moving vehicles.
      e.g. mud on cart-wheels, dust carts, trains, etc.
2. Dispersal among crop-seed:
      e.g. many cornfield weeds.
3. Dispersal among other plants:
      e.g. fodder and packing materials.
4. Dispersal among minerals:
      e.g. soil export, ballast, road metal.
5. Dispersal by carriage of seed for purposes other than planting:
      e.g. this includes a whole range of possibilities. One mentioned by Ridley is the spread of drug plants from the seeds escaping from druggists' shops.

So much for some of the more qualitative aspects of introductions. An idea of the quantitative side of the question is best conveyed by a reference to some particular country, and in view of Thomson's work just mentioned New Zealand may well be selected. The reader may also be reminded that the introduction of plants into Great Britain was dealt with at some length in Chapter 13.

The Naturalisation of Plants in New Zealand

According to Thomson (733) more than 600 species have been introduced into New Zealand and have become more or less truly wild in the sense that they reproduce habitually by seed and have become permanent features of the plant life there.

A great many of these have become abundant or common throughout the country (12, 13, 14). They include many well-known weeds but also a few others, and the following is a list of some of them:

Ranunculus repens	*Stellaria media*
Nasturtium officinale	*Sagina procumbens*
Cardamine hirsuta	*Spergula arvensis*
Capsella bursa-pastoris	*Hypericum androsaemum*
Silene quinquevulnera	*Malva rotundifolia*
Cerastium vulgatum	*Ulex europaeus*

Sarothamnus scoparius	Prunella vulgaris
Trifolium pratense	Verbena officinalis
Vicia sativa	Plantago lanceolata
Foeniculum vulgare	Plantago major
Arctium lappa	Rumex acetosella
Cirsium arvense	Rumex crispus
Cirsium vulgare	Rumex obtusifolius
Chrysanthemum leucanthemum	Chenopodium album
Bellis perennis	Euphorbia peplus
Senecio jacobaea	Phalaris canariensis
Senecio vulgaris	Anthoxanthum odoratum
Hypochoeris radicata	Phleum pratense
Crepis capillaris	Polypogon monspeliensis
Sonchus arvensis	Holcus lanatus
Anagallis arvensis	Dactylis glomerata
Centaurium umbellatum	Cynosurus cristatus
Digitalis purpurea	Poa annua
Mentha pulegium	Poa pratensis

Of these *Hypochoeris radicata* is often considered the most ubiquitous of all. *Nasturtium officinale* and *Verbena officinalis* have occurred or still often occur in very large forms. *Trifolium pratense* (red clover) is of exceptional interest because its abundance is directly associated with the presence of humble-bees, which seem to be the only insects capable of pollinating it. These bees were deliberately introduced into New Zealand, and before their advent the red clover rarely if ever set seed. All the species mentioned are common European plants, and the only other species which has become widely established appears to be *Eschscholzia californica*, which, as its name implies, is a native of western North America. Some species have become so completely established and form so intimate a part of the natural vegetation that they have often been considered to be native. They are, however, almost certainly introductions and include *Geranium molle*, *Sonchus oleraceus*, *Plantago coronopus* and *Polygonum aviculare*.

On the other hand a number of species are much less common that might be expected. Among them are:

Papaver rhoeas	Lamium album
Geranium robertianum	Lamium purpureum
Daucus carota	Urtica dioica
Centaurea cyanus	Urtica urens
Cichorium intybus	Arrhenatherum elatius
Calluna vulgaris	Agropyron repens
Convolvulus arvensis	Brachypodium sylvaticum

Others have become firmly established locally as garden escapes, as *Pelargonium zonale* and *Tropaeolum majus*. The peach, *Prunus persica*, is of interest here too. In the earlier days it established itself freely, but now it does so far less frequently and seems to be restricted by the occurrence of certain diseases from which it suffers.

Perhaps more interesting than any of these are the plants which have never been able to establish themselves, even with the repeated help of man. *Viola odorata* and various species of *Primula* such as the primrose, cowslip and polyanthus are noteworthy examples of this, and the reason seems in some measure at least to be the absence of the normal pollinating insects. In the case of the Primulas the plants refused even to seed before the introduction of bees. They now do so in gardens but have never become established. Heaths of various kinds also have never been naturalised. Other species which, fortunately or unfortunately, have never become established are *Linum usitatissimum, Pisum sativum, Lathyrus odoratus, Petunia parviflora, Opuntia vulgaris* and *Scilla non-scripta*.

A group of species has become widespread only since the introduction and subsequent multiplication of such fruit-eating birds as thrushes and blackbirds. The prevalence of the blackberry, *Rubus fruticosus*, which is perhaps the worst of all weeds in New Zealand, is a case in point, and others are *Berberis vulgaris, Rosa rubiginosa* (which incidentally is far more widespread than *R. canina*), *Crataegus, Ribes uva-crispa, Sambucus nigra* and *S. racemosa, Leycesteria formosa* and *Phytolacca*. There are, of course, native fruit-eating birds, but presumably their natural diet is in general confined to native species.

In the course of his remarks Thomson refers frequently to the dispersal mechanisms of the various plants, and it is interesting to note that in the following species the seeds or fruits become sticky when wet: *Capsella, Lepidium sativum, Viola tricolor, Artemisia absinthium, Senecio vulgaris, Gilia* spp., *Glecoma hederacea*, and species of *Plantago*.

Finally there are a few cases of special interest. *Brassica oleracea* was planted by the earliest visitors to the country, and the progeny of this stock has gradually reverted to the wild type, which now inhabits sea cliffs in various parts of the dominion as it does in Europe. *Matricaria matricarioides*, which has been referred to before in another connection, was locally abundant as early as 1882 and has since spread almost everywhere. *Verbascum thapsus* is especially common where there are big populations of rabbits, a feature which is noticeable in its distribution in England also. The broad bean, *Faba vulgaris*, has been noted sprouting from the skeleton of a pigeon, the inference being that germination was possible only after the body of the carrier had decayed. Some people think that many seeds are distributed in this particular way.

Certainly the most conspicuous feature of the long list given above is the fact that practically all the plants mentioned are what may be called common European weeds belonging to what has been distinguished as the Scandinavian floristic element. The great prevalence of these as adventives not only in New Zealand but in almost all countries (see Chapter 4) has been commented on again and again from the time of Hooker, who in his *Introductory Essay to the Flora of New Zealand* (371) discussed the matter at length. So impressed was he by what he considered to be the aggressive colonising power of the Scandinavian flora that he foresaw the gradual extermination of indigenous floras by these adventive species. This extreme point of view was no doubt connected with the fact that at first sight these adventive species appear much more ubiquitous than they really are, because they follow so closely in the footsteps of man, and it is fairly certain now, as Thomson and others have shown, that there is no strong likelihood of this eventuality. It would seem that it is not so much the inherent aggressiveness of the species in question as the advantages which their association with man confers on them. Man's actions tend to provide a series of habitats, those of disturbed ground, which are specially the domain of these plants and which do not occur in nature. This certainly leads to local destruction of the native vegetation and some native species inevitably become rare in the process, but Thomson has stated definitely, in respect at least of New Zealand, that he knows of no case where a native species has been completely exterminated by adventives, and his general opinion, as it is also that of others, is that when man's influence is removed the native flora can everywhere hold its own.

But there is also another very interesting aspect of this problem. The northern hemisphere generally and Europe in particular has been the stage of man's development for vastly longer than any southern countries, and the kinds of artificial habitats which this development produces have in the north been available for local plants for much longer. May it not be then that the common northern weed species are in fact species or strains peculiarly fitted for these habitats, and in fact slightly different from the corresponding forms which grow in more natural situations? If this is so, then it might be expected that these weeds would flourish in all artificial habitats no matter where they might be, and would tend to produce the effect of aggressiveness observed.

CHAPTER 20

THE FACTORS OF DISTRIBUTION—V. CHANGES OF CLIMATE

THE belief that the climatic values have in the past fluctuated greatly with the passage of time is now so generally held as to have become almost axiomatic, but it is nevertheless desirable here to consider shortly the reasons that have given rise to it. For more complete presentations of the subject the reader may refer to the work of Simpson (650, 651), Brooks (88, 90), Huntington and Visher (392), Russell (611), Shapley (644), Nairn (535) and Nairn and Runcorn (822).

The direct and indirect evidences for climatic variation in the past are of five kinds, namely mathematical and geodetic, geological and topographical, botanical, archaeological, and meteorological.

The first need not detain us long because it is rather remote in all senses of the word from our present subject. It comprises the relations between the earth and other heavenly bodies, and also the question of the mode of formation of the earth and its subsequent vicissitudes, these being such that it is impossible to suppose that the present conditions of climate can have existed unchanged for any considerable part of secular time or of the earth's history. Indeed, there is reason to believe that for long after the formation of the world no climate in the modern sense existed.

Geological and topographical evidence of climatic change is of three chief kinds, the first being that afforded by the appearance and texture of certain rocks. Thus some sandstones appear to be formed of dune sand, while some Tertiary granites show signs of having been weathered by sand blasts, both suggesting that contemporary conditions were very arid (640). On the other hand many clay deposits can scarcely have been formed except under pluvial conditions. Not only are these rocks found where now the climate is very different from that indicated by their origin, but the various types may be found superposed or intermingled, showing that the climate of their region of deposition must have undergone considerable changes. Indeed a vertical section through almost any series of geological beds will show a variation of type that can only be explained by an equal variation of climate. Moreover, freshwater deposits will be found among and between marine deposits, indicating at least geographical changes such as are unlikely to have been without effect on climate.

The second kind of geological evidence of climatic change, and perhaps the most familiar one, relates to glaciation. Ice-sheets and glaciers scour and mark the surface of the earth where they occur in ways which leave unmistakable evidence of their former presence long after they have disappeared. The nature of these traces has already been described and it need only be remembered here that they are found over wide areas of the world where now the climate is far from polar. Glacial conditions are now generally supposed to have been more or less widespread on the earth on a number of occasions during geological history, that is to say it is believed that there have been in the past a series of glacial epochs or ice ages. These were, however, separated by vast periods of time. Only two (if we ignore the debatable indications of a Cretaceous or early Eocene glaciation) have occurred

PLATE 24

Map of the World showing the seasonal distribution of rain. After Bartholomew's *Physical Atlas*, vol. III.

constant drought

rain at all seasons

rain chiefly in summer

rain chiefly in winter

Areas correct Distortion increasing towards border of map.
Approximate Scale 1:100,000,000 (1600 miles=1inch) along Equator
on Mollweide's Homolographic Projection

Copyright

Tropic of Cancer

Equator

Tropic of Capricorn

since the beginning of the Palaeozoic, and of these only the latter involves the Angiosperms and is therefore of more than passing interest to us here. As will be seen, these glacial ages are to be regarded as long intermittent catastrophes in the general story of climate, and as such are perhaps the most striking evidence of the fact that climatic values have not always been as they are to-day.

The nature of the changes which accompanied the Pleistocene glaciation, and their far-reaching effects on the existing vegetation, have already been described, but it is well to stress again here that the climatic change at this time was both great in its degree and vast in its significance and that it has been the main influence in moulding the world flora into its present state. Nor, it is now generally held, was this change confined to those parts of the world which were actually covered with ice, but expressed itself widely elsewhere, particularly in many parts of the tropics, as a corresponding series of pluvial and dry periods, which in all probability, as has been suggested by Gilliland (270) and many others, caused plant migrations of a similar though perhaps less drastic kind. If, indeed, as many now believe, high precipitation values are an essential feature of glacial periods, then we may expect comparative dryness to be an equally characteristic feature of non-glacial conditions like the present, and this falls satisfactorily in line with the growing evidence that there is generally increasing dryness now at lower latitudes, or in other words that aridity is spreading in many parts of the tropics.

This problem of what has been called the "désertification" of tropical regions is a most interesting and important one. That semi-desert or desert conditions are, in many places, spreading, as Aubréville has admirably demonstrated for tropical Africa (29, 30), seems indisputable, but whether this is to be attributed solely to natural causes is more debatable. Hitherto this has been generally assumed to be the case but the work of Aubréville and others has thrown considerable doubt on this view and suggests that the spread of desert conditions may often be caused by human rather than natural factors. Van Steenis (701) goes even further and believes that man has in many cases actually converted his areas of settlement into deserts and has consequently been obliged to abandon them.

A third direct line of geological and topographical evidence is afforded by the occurrence, in regions now comparatively arid, of physiographic features obviously caused by the action of large bodies of water. Empty gorges and dry, or almost dry, river beds are the commonest of these and may be seen in many parts of the world. Among striking instances are some of the tributary valleys of the lower part of the Orange River in southern Africa, and the great wadis in parts of the Sahara and in Arabia, which, presumably not so long ago, must have carried rivers capable of watering great tracts of land.

Among the more indirect evidences of climatic change caused by geological and topographical factors two may be mentioned here. Mountain ranges are one of the most potent influences in determining local climate in many parts of the world, because they intercept moisture-laden winds from the sea, thereby causing on their leeward sides not only conditions of drought but also many consequent climatic changes. It is fairly clear that mountain building on the grand scale has been particularly the characteristic of certain times, as for instance the later part of the Tertiary when most of the present high ranges were elevated, and that at other periods relief was much less marked. This cannot fail to have had an enormous effect on the distribution of climatic values, and hence the very presence of mountain ranges of different ages is evidence of appreciable climatic change in the past. This point may be illustrated by the often-quoted case of North America (63) where there is abundant

25

evidence that the elevation of the western mountain line radically altered the climatic values of almost the whole subcontinent.

In much the same ways any considerable alterations in the relative outlines of land and sea are likely to lead to changes in climatic values by increasing, diminishing or diverting oceanic effects. Something of this kind will doubtless have happened following alterations in relative level, with its consequential broadening or narrowing of seas, but the point is of much greater importance in relation to ideas of continental drift (see next chapter) for it is almost impossible to imagine that this can have occurred on any appreciable scale without causing climatic changes of a profound character, and it is particularly necessary to bear this in mind when theories involving continental movement are under discussion

The botanical evidence is similarly twofold, but by far the more important aspect is that afforded by the nature and characteristics of fossil plants. The question of the extent to which fossil floras are tests of climate has already been discussed in Chapter 15, and it is clearly dangerous to push conclusions too far, but it cannot be denied that in a broad sense the general appearance and structure of plants do to a large extent indicate the types of climate under which they flourish. To take the most obvious example, it is contrary to all experience to associate highly succulent plants such as the cacti with any but very dry climatic conditions. Unfortunately the problem of fossils is not so clear-cut as this, but they may nevertheless be very significant indicators of climatic values, and at least it seems certain, on their evidence, that temperate or warm-temperate conditions were formerly more widespread latitudinally than now. It was once thought that they may have reached far into what are now the Arctic and Antarctic regions, but modern opinion is more moderate, indicating that temperate conditions may have prevailed about 15 degrees farther north and south than they do now, and tropical conditions perhaps 10 degrees. Such fossil floras as are known from the tropics also add to the picture because they appear to be very like the floras of the same places to-day and so indicate that past changes of climate concerned the temperature gradients between the poles and the equator rather than absolute differences in world values. At the same time it must be remembered that no amount of increase in temperature will alter the light values and relations at higher latitudes (see p. 393).

The second and minor type of botanical evidence is that afforded by the annual rings of certain large and long-lived trees, especially the sequoias of California (275). The width of the annual rings in trees is a rough measure of the amount of growth which the tree has achieved season by season. This in turn is generally supposed to be a function of the climatic conditions, and especially of the precipitation. Developing this argument, it may be suggested that variation in width of ring will reflect and correspond to variation in rainfall from year to year. Examination shows that the rings of a large tree do in fact vary greatly in width, and also that this variation is a fluctuating one, the rings over one series of years being small and over another series being large. They tend to wax and wane through the years, and this is generally interpreted as indicating a corresponding oscillation in climatic values. Naturally the length of life of any single tree is negligible in terms of geological time, but some of the big trees mentioned live for some thousands of years and thus cover comparatively long periods. This subject of the correlation of ring growth and climate has received much attention, especially in the work of Douglass (196), and the general conclusion that there is something approaching a persistent fluctuation in climatic values is inescapable. Actually investigation on these lines has been pursued very intensively, and there have been built up on the basis of ring-size climatic curves for the area in which these trees live extending back for hundreds of years. These curves, as has been said, seem to show beyond doubt that rainfall at least has varied almost continuously during the period concerned and, also, that there is a relation between tree-growth, climate and the sunspot cycle (806).

It will be noticed that these various lines of evidence have gradually brought the problem of climatic change more and more towards the present time, and the next type of evidence, the archaeological, is almost entirely concerned with changes in recent, and especially in historical, time. In many ways this evidence is the most interesting of all, because the earlier ones concerned periods and events so remote that they necessarily seem a little unreal. With the archaeological evidence the question of climatic change becomes more tangible and realistic. On the other hand, the changes themselves are naturally smaller, though not for this reason of any less interest.

At this point it is desirable to draw a careful distinction between climatic changes and climatic fluctuations, as there is some ambiguity in the use of these terms. The geological and botanical evidence has shown that there has been considerable long-term alteration in the climate of the world, and that this has included a series of catastrophic alterations. It is to these secular alterations and oscillations that the word change can be best restricted. Other botanical evidence has shown, and the archaeological evidence will also show, that in addition to these there have been constant minor variations, variations superposed, as it were, on the general trends of change. Major change seems never to have been quite smooth and unbroken but to have progressed in the form of irregularities. It is to these minor irregularities and variations that the word fluctuation is best applied. For instance, the general trend of climatic *change* since the end of the Pleistocene has been a gradual amelioration of condition, and this process has been sufficiently noted in Chapters 13 and 15. At the same time there have been almost constant *fluctuations* and advances and retreats in the main process of amelioration, and it is with these that we are now concerned. It must be emphasised that, although these fluctuations are minor compared with the main changes, they are nevertheless more than adequate to influence plant distribution, and indeed this may be the more normal way in which this influence makes itself felt. It must also be remembered that there is a close relation between change and fluctuation, and that the accumulation of the latter may and no doubt does often produce the former.

The archaeological evidences of climatic variation are very numerous but for the most part inferential rather than direct. That many of them represent indeed some measures of change can scarcely be doubted, but the nature and extent of that change are often matters of considerable argument. We are not, however, concerned here with details, but rather in demonstrating that change of one kind or another has occurred, and for this purpose deductions on archaeological grounds are valuable and important.

These indications of climatic fluctuations are really of four types. The first concerns the relatively minor oscillations that have taken place in the north polar ice-cap during the historical period. In the Norse period settlements were established on both the western and eastern coasts of south Greenland, and there is evidence that a fairly well-developed agriculture was carried on there. Now the region is permanently glaciated and even habitation by Europeans is out of the question. Of special interest are the excavations which have been made in a burial ground attached to the settlement near Cape Farewell because the details and methods of burial here clearly point to a gradual oncoming of severe conditions leading eventually to the disappearance of the whole settlement. Like changes are evidenced by the oscillations of ice-advance and retreat in the glaciers of the Alps and other European mountains. Some of these are comparatively modern and Brooks (90) notes particularly the great outburst of mountain glaciation which began about 350 years ago and which was so remarkable as to gain the name of the "Little Ice Age". This was followed by a retreat, a re-advance, and in the last hundred years a more rapid retreat. There is also much information about glacier variation in Ahlmann (8).

A second general indication of climatic fluctuations, and especially of rainfall, is seen in various directions where changes in the level of bodies of water can be estimated. The best known of these is the record of the annual level of the Nile which is known from about A.D. 600 and which shows almost continuous fluctuation superposed on a gradual and steady rise. Similar variations have been observed in the Caspian and in parts of North America, especially in the old lakes associated with the Pleistocene glaciations. In Africa there is the well-known shrinking of Lake Chad.

Another more general inference is that afforded by the distribution of some of the great city civilisations of the past, an aspect of the subject which is of special interest in view of the growing belief already referred to that the actions of man himself has made no small contribution to the ultimate results. Thus, in the familiar case of Mesopotamia, where there are many vestiges of civilisations which could scarcely exist there to-day because of the general dryness of the country, it is known that there formerly existed water storage and irrigation systems which were destroyed in the course of human warfare. Again, in one of the most striking cases, that of the Syrian deserts, once so densely populated but now abandoned, so vividly described by Butler (98), the conclusion is that the vital changes have taken place in not much more than a thousand years, and though partly no doubt due to natural causes, were in large measure the results of bad government. Much the same is suggested by the remains of the once flourishing Roman cities of North Africa which to-day stand in regions so arid that it is difficult to see how any very considerable population could be supported there, and also by the remains of the earlier civilisations of the Indus plain where conditions seem formerly to have been much moister than now. All these give evidence of change which, though it may have been greatly intensified by man, can scarcely have been entirely due to him. The Kharga Oasis on the eastern edge of the Sahara illustrates a related state of affairs. In earlier historical times the oasis was a lake which gradually degenerated into a swamp, since when the water in the oasis has varied greatly and the human population with it. The extraordinary local changes which may be caused by a few seasons or even a single season of abnormality have been most strikingly demonstrated by Lake Eyre in South Australia. This is part of the drainage basin for much of the country to the north-east of it and for very many years it had contained no water and its affluents had been dammed by sand, but about 1950 the rainfall in Queensland was sufficient to form rivers capable of overcoming the sand obstacles and at one period the lake had become a sheet of water more than 3,000 square miles in extent. It was, however, dry again by January 1953.

The reverse condition, of ancient cities now lying buried in dense tropical forests, and which seem to have been overwhelmed by an increase in precipitation, is seen well in the country of the Mayas in Central America. Here the cities appear to have been at their zenith about the first few centuries of the present era. Now, as Brooks says (90), "this country is at present covered by almost impenetrable forests, the climate is hot, moist, and enervating, while the inhabitants are idle and uncultured". A less familiar example is furnished by Angkor, the great abandoned city now buried in the tropical jungle of Cambodia. It was founded about A.D. 600 and flourished for the next 500 years or so, and at one time is estimated to have had a million inhabitants. It is thought to have been abandoned in about A.D. 1200.

This brings us to the last and most detailed evidence, that afforded by actual meteorological observations during the last 200 years or so. All such observations go to show that in most respects, and perhaps particularly as regards rainfall, climatic values tend to fluctuate more or less continuously, a series of years below the norm being followed by a series of years above the norm. This at any rate is a general conclusion, and it can be substantiated in detail and particularly from many meteorological records.

One aspect of this fluctuation and its effect on plant distribution has been studied in some detail (292). The lizard orchid, *Himantoglossum hircinum*, has an interesting geographical history in Britain, of which the main features are its fairly regular occurrence locally up to about the middle of the nineteenth century, its decline and virtual disappearance between that date and 1900, and its marked increase in numbers and range during the present century (or at least to 1933 when the study was made). So conspicuous is the last feature that enquiries were made to discover whether there was any meteorological explanation of it and the result showed that the facts correlated well with a general climatic change in the direction of winter temperature amelioration which became notably accentuated after 1900 (70, 89, 457, 483).

That this fluctuation has not been confined to Britain has been shown by the work of Ahlmann (7, 8) and others (378, 624), and Lysgaard (472) concludes that in the thirty years, 1911–1940, compared with the thirty years, 1881–1910, both temperature and rainfall have been *higher* in temperate latitudes and *lower* in the tropics.

Krause (820), on the other hand, dealing with the subtropics on the edges of the arid zones, concludes that a drier period began abruptly at the beginning of the present century and lasted until the nineteen-forties. On a still shorter scale fluctuations of climate from year to year are in everyone's experience, and as far as Britain is concerned it is necessary only to mention the markedly hot and dry summers of 1933–1935; the frequent cold winters between 1940 and 1947; the exceptionally wet autumn and winter of 1960–61; and the extraordinarily severe winter of 1962–63 as instances of this.

The combined effect of all the lines of evidence which have just been reviewed has been sufficient to demonstrate beyond doubt the two main facts that climate has suffered changes both great and small, and that these have been reflected directly in the distribution of plants. We may now go on to see whether it is possible to give a more general picture of climatic change during geological time, and especially during the history of the Angiosperms.

This has actually been done with a wealth of evidence and detail by Brooks (90), and we cannot do better than describe shortly the conclusions to which he comes. Put very concisely, these are that the climate of the earth has normally been a genial climate interrupted only at long intervals and for short durations by glacial periods, "as at long intervals a passing cyclone disturbs the peaceful life of a tropical island". The long genial or warm periods were all times during which the relief of the world's surface was low and during which, as a result, shallow seas encroached more or less extensively over the land surfaces. These periods too were characterised especially by comparatively small and gradual differences between the equator and the poles. On the other hand, the glacial periods seem to have followed periods of active mountain building and were characterised by steep and extensive temperature gradients from equator to poles.

One of these long warm periods apparently persisted from the glaciations of the Permian to those of the Pleistocene, and it was during this long time that the Flowering Plants were evolved. As regards these plants then, they originated during a long warm period, and these conditions continued to prevail for millions of years after they had appeared. Only comparatively recently, from a geological point of view, did these optimum conditions give place almost suddenly to one of the catastrophic periodic glaciations whose vibrations still persist.

This conception throws much light on the geographical development of the Flowering Plants. Arguing from it we are justified in regarding this great group of plants as developing in response to and in correlation with more or less constant and optimum climatic conditions, and perhaps as having reached, towards the end of this period, what may be described as something approaching an equilibrium. With the onset of glaciation this equilibrium was suddenly and rudely disturbed. An almost completely new range of climatic conditions arose in the higher latitudes at any rate, conditions to which the Flowering Plants were quite unaccustomed, and their subsequent history has undoubtedly been the story of their attempts to exploit this new environment. It is to this more than any other factor that many of the more puzzling details in the present distribution of plants are due.

This point of view can be conveniently illustrated by a consideration of certain aspects of arctic plants. From the various evidences available it is an almost inevitable conclusion that during the long warm period of the Cretaceous and earlier Tertiary temperate or warm-temperate conditions must have been the rule throughout the upper latitudes, and that arctic conditions, that is to say glacial conditions at sea level, were unknown anywhere in the world. Apart from the circumstantial evidence afforded by fossil plants, there is, according to Brooks, definite meteorological and mathematical evidence for this view. He shows, for instance, that even to-day a comparatively small rise in mean annual temperature of the order of 5° F. would be sufficient to cause the gradual melting of the polar ice-caps and to prevent them re-forming, and the temperature of the warm periods was certainly above this figure. Moreover, once the ice-caps disappeared their effects on the climate would be removed and almost certainly an even warmer climate would be the rule. There is an interesting comment on this by Wolbach in Shapley (644).

As regards the Angiosperms then the essential feature of the glacial period of the Pleistocene was to produce, for the first time in their history, what we now call arctic or polar conditions, that is to say glacial conditions at sea level, and these over a comparatively wide area. This being so, and there seems little reasonable doubt about it, several consequences follow, the chief of these being that cold temperate and arctic plants must be regarded as among the more recent in origin, and this element as one of the youngest in the world flora. But the problem of the actual source of this cold flora is not so simple. At the present time the snow line is nowhere so high that there are not some snow-capped mountains, even on the equator, as in East Africa and in the Andes. On the other hand there are high mountains so far north and so far south, as for instance in Alaska where there are elevations of over 20,000 ft. and in Antarctica, that they are virtually entirely above the snow line. Thus a temperature change which would suffice to raise the snow line above the tops of all the mountains at all latitudes would have to be enormous and indeed theoretically quite inconceivable. It would therefore seem that although arctic conditions may be recent alpine conditions must have existed somewhere much longer and these places would afford an obvious source from which the polar flora could have developed.

On the other hand the long genial period of the Cretaceous and earlier Tertiary is pictured as one of low relief and least continental area (90) and if this is a true representation then it may well have been that until the orogeny of the later Tertiary there were in fact no elevations sufficient to bear ice and snow, at all events in the north, where there is polar sea, though it is not so easy to visualise the possible conditions in the south where there is a land pole. All that can be inferred with profit is that alpine conditions must have existed at least since the Miocene and Pliocene and may have been present in some form much earlier, especially on some of the more ancient mountain systems. Bearing in mind that there was a considerable time gap between the Miocene/Pliocene orogeny and the Pleistocene glaciation to which it contributed it seems clear enough that alpine vegetational conditions are older than polar conditions and hence that the relationship between the arctic and alpine floras expresses the origin of the former from the latter rather than the reverse, a conclusion which is fully in agreement with the distributions of their respective constituents.

Finally let us turn to the vegetation of the low-lying tropics. There are no indications either from fossil or other evidence that the maximum or equatorial world temperature has, since the rise of the Angiosperms, ever been much greater than it is to-day. Indeed on astronomical grounds there are *a priori* reasons for the view that it has not. The difference between the climate of a genial or warm period and that of the Pleistocene was therefore, as has been already said, essentially the difference between a generalised latitudinal climatic zonation and a steeper zonation. In other words, the tropics in the warm periods were probably not much warmer, but the higher latitudes in the glacial periods were much colder. Nor does it appear likely that the equatorial values were very greatly diminished during glaciation. In floristic terms then it may be said that while, in the warm periods, circumstances favoured the development of a few widespread and generalised plant types, of which some of the present tropical flora are probably good examples, circumstances in the glacial periods produced not only a tendency towards the production of more specialised types in correlation with the more specialised conditions, but also brought about some world-wide telescoping of the climatic zones, so that, if nothing else, there must have been an intense competition for space, although this may have been offset to some degree by the relative greater elevation of the continents and their consequent greater areas. This in turn doubtless led to further and more local specialisation, and thus the whole effect of the glaciation appears to have been to hasten the conversion of a generalised world flora into a number of more or less specialised floras. Certainly this specialisation is one of the leading features in the world flora to-day, and it would seem that this is at least a partial explanation of it.

Attention has often been called to the fact that on oceanic islands where there is a high degree of endemism, the endemics are commonly mesophytic woody plants. This is not surprising in view of the oceanic climates of most such islands but it has been suggested that it has a greater significance than this and that these floras are relics of older, moister world conditions like those indicated above for the genial periods. Wallace (756), for instance, expresses the view that every island represents the flora and fauna of the period when it was last separated from the adjacent continent, while Guppy (327) has put the matter even more plainly when he says, "islands appeal to me more as registers of past floral conditions in the continents than as representing their present state. Their marked peculiarities bear the impress of the past on the continents, whilst their common features tell the story of the present".

On the other hand in continental floras where there is much endemism, as for instance at the Cape and in south-western Australia, the endemics are notably associated with the more arid kinds of habitat and this raises the very interesting and important question of how far arid conditions or "desert habitats" have existed in the past, and whether the existent floras of such regions are to be regarded as of recent or of more remote origin. The undoubted facts that mountain building tends, by excluding rainfall, to produce desert conditions and that the extension of continental areas intensifies similar aridity towards their centres, suggests that arid habitats are now much more prevalent than in the early stages of Angiosperm history, and hence that most desert floras are young floras, but it is well to be cautious in accepting the validity of this conclusion. It must be remembered that rocks of desert origin are frequent in the geological record and are by no means always associated with periods of mountain building or glaciation. Also the long genial periods of the past which constitute what is called by Brooks the normal climate of geological time, are described as warm and dry. This does not of course necessarily mean aridity everywhere and always, and the Eocene, which is of special importance in Angiosperm history is admitted to have been more than usually moist, but it does suggest that desert conditions are not so modern as might at first be thought. In short it permits the view that the present deserts of the world, and their floras, are not all of the same age, a view which may go far to explain the several notable differences, both qualitative and quantitative, between these, and in particular the curious fact that the largest desert area of all, the North African–Indian region has a less specialised flora and fewer characteristic forms than almost any other.

But when all due allowance has been made for the possibility that certain extreme environmental conditions, such as those of mountain snows and those of deserts, have existed since the Flowering Plants first appeared, it seems reasonable to regard the changes of climate during the history of these plants as having led gradually to a more and more specialised series of local climates, particularly during and since the Pliocene, with consequent differentiation in the vegetation. This point has been well put by Bews (69), who says, "the evidence from phylogeny . . . affords convincing support to the view that climatic differentiation has been responsible for the production of plant forms adapted to more open grassland conditions, to scrub, semi-desert and also, though this began very early, to the temperate floras as well".

This view involves the belief that the earlier Angiosperm flora was of a generalised forest type and very widespread, and that the development of the vegetation as we see it to-day has been in the various directions of specialisation from this original condition. This is differentiation, and this particular aspect of Angiosperm history is, as we have seen, an important basis of Guppy's Theory of Differentiation.

So far in this chapter we have been concerned chiefly with the more definite evidences of climatic change in the past, and the point has now been reached at which there can be most properly discussed certain contingent conditions and their possible consequences which have a direct bearing on the subject of climatic change and which may, indeed, be a strong pointer towards an explanation of it. This is the subject of the variable elements in the earth's movement and orbit which are called inequalities or perturbations and which are known to have certain periodicities, and to which some useful references are in Shapley (644). Although to discuss these at length here is impossible the general nature of the possibilities can be sufficiently explained by a consideration of the one of these perturbations with which problems of plant geography would seem almost inevitably to be most closely related, the obliquity of the ecliptic.

It is well enough known that the axis of rotation of the earth is not at right angles to the plane of its orbit or path round the sun, but it may not be so generally realised that this obliquity is the cause of seasonal differences, which become increasingly marked from the equator, where conditions are almost constant, to the poles. In consequence also of the obliquity, and constituting a leading element in seasonal change, there is an increasing variation pole-ward in the length of day and night throughout the year, so that while, at the equator, day and night are each of about twelve hours all through the year, at the poles the year consists of one "day" of six months and one "night" of six months. The change in this respect with latitude is not, however, constant and whereas from the equator to latitude 45° or so the variation in length of day is comparatively small, it becomes greatly accentuated above 45°. The present distribution of plants is plainly correlated with this matter of length of day, as was shortly stated in Chapter 15, and any serious alteration in its values would be likely to have a profound effect on plant geography.

Within the tropics, there is not much seasonal change in length of day or in temperature, but, in the course of the year, the latitude at which the sun is directly overhead at noon swings from one tropic to the other and back again. Hence all places in the tropics have two equinoxes *less* than six months apart, except actually on the equator, where they are exactly six months apart.

It is not surprising therefore that the perturbations of the earth have been much considered by those who seek an explanation of the major climatic changes of the past, and a useful summary of the position in relation to one particular change of this sort, the Pleistocene Ice Ages, has been given by Zeuner (805) in a discussion of the Astronomical Theory of Glaciation. He considers four perturbations—the length of year, which he concludes has been virtually unchanged since the Palaeozoic; the eccentricity of the orbit, which fluctuates with a period of 92,000 years; the precession of the equinoxes, with an effective period of 21,000 years; and the obliquity of the ecliptic, which at present fluctuates within narrow limits with a period of about 40,000 years. Doubtless major alteration in any perturbation would gravely affect plant distribution, but the last has particularly interesting possibilities in this connection.

Were there no obliquity of the ecliptic there would be, at all latitudes, a condition of perpetual equinox, in which, although the shape of the earth would still cause a temperature gradient from equator to poles, there would be no seasonal variation. Since equinoctial conditions are to-day characteristic of equatorial regions it might at first be thought that this would ameliorate the climate of temperate regions, but this is not so, and the meteorologists conclude that a *decrease* in obliquity, while diminishing seasonal differences, would increase the distinctness of the climatic zonation, so that the climate would tend to be less clement than now at high latitudes. Conversely, any *increase* in obliquity would intensify seasonal variation but diminish the climatic zonation, and Zeuner quotes Milankovitch in Koppen and Geiger (431) for the proposition that if the obliquity reached an amplitude of as much as 54° (it is now about 23°) the annual total of radiation would be the same for each of the poles as for the equator, and the general climatic conditions would be much alike all over the world and characterised by very marked seasons.

It would take too long to deal here with all the botanical implications of such hypothetical changes in the obliquity of the ecliptic and the reader should consult the interesting summary of these by Allard in Murneek and Whyte (531), from which it is clear that changes of this sort, if appropriate in scale and in time, might explain not only many problems of plant geography but also many puzzling aspects of Angiosperm history, such for example as the development of the great herbaceous element in the northern flora. But on the broader general issue of climatic change in the past which has been the subject of this chapter, it would certainly also seem that further knowledge of what we have called the earth's perturbations may well make plain much that is still obscure to-day.

CHAPTER 21

THE FACTORS OF DISTRIBUTION—VI. GEOGRAPHICAL CHANGES

THERE are few clearer illustrations of the bearing of the evolutionary conception on problems of plant distribution than that of the importance of the distribution of land and sea. On the assumption that species were created in or near the situations in which they occur to-day, discontinuity is not necessarily of any great significance, because it can be explained on the assumption that creation took place on more than one occasion and in more than one place, but if an evolutionary origin of species is assumed with its generally accepted premise that species are monophyletic, then clearly the discontinuity of species becomes a matter of much greater interest and importance. It is not surprising therefore to find that the pioneers of the idea of evolution realised almost from the first that discontinuity was a subject likely to hold the key to many riddles. More remarkable is the fact that in those early days, and actually antedating the *Origin of Species*, there was a widely held view that the present distribution of living things could not be explained on the present distribution of land and sea, and that changes in this feature must be a potent factor in plant and animal geography. For instance, Hooker (371) quotes Lyell as saying: "As a general rule species common to many distant provinces, or those now found to inhabit many distant parts of the globe, are to be regarded as the most ancient . . . their wide diffusion shows that they have had a long time to spread themselves, and have been able to survive many important changes in Physical Geography", and Hooker himself (372), in his *Introductory Essay to the Flora of Tasmania*, writes: "These and a multitude of analogous facts have led to the study of two classes of agents, both of which may reasonably be supposed to have had a powerful effect in determining the distribution of plants; these are changes of climates, and changes in the relative positions and elevations of land." The final phrase of this statement is especially interesting because it distinguishes between the spatial relations of land surfaces, that is to say the distances between them, and their relief and outline, and it is important before going further to amplify this.

That Hooker's remark is true and that neither the distribution of the land nor its elevation has remained unchanged during the past is shown by a glance at any stratigraphical map of the world or of any one continent, for it will be plain that marine and freshwater sedimentary deposits cover many parts of the surface, and hence that these areas must at one time have been below the sea (though not necessarily all at once) and many maps purporting to show the state of world geography at different geological epochs such as those of Mathew (498), Grabau (310), Arldt (27) and others have been constructed on this basis. At the same time the problems involved in the circumstances, dates and intensities of these changes are many, and certain of them must be considered with some care here. In particular must an attempt be made to come to some conclusion about the last of these, the *degree* to which there has been change.

An enquiry of this kind, which can be made to include almost every aspect of earth history is fascinating but liable to lead all too easily into realms beyond the scope of this chapter, and the following observations are therefore confined as strictly as possible to some of the matters which especially concern the distribution of plants, and for further information on other topics the reader should consult such general works as those of Arldt (27), Umbgrove (745), Daly (169), Shepard (646) and Gutenberg (330).

With regard to the minor and less controversial kind of change, that which merely involves elevation, a perusal of geological maps also shows that in all the larger land masses of the earth there are great areas where very ancient Archaean (pre-Cambrian) rocks are exposed at the surface, and that in general these areas are central rather then peripheral. Furthermore, these ancient rocks, which represent the original materials of the land masses, normally extend widely beneath the sedimentary deposits already mentioned. In short a continent or subcontinent is to be regarded as composed of a core or base of these Archaean rocks on parts of which, from time to time, sedimentary younger rocks have been laid down. Such ancient rock surfaces, or Archaean shields as they are often called, are conspicuous in Canada, in eastern South America, in Scandinavia, in India, in Manchuria, in Africa, in Arabia, and in Western Australia, but they are also represented on a smaller scale in many of the larger islands.

There is also good geological reason for believing that all or nearly all of the superposed sediments are deposits formed under comparatively shallow water in which the Archaean shield lay not far below the surface, and on this evidence it is generally supposed that the sedimentary deposits of the larger land masses were formed during times when certain of their parts were shallowly submerged. These sediments vary greatly in age and it is therefore unnecessary to assume that any land mass was submerged to the total extent of such deposits at any one time. Rather may we visualise the successive shallow submergence of different parts of the continents in different periods, the various sediments being laid down accordingly. We may therefore also imagine that the seas around the masses have encroached upon them locally and at different times according to changes in the relative levels of land and water. This conception raises the question whether the present extent of the continents is a maximum one or whether in fact some parts of them are even now invaded by shallow seas. The question is whether or not the present land outline of the continents actually represents the boundaries of their Archaean bases.

To answer this it is necessary to consult a map showing the submarine relief. Here it will at once be noticed that the shallower submarine contours closely follow the outline of the land, but that as depth increases so they become more irregular. This means in effect that round most land surfaces there is a narrow edging of very shallow water beyond which the sea becomes rapidly deeper. The details of this distribution leave no room for doubt that the line where the sea passes from shallow to deep represents the real edges of the continents, but that these are in general at present slightly encroached upon by the sea. Such submerged edges of the continents are called continental shelves, and one of the most striking is in western Europe, where the true edge of the continent runs west of Ireland, so that the British Isles are islands rising from the surface of the continental shelf which elsewhere forms the beds of the shallow seas which separate them from what is generally called the "continent". Seas of this kind, which are clearly intrusions over the land surfaces of the continents, are called epicontinental seas (see Chapter 1), and by a justifiable extension of the phrase, sedimentary deposits formed on their beds may be called epicontinental deposits. Although the British Isles have been cited for their familiarity they are by no means the best example of such conditions, and far greater areas of shallow waters, which are presumably also epicontinental, are to be found in south-east Asia, where they extend over much of Malaysia. On the other hand many parts of the world are conspicuously without these epicontinental seas, and here the shore edge is more or less exactly the real continental edge. The west coasts of Africa, America and Australia are perhaps the best instances of this.

A point of considerable interest as well as of great theoretical importance is whether or not the real edges of all the continents are at about the same level or whether some are more deeply invaded by water than others because their general level is lower, but this is a difficult point which can only be answered rather inferentially here. Returning to our examination of submarine contours we shall notice that one of those most generally depicted is the 200 metre or 600 ft. contour. There is no inherent virtue in this figure, except perhaps that it is also 100 fathoms, and its repeated use is partly based on the fact that it serves particularly well to reveal vividly the salient points of under-water relief, and that it does usually mark the point at which a gradual deepening of the sea round a continent becomes suddenly and intensely accentuated. On this account it is a reasonably fair inference that this depth broadly represents that to which in present circumstances the true edges of the continent are submerged, and since the depth is equally significant for all, that these have more or less the same common level, a conclusion which, it may be added, accords with that reached by entirely different lines of reasoning. We may, indeed, for present purposes, be allowed to regard the 600 ft. submarine contour as giving a generalised if not an exact impression of the actual outlines of the chief land masses of the globe.

This enables us to gain a much clearer picture of what changes in the relative levels of land and sea, especially of what, to coin an ugly word, "epicontinentality" may mean, because by following this particular contour there can be drawn an outline of the continents as they would presumably appear if they were at such an elevation that they were free from the encroachment of epicontinental seas. Plate 3 is such a map and it is illuminating. It will already have been realised that Great Britain and Ireland would be joined to the continent, but this is a minor aspect of the whole. Taking the continents in order we should see that in Europe there is not much other change except that the narrower straits of the Mediterranean disappear. That sea as a whole survives but in diminished form. In Africa, too, the only change of note is the joining of the Canaries to the mainland. In America the changes are much greater. Working from north to south, the Arctic Archipelago would disappear and become a continuous extension of the northern mainland, and the North Atlantic would be almost bridged; Newfoundland would be united to Canada; the Bahamas and Cuba would be practically continuous, not only with Florida, but also with Yucatan; the rest of the West Indies would be much enlarged; and the Falklands would be connected up with Fuegia. Extensive as these American changes would be, they are slight compared with what would happen in Asia and Australia. Here, once more starting in the north, the Bering Strait would disappear; Japan and Sakhalin would be joined to the mainland; the Philippines, Borneo, Java and Sumatra would all be united to the continent of Asia by way of the Malay Peninsula and Siam; and New Guinea would be joined to Australia. All this would happen were there an effective lowering of the sea level by 600 ft., but much of it would follow even if the change was much less than this. For instance, a difference of 150 ft. would connect Asia and America by a belt of land nearly 200 miles wide (284); a similar difference would be effective in western Malaysia; and one as slight as 65 ft. would widely unite Australia and New Guinea (745).

Conversely, it is just as interesting to note, a relative lowering of the land by the same amount of 600 ft. would, except in western Europe and central Asia, have but comparatively little effect, and would put but few new obstacles in the path of plant migration.

Is it justifiable to believe that changes of this kind of dimension, and especially a relative rise in the land of such degree that, for example, with few quite minor exceptions almost all the islands of the northern hemisphere would be replaced by continuous land surfaces and the only major discontinuity would be that of the ocean basins, have indeed occurred during the history of the Flowering Plants?

There are several lines of evidence which go to show that the present state of affairs is not extreme in either direction. The distribution of Tertiary epicontinental deposits shows clearly that the continents must, as wholes or in part, have been much more submerged than now at some period since the Angiosperms became widespread and the same is true of somewhat earlier times, the great Cretaceous transgression being a striking case in point. Turning to more recent times there are in many parts of the world raised beaches far above present sea level. On the other hand a mass of evidence shows that there must have been much relative elevation. The British Isles are generally supposed to have been joined, on one or more occasions, to the continent (788) and also to one another, and evidences of like elevation are considerable in mid-America and in parts of Malaysia (53, 676). All these would presumably involve changes of the order of magnitude described above and there seems no reason to doubt that they have occurred.

There is no sure means of judging how much the land surfaces of the world may have been reduced and their isolation increased at times of greatest depression but some idea can be obtained by tracing their outlines from a geological map as they would appear if the deposits of Tertiary or of more recent times are excluded as if they were in fact below the sea. It would take too long to go through the whole world on this basis, but the case of Europe and Asia for instance will show the sort of degree of change that might be expected. Great areas of north-east Siberia are covered with Tertiary deposits, as is also much of the interior of Asia. Similarly in Europe, Asia Minor, Arabia and parts of North Africa, and at least it can be said that an appreciable proportion of the whole might well have been simultaneously submerged at a time of maximum relative depression. There are also considerable Tertiary deposits in other continents, but they are least perhaps in Australia, where the Eocene is lacking.

We cannot here discuss all the possible causes of depression and elevation but they are of two main sorts (50), eustatic changes which are due to alterations in the overall sea level and which therefore make themselves felt equally all over the world, and orogenic and epeirogenic changes due to deformation of the land masses by such agencies as mountain building, which are usually of comparatively local significance only. Both these may be illustrated by a short reference to one sequence of events in which both are concerned, and which because of its unusually accurate time relation is of special interest to the plant geographer.

During the Pleistocene glaciations (see Chapter 15), great quantities of water must, from time to time, have been locked up in the enormous polar ice-caps and the amount of water in the oceans must have been correspondingly less, resulting in a world-wide (eustatic) lowering of sea level. What this lowering may actually have amounted to is controversial and estimates range from 100 ft. or so to many times that figure but even at its lowest it is generally believed to have been sufficient to have eliminated many of the shallower sea-water barriers. True, it is believed also that the actual weight of the ice-caps must have depressed those parts of the land surfaces on which they rested (169) so as to compensate to some degree for the general lowered water level, but this effect would not have been eustatic and would have affected only the land areas under or near the ice and would have been without significance further afield, and, with the melting of the ice these depressed areas are thought gradually to have risen again as the weight lifted (see p. 327). The Pleistocene glaciations thus illustrate both kinds of relative elevation and also demonstrate that as recently as this many of the shallow-water epicontinental areas were dry land and open to plant migration. It may be too that the evidence of the tilting of Great Britain along a north-south axis, which, from a study of raised beaches, seems to have taken place comparatively recently (584), is associated with these times.

But whatever the actual details may have been, it is certain that we must think in terms of considerable epicontinental changes during the lifetime of the Angiosperms, and, moreover, that these changes must at one time or another have affected the distribution of these plants in three ways. First, they must have controlled plant movement and dispersal by the formation or elimination of barriers. Second, they must have led to tremendous changes in the actual amount of land available for plants. Third, they must have caused correspondingly great alterations, not only in the zonation of climate, but also, and as a consequence, in the prevalence of habitat types.

So far we have been concerned only with changes in the level of the land masses. Certainly, changes of this sort may, by submerging some parts and raising others above the sea, cause considerable alterations in superficial geography, but they do not involve modifications of either the basic area of the continents or their relative positions in respect of one another. Thus, the changes already described, important though they may be, are not of the magnitude required to explain the larger problems in the distribution of plants. We must therefore now enquire what evidence there may be of geographical change on this much greater scale. Here again there are two aspects of the matter and it is convenient to deal first with the smaller, which concerns the subject of mountain building.

The fact that certain geological epochs, and especially the Miocene and Pliocene, were periods of intense mountain elevation has already been referred to more than once. Mountain building on a large scale may be described as a corrugating of the earth's surface widely or locally according to its extent. This can be illustrated in a familiar way by compressing a flat surface such as a sheet or pile of paper laterally. In so doing, not only is the surface thrown into folds but the ends of the paper are brought closer together, so that the horizontal distance between the ends is decreased. That such compression folding has indeed been the mode of formation of many mountain systems has been shown conclusively in the case of the Alps for instance (145), where it appears that part of North Africa has actually been pushed into south Europe. The difference between the model and the real is that in the paper the folds are hollow, but in the earth they are solid, so that mountain building must mean a considerable redistribution of the material of the land mass concerned, not only in order to provide for the thickening caused on the surface by the folding but also to provide for the compensation on the underside of the mass required to bring about isostatic equilibrium and, as it were, to buoy up the increased local load. This material can come only from more outlying parts of the land mass and hence it may be expected, on quite general grounds, that mountain building will cause some contraction of area, which in turn means that the distance between land masses so affected will increase. By how much will of course depend on the amount of folding and overfolding in the mountains and may be very great, as for instance has been suggested in the case of the Himalayan systems, which, it is thought, may have caused such a contraction that India may have been drawn away from the neighbourhood of Africa across the western part of the Indian Ocean. Similarly the width of South America may well be a good deal less now than before the Andes were uplifted.

We see then that geographical changes may be brought about in at least two ways, by relative elevation and depression of land surfaces and by changes in their actual areas and that in the latter particularly the amount of alteration may be considerable. But it is still not of sufficient dimension to explain many of the problems and we must now consider a fresh possibility which would be sufficient in this respect, namely the possibility that there have been major changes in the relative positions of the continents.

The brief mention above of isostatic compensation was made because it served two useful purposes. Not only was it appropriate to the more restricted question there under discussion but it was a valuable introduction to the wider question of continental position now to be discussed, because it clearly indicates that what may be regarded as the normal idea of continental structure and behaviour may have to be radically revised. To the ordinary man in the street a continent or other large land mass is symbolic of all that is solid, rigid and unchangeable, but the geophysicist has quite a different conception, because to him such attributes as solidity and rigidity have a more precise meaning. On his criteria very few kinds of matter merit these descriptions, and a continent is certainly not one of them. How then is it to be regarded? The best way of explaining this point is to pass straight into a simple account of the crust of the earth as it is believed to exist in the light of modern physical ideas.

In brief, the outer layers of the earth's core are pictured as being of the consistency of a very viscous liquid, "solid" by all ordinary standards but essentially fluid in the more strictly scientific meaning of the term. On the outermost layer of this fluid core the continents, themselves more rigid though far from absolutely so, float, like a series of rafts, partially immersed. The layer of the core in which they float is called the "sima", because it is composed of more basic material containing much silica and magnesia, and the continental slabs themselves are composed of a material called "sial" which is more acidic and contains much silica and alumina (Fig. 84). The continental slabs are regarded as of the same average thickness but their absolute thickness varies locally, of course, according to their relief and to compensation on their undersides in accordance with isostasy. Between the continents, over the beds of the oceans, the surface of the sima is generally in direct contact with the water. The continents are thus pictured as isolated slabs of one sort of material floating partially immersed in another sort of material.

With this picture before us we shall at least be partially equipped for an enquiry into one of the most topical of such subjects to-day—the question of whether or not the continents have always occupied the same relative positions as they do now.

There seems little doubt that the idea of continental movement, for which other names now current are displacement, drift and shift, has been vaguely in the minds of men for many years, but the whole conception is so revolutionary and so opposed to traditional teaching that it was not put forward as a definite hypothesis until the present century, and it was not indeed until Wegener (767) published his book *Die Entstehung der Kontinente und Oceane*, in 1915, that the theory came into full prominence. Because this was the first really illustrative attempt to put continental drift into words Wegener's name has become rather too exclusively linked with the

Plate 25. A grove of palms (*Washingtonia filifera*) in California

general theory, and it should be remembered that he was but one of a number of apostles. His theory is as follows. During the early part of the Palaeozoic the continents of the world as we know them were all joined together in one huge land mass or Pangaea, but subsequently separated and drifted apart until they have come to reach the positions they now occupy (Fig. 85). This movement centred on Africa, which, with the main part of continental Asia, has retained its original position more or less unchanged. The theory also postulates a movement or wandering of the poles, in order to account for considerable alterations in the distribution of the climatic zones. After the publication of Wegener's book the Theory of Continental Drift received a great deal of attention (e.g. 113, 208, 209, 364, 465, 612), and many improved forms of it, correcting or modifying some of the more obvious weaknesses of Wegener's ideas, have been put forward. Du Toit (208) in particular

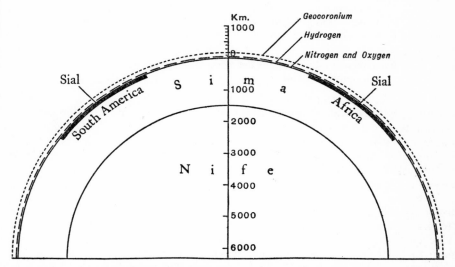

FIG. 83.—Diagram of a section of one hemisphere to show the position of the sial and sima. (Redrawn from Wegener, *Origin of Contents and Oceans*, Methuen & Co.)

brought together in one volume much of the relevant matter relating to these theories, to which he added many of his own beliefs, and it is to this work that the present writer is most indebted in the following discussion.

It would be out of place to consider here the many very controversial aspects of this subject, but it is essential to survey very shortly the evidences on which the idea of drift is based, and these Du Toit usefully summarised as the "criteria of drift", and a much simplified presentation of them is as follows:

1. Physiographic:
    The general similarity in shape of many opposed coast-lines such, for instance, as those of eastern South America and western Africa.
    The correspondence of physiographical features in lands now widely separated.
    The occurrence of various submarine features producible by drifting blocks.

2. Stratigraphical:
    The occurrence of similar geological formations on opposite coasts.
    Other geological resemblances on separate masses.

26

3. Tectonic:
   The occurrence of comparable geosynclines, fold systems, fault systems, and rift valleys on different continental masses.

4. Volcanic:
   Similarities between the volcanic geology of separated masses.

5. Palaeoclimatic:
   The peculiar distribution of glacial deposits and of other extreme climatic types of deposits over the different continents.

6. Palaeontological:
   These may be comprehended in the single statement of the difficulty or impossibility of accounting for the present distribution of organisms on the assumption that the major distribution of land surfaces has been constant. It involves in detail a great many important special aspects, as for instance the floral relation between America and Africa, and between the widely sundered lands of the southern hemisphere. The distribution of marine organisms also presents many very difficult problems on such an assumption.

7. Geodetic:
   This may be interpreted as the evidence afforded by the actual measurements of longitudinal and latitudinal values.

For further details of these criteria the works of the authors cited should be consulted, but it is well to say here that while these show considerable differences in detail there are no essential discrepancies between them. For example, there are differences of opinion about the course of continental drift and also about the condition of the world at the time it began (in contrast to Wegener's Pangaea, Du Toit postulates two primaeval continents, Laurasia in the north and Gondwanaland in the south separated by the Tethys Sea) but these do not affect the general theory.

The last two of the above criteria, however, call for further comment and we may dispose of the final one first. It is particularly important here because to those who are not expert geologists or geophysicists it is by far the most easily understood evidence, and even to them it must if substantiated be the most conclusive. In brief, has actual astronomical and mathematical measurement shown that the continents have moved or are moving? Du Toit, who considers the evidence at some length, concludes that a positive shift of crustal matter has been instrumentally demonstrated, but Longwell (464) and others do not agree, and the evidence on this most crucial point must unfortunately still be regarded as uncertain.

The evidence based on the distribution of organisms, and especially of plants, is obviously of special relevancy here but we need not repeat it because it has already been set out in the earlier part of this book and more especially in those pages dealing with discontinuity, and has also been summarised elsewhere (297). The theoretical importance of that aspect of plant geography is largely in relation to this question of continental drift and the chief facts about it are stated both in Chapter 6 and in Appendix B.

From what has already been said it might be supposed that the more or less unanimous opinion that the distribution of plants cannot properly be explained on the present distribution of land and sea which has already been commented upon implies acceptance of the theory of continental displacement, but this is not so, for there is an alternative view which, until recent times, held the field unchallenged. There are obviously two possible methods by which, in theory, sundered units may be joined. The first is by the movement of one towards the other or both towards one another, the second is by throwing a bridge across the gap between them (626). The

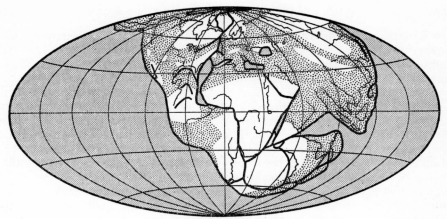

Upper Carboniferous

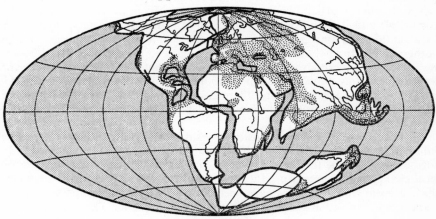

Eocene

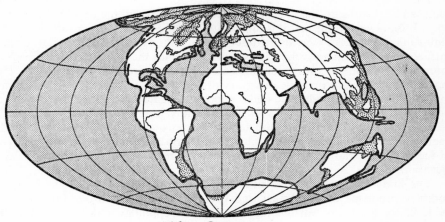

Older Quaternary

FIG. 84.—Reconstruction of the map of the world at different periods in geological history, according to Wegener's Theory of Continental Drift.
(Redrawn from Wegener, *Origin of Continents and Oceans*, Methuen & Co.)

403

first is in effect, as regards continents, the displacement theory, and the second is the Theory of Land-bridges, which supposes that there have existed in the past great additional land surfaces which served to unite the now-severed continents in various ways, and to this we must now turn our attention.

As regards direct evidence the land-bridge theory, which postulates that former huge land areas have now vanished and foundered beneath the sea, is in no better position than the theory of continental drift, for of this foundering of land masses there is no satisfactory evidence, and it would seem clear that the theory must have originated as a theory *faute de mieux*, that is to say as the only conceivable explanation of other facts. But this makes the criterion of it largely that of what can or cannot readily be conceived by the human intelligence. Until the coming of the idea of evolution human thought in general and scientific thought in particular were bounded by conceptions of cosmogony of so ponderous a traditional weight that only exceptional intelligences could become free of them. It is therefore not surprising that the idea of continental drift was not seriously entertained earlier, and in its absence the theory of land-bridges was inevitable. Even to-day tradition is by no means dead and it is the freshness of thought in the displacement theory which arouses at the same time the strong antagonism of some and the enthusiastic support of others. Unfortunately these circumstances gave to the theory of land-bridges a long freedom from criticism, and it became established so firmly that its overthrow became exceedingly difficult, though by no merits of the theory itself. Indeed it is in many respects a weak theory and there is much weight against it. The nature of this evidence has been discussed elsewhere (288, 642) and need only be summarised here in a general way.

The occurrence of marine deposits on what is now land, and the occurrence of land or freshwater deposits where there is now sea, might be taken at first sight to afford evidence of the former existence of bridges or at least of the sort of geographical changes which might produce them, but the earlier part of this chapter has sufficiently shown that the first have been the work of epicontinental seas and have no relation to the actual shapes and areas of the continents. The second, however, requires more attention since it is in fact the crux of the land-bridge theory.

There are two likely sources of evidence for the former existence of now-vanished land surfaces, the structure of oceanic islands and the nature of the ocean floor. With regard to the first it is difficult to imagine the existence of shallow water sedimentary deposits except as a consequence of the subaerial denudation of land surfaces over a comparatively long period, and hence the presence of such beds on more or less isolated islands would indicate that these were once parts of larger land masses. From time to time the discovery of deposits of this kind has been claimed but none has been substantiated and it appears to be true to say that there is still no knowledge of the existence of such beds on any islands which can properly be described as oceanic in the strictest sense. Certainly some of the high coral islands bear sedimentary deposits but these have been formed from the denudation of parts of the coral material of the islands themselves during periods of different relative elevation.

The study of the nature and formation of the ocean floor, which involves very complex problems of geophysics and geology is the most promising source of evidence for or against various theories of geomorphology and it is therefore not surprising that it is receiving special attention to-day and is itself in a state of very rapid development (169, 646, 745). In consequence only the briefest reference, to one or two of its aspects most relevant to plant geography will be made here.

The main point is that sedimentary rocks of the sort just discussed are not the only kind of rock formations which are regarded as of a "continental" rather than an "ocean floor" nature, that is to say which are found especially associated with the floating continental blocks. All the rocks which are comprised within the term *sial* are of this kind, as well as certain related others, being derivable either directly or indirectly from the more or less sialic materials of which the primaeval continents were formed. Therefore if the presence of sialic or sialic-related rocks can be detected on the ocean floor the presence there of continental material may be inferred. It is therefore of great interest that granite (which is a sialic rock) is present in certain oceanic islands (832), notably in the Azores, on Ascension Island, and in the Seychelles, and that related rocks are found on Fiji and some of its neighbours (see p. 852). The first two of these instances arise from a long bottom elevation which runs almost exactly centrally down the middle of the north and south Atlantic, and which is called the mid-Atlantic swell. The Seychelles rather similarly arise from a less well-defined ridge which underlies part of the Indian Ocean between Madagascar and India. The case of the south-western Pacific is a little different. Here Fiji and many other of the islands contain andesite, which though not strictly sialic is nevertheless regarded as associated with continental formations, and on this basis it has been argued that the islands concerned mark the eastern edge of a former Melanesian continent. There are thus at least three areas in which there seems to be continental material on the floors of the oceans but how far these can be regarded as traces of former land surfaces of the land-bridge sort in these positions is very doubtful. The mid-Atlantic swell for instance runs down the ocean and not across it, while the situation with regard to the south-west Pacific is still largely hypothetical. Only in the Seychelles does the case look stronger, but here the land-bridge explanation is least required because of the direction and fair proximity of the East African and Arabian coasts. Indeed it seems more reasonable to suppose that these areas, if indeed they are extensive areas of sialic rocks, are thin residual patches torn or thinned away by stretching from a continental block according to one or other of several modern theories of crustal behaviour, and if this is so the view that this may have occurred in connection with some kind of horizontal rather than vertical displacement of the continents would seem a very reasonable one. In this context, it is interesting to note that Jeannel (403) believes that the south temperate oceanic islands lie along ridges of continental basalt which were left behind in the course of continental drift at the beginning of the Tertiary, and that they are thus fundamentally continental in type. He cites in support of this the presence of sialic granites on Keguelen.

But apart from all this the actual idea of land-bridges is less promising than would appear at first sight. To begin with the phytogeographical problems which land-bridges are particularly called to explain are mostly those of Angiosperms, and hence any bridges must be of Cretaceous or later date to be effective. Again, the list of discontinuities in Appendix B shows that in this period since the Cretaceous it would be necessary to postulate bridges in almost every direction, between America and Africa, between Africa and Asia, linking the scattered lands of the south, joining oceanic islands with some mainland, and stretching across the Pacific. In short, it is necessary largely to cover the oceans with land-bridges, and more or less contemporary ones at that. Such an assumption is unwarrantable on any grounds, including geophysical arguments, and it is no small point in favour of the idea of drift that it avoids postulating such enormous and unlikely increases in the land surfaces of the globe.

It must not be supposed from this that no land-bridges can have existed in any circumstances or time, nor even that faith in them has been entirely abandoned (315, 316) and, as Darlington (175) has shrewdly pointed out, Central America is in fact a land bridge, which has existed only since the Pliocene. He notes also that, from the Isthmus of Tehuantepec in southern Mexico to the Isthmus of Panama, it is 1,300 miles long, that is to say, two-thirds of the distance between West Africa and Brazil across the Atlantic. Even more recently van Steenis (829) has given an elaborate presentation of many of the facts and arguments most commonly quoted in support of the theory of land-bridges. It has also already been shown that comparatively small elevations would serve to link what are now some quite widely separated areas, but land-bridges proper, such as are required in order to explain many of the phytogeographical facts, are land areas crossing the main oceans and for such it can only be said that the evidence is in no case adequate. It is fair to say that many of these difficulties are realised and attempts have been made to meet them, and that few geologists would accept the bare land-bridge theory to-day without saving clauses. For instance, one view supposes that there was in the Palaeozoic a huge mainly southern continent, and that this, to use the current phrase, "broke up" in the Mesozoic, the breaking up being pictured as a differential sinking of its constituent parts so as to produce a discontinuous series of land masses. The interesting point about this is that it takes liberties with the stability of continents which are not always allowed to the protagonists of drift. There are other reasons too why land-bridges are far from being the universal remedy that they appear. One in particular is that the submergence of great extents of land will not necessarily produce the phytogeographical results actually to be observed. For instance very wide discontinuity of types will follow only if those types are completely distributed throughout the bridge before it founders and, moreover, in very constant form. Otherwise the subsidence of the bridge would have to take the most peculiar and special course to produce the observed discontinuity. These difficulties have indeed been realised often enough, and frequently, it should be noted, by some foremost authorities on distribution. Wallace (756), for instance, believed firmly in what he called the permanence of continents and would not admit the possibility of land-bridges. Unfortunately he knew not continental drift and was thus faced with the necessity of explaining the awkward facts of discontinuity largely on the basis of dispersal, and this, to say the least, is a very uneasy standpoint.

As the last few paragraphs have implied it is in relation to the problem of oceanic islands and the process by which they may have become populated that the land-bridge theory appears in the most favourable light because of the easy opportunity it affords of regarding them as the remnants of foundered continents, from which, of course, their biota will have been derived, though as has been shown there is little or no evidence of this. It must be admitted that the theory of continental drift cannot provide so simple an explanation as this of the formation and population of isolated islands but one view is that the elevation of many of them was associated with the disturbed crustal conditions which would be expected to occur immediately in the wake of a drifting continent, from which their biota would have been derived at a time when it was still comparatively near at hand. An explanation of this sort may certainly be feasible enough for some islands, such for instance as those of the north and south Atlantic, but for others, among which the Hawaiian Islands are particularly prominent, it will hardly do, though neither, it should be made clear, will the theory of land-bridges. In these more difficult cases it may well be that the solution of the puzzle depends on knowledge not yet at our disposal.

Turning now once more to the theory of continental drift, it is not unfair to say that many of the criteria mentioned by Du Toit—that is to say the direct evidences of the theory—are very compelling. It would be presumptuous to make further comment on the inorganic arguments but it is permissible and indeed desirable to refer once more to the evidences afforded by plant geography, and of this it can be said, in the writer's opinion, without fear of rebuttal, that the theory of continental drift explains the peculiarities and leading features of Angiosperm distribution more simply than any other hypothesis. By this is meant that not only is drift more likely than bridging on phytogeographical evidence, but that drift can explain the details and sequence of distribution in a way quite beyond the power of any reasonable theory of land-bridges or of the theory of distribution entirely by dispersal. The writer also believes that few will read the early chapters of this book dispassionately without coming to the same conclusion.

Nor, despite the fact that discontinuity has been so particularly mentioned, is the botanical evidence restricted to this. On the contrary there are other features in the geography of the Flowering Plants which are even more difficult to explain otherwise and it is worth while to stress these at this point. Paramount among them is the remarkable degree of underlying similarity and community between the floras of all parts of the world, which, because differences are often so much more obvious than resemblances, is seldom commented upon. There are Angiosperm floras in all the plant-habitable parts of the globe and no one of them is significantly distinct from any of the others, or so unlike them as to suggest some quite peculiar history. Naturally some have greater degrees of particularity than others, as for instance the flora of Australia (see Chapter 12), but this peculiarity is superficial compared with the degree of basic similarity, so that even in Australia we find the more prevalent families in much the same order as in other places. Even in what is perhaps the most distinctive of all floras, that of New Caledonia, the difference in this respect is comparatively little. Again, as Chapter 4 has shown, there are practically no large endemic groups of Angiosperms such as would surely be inevitable if the continents had always been as isolated from one another as they are now. And finally there is the extraordinary circumstance of the Monocotyledons, which compare almost completely with the Dicotyledons in distribution and which are almost everywhere present in the same minor proportion to them (301). In short the Angiosperms have spread all over the world with a degree of completeness and constancy which it may well be argued is inconceivable if the continents had never been more closely adjacent than they are now. Indeed taking all these facts into consideration it seems an almost inescapable conclusion that the Angiosperms must have achieved a great part of, and even perhaps nearly all, their distribution during a period prior to the sundering of a super-continent into its constituent parts (297).

But why, it may be asked, in view of this biological evidence, is the theory of continental drift not more widely accepted? The reply is that there are at least three important objections to it. Important at least in theory though it is to be noted that each is peculiarly unsatisfactory in some way. The first is the purely psychological objection to something which not only breaks entirely new ground but which in doing so does violence to long-established opinions. If the theory of drift is true, then much that has been written on all kinds of other topics is untrue, and there is thus an enormous inertia against the theory. Du Toit expressed this so vividly that we cannot do better than quote his words (the italics are his), in which he says: ". . . it must frankly be recognised that the principles advocated by the *supporters of Continental Drift form generally the antithesis of those currently held.*

The differences between the two doctrines are indeed fundamental and the acceptance of the one must largely exclude the other. Indeed, under the new hypothesis certain geological concepts come to acquire a new significance amounting in a few cases to a complete inversion of principles, and the enquirer will find it necessary to re-orient his ideas. For the first time he will get glimpses—albeit imperfect as yet—of a pulsating restless earth, all parts of which are in greater or less degree of movement in respect to the axis of rotation, having been so, moreover, throughout geological time. He will have to leave behind him—perhaps reluctantly—the dumbfounding spectacle of the present continental masses, firmly anchored to a plastic foundation yet remaining fixed in space; set thousands of kilometres apart, it may be, yet behaving in almost identical fashion from epoch to epoch and stage to stage like soldiers at drill; widely stretched in some quarters at various times and astoundingly compressed in others, yet retaining their general shapes, positions and orientations; remote from one another throughout history, yet showing in their fossil remains common or allied forms of terrestrial life; possessed during certain epochs of climates that may have ranged from glacial to torrid or pluvial to arid, though contrary to meteorological principles when their existing geographical positions are considered— to mention but a few such paradoxes!"

This extract illustrates a point which should be stressed, namely that the conceptions of continental structure described above, such as the sial and the sima, floating blocks and isostasy, are not peculiar to the theory of drift, but rather quite generally accepted views of modern geomorphology. That they are so apposite in view of possible drift is then distinctly in favour of that theory. This emerges in an interesting way from the consideration of the other general objections to the theory. The second of these, and the only one which approaches the scientific, is that there is not known any force which could possibly be regarded as sufficient to move the continents in the way suggested. That is to say, there is no satisfactory explanation of their movement. This objection has all too often been accepted as final, but it must be realised that at best it is only negative, and it would surely be untenable to suppose that there *cannot* be any such force. It is simply that no such force is understood at present. The ordinary observer is not likely to be much impressed by such negative evidence and it has also been most appropriately pointed out (579) that this is exactly the position also with certain other geological beliefs which have been generally accepted on their circumstantial evidences, such as the sinking of land-bridges and the occurrence of the ice ages. There is no properly understood physical explanation of them either.

The third objection or series of objections is based on weaknesses in the presentation of the drift theory by earlier writers, and especially by Wegener. He, for instance, painted much too detailed a picture for the contemporary state of the theory and laid both himself and it open to criticism on matters of really unimportant detail. Probably no one among even the most fervent advocates of drift is prepared to accept the theory in the precise form of Wegener, but this cannot be considered to be evidence against the broad conception underlying it. Again, he made his chronology so definite that it is easy to pick holes in it, but this has no real bearing on the absolute likelihood or otherwise of drift. Similarly he pictured more or less constant movement of land masses over very long periods of time and the possibility of this again is controversial. He also postulated displacement of the poles, though it is not essential to the basic geophysical argument, and in doing so gave his adversaries a valuable weapon, since there are arguments against this idea.

As a matter of fact this very abstruse problem of polar change is, from the botanical point of view, of some special interest in relation to the light requirements of plants, and calls for further notice on that account. It is generally agreed that in Tertiary times Antarctica sustained a flora of temperate *facies* (see p. 323 above) probably similar to the present floras of New Zealand and Fuegia (157, 158, 207). To-day, Antarctica, because of its position in relation to the polar axis of rotation, has very long days, and even, according to latitude, continuous daylight in summer, and very short days, or even continuous darkness, in winter. It is difficult to believe that the kind of flora which has been described could have existed in these circumstances and there would seem inevitably to have been a subsequent change of some considerable degree. There are two leading possibilities—either the length of day relation at high latitudes (see p. 393) has altered through some such cause as a variation in the obliquity of the ecliptic or these values have remained constant. If the latter it must be supposed that Antarctica is not now in the position, *relative to the pole*, which it occupied during that part of the Tertiary, and this may be due to polar movement, or to continental movement or to a combination of the two. The more unlikely the former, the more likely the latter. In this connection it is interesting to notice the opinion, re-expressed by Joyce (415), that the form of the Scotia arc of islands between South America and Antarctica may be the consequence of some such movement of the latter.

Although many geophysicists and geomorphologists have felt themselves unable to accept the theory of drift some of them seem to have appreciated the weakness of their position and to have put forward theories of their own to rationalise it. These may be illustrated by references to one of them, Joly's Theory of Climatic Cycles, which to the present writer seems to indicate very clearly the direction in which a synthesis between opposing views about drift is likely to be achieved eventually, an opinion already expressed by Bews (69) who looks forward to a combination of the views of Wegener and Joly. Joly (412) supposed that in the course of time the internal heat of the earth accumulates as a result of radioactivity, and that the effect of this is to melt the sima progressively outwards till that layer of it supporting the continents and oceans becomes molten. This has two consequences—a reduction in the density of the supporting sima and a resultant sinking of the continents, with some inevitable transgression of the seas, and a rapid conduction away of the heat of the sima by the oceans and continents, so that the molten layer soon resolidifies and there begins a new cycle. This theory was propounded to account for certain major features of geological history, and especially for the repeated but long-separated period of climatic catastrophe (glaciation), epicontinentality and mountain building. Joly supposed, in the theory, that these are the inescapable consequences of the stages at which the outer layer of the sima becomes molten. Strangely enough, however, he did not admit the possibility of continental movement to any great degree in these circumstances, despite the fact that they might on general grounds be supposed to be exactly the conditions to favour it. Because of the association of glaciation and mountain building the latest melting of the sima must have occurred, as Joly postulated, some time since the beginning of the Tertiary, so that any drift it might involve is likely to have been more or less of similar date, and this it will be noticed accords very well with the requirements of the botanical evidence which favours the view that drift was not marked or continuous till well on in the Tertiary. Thus Joly's theory, if it permitted the conception of continental displacement or drift as a consequence of one of the cyclical revolutions described, would provide an almost ideal geomorphic theory from the point of view of the plant geographer. It is therefore significant that some regional studies of crustal movement, such as those of Smit Sibinga in Malaysia (676) as quoted by Lam (440), clearly suggest circumstances which might have led to drift, and even to intermittent drift, at a comparatively late date. On the other hand some believe that during the Pleistocene the position of the continents was much as it is to-day (745), which suggests that had drift occurred it would have effectively ceased by that time. Holland, too (364), has stressed the evidence that some 50–70 million years ago, a date presumably in Tertiary times, there was a widespread physical revolution and thinks that this was of a kind which might well have facilitated continental drift, while Seymour Sewell (364, 643) believes that the Indian, Atlantic and Arctic Oceans may have been formed during the Tertiary.

In the ten years that have elapsed since the foregoing account of continental drift was prepared for the second edition of this book, a great deal of progress has been made in subjects relating to it.

In 1955 Gold (817) showed that changes in the distribution of mass in the earth's crust, for example through mountain building, could be sufficient to cause such movement of the outer layers of the earth relative to its rotational axis as would produce the effect of polar shift; and at about the same time, Hospers (380) and Runcorn (607, 608) were among the first to develop, under the name of palaeomagnetism, earlier suggestions that rock-magnetism might eventually help to solve the problem of continental drift. As they pointed out, there is strong reason for believing that the direction of magnetisation of rocks perpetuates that of the earth's magnetic field at the time of their formation, so that, in suitable circumstances, rocks in this way reveal their original positions in respect of the contemporary poles. Assuming this belief to be correct, it follows that if the surface layers of the earth have shifted on the deeper layers as a whole and without distortion, the palaeomagnetic data from their rocks will be mutually inconsistent, and also inconsistent with their present geographical positions. Thus inconsistencies of this kind can be held to afford evidence of differential continental movement. Not all rocks are suitable for palaeomagnetic determination, and results have yet to be obtained from some of the more crucial parts of the world, but much has been done and some important tentative conclusions reached. To mention some examples, Nairn (533, 535) concluded that some Rhodesian lavas indicate a drift of about 2,000 miles; Irving calculated that when certain Tasmanian dolerites were formed in the Mesozoic, the South Pole was at a point which is now 50° S. and 157° E.; Runcorn (608) gave results which, in his opinion, seem to require about 24 degrees of displacement of America westward from Europe in post-Triassic times, and, in another paper, has suggested that in the southern hemisphere continental displacement may have been extensive since late pre-Cambrian times, and even perhaps of the order of 6,000 miles since the end of the Palaeozoic; Irving and Green (401) have suggested that in early Tertiary times Australia and Antarctica were closely adjacent to each other, but that by the end of that period they had become situated as they are now; and Opdyke and Runcorn (545) have shown that the position of Australia in respect of the South Pole has greatly changed since the Upper Palaeozoic. In 1958 there appeared a useful collection of papers relating to continental drift edited by, and contributed to by, Carey (119), and in 1960 two long papers by Collinson and Runcorn (146) and by Cox and Doell (156) respectively gave valuable summaries of the contemporary situation in regard to palaeomagnetism and related matters. More recently, Runcorn (609) has given a general summing up of the position to-day, in which he concludes that South America, Africa, India, Australia and Antarctica were, during the middle Mesozoic, clearly grouped together near the present South Pole. These at least are some of the many references to subjects too technical to be covered any more fully here, and though it may be that some of the conclusions will have to be modified in the future, there can be no doubt that this work has given most important fresh support to the idea of continental movement, and, in particular, has done much to remove some of the previous difficulties.

Increasing support for the view that there may have been a real or apparent shift in the position of the poles in the past is of special interest to plant-geographers because of the almost infinite variety of change in climatic values, especially, of course, temperature, that such change would bring, an aspect of the matter which Irving (400) has considered. Two points are worth stressing here. The first is that the equator is, in effect, a ring which is equidistant from the poles at all points, so that if the poles move the equator must swing in order to maintain this relation to them. Hence, no matter whither the poles may drift, the equator must move accordingly, with the consequence that the temperature will rise in some parts of the world and fall in others. At the same time the equator can never assume an entirely new position; it must always encircle the earth through its maximum circumference, and so, no matter how or where it swings, the conditions at two points on it will remain unchanged. The second point is that the biological effect of shift will depend greatly on how land and sea is distributed along the new equator. In some positions of the poles, the equator might cross much more land than it does to-day, but, with the poles in other positions, the equator might be largely or even almost entirely over water, in which case the effect on tropical life would be profound because there would be little or no equatorial land surface. These hypothetical changes in the position of the equator are not easy to visualise, but they have great theoretical importance and Figs. 85 and 86 illustrate some of the more suggestive of them.

Another interesting consideration in the theme of polar shift is whether a change in this respect would eventually lead to a redistribution of the world's land masses. As has already been noted on p. 11, these are to-day arranged in a highly symmetrical pattern in respect of the polar axis on which the earth revolves, and it is at least justifiable to speculate whether, in the event of this axis shifting and destroying this symmetry, there might not be set in motion strong forces tending towards its restoration through a redistribution of land and sea, perhaps by some form of drift or plastic deformation.

The idea of continental movement has also had reinforcement of a more purely physiographic kind from Carey's Orocline Concept. He points out (118) that the face of the globe shows many areas where orogenic (mountain) belts turn in trend through large angles, in places as much as 180 degrees, or, in other words, where mountain systems are sharply bent, as for instance in Europe, in Baluchistan and in Alaska. This, he considers, can have one of two origins. Either the orogenic belt had that shape from the beginning, or else the bend represents an imposed strain, and it is this latter which he calls an orocline. He claims that, when all such oroclines, together with other identifiable strains, are straightened out, the distribution of land masses is much altered, and in particular there appears a Laurasia substantially identical with that deduced by Du Toit on wholly different grounds.

Other developments which have lessened the difficulty of accepting a concept of continental drift, are concerned more directly with the structure of the earth as a whole, and two of these call for brief notice here.

It is often, and perhaps generally, assumed that the earth is a shrinking body, though some have believed that it is, on the contrary, expanding. Recently Egyed (213, 814) has produced new data and arguments in support of this view. He supposes that, in consequence of the release of unstable ultra-high pressure in its interior, the earth is expanding, and that this has involved the fragmentation and increasing

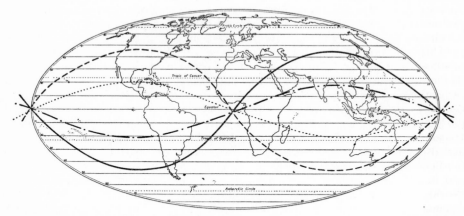

FIG. 85. Map of the world showing the positions of the equator at various positions of the North Pole.

——————— N. Pole at 45° N. 90° W.   N. Pole at 70° N. 90° W.   —— · —— ·
– – – – – – – N. Pole at 45° N. 90° E.   N. Pole at 70° N. 90° E.   · · · · · · · ·

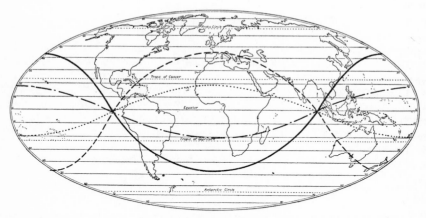

FIG. 86. Map of the world showing the positions of the equator at various positions of the North Pole.

——————— N. Pole at 45° N.   0° W.   N. Pole at 70° N.   0° W.   —— · —— ·
– – – – – – – N. Pole at 45° N. 180° W.   N. Pole at 70° N. 180° W.   · · · · · · · ·

separation of the continental material of the crust. Another less direct indication of this expansion of the earth is the nicety with which the major land masses fit closely together on a hypothetical globe of about two-thirds the diameter of the present earth.

Much the same result, though from a different cause, is postulated in the theory of Dietz (191), which was discussed by that author, Bernal and Wilson (*loc. cit.*). He supposes that the oceans began as rifts in the continents and that these rifts became progressively widened by the extrusion of material into them from the magma below, through "convection currents" set up by the greater heat and pressure deep down. Indeed the whole outer layer of the earth below the continents and oceans has, elsewhere, been pictured in popular language as sluggishly churning over like slowly boiling toffee. These rifts are marked, according to Dietz's theory, by elevations along the lines of split, and the long mid-Atlantic swell, on or close to which St. Helena and Ascension lie, is a well-known example.

This theory is of special interest in view of Jeannel's work already referred to on p. 405 and his belief that all the south temperate oceanic islands from Marion to St. Paul and Amsterdam, lie on ridges of continental basalt conforming to the general eastern edge of South America and Antarctica, and left behind when these continents drifted towards their present positions. It is also worth noting that Zimmerman (807) quotes the view that the swell on which the Hawaiian Islands stand is formed by volcanic material extruded through a rift or fissure in the floor of the ocean. There are also very recent contributions to this problem by Wilson (830, 831) and by Girdler (816), who bring forward evidence that in the Red Sea, in the Gulf of Aden and in the Rift Valley in the Old World, and in the Gulf of California in the New World, there are to be seen to-day the beginnings of the process of continental fragmentation and drift.

To summarise, the theory of continental drift would explain plant distribution to-day to a remarkably complete degree if it could be substantiated in the following terms and made to incorporate the following points:

1. That at least at some time after the origin of the Angiosperms, and perhaps between the Cretaceous and the middle or later Tertiary the continents were, more or less, joined into one and were fixed in position.

2. That as a consequence of some thermal reaction of the kinds mentioned above the sima became molten in the latter part of the Tertiary.

3. That continental drift resulted, first, perhaps, at a rapid rate and then as the sima cooled, more slowly.

4. That an immediate result of this drifting was the uplifting of mountain ranges on the forward sides of the moving masses.

5. That a later consequence of the rapid loss of heat was the onset of the glaciations of the Pleistocene.

If, as is said, a theory incorporating these points could be put forward, then it would not only explain most points of plant geography but would also reveal the main outlines of the sequence of events by which the Angiosperms have attained their present development and distribution in the world. Each point in the above summary is provided for by one hypothesis or another, and if these at present apparently divergent details could be welded into a whole, it would be a very satisfactory theory of historical plant geography.

To conclude a chapter which has in places taken us far from this subject, let us describe the position (in respect of the matters which have been discussed) as it appears to be to-day:

1. Many features in the present distribution of plants, and especially those associated on the one hand with the overall similarities of floras and on the other with the particular phenomenon of discontinuity, cannot easily be explained.

2. Three general explanations are possible:

    (*a*) That they are due solely to dispersal factors.

    (*b*) That the now separated continents were once joined by land-bridges.

    (*c*) That the continents have changed their relative positions.

3. All three of these have probably had some effect, and the question is to decide which has been of paramount importance.

4. The inadequacy of dispersal has been particularly demonstrated in Chapter 19.

5. There are grave objections to the theory of land-bridges.

6. The idea of continental drift affords a satisfactory explanation.

7. The obstacles to the acceptance of the idea of continental drift have been much reduced in recent years and there is a reasonable prospect that the theory will, in some final form, not only receive general support but will provide the desired explanation of many problems in the geography of the Flowering Plants.

In the latter part of this chapter attention has been concentrated upon the subjects of land-bridges and continental displacement not solely because these have a particular appeal to the plant geographer but also because they illustrate in a specially vivid way the necessary relation that exists between plant geography and these theories of earth structure and geochronology, and it is therefore very desirable to make clear here that these are by no means the only hypotheses of this kind. Certainly, as far as can be seen at present, these seem to be more directly applicable to problems of phytogeography than any others but they should not be regarded as the only conceivable explanations or allowed to exclude the consideration of many other aspects of the matter such as are conveniently summarised in a single chapter by Gutenberg (330). Nor is this all. One of the most perplexing things about Angiosperm geography is its inherent chaos, which expresses itself in the difficulty of accounting satisfactorily for any appreciable proportion of the total facts by any one single theoretical explanation of the more detailed sort. It is, indeed, as if there still remains to be discovered the key to knowledge which will convert this discordance into harmony, and while this state of affairs continues plant geographers will be wise if they are as receptive as they can be to the implications and possibilities not only of such hypotheses as have been the subject of this chapter but even perhaps of some of the more fantastic theories of cosmogony and earth-history.

Chapter 22

THE THEORY OF TOLERANCE

In the last six chapters the factors of distribution were first reviewed in general and then discussed in particular. The purpose of this chapter is to consider how far and in what manner they can be made to provide a theoretical explanation of the geography of the Flowering Plants.

What has already been said makes it clear that there are certain general statements which can be made regarding the causes of plant distribution, and that these are so incontestable that they may rank as general principles of plant geography. These principles are fundamentally six and may be expressed most concisely as follows:

1. Plant distribution is primarily controlled by the distribution of climatic conditions (see Plates 2, 4 and 5).

2. Plant distribution is secondarily controlled by the distribution of edaphic factors.

3. Great movements of species and of floras have taken place in the past and are apparently still continuing.

4. Plant movement, especially in its larger aspect of plant migration, is brought about by the transport of individual plants during their dispersal phases.

5. There has been great variation and oscillation in climate, especially at higher latitudes, since Angiosperms became prominent.

6. At least some, and probably considerable, variation has occurred during the same period in the relative distribution and outline of land and sea.

Although in the light of what has been said earlier these principles need no further demonstration, there are one or two points connected with them which have not yet been adequately noted. The first is the relation between the first two principles. The facts of plant geography everywhere show that the first of these is the more fundamental and that plant distribution is basically a climatic distribution. Edaphic factors can have but a secondary rôle, if for no other reason than that they themselves are often controlled by climatic considerations. Moreover, edaphic factors tend to be distributed without much regard to latitude, whereas plants are normally correlated in range with latitude unless the factor of altitude, which is itself a climatic effect, comes into play. Actually the difference between the two factors is best expressed by saying that while climatic factors control the extent of distribution, edaphic factors control its intensity. On climatic factors will depend whether a given species shall be a potential occupant of a given area; on edaphic factors will depend whether it will in fact occupy it, and if so in what relative abundance. Climatic factors must decide whether an area is open to colonisation by a species in view of its general atmospheric requirements; its eventual presence will depend on whether or not there are habitats suitable for it. Usually the more numerous and larger such habitats are, the more plentiful within this area will the species be. Naturally other factors may also be involved, but this is a fair general statement.

Except for the third, each of the six principles comprehends one of the main factors of distribution already discussed at length, and one of the most important

415

points is that they and the factors involved in them are of two kinds. The first two and the fourth can be distinguished from the rest as being *internal*, in the sense that they concern the inherent constitution of the plant. In the first two the aspect of constitution concerned is the physiological, and in the fourth it is the structural. Numbers five and six are *external* or extraneous, in the sense that they are no more than guides controlling the direction of effects resulting from the inherent conditions of plants. The relationships between the six principles are fairly clear and generally accepted. That between the first two has just been dealt with; that between the third and fifth is believed to be one of effect and cause; the fourth explains the mechanism of the third; and the sixth will control to a greater or lesser extent the result of the third. Indeed, taking the whole six principles together, they clearly indicate what is in effect a theoretical explanation of plant distribution, namely that it is the result of complicated plant movement or migration under the influence of climatic change, this movement being achieved by dispersal and being modified by contemporary topography, and this, with or without minor modification, is the view generally held to-day by those who are familiar with the facts and history of plant geography.

At first sight this view, which is at least one hundred years old and which may be called for convenience the Theory of Climatic Migrations, appears to be all that is to be desired, but on close examination it will be seen to be deficient in one very important and fundamental respect. It visualises plant movement; it indicates exactly how such movement may be made; it indicates the primary cause of such movement, but what it does not do is to explain why the cause (climatic change) should actually result in the movement or migration of plants. How the result can be achieved is clear, namely by dispersal. As to *why* the cause should have this particular result there is no indication. There is no conception of how and why climatic change is able to bring about plant movement by the agencies of dispersal. As it stands the theory is like a locomotive which lacks connecting rods. Climatic change may be compared with the steam power generated in the boiler, and plant movement, by means of dispersal, may be compared with the mechanical movement of the locomotive by means of its wheels, but just as without the connecting rods the first cannot be converted into the second, so the theory cannot be made to explain plant movement without some definite provision which, as expressed above, it lacks.

This deficiency is met by the tacit and therefore to such extent unsatisfactory assumption of what is in fact the conception of specific tolerance, namely the view that each and every species can exist only within a given range of external conditions, and that this tolerance to environmental values does not and cannot change so rapidly as to "adapt" itself to change in external conditions. On this assumption the species can only survive in so far as its dispersal methods are able to keep pace with the changing external conditions in such a way that its range is always that of the conditions which it requires for its development. On this assumption the necessary connecting rod is provided in the form of a rigid relation between the species and the conditions under which it can exist. This relationship prevents the species from staying where it is and modifying its existence to the new surroundings which the movement of climatic values (climatic change) has brought about.

Let it be said at once that no criticism of this assumption on the score of its probability is possible. It may be that in the early days of the Flowering Plants climatic changes were so slow and gradual that species were able to adapt themselves to them by the processes of evolution, but in more recent times climatic changes have been so rapid and so drastic, at any rate outside the tropics, as to make this suggestion in general quite untenable, and it is to these rapid and recent changes that are undoubtedly to be attributed the major features of plant distribution to-day. The point at issue is that this all-essential part of the Theory of Climatic Migrations has grown up without proper presentation and without the standing which would be its due as a properly expressed and tested hypothesis.

To remedy this deficiency the present writer published some thirty years ago a paper reconsidering the conception of tolerance and expressing it in the form of a definite theory (289). In that paper the six principles enumerated above were first dealt with, and there was then enunciated the Theory of Tolerance in the following terms:

"Each and every plant species is able to exist and reproduce successfully only within a definite range of climatic and edaphic conditions. This range represents the tolerance of the species to external conditions.

"The tolerance of a species is a specific character subject to the laws and processes of organic evolution in the same way as its morphological characters, but the two are not necessarily linked.

"Change in tolerance may or may not be accompanied by morphological change, and morphological change may or may not be accompanied by change in tolerance.

"Morphologically similar species may show wide differences in tolerance, and species with similar tolerance may show very little morphological similarity.

"The relative distribution of species with similar ranges of tolerance is finally determined by the result of the competition between them.

"The tolerance of any larger taxonomic unit is the sum of the tolerances of its constituent species."

This enunciation was followed by a long discussion of the meaning and application of the theory, and, because they serve to illustrate many points of general interest to the student of plant geography, the main features of this discussion may appropriately be summarised here.

According to the theory there must be a total area which a species can, in virtue of its tolerance, occupy, and this may be termed its "potential area". Its ability to cover this area depends first upon its dispersal over the area and then upon the result of the competition it may encounter in the process. If the potential area is large, competition will tend to vary in intensity in different parts of it so that establishment will not be equally easy everywhere. A species never can or will, under natural conditions, become established outside the potential area, and the size and position of the potential area will tend to vary with change in external conditions. If tolerance is a specific character amenable to the laws of evolution and genetics, it may change in the same manner and from the same causes as structural characters, and since these latter are normally more or less closely correlated with conditions of life, some distinct relation between morphology and tolerance may normally be expected.

It is important to note that the theory as a whole visualises three kinds of changes, each with its own particular speed. First, there is the rate of evolutionary change; secondly, there is the speed of change in external conditions; and, thirdly, there is the speed of movement of the species by means of dispersal. It is a fundamental postulate of the theory that the first speed (evolutionary) is nowadays immeasurably slower than the other two, and that these (external change and dispersal) are normally comparable.

27

The tolerance of a species will be composed of many ranges of tolerance to individual conditions, but in practice one of these will usually become a distributional limiting factor. A narrow range of tolerance as regards one condition—say, for instance, rainfall—will control the distribution even though the tolerance to other conditions, perhaps to soil constitution, is much wider. If tolerance to a particular condition or factor is so wide as to include the whole existing world gamut of this factor, the tolerance may be described as complete in respect of it. In the theoretically conceivable case of a species exhibiting complete tolerance to all factors and conditions, its potential area will also be complete, namely cosmopolitan, but there are no species which can be cited as possible examples of this. The world gamut of most external conditions is relatively small, and, taking into account the great number of plant species, it must be presumed that many species will tend to have very similar tolerances, especially as regards one or a few factors. This is in accord with the observed facts of competition and affords a possible explanation of it. The result may be anything from the complete supremacy of one species to a balanced deadlock between two or more.

Many detailed studies in plant distribution (295, 307) suggest strongly that within any range of tolerance as a whole there are minimum, optimum and maximum conditions. Existence, in absence of competition, will be possible within the whole range, but the species will only be at its strongest, in relation to competition and also to vigour, within certain optimum figures. It also seems certain that minute differences in tolerance between species, such as are imperceptible to the ordinary human observer, may be quite critical and decisive in determining the issue of competition. Conversely, very minute differences in external conditions may be vital to the plant.

The assertion that the tolerance of a larger unit is the sum of the tolerances of its constituent species needs no elaboration except to point out that these specific tolerances need not form a continuous range of values for any or all factors. Thus the tolerances of the species of a genus towards temperature, for instance, may have wide limits but they may not cover all values between these limits. As there is usually continuous variation in climatic values, this may well lead to the potential area of the genus being discontinuous, that is to say composed of spatially separated parts. This obviously has a direct bearing on the subject of discontinuous distribution, and is only one example of the way in which the conception of tolerance impinges on all sorts of geographical problems.

The corollary to this final phrase of the theory is that the tolerance of a species will, in its turn, be made up of the tolerances of its constituent individuals, since (as the third sentence of the statement says) these individuals will vary in tolerance among themselves much as they vary in form, and it is important for several reasons to appreciate this fully. For one thing it follows that the tolerance of a species will depend on what individuals are included within it, that is to say on the taxonomic conception of it, and there is thus no necessity in connection with the theory to attempt any definition of what a species may or may not be. Any population of individuals will have its own tolerance and this will be unaffected by what taxonomic rank may or may not be given it. Again, the conception of individual tolerance is consistent with many of the results observed in the study of geographical races and ecotypes, and with much of what is now often called cytogeography (see pp. 36, 177 above). It would be out of place here to attempt any detailed appreciation of these lines of work but the reader will find a useful guide to them in three papers by Clausen, Keck and Hiesey (137, 138, 139) of which the most recent contains a summary of other investigations of the same kind. Most of all, however, the idea of the variation of tolerance among individuals is important because of the way in which it affords to populations a means of protection against the effects of alterations in external conditions. Were all the individuals of an assemblage rigidly similar in their tolerances then a serious change in some environmental value might, even if it were no more than a short-term fluctuation, have the most serious consequences, since a transgression of this rigid tolerance limit might easily result in total elimination. Individual differences of tolerance on the other hand, diversified as they are likely to be by a multiplicity of components, provide a buffering or damping effect which serves to spread the harmful effect of external fluctuation so widely over the population that only from an exceptionally severe or prolonged change is there real danger of the extinction of every member of the population even if the change is so widespread as to affect the whole of the population distribution. Some may perish but not all, the incidence of mortality depending upon such factors as the nature and direction of the external alteration, degree of exposure, stage of development, and so on.

This conception of individual tolerance may indeed be looked upon, without undue exaggeration, as one of the most vital aspects of the theory because it provides an explanation of an obvious difficulty, namely the fact that the occurrence of temporary exceptional environmental conditions does not produce an immediate wholesale effect. True, it is possible to conceive of circumstances in which this might be the result, as for example the sudden occurrence of severe frost in an area hitherto without it, but all experience shows that environmental fluctuation is, even in its most extreme form, something of a much less drastic order than this, and that individual tolerance variation is sufficient to meet it to a considerable degree. Thus a single exceptional season is not often observed to have, under natural conditions, a widely destructive effect, though some proportion of individuals may suffer. Indeed it may well be that the measure of individual variation in tolerance has become, in the course of ages, generally attuned to the amplitude of environmental fluctuation and its distribution over the different portions of the world's surface as a whole.

The Theory of Tolerance bears also on the conception of Age and Area (see Chapter 3). A species or genus may be very restricted in range for one or other of two totally distinct reasons. It may be because the unit has such a tolerance that the area occupied is in fact its whole potential area, in which case it is in at least a temporary state of equilibrium, or it may be because the unit has not succeeded in occupying more than a part of its potential area. Lack of time must always be a probable explanation of this, and thus area may be a matter of age, but only in certain circumstances. For instance, where a potential area is discontinuous, failure to occupy it may be attributable to such difficulties as those of crossing the space between the parts of the area, and this may have little or no relation to age, except that the longer a species exists the greater the chances of a successful crossing. Where the range of a unit is complete, that is to say where the whole of the potential area is occupied, area obviously can give no indication of age. It is practically impossible to say which of these circumstances prevails in any given case, and hence from the point of view of tolerance there seems little hope of deducing age from area.

It must always be remembered that change in external conditions is independent of change in tolerance except in so far as the latter is the result of the former. Hence potential area must not be regarded as something fixed but as something that fluctuates according to the distribution of external conditions. Supposing, for instance, that a species is able to exist only within certain precipitation values, its potential area at any time will be the area over which these values pertain. This clearly will vary in one way or another with the passage of time. This is no doubt a partial explanation of the well-known cases where a genus is known to have had in former geological periods a range much greater than it has to-day. Both the former extensive and the recent restricted areas may represent its potential area at the respective times. To this, of course, must be added the possibility that the constitution of the genus has altered by the extinction of species.

These are some of the points which arise in the consideration of tolerance, and there must now be considered exactly how tolerance works, that is to say, exactly how it makes movement inevitable if the species is to survive.

Imagine a species which is tolerant to a range of mean annual temperatures between 50° and 55° F. (the figure is purely illustrative), and suppose that the area over which these figures prevail, that is to say the potential area of the species is continuous. Also suppose that its distribution is complete and that the range of the plant and the range of these temperature values are the same. Every generation, if the species is monocarpic, and every reproductive season if the species is perennial, the individuals composing it will produce dispersal units (usually seeds or fruits), and these will tend to be disseminated in all directions from the parent plants. Except along the edges of the species area, dispersal, unless very wide, will cause the units to come to rest at a point within the existing area of the species. Along the edges of the area, however, the result will be different, since, if dispersal is in all directions from the parents, some at least of the dispersal units from the outer individuals will fall beyond the specific limits, that is to say outside their necessary temperature conditions, and will therefore be unable to develop successfully. This process will continue at reproductive intervals of time as long as the specific tolerance and the distribution of temperature remain unchanged, some disseminules each time failing to develop. Now suppose that a climatic change associated with general lowering of temperature begins. Other things (such as topography) being equal, the temperature area of 50°–55° F. will move towards the equator. What will be the effects on the individuals of the species? On the northern edge of their area there will be, as climatic movement begins, the equivalent of a contraction of potential area so that some of the disseminules, not only of the outermost plants but also of those slightly further in, will fall outside the necessary conditions. Before very long the parents which were originally the outermost will be themselves outside the potential area and will therefore perish. As the climatic movement continues the belt of destruction in its wake will widen. On the southern edge of the specific area the circumstances will be exactly reversed. After a time none of the disseminules of the outermost individuals will any longer fall outside the potential area, but within it, and will mature successfully, producing disseminules in their turn. These new parents will at first disseminate themselves partly outside the area, but very soon, with the continuance of climatic change, their disseminules, too, will fall within the necessary conditions, and this process will be repeated in succeeding generations. The combined effect on the southern and northern edges of distribution, together with the similar but modified effects on other parts of the periphery, will in fact be such that correlation is maintained between climatic and specific area, and hence, since the former moves, so also does the latter.

But this movement will only result if tolerance remains unchanged while climate alters. This is the most crucial part of the whole theory, and the reason for the comparison, in the enunciation, of tolerance and morphology in relation to evolution. It is essential to remember that the rates of climatic change and evolutionary change are in present conditions unlike, and that this disparity has prevailed for a long time past. The great climatic changes which have occurred since the Pliocene period have occupied an almost negligible portion of evolutionary time and are entirely out of phase with the normal slow changes of evolution. That is to say, it is inconceivable that during this time evolutionary change and climatic change have continued *pari passu* but unrelatedly. Climatic change may have been the *cause* of evolutionary change, that is of the production of new forms, but these will, if they are indeed distinct forms, have by the Theory of Tolerance their own ranges of tolerance.

Actually the theory is of considerable interest in regard to the possible mechanism of species production. In the simple case described above there is a very great difference between the individuals in the van of movement and those in the rear. In the van the correlation between climate and area is never seriously upset; there is simply a gradually unfolding space into which dispersal can be effective. In the rear the conditions are quite different. Here the potential area is continually diminishing and the possibility of successful dispersal is, for many individuals, becoming increasingly small, so that the plants are constantly in incomplete harmony with their external conditions. They are, in short, in a state of environmental stress. There is still no perfect understanding of the causes of the changes in genetic constitution which are the heralds of new morphological forms, but there is plenty of experimental evidence that such changes can be induced by external means and it at least seems possible that the conditions of stress outlined may do this. This conception is a very important one. It was seen in Chapter 20 that climatic changes during the history of the Flowering Plants have been of two kinds, or rather of two degrees. There have been first of all the long-term gradual secular changes which appear to be inseparable from the circumstances of cosmogony, and there have also been the rapid and catastrophic changes associated with periods of glaciation. These may well be reflected in two kinds of species formation, an equally gradual and inherent production of new forms in which time is the main factor, and the more rapid production of forms induced by the stress of catastrophic changes. This is in good accord with the view, frequently expressed, that the families of flowering plants are of two kinds, ancient and generalised, and modern and specialised, and may indeed be the explanation of this difference.

Although, as mentioned above, many species must have generally similar ranges of tolerance, any exact similarity between species in this respect is, if only on account of the number of factors involved, likely to be improbable, and even very slight differences may be of great significance. This being so, the influence of the tolerance relation will tend to be a selective influence, so that there is a sifting out of the species affected. As a result of this a climatic change need not be visualised as leading to equal movement among all of a large number of species, but as acting differentially, so as to increase the intermingling of floristic elements. Some species will be moved at a maximum rate while others will, to a more or less marked extent, lag behind, and hence there will tend to arise the blurring of floristic boundaries which is so characteristic a feature of plant distribution in many parts of the world.

The Theory of Tolerance also provides support for the views concerning the essentially limited real function of dispersal as described earlier. In terms of the theory, exceptionally wide dispersal is likely to be ineffective, because it will tend to deposit the disseminules in regions outside their potential areas, and they will therefore not establish themselves. Moreover dispersal, as a means of increasing geographical range, will probably be of appreciable value only in cases where the species has already occupied but part of its potential area. On the other hand, the minimum powers of dispersal required by the theory are no more than will suffice to enable the movement of species to keep pace with the movement of climatic zones, and there is every reason to suppose that even the smallest degree of dispersal is sufficient to do this.

It will, of course, be evident that in the attainment of the potential area barriers of various kinds must exercise a considerable influence. The symmetrical distribution of climatic values on both sides of the equator suggests that the potential area of many temperate species may in fact consist of two parts, one in the northern hemisphere and one in the southern, and that many of the plants confined to one or other have incomplete distributions. No doubt two causes contribute to this. First, there is the barrier presented by the tropical latitudes, a barrier across which the only obvious passage is by north-and-south mountain systems. Second, there is the constitution of the floras in the two temperate regions. The flora of each has probably developed more or less completely in isolation from the other owing to the barrier just mentioned, and thus there tend to be corresponding plant forms occupying the corresponding niches in the vegetations of the two. As a result of this, competition to an intrusive species must almost certainly be exceptionally severe.

Two common observations bear directly on these points. Where a temperate genus is found in both hemispheres it will generally be noted that there are connecting species along one or other of the trans-tropical mountain systems; and southern temperate species commonly grow well in the north in circumstances where the factor of competition is eliminated and *vice versa*.

Although the paper enunciating the Theory of Tolerance and discussing its application to problems of plant geography appeared only in 1931, the conception on which the theory is based is implicit at least in many earlier writings. This has been pointed out by Wulff (800, 802), who gives several references, and especially one to the work of Engler (216). Some other writers have expressed themselves even more definitely. Thoday (731), for example, writing of the genus *Passerina*, says, "the distribution of the species . . . indicates that each has a distinct physiological constitution and is specialized to a definite range of environmental factors". Salisbury, in a particularly important paper (614), makes frequent and direct allusion to the conception of tolerance, actually employing the phrase "climatic tolerance". He considers that a species has three zones of distribution: one where reproduction in full can take place; one where only vegetative propagation is possible; and one of cultivation where purely artificial reproduction is necessary. Thus he introduces the interesting subsidiary point that tolerance may not be the same in respect of all aspects of a plant's life and that, while certain conditions may suffice for ordinary vegetative growth, more particular values are necessary for reproduction. Since reproduction is the crucial stage of life, it is of course these latter values which will actually determine the distribution of the species. He mentions, too, the well-known fact that many garden plants do not flower because the special conditions necessary for this process are lacking, and also states that *Ranunculus ficaria* reproduces by vegetative means near its northern limits of range. Even more interesting is his reference to *Stratiotes aloides*, of which he says that the male plants have a more northerly distribution than the females. Where they overlap there is seed production, but otherwise reproduction is vegetative. Setchell

(632) records the rather similar circumstances that the marine Angiosperm, *Halophila ovalis*, has not been found fertile in the wide southern extension of its range in Australasia.

Another noteworthy reference to tolerance is that of Hutchinson (393) in a paper with the significant title "Limiting factors in relation to specific tolerance of forest trees". He refers to Schimper's statement (619) that "*the differentiation of the earth's vegetation is thus controlled by three factors—heat, atmospheric precipitation (including winds), soil.* Heat determines the flora, climatic humidity the vegetation; the soil as a rule merely picks out and blends the material supplied by these two climatic factors, and on its own account adds a few details." He goes on to discuss the distribution of many tree species in North America with special reference to their southern limits, and shows that many of these are coincident, while others intersect. In some precipitation seems clearly to be the determining factor, but others are also involved. He finally discusses various species particularly in relation to their tolerance, and gives several valuable diagrams illustrating the different points which emerge in the discussion.

The presentation of the Theory of Tolerance by the present writer (289) has been discussed at length by Wulff (800, 802), who deals with the history of the conception involved and emphasises a number of facts which in his opinion serve to support it. He also stresses the importance, not perhaps made sufficiently explicit in the original presentation of the theory, of the fact that climatic changes cause not only horizontal but also vertical plant movement, an effect that may lead to significant floristic mingling. The theory has also received lengthy consideration by Mason (493) and by Mason and Stout (497), who, working with special reference to the flora of California, has reviewed the general principles therein set out, and in addition to making them more precise in their application, has increased their number to ten by including four based upon the acceptance of the Theory of Tolerance. In so far as these afford an amplification of the earlier exposition they may well be quoted in full here. They are, as the author points out, "organized under four headings. The first deals with the general subject of the environment in a dynamic sense, including the factors of the environment and the physical basis for their modification and control. The second group deals with the responses of the plant as governed by the Theory of Tolerance and the Principle of Limiting Factors. The third group is concerned with migration and establishment, and the fourth group deals with the perpetuation of vegetation, and the evolution of floras."

A. The Environment of the Plant

1. Plant distribution is primarily controlled by the distribution of climatic factors, and in any given region the extremes of these factors may be more important than their means.
2. Plant distribution is secondarily controlled by the distribution of edaphic factors.
3. There has been great oscillation and variation in climate, especially in the higher latitudes, during the geological past.
4. At least some, and probably considerable, variation has occurred in the relative distribution and outline of the lands and seas in the geological past.

B. The Responses of the Plant

5. The functions governing the existence and successful reproduction of plant species are limited by definite ranges of intensity of particular climatic, edaphic and biotic factors. These ranges represent the tolerance of the function for the particular factor.

6. In the life history of the organism there are times when it is in some critical phase of its development which has a narrow tolerance range for a particular factor of the environment. The distribution of this intensity span of the factor during the time the plant is in this particular phase limits the area in which the function can operate, and hence governs the distribution of the species. The narrower the range of tolerance, the more critical the factor becomes.

C. The Migration of Floras

7. Great movements of floras have taken place in the past and are continuing to take place.
8. Migration is brought about by the transport of individual plants during their motile dispersal phases and the subsequent establishment of these migrules.

D. The Perpetuation and Evolution of Floras

9. The perpetuation of vegetation is dependent first upon the ability of the species to migrate, and secondly upon the ability of the species to vary and to transmit the favourable variations to their offspring.
10. The evolution of floras is dependent upon plant migration, the evolution of species, and the selective influences of climatic change acting upon the varying tolerances of the component species.

The theory and, particularly, the principles of plant geography associated with it have also been made the subject of an introductory chapter by Cain in his *Foundations of Plant Geography* (104), the remainder of the book consisting, to quote the author's own words, "in part, of an amplification of these principles with illustrative data and discussion, and such additional materials as compose the framework of plant geography . . . conceived as an explanatory science which attains its unity and justification by abstracting and synthesising from the contributions of more specialized sciences".

Cain begins with a further statement of principles, which besides incorporating all those of Mason's extended presentation, increases the total number to thirteen by expressing more explicitly, and thereby rightly emphasising, certain points which hitherto were more or less implicit, namely, that biotic factors may be of importance; that the environment is holocoenotic; and that tolerances have a genetic basis. The first of these is extracted from the principle that edaphic factors play a secondary part in plant geography. Biotic factors are not capable to any appreciable extent of influencing climatic conditions, but they may have a profound effect on the substratum and thus become, at second hand, edaphic factors. By the statement that the environment is holocoenotic is meant that its various factors react upon the plant life in concert and not independently, that is to say they react upon or qualify one another at the same time. From the discussion accompanying this statement it seems clear that its main purpose is to emphasise the dangers of deducing causes and correlations on insufficient grounds, and to this end it is valuable, but it involves very complex problems as yet far from fully understood, and it is doubtful whether the clarity of the presentation of principles is enhanced by its particular mention. The principle that tolerance has a genetic basis, which, as Cain states, is due to Mason, is of special interest here because it is the essence of the Theory of Tolerance, and indeed its statement is very close to that of the third sentence of the theory. Besides these additions Cain's presentation of principles makes much more clear the point that the different ontogenetic phases of a plant may have different tolerances. This is a very important conception closely related to the subject of phasic development noticed on p. 429 and is valuable because it adds an extra variable, namely the age of the individual, to the interaction of plant and environmental factor, and this in turn gives a time component of great theoretical significance and capable of widely spreading the incidence of harmful factors.

The Evidences of Tolerance

The Theory of Tolerance, it has been clearly shown, is intimately related to various evolutionary theories and shares with them the inevitable limitation that because of the immense time values involved no direct experimental proof is possible, and evidence must be circumstantial.

Actually the onus of proof is but a light one. The theory is built up on a generally accepted assumption of standing, and it may therefore be said that the reasons for the assumption may rank as evidence for the theory. These reasons are no more and no less than the observed facts of plant distribution as a whole and the impossibility of explaining them on any other basis, and the main thesis of the theory may therefore be considered to be upheld by the whole array of facts contained in the earlier chapters of this book.

As enunciated, however, the theory particularises the general assumption in various ways, and it is desirable to deal shortly with certain facts which support these more detailed opinions.

There is first the case of garden plants. These are habitually classified as hardy, half-hardy or tender, and there are no known instances of a plant departing from the behaviour which such terms imply. By half-hardy is meant roughly a limited tolerance to conditions of severe cold such as must be met by protection in the winter in such latitudes as those of Britain, or by germination in artificial heat of some kind. The point is that this half-hardiness is obviously a specific character, and a plant with such tolerance relations does not lose them on being transplanted from its native place to some other country. Moreover, this is a general character of the individuals of the species, and we do not find there is appreciable difference in tolerance between different plants. It may be that under cultivation some individuals may seem more resistant than others, but this can always be explained either by individual tolerance variation or on the grounds that the conditions under which the species is growing are slightly different.

What is true of individuals may, however, not be true of the different strains of a species. Cultivated strains vary greatly in their tolerance, some being much more resistant than others to cold or other unfavourable conditions, and it is but one aspect of the art of gardening to realise which are the appropriate strains to grow in varying circumstances. This, however, is exactly what might be expected according to the theory, because the strains are genetically distinct from one another and may be compared with incipient species, and their differences in tolerance are almost certainly reflected in their gene complement.

It may be urged that reference to cultivated plants is undesirable because of the artificial conditions in which they grow, but this really only increases their value as evidence, because the essential feature of cultivation is the removal of competition, a factor which always tends to obscure the relation of plants to external conditions in nature. In addition cultivated plants illustrate most vividly the way in which new forms can be induced by external means. It is true that cultivation may lead to an evolutionary change which in nature would have taken immeasurably longer, but this again is only in accordance with the theory.

What is true of the climatic portions of a plant's tolerance is also true of its relation to edaphic factors, and this also is commonly illustrated in horticulture. Every gardener knows that different plants need certain soil conditions and will tolerate no others, and that to grow plants otherwise is to court disaster. Here, again, closely related species may differ in requirement, but the individuals of the same species or strain do not do so, except, of course, within the limits of their tolerance variation.

Both aspects of tolerance are combined in the general difficulty which is experienced in cultivating certain plants. Many most desirable garden plants either will not grow in gardens or glass-houses or only do so clearly under protest, and the explanation of this can hardly be other than that the resources of the cultivator are insufficient to provide the plant with the conditions which it needs. The greater the number and variety of plants to be cultivated, the greater the variety of facilities required for doing so. The scope of the ordinary outdoor gardener is comparatively limited compared with that of one who has a whole range of glass-houses, each reproducing some special condition, at his disposal.

One special aspect of this is of particular interest. Practical growers often believe that in the special circumstances of their work it pays to obtain the seed of a given species from a particular source because this seed suits their special conditions and place of cultivation better than any other—that is to say that this seed produces plants more in harmony with the conditions available. At first sight this may seem to cut across the thesis that all the individuals of a species have the same general tolerance, but it actually affords one of the most interesting confirmations of it. As has been shown by experiment, the state of affairs described is generally due to the fact that the "species" comprises two or more strains, indistinguishable by visual characters but having definitely distinct ranges of tolerance, exactly the situation envisaged in paragraphs three and four of the theory (see p. 417).

Another important line of evidence is afforded by the subject of "acclimatisation". This, again, appears at first sight to be against the theory, but it can actually be explained quite simply in accordance with it. Species which do well in cultivation under conditions different from those in which they are found in a wild state are often supposed to have modified their external relations in conformity with their new surroundings. This is an unnecessary explanation. It has been shown that many species do not, for various reasons, occupy in nature the whole of their potential areas, and this means, in terms of the theory, that their tolerance to certain external conditions may be much wider than appears from a study of their natural ranges. If this is so, then species may be grown artificially, especially in absence of competition, under conditions which do not exist in their natural habitats, because such conditions may be well within their tolerance, although this fact is not apparent in nature. For instance, many South African plants can be cultivated out of doors in Britain. This does not necessarily imply that these species have altered their tolerances to accord with conditions in this country, but is explained on the assumption that such conditions are within the tolerances of the plants in question, although for reasons of topography or competition this is not apparent from their distributions in their native countries.

It is probable that many and perhaps all the supposed examples of acclimatisation are of this kind, and it is significant that many authorities have expressed the view that there is no such thing as real acclimatisation in the sense in which it is popularly meant. Hooker (371), for instance, says, "the fact now universally conceded by all intelligent horticulturists, that no plant has been acclimatised in England within the experience of man, is a very suggestive one. . . ".

It is perhaps natural to think of acclimatisation as primarily a process by which plants may be grown in countries in which conditions are more rigorous than their own, but it is important to remember that the reverse is also true. Van Steenis, in the second part of his study of the Malaysian mountain flora (700) has brought together a great deal of scattered information about the results of plant introduction and transplantation in that region, including a lengthy quotation from two papers by Ridley on acclimatisation (593). This makes abundantly clear that the responses of the plants concerned to their changes of circumstances are, as would be expected in terms of the Theory of Tolerance, extremely varied. Some northern temperate plants, such as *Digitalis purpurea*, will do well in Malaysia, provided they are planted at sufficient altitude, and some local montane species will grow well, at least for some years, when transplanted to the lowlands, but in the great majority of cases the change is detrimental, and the plants either fail to hold their own, or persist in a reduced and unreproductive state (see p. 422). Two points of special interest in relation to the discussion on the true function of dispersal, in Chapter 16, are that certain mountain species which are habitually and normally dispersed downwards do not become established below certain altitudes, and that among the temperate plants which do less than usually well are some familiar northern weeds, and many well-known northern garden plants.

Although considerations of hardiness and acclimatisation usually involve cultivated plants, there is an increasing amount of work on these problems in relation to wild plants. We have already mentioned one such (647), and another is the paper of Dexter and others (187) in which an interesting attempt to estimate frost resistance quantitatively is described. Of particular interest and importance, in that they bear very directly on the conceptions of the Theory of Tolerance, are also two papers by White, the second being largely a reprint of the first (773, 774).

White begins by referring to the common horticultural practice of using seeds collected from towards the northern limits of specific ranges to give the most cold resistant seedlings, and instances the case of the black walnut (*Juglans nigra*). In this plant the individuals native to the southern States like Texas and Alabama are said to be incapable of living in such northern States as South Dakota and Minnesota. There are other cases of the same thing too, and there is distinct evidence favouring the belief that varieties, strains and geographical races, within species, vary considerably in their ability to resist cold (that is to say, in their tolerance to that external condition). White refers to de Candolle (117) in this connection, who finds no indication that perennial species have become adapted to greater cold and have thus extended their ranges northwards within the historical period, despite the fact that their seeds are continually being carried northwards. He quotes de Candolle's own words in which he says, "Periods of more than four or five thousand years . . . are needed apparently to produce a modification in a plant which will allow it to support a greater degree of cold."

White himself believes that the walnuts from the northern States may differ from those from the southern States by a gene, or perhaps a series of genes, that determined their ability to withstand different winter temperatures but in no other way expresses itself, at least so far as external characters are concerned. In other words, he supposes there may be two or more walnut genotypes indistinguishable at sight but restricted geographically by the nature of their tolerance to cold, and thus visualises exactly one of the conditions postulated in the enunciation of the Theory of Tolerance. He thinks it probable, moreover, that many tropical and warm-temperate species give rise, by mutation, to individuals much more cold-resisting and that these remain for the most part unrecognised because they occur and grow under conditions where the character in question could not be expressed. If this is so, then the Pleistocene glaciation would have a sifting effect, some genera being able to continue living in what would appear to be more rigorous conditions, while others would be destroyed there, only later re-immigrating from the south as they produced more hardy genotypes by mutation (485, 486). He mentions a number of plants which, having a wide north-south range, are known to have hardy and less hardy forms, and also points out that if a species is restricted in its range by conditions other than temperature it may in fact be much more resistant to cold than its natural range indicates. Also, since some wide-ranging species are apparently without different forms, species may clearly be of two types as regards their resistance to temperature. In one type all the individuals can exist over a wide range of temperature, but in the other the species is composed of numerous groups, each with its particular temperature range, although these groups are indistinguishable morphologically. Finally he refers to a number of species which occur over a wide range of temperature, such a *Tillandsia usneoides*, *Asimina triloba* and *Nymphaea odorata*, and to species which are tropical in natural range but which on cultivation prove to be unexpectedly hardy. Among these latter he cites *Leitneria floridana*, *Gleditsia aquatica*, *Lavandula spica*, *Yucca filamentosa*, *Maclura pomifera*, *Magnolia grandiflora*, *Hamamelis vernalis* and *Nymphaea mexicana*.

In a later paper White (775) takes his conception of tolerance to temperature, or cold and heat susceptibility, which he believes has been proved to be hereditary, rather further. He considers that mutation towards increased cold resistance has taken place in many plant groups irrespective of their geographical or climatic locations, and that in consequence many units will be mixtures as regards cold and heat tolerance. Temperate as well as tropical species give rise to temperature tolerance mutations in either direction, but in temperate regions those towards cold susceptibility tend to perish. Hence, one would expect to find, outside the tropics, only mutations of greater cold resistance, while within the tropics there would be cold-resistant as well as cold-susceptible individuals, although these would be indistinguishable. His paper ends with several tables incorporating experimental observations on cold resistance, including one of species which are known to have strains and varieties differing in this respect.

What is usually looked upon as incomplete acclimatisation is also explicable in terms of the Theory of Tolerance. There are various exotic species for example, such as the myrtle (*Myrtus communis*) and the bay (*Laurus nobilis*) which maintain themselves successfully in cultivation in various parts of Britain until some particularly severe climatic condition destroys them. One explanation at least of this is that conditions in these places are, in general, within but only just within the tolerance range of the species concerned, so that any excessive departure from the mean will pass outside them, and since the conditions in which the plants are living are so marginal, their individual variations of tolerance (see p. 418) will be insufficient to meet the crisis, and they will, unless protected by some particularly favourable circumstances of local situation, perish.

But the conditions under which the plants referred to are in cultivation are not widely different, except possibly for the absence of space competition, from the natural environments of many individuals on the edges of wide distributional areas, and there is much evidence that life for these plants is something rather different from and more rigorous than that of their fellow plants in the more central parts of the range. For many of these latter conditions are sufficiently near the centres of their ranges of tolerance to allow for a good deal of oscillation in one direction or the other without much risk to the plants, but for the former the crucial environmental values are so near one end of the tolerance gamut that much less oscillation is likely to result in a situation which is insupportable.

The conception of ecesis, or "adaptation to environment", also infers the application of the Theory of Tolerance. Many species have a peculiar and particular morphological structure which, so far as can be seen, enables them to inhabit certain equally definite types of habitat or to live under equally definite conditions. It is generally believed that these structures have the effect of thus restricting the species possessing them. This is tantamount to saying that these species can exist only in these special habitats or conditions, at least while their peculiar morphology persists, and this in turn is equivalent, in fact at least, to an acceptance of the main thesis.

Next, the early researches of Klebs on phasic development in plants, and their subsequent great elaboration by Lysenko and other Russian workers (810) in connection with the vernalisation of seeds, have a very direct bearing upon the conception of tolerance. Lysenko's work and views have now been presented in the form of a theory of which the most important and apposite portions are as follows. Lysenko believes that the growth of a plant is not a single and simple process of increase in quantity but is in fact made up also of a series of stages at each of which changes of a qualitative nature occur. These two he distinguishes as "growth" and "development". The two may go on dependently or independently and plants may show rapid growth but slow development, slow growth but rapid development, or rapid growth and rapid development. The culmination of the life of the plant is the production of ripe fruit, and this particularly is believed to be achieved only by the fulfilment of each of a number of developmental stages. Moreover, these stages always proceed in one order and no stage can be initiated until the proper preceding one has been completed. Finally, the most important postulate from our point of view is that different stages of development of the same plant require for their completion different external conditions.

For any detailed account of vernalisation the reader must refer to other works, of which perhaps the most convenient are the Bulletins of the Imperial Bureaux of Plant Genetics (505, 777, 808, 809) and the symposium by Murneek, Whyte and others (531) in which reference to much other literature will be found, and to the excellent review of the subject of phasic development in plants by Whyte (776), but a very brief account is of sufficiently direct relation to geographical problems to warrant inclusion here.

The time that it takes for an individual plant to pass from the condition of a dry seed to that of producing ripe fruit—that is to say, the time which must elapse between sowing and reaping—obviously depends (on the old view) upon the rapidity of growth, but according to the theories just described it depends more accurately upon the time occupied by each of the developmental stages through which the plant has to pass during its life. In the ordinary way much of the time is occupied by the period between sowing and the emergence of the seedling above ground. According to the modern view this period is in fact one of the developmental stages and during it the seed must be provided with certain definite conditions, and until these are fulfilled it will not proceed to the next stages of development. In theory, then, if the seed's requirements at this stage can be discovered, it should be possible to provide the seed with them before it is sown. In other words, it should be possible to make the seed pass through this initial stage in development before it is put in the ground, so that when it is so planted it will almost immediately germinate. This has actually been done with a number of crop plants, especially some of the cereals, and is the process known as vernalisation. Vernalised seeds therefore take a shorter time to come to fruition after they are sown, and it need hardly be said that this is a consideration of the utmost importance. Especially is it so in countries where the latitude gives so short a growing season that many crops cannot reach maturity in the time available. If the growth period can be shortened, then many crops may be grown that would otherwise be impossible. This state of affairs prevails over much of Russia, and this is the reason why vernalisation and related problems have received so much attention from Russian scientists. It should perhaps be emphasised that vernalisation does not in any way alter the developmental necessities or stages of the plant. Its value lies in the fact that it permits the first stage of development to be carried out when and where required and before external conditions allow of ordinary sowing in the field.

The importance of these theories and of vernalisation to the Theory of Tolerance is the very important supporting evidence they provide that the individual plant and also each species as a whole require certain perfectly definite external conditions for their development, and that without those particular conditions they cannot mature. There are, of course, plenty of other indications that this is so, and the special importance of Lysenko's work is in the demonstration it affords that the life of the plant is divided into a number of stages each of which not only requires exact external conditions but more often than not quite different external conditions. This means that different external conditions will be crucial to the plant at different stages in its history, and its tolerance must be something even more detailed and exact than appears at first sight. For instance, according to the researches described, the first stage in development is intimately connected with temperature and moisture values, while the second involves more deeply than anything else the factor of light.

Finally, there is the belief widely held by palaeobotanists, and the basis for much of their hypothesis and determinations, that the occurrence of fossils similar to or identical with living plants indicates that the conditions under which they existed were similar to or identical with the conditions under which their modern counterparts exist to-day. This opinion has already been mentioned, not only in Chapter 15 but also as one line of evidence for climatic change in the past. It is true that there is little direct evidence for the view, but it is nevertheless generally accepted in broad outline. It is important here because tacitly, if not admittedly, it is based upon the primary postulate of the theory, namely that the relation of a species to external conditions is a character of that species and that it may persist unaltered as long as morphological features persist. Actually it will be realised that this belief involves an even more rigid outlook than is required by the theory, in that it does not allow due latitude for the *possibility* of tolerance change without morphological change during time of evolutionary magnitude.

Summary

From the discussion of the Theory of Tolerance in the foregoing pages the following three major conclusions emerge.

First, the main thesis, that any species shows a definite range of tolerance to external conditions at any given time is scarcely to be denied, because the whole picture of plant distribution is so intimately related to the distribution of external factors that no other view can reasonably be maintained.

Second, supporting evidences of this, if they are needed, are furnished by the behaviour of plants in cultivation; by the non-occurrence of "acclimatisation"; by the whole conception of "adaptation to environment"; and by such matters as phasic development and vernalisation.

Third, certain more detailed aspects of the application of the theory are more debatable. In particular the value of the theory as an *explanation* of phytogeographical facts stands or falls by the subsidiary hypothesis which postulates that environmental change has, at least during the more recent past, been more rapid than change in tolerance or morphology, or, in other words, by the view that progressive adaptation to external change has not had time to occur *in situ*.

Clearly the problem here involves the past as well as the present, and it is to palaeobotany that we must turn in search of evidence. This is not far to seek. The history of the British flora since the latter part of the Tertiary period amounts, by itself, to almost conclusive evidence in support of this thesis. It shows clearly that since Pliocene times species have altered but little morphologically, yet in the same period there have been drastic changes in climate and environment. It is surely beyond the bounds of reasonable probability to suggest that tolerance has varied coincidently with and proportionately to these changes, but has been virtually entirely unaccompanied by morphological change. Were this indeed the case it would inevitably be betrayed, either rarely or more commonly, in the habits and habitats of living plants. In fact all these, as has been demonstrated in the last few pages, point to the reverse, and this being so, this second and more particular postulate of the Theory of Tolerance may also be claimed to be the truth.

But it is this particular part of the general theory which converts the whole, at least as regards plant geography, from a mere conception to a means of elucidation, because, if it is accepted, it is possible to construct in the way indicated in the earlier pages of this chapter a general explanation of the facts of plant geography and, as will be done in the next and final chapter of this book, to weave into one single pattern the many diverse and separate threads of the subject.

CHAPTER 23

CONCLUSIONS

IT is the task of this final chapter to attempt a synthesis of all that has gone before and to present to the reader a brief but comprehensive summary of the processes and events which have led to that state of plant distribution observable to-day. On first considerations such a task may, with reason, seem almost impossible, so great and multifarious is the mass of fact and theory to be taken into account. But by carefully sorting and sifting the material a gradual outline emerges, and this outline becomes clearer with every increment to our knowledge. The form which that outline takes has been made sufficiently apparent by the discussions which form so large a part of Chapters 16 to 22, and from these, reinforced by the innumerable facts cited in earlier chapters, it is possible to paint a picture which may claim at least some degree of completeness.

First and foremost we must visualise the constant production of new forms (the taxonomist's species) by the processes of evolution. This is as it were the primary determinant of the picture; it is the medium in which it is painted. This must be so because the very appearance and development of the great group of the Flowering Plants is an expression of it. It is the fundamental cause of the geographical facts which we observe. The picture must therefore have as its background the historical development of these plants, and this, in so far as it has been revealed, can be described fairly shortly.

Some time in the middle or later parts of the Mesozoic epoch there arose, presumably from some already existent type of seed-plant, a group of plants characterised by possessing special closed structures known as carpels, and having other associated features. Thus there came into being the group of plants—the Angiosperms or Flowering Plants—destined to become the dominant vegetation throughout the land surfaces of the globe. Of this actual origin very little is known. There are indications here and there in the rocks of what may be regarded, with varying certainty, as forerunners or ancestral types, but the Flowering Plants proper appear with bewildering suddenness in the deposits of the later Cretaceous. In the horizons below this they are few; in this and succeeding horizons they predominate to a greater or lesser extent and indeed almost at once attain that position in the general vegetation that they hold to-day. The reason for this sudden appearance is not clear, but it is enough to know that the Flowering Plants have been the dominant world group since the end of the Mesozoic era. For the reasons which have been explained in Chapter 15, caution must be exercised in making deductions from the fossil record, but this and other evidence certainly suggests that the earlier Flowering Plants were mostly woody plants living under fairly moist and rather warm conditions. The great herbaceous families of to-day, associated as they so often are with extreme climatic conditions, such as lack of water and severe cold, are practically unrepresented in the earlier parts of the fossil record of the Angiosperms, and on this ground at least may be considered as a later development, though we must not forget that their absence from the record may be due to causes other than their non-existence.

This is in accordance, moreover, with what is known of the climates of the past. There are cogent reasons for believing, and it is generally accepted to-day, that the later Cretaceous and all but the latter part of the Tertiary period were a time of relatively constant or but slightly fluctuating climates, characterised by genial, moist conditions varying little with the passage of time and associated with a minimum of relief on the world's surface. The Angiosperms, then, may be pictured as originating and slowly diversifying for millions of years, comparatively little affected by changes in their external circumstances, and it is believed that during this period the main outline of the group as it is seen to-day was determined. It was, as has so frequently been said, an age of generalisation—an age of natural evolution by the inherent processes of change with time.

During this period there is little doubt that the distribution of the Flowering Plants was also far more generalised than it is to-day. Temperature and other climatic gradients were everywhere more gradual, and there is reason to think that what are now called temperate conditions, with their accompanying vegetation, reached almost if not quite to the poles. In terms which have been frequently used above, potential areas were probably much larger, much more extensive, and their attainment was much less impeded by barriers. Mountains were lower and their climatic effects less pronounced. In addition there is a general belief that the land surfaces of the globe were less scattered. As to this last belief, it is only the explanation which is contentious. An older school believes in the former existence of connecting land surfaces which have now disappeared. A more modern belief is that the continents have drifted away from one another. Whichever is correct—and there is an ever-increasing movement towards the latter view—it is generally accepted that geographical isolation, which is the direct result of the separation of land-masses, has increased to what may be regarded as a maximum to-day. With this increasing isolation came, inevitably, local specialisation by the effects of segregated and isolated evolution, and this was probably the first kind of specialisation superposed on the earlier generalised distribution of the Flowering Plants. All this time the distribution of plants was being attained almost entirely by spread in all directions by means of dispersal, this dispersal being directed and controlled by external factors only to a minimum extent. It may, indeed, be described as essentially a period in which this newly evolved group of plants multiplied, and in doing so established something like a geographical equilibrium with the fairly constant external conditions. It was a period of steady and widespread colonisation of the land surfaces of the globe by a new and superior type of vegetation.

It is no exaggeration to say that towards the end of the Tertiary epoch the picture changed in almost every respect. At that time causes of which little is known brought on one of the periodical catastrophic periods which there seems little doubt have been an intermittent feature of all past time. The catastrophe effectively consisted of a drastic and, in a geological sense, sudden alteration in the temperature relations of the world's surface, a change which brought in its train all kinds of minor and secondary variations. It culminated in what is called a glacial period during which, probably for the first time in the history of the Angiosperms, glacial conditions developed at sea level near the poles. It is possible that equatorial temperature values were but little affected, but, whether this is so or not, it is certain that the main result of the change was to telescope up the latitudinal zonation of climate. That is to say the gentler gradient from the equator to the poles was replaced by a steep gradient culminating at higher latitudes in what are now called arctic and antarctic conditions. From the point of view of the vegetation this meant a

28

marked diminution in the areas available for the different sorts of plants and the diminution nearly everywhere of the average size of potential areas. It is unlikely that the effects were felt everywhere equally. In some parts of the northern hemisphere, for instance, the effects of the polar ice-cap were felt far less than elsewhere, but it is safe to say that nowhere was its influence entirely negligible.

This great climatic change was heralded or anticipated by a period of intense mountain building such as has also been an intermittent feature in world history. This process is generally associated more particularly with the Miocene period, and from it date practically all the great mountain systems of the world to-day. Their effect on the climate also was, quite apart from the subsequent glaciation, immense. Not only were appreciable areas of the earth's crust raised into colder layers of the atmosphere but, even more important, the newly elevated mountain ranges intercepted the moisture-laden winds from the oceans and condemned many parts of the interior of the continents to aridity. These changes in turn brought alterations in all sorts of other climatic aspects, such as those of pressure and wind, and every kind of external condition for plant life suffered some modification. It may well have been in direct association with these orographic and climatic changes that changes in the distribution of land and sea were especially notable, and there is even some reason to suggest that continental drift and displacement may have been an essential feature of this period, and even perhaps was initiated then rather than earlier.

The effect of all this on the Flowering Plants was profound. Everywhere their long-familiar world and surroundings were changed, and survival in the face of such disasters became the main theme and problem of their life. Those, for instance, living at the higher latitudes were faced, very likely for the first time, with the problem of frost, a danger which it can scarcely be doubted they were unequipped to meet. Moreover, their potential areas were everywhere being moved under the influence of climatic change. Rarely could this movement be unaccompanied by change in area, and with the general shrinking of the more genial parts of the world there was an almost inevitable general tendency to shrinking of their potential areas. More than this, some of them no doubt were completely eliminated. Everywhere conditions of stress as between plant and environment became inevitable. These were least, no doubt, in the equatorial regions, and it is noteworthy that it is the vegetation of this zone which to-day is considered on quite other grounds to be the most primaeval, but they must have been felt to some degree almost everywhere.

There can be little doubt that this had a profound effect not only on the results of evolution in the Flowering Plants but also, it may be, on the processes of evolution themselves. No longer can evolutionary change be pictured as something inherent and perhaps unrelated to external conditions. No doubt this type of evolution continued, as indeed it must, but the changes which it produced were henceforth to be judged by the stern test of practical success. Such changes as contributed appreciably to increasing the correlation between plant and environment were effective; those which had no such value, or which, owing to external conditions, may have had an opposite import, were ineffective. There thus arose quite a different conception of evolution: the conception of something which was capable in certain circumstances of meeting the dangers to which the plants involved were exposed. Similarly the factors of distribution took on new rôles and new values. The potentiality for dispersal became, with the increasing heterogeneity of external conditions, of less significance. Range of tolerance, on the other hand, must have increased in importance. Distribution of land and sea became a matter of great moment, determining as it did the directions of possible retreat from danger. Changes of climate not only enforced migration but also partly at least determined its direction.

It is perhaps permissible to summarise what has been said by asserting that while in the pre-glacial portion of their history the Flowering Plants were the masters of their environment, in the sense that they were probably, to some extent at least, in equilibrium with it, their post-glacial history saw the development of the reverse state of affairs. No one general feature of plant development and distribution since the Pliocene is so prominent as the marked lack of equilibrium between vegetation and its environment. This must not be taken to mean that many plants are not peculiarly and beautifully in harmony with their surroundings. This fact is rather to be emphasised as indicating how far from general, correlation of this kind is.

Returning to the difference in evolution mentioned above, there is ample evidence that mutation, which is so often the physical basis of new forms, can be induced at unusual rates by the application of certain external factors, and especially by changes in external factors. It can scarcely be denied that the changes consequent upon the Pleistocene glaciation constituted such influences and that they may thus have greatly accelerated the production of new forms by this method. The species constitution of some genera, especially, be it noted, those living in what were once glaciated regions, can indeed hardly be explained on any other basis.

But no matter what the aspect, the constitution of groups as well as their distribution everywhere reflects the disastrous result of the Ice Ages. The extraordinary development of many herbaceous types, and especially of those with well-marked methods of perennation, seems clearly to be correlated with a distribution of climatic conditions such as would put a premium on the possession of these features. In particular perhaps many semi-desert families and genera may be mentioned, as well as many constituents of the more northerly temperate or subarctic zones. Again, it is probable, as has been shown, that the arctic flora and to a certain extent the alpine flora as known to-day are to be regarded as a consequence of the glacial ages. Yet again, there is clear evidence that this time brought in its train extensive annihilation of plants in many parts of the world. That, for instance, is the generally accepted explanation of the poverty of the European flora (as distinct from the purely Mediterranean) compared with that of eastern North America and eastern Asia, and there are many other examples.

No longer then is the development of the Flowering Plants something that is proceeding with a slow, stately, and inevitable progress scarcely modified by the more detailed aspects of environment. On the contrary, to-day this development must be visualised as something everywhere controlled by factors beyond the response of the plants themselves. As with evolution, so with distribution. The distribution of plants to-day gives every evidence that it is in a state of almost complete flux. The movement of species and of floras over the world is everywhere being forced upon them by the exigencies of environmental change, and everywhere the plants can survive only by keeping pace with this movement, or by giving place to new forms less critically affected by these conditions. As has been said, all these influences appear, as might be expected, to be expressed least in the equatorial regions and, conversely, are most marked in the higher latitudes, and this is in accord not only with the story which has been outlined here but also with the assumptions of plant relationship and phylogeny based upon and derived from other sources.

In a word, the distribution of plants to-day unquestionably suggests that the Flowering Plants are recovering from a catastrophe, and that they are actively in process of reconstituting that generalised balance or equilibrium between vegetation and environment which has been pictured above as the outstanding feature of pre-glacial plant geography. So far the period of recovery (if, indeed, it is one of absolute recovery) has been very short and one can only be amazed at the progress which the plants have made in the course of it. Whether it will continue at its present rate to its culmination without setbacks or whether fresh disasters are still to come cannot and will not be revealed, but that eventually, though perhaps only after the passage of enormous time, such result will be achieved can scarcely be doubted. Whether the Angiosperms will still be recognisable or whether they will, before then, have given place in the process to some still more highly developed group is a question which admits of no answer now.

APPENDIX A

Statistics of the World's Land Surfaces

IF the latitudinal and altitudinal zonations described in the early pages of Chapter 2 are modified, for statistical purposes, into simpler and rounder figures, it is possible to obtain from a paper by Murray (532) a useful and reasonably accurate mathematical impression of the proportionate distribution of the more important climatic types of vegetation at different latitudes.

Let it be assumed then for this purpose that latitudinal zonation is expressed sufficiently accurately as follows:

0°–20°	.	.	.	Tropical
20°–40°	.	.	.	Subtropical and warm temperate
40°–60°	.	.	.	Temperate
60°–80°	.	.	.	Arctic and antarctic

and that altitudinal zonations may be set out in the following scheme:

In the tropical zone   0– 3,000 ft. bears tropical vegetation.
     3,000– 6,000 ft. ,,   subtropical vegetation.
     6,000–12,000 ft. ,,   temperate vegetation.
     12,000–18,000 ft. ,,   arctic-alpine vegetation.
In the subtropical zones 0– 3,000 ft. bears subtropical vegetation.
     3,000– 6,000 ft. ,,   temperate vegetation.
     6,000–12,000 ft. ,,   arctic-alpine vegetation.
In the temperate zones   0– 3,000 ft. bears temperate vegetation.
     3,000– 6,000 ft. ,,   arctic-alpine vegetation.
In the arctic zones   0– 3,000 ft. bears arctic-alpine vegetation.

On the basis of these classifications the relevant figures from Murray can be arranged in a series of three tables.

TABLE 1

Total Land Surfaces of the *Latitudinal* Zones, in Thousands of Square Miles.

80°–90° N.	.	.	.	.	112
70°–80° N.	.	.	.	.	1,379
60°–70° N.	.	.	.	.	4,767
50°–60° N.	.	.	.	.	5,300
40°–50° N.	.	.	.	.	6,225
30°–40° N.	.	.	.	.	6,436
20°–30° N.	.	.	.	.	5,773
10°–20° N.	.	.	.	.	4,278
0°–10° N.	.	.	.	.	3,832
0°–10° S.	.	.	.	.	3,973
10°–20° S.	.	.	.	.	3,630
20°–30° S.	.	.	.	.	3,550
30°–40° S.	.	.	.	.	1,659
40°–50° S.	.	.	.	.	408
50°–60° S.	.	.	.	.	87
Antarctica	.	.	.	.	3,565 (virtually no flowering plants)

TABLE 2

Total Land Surfaces of the Main *Vegetation* Zones, in Thousands of Square Miles.

North	arctic-alpine	6,146
,,	temperate	11,525
,,	subtropical	12,210
,,	tropical	8,110
South	tropical	7,605
,,	subtropical	5,208
,,	temperate	495
,,	antarctic-alpine	——

Or, combining the equivalent zones in each hemisphere:

Arctic- and antarctic-alpine vegetation zones	6,146
Temperate zones	12,020
Subtropical zones	17,418
Tropical zones	15,715

that is to say, in rough proportion:

arctic-alpine 1; temperate 2; subtropical 3; tropical 2·5.

The next table shows the figures further analysed and segregated according to altitude as well as latitude:

TABLE 3

Areas open to the several Vegetation Types at different Latitudes.

	No. Vegetation	Arctic-alpine	Temperate	Subtropical	Tropical	Total
80°–90° N.	112	—	—	—	—	112
60°–80° N.	729	5,417	—	—	—	6,146
40°–60° N.	895	2,137	8,493	—	—	11,525
20°–40° N.	921	1,487	2,318	7,485	—	12,211
0°–20° N.	1	24	326	1,188	6,571	8,110
0°–20° S.	17	193	261	1,583	5,551	7,605
20°–40° S.	110	180	652	4,266	—	5,208
40°–60° S.	28	63	404	—	—	495
60°–80° S.	—	—	—	—	—	—
80°–90° S.	—	—	—	—	—	—
Totals	2,813	9,501	12,454	14,522	12,122	51,412
Northern hemisphere	2,658	9,065	11,137	8,673	6,571	38,104
Southern hemisphere	155	436	1,317	5,849	5,551	13,308

Finally it is worth while to show the proportion of the land in each zone which, *on account of elevation*, is not occupied by the type of vegetation characteristic of the zone at sea level. The figures are:

North temperate	0·26 or about	one-fourth
North subtropical	0·39 ,, ,,	three-eighths
North tropical	0·19 ,, ,,	one-fifth
South tropical	0·27 ,, ,,	one-fourth
South subtropical	0·18 ,, ,,	one-fifth
South temperate	0·18 ,, ,,	one-fifth

The chief points emerging from the foregoing tables are:

1. Excluding the arctic and antarctic, there is two and a half times as much total land in the north as there is in the south.

2. There is virtually no available land south of 60° S.

3. Land sufficiently high to bear arctic-alpine vegetation occurs in all zones, but by far the smallest proportion is in the north tropics.

4. The total area of temperate vegetation in the northern hemisphere is between eight and nine times as great as in the southern.

5. The total area of arctic-alpine vegetation in the northern hemisphere is more than twenty times as great as in the southern.

APPENDIX B

Discontinuous Genera

THE following is a fourth edition of the list of widely discontinuous genera which first appeared in the *New Phytologist* (285). As there, authorities for the names are given; genera which are to be considered *in sensu stricto* are indicated by asterisks; and certain pairs of genera are combined. In addition the comparable figures in each of the two latest editions are given at the end of each major and minor category.

Since the last edition (1953) three genera have been deleted, namely *Brasenia* (as being too nearly pantropical): *Carpha* (as too weakly defined); and *Osmanthus* (following a revision of its group). Ten genera have been added, namely *Elliottia* and *Tripetaleia*, *Cayratia*, *Irvingia*, *Heteropholis*, *Leea*, *Brexia* and *Ixerba*, *Gevuina*, *Boisduvalia*, *Elaeocarpus*, *Gymnolaea*. The total is now 765.

The chief purpose of the names and, particularly, the authorities given being to define the groups of species intended, as unmistakably as possible, for those readers who may not be expert taxonomists, I have, in general, used those which seem most likely to achieve this aim, even if they are not those which, according to the strict letter of the Rules of Nomenclature, should be cited.

A. Genera found entirely or predominantly in the North Temperate Zone.

   a. Discontinuous over the whole North Temperate Zone.

   Aesculus L. and *Hippocastanum* Rupp., *Apocynum* L., *Bifora* Hoffm., *Carpinus* L., *Cercis* L., *Epimedium* L. and *Vancouveria* C. Morr. et Decne., *Fagus* L.*, *Gleditsia* Clayton, *Harrimanella* Cov., *Hypopitys* Dill., *Liquidambar* L., *Narthecium* Moehr., *Ostrya* Scop., *Paeonia* L., *Philadelphus* L., *Pistacia* L., *Staphylea* L., *Tilia* L. 18 (18)

   b. Europe and/or W. Asia and E. Asia.

   Bosea L. and *Rodetia* Moq., *Forsythia* Vahl., *Leontopodium* R. Br., *Ligustrum* L., *Meconopsis* Vig.*, *Parrotia* C. A. Mey. and *Fothergilla* Murr. p.p., *Pterocarya* Kunth, *Theligonum* L., *Wulfenia* Jacq., *Zelkova* Spach . . . 10 (10)

   c. N. America, Europe and W. Asia.

   Ammophila Host, *Arbutus* L., *Cakile* Mill., *Cinna* L., *Comandra* Nutt., *Corema* D. Don, *Datisca* L., *Douglasia* Lindl., *Eurotia* Adans., *Heberdenia* Banks, *Helianthemum* Tourn., *Hottonia* L., *Loeflingia* L., *Lupinus* L., *Peganum* L., *Platanus* L., *Spartina* Schreb.*, *Specularia* Heist. . . . 18 (18)

   d. N. America (especially or entirely in the West) and in Central and/or E. Asia.

   Achlys DC., *Boschniakia* C. A. Mey., *Boykinia* Nutt., *Chamaesaracha* A. Gr., *Clintonia* Raf., *Dicentra* Bernh., *Echinopanax* Decne. et Planch., *Enemion* Raf., *Glehnia* Schmidt, *Mahonia* Nutt., *Mitella* L., *Monotropa* L.*, *Nephrophyllidium* Gilg, *Phyllospadix* Hook., *Stenanthella* Rydb., *Thermopsis* R. Br., *Tiarella* L., *Trillium* L. . . . . 18 (18) *e.* Eastern N. America (especially or entirely) and both continental and insular E. Asia.

Apios Moench, *Buckleya* Torr., *Caulophyllum* Michx., *Chionanthus* L., *Cladrastis* Raf., *Cryptotaenia* DC., *Diarrhena* Beauv., *Diervilla* Mill. and *Weigela* Thunb., *Diphylleia* Michx., *Hamamelis* L., *Houttuynia* Thunb. and *Anemopsis* Hk. et Arn., *Kraunhia* Raf. and *Wisteria* Nutt., *Menispermum* L., *Pachysandra* Michx., *Panax* L., *Penthorum* L., *Phryma* L., *Podophyllum* L., *Pogonia* Juss., *Saururus* L., *Shortia* Torr. et Gr., *Stewartia* L., *Symplocarpus* Salisb., *Tipularia* Nutt., *Trautvetteria* Fisch. et Mey., *Triosteum* L., *Zanthoxylum* L.*, *Zizania* L. .   .   28 (27)

f. Eastern N. America (especially or entirely) and continental E. Asia only.

Aletris L., *Calycanthus* L. and *Chimonanthus* Lindl., *Campsis* Lour., *Criosanthes* Raf., *Decumaria* L., *Gymnocladus* Lam., *Halesia* L., *Jeffersonia* Barton, *Liriodendron* L., *Pyrularia* Michx., *Stylophorum* Nutt., *Symphoricarpos* Juss.   12 (13)

g. Eastern N. America (especially or entirely) and Japan only.

Amsonia Walt., *Arethusa* L., *Chiogenes* Salisb., *Croomia* Torr., *Elliottia* Muehlenb. and *Tripetaleia* Sieb. et Zucc., *Epigaea* L., *Hydrastis* Ellis and *Glaucidium* Sieb. et Zucc., *Mitchella* L. 8 (7)

h. Eastern N. America and E. Asia, with extensions southward in one or both hemispheres.

Abelia R. Br., *Aralia* L., *Astilbe* Buch.-Ham., *Berchemia* Neck., *Catalpa* Scop., *Disporum* Salisb., *Gelsemium* Juss., *Gordonia* Ellis, *Hydrangea* L., *Illicium* L., *Itea* L., *Magnolia* L., *Nyssa* L., *Photinia* Lindl.*, *Schisandra* Michx.   16 (18)

B. Genera found entirely or predominantly in the tropical regions, but excluding pantropical genera.

a. America, Africa and/or the Madagascar region.

1. America, Africa and the Madagascar region.

Asclepias L. and *Gomphocarpus* R. Br., *Ascolepis* Steud., *Bertiera* Aubl., *Caperonia* St. Hil., *Carpodiptera* Griseb., *Cassipourea* Aubl. and *Weihea* Spreng., *Eichhornia* Kunth, *Elaeis* Jacq. and *Corozo* Giseke, *Eulophidium* Pfitz., *Hirtella* L., *Landolphia* Beauv., *Loudetia* Steud., *Mostuea* Didr. and *Leptocladus* Oliv., *Paepalanthus* Mart., *Paratheria* Griseb., *Paullinia* L., *Pentodon* Hochst., *Piriqueta* Aubl., *Raphia* Beauv., *Sabicea* Aubl., *Savia* Willd., *Symphonia* L., *Trachypogon* Nees, *Trichilia* L., *Tristachya* Nees, *Vellozia* Vand. and *Barbacenia* Vand.   26 (26)

2. America and continental Africa only.

Amanoa Aubl., *Andira* Lam., *Anthephora* Schreb., *Antrocaryon* A. W. Hill et B. L. Burtt, *Aptandra* Miers, *Bartsia* L.*, *Bouchea* Cham.*, *Brachypterys* A. Juss. (?), *Buforrestia* C. B. Cl., *Cacoucia* Aubl., *Chlorophora* Gaudich., *Chrysobalanus* L., *Conocarpus* L., *Copaifera* L., *Corrigiola* L., *Drepanocarpus* G. F. Mey., *Eriochrysis* Beauv., *Erisma* Rudge and *Erismadelphus* Mildbr., *Euclasta* Franch., *Genlisea* St. Hil., *Guarea* Allem., *Heisteria* Jacq., *Heteranthera* R. et P., *Heteropteris* H., B. et K., *Hoffmanseggia* Cav., *Hydranthelium* H., B. et K., *Hypogynium* Nees, *Laguncularia* Gaertn. f., *Lindackeria* C. Presl, *Macrolobium* Schreb., *Malouetia* A. DC., *Maprounea* Aubl., *Mayaca* Aubl., *Melasma* Berg.*, *Microtea* Sw., *Neurotheca* Salisb., *Ochthocosmus* Benth. and *Phyllocosmus* Klotzsch, *Olyra* L., *Parkinsonia* L., *Pentaclethra* Benth., *Pitcairnia* L'Hérit., *Prevostea* Choisy, *Priva* Adans., *Ptychopetalum* Benth., *Quassia* L., *Renealmia* L.f., *Saccoglottis* Mart., *Schaueria* Nees, *Schultesia* Mart., *Sclerocarpus* Jacq., *Sibthorpia* L., *Sparganophorus* Crantz, *Sphaeralcea* St. Hil., *Symmeria* Benth., *Syngonanthus* Ruhl., *Talinum* Adans., *Tapura* Aubl., *Thalia* L., *Thamnosma* Torr. et Frem., *Trianosperma* Mart., *Tristicha* Thou., *Vismia* Vand., *Voyria* Aubl. and *Leiphaimos* Ch. et Sch. 63 (62)

3. America and the Madagascar region only.

Pedilanthus Neck., *Ravenala* Adans. and *Phenakospermum* Endl., *Rheedia* L.

3 (4)

b. Africa, the Madagascar region and Asia.

1. Africa and Asia (often extending into Australasia and the Pacific Islands).

Adenanthera L., *Adina* Salisb., *Adinandra* Jack, *Aegle* Corr. and *Afraegle* Engl., *Alstonia* R. Br., *Ancistrocladus* Wall., *Anogeissus* Wall., *Antiaris* Lesch., *Aphania* Bl., *Argostemma* Wall., *Artanema* D. Don, *Baissea* A. DC., *Bowringia* Champ., *Brachylophon* Oliv., *Brackenridgea* A. Gr., *Brucea* J. F. Mill., *Bryonopsis* Arn., *Cajanus* DC., *Calamus* L., *Capillipedium* Stapf, *Cayratia* A.L. de Juss., *Centotheca* Desv., *Clausena* Burm. f., *Cleistachne* Benth., *Coccinia* Wight et Arn., *Combreto-dendron* A. Chev., *Ctenolophon* Oliv., *Cyanotis* D. Don, *Cyrtococcum* Stapf, *Dalhousiea* R. Grah., *Dichanthium* Willemet, *Dovyalis* E. Mey., *Droogmansia* De Wild., *Elatostema* Forst., *Elsholtzia* Willd., *Elytrophorus* Beauv., *Englerastrum* Briq.*, *Epithema* Bl., *Erythrophleum* Afzel., *Fingerhuthia* Nees, *Firmiana* Marsigli, *Flacourtia* L'Hérit., *Flemingia* Roxb., *Fluggea* Willd., *Ganophyllum* Bl., *Geissaspis* Wight et Arn., *Halopegia* K. Sch., *Harrisonia* R. Br., *Heritiera* Ait., *Holarrhena* R. Br., *Hunteria* Roxb., *Hymenocardia* Wall., *Illigera* Bl., *Irvingia* Hk. f., *Kaempferia* L., *Kedrostis* Medik., *Lasianthus* Jack, *Lecanthus* Wedd., *Lepistemon* Bl., *Leptonychia* Turcz., *Limonia* L. and *Citropsis* Swingle et Kellerm., *Mallotus* Lour., *Manisuris* L., *Mansonia* J. R. Drum., *Microdesmis* Hk. f., *Millettia* Wight et Arn., *Mitragyna* Korth., *Monochoria* C. Presl, *Musa* L., *Naregamia* Wight et Arn., *Neuropeltis* Wall., *Opilia* Roxb., *Oropetium* Trin., *Orthanthera* Wight, *Ottochloa* Dandy, *Oxytenanthera* Munro, *Parochetus* Buch.-Ham., *Perotis* Ait., *Petalidium* Nees, *Petersianthus* Merrill, *Platostoma* Benth. et Hk., *Pterolobium* R. Br., *Pterygota* Schott et Endl., *Pygeum* Gaertn., *Pyrenacantha* Wight, *Quisqualis* L., *Ranalisma* Stapf., *Remusatia* Schott, *Rothia* Pers., *Roureopsis* Planch., *Sansevieria* Thunb., *Santaloides* Schellenb., *Santiria* Bl. and *Santiriopsis* Engl., *Sarcocephalus* Afzel., *Sauromatum* Schott. *Schoenefeldia* Kunth, *Sesamum* L., *Shuteria* Wight et Arn., *Stephania* Lour., *Strombosia* Bl., *Telosma* Cov., *Tenagocharis* Hochst., *Thelepogon* Roth, *Tiliacora* Colebr., *Tinospora* Miers,*Vossia* Wall. et Griff.

106 (104)

2. Africa, the Madagascar region and Asia (often extending into Australasia and the Pacific Islands).

Achyrospermum Bl., *Acridocarpus* Guill. et Perr., *Acrocephalus* Benth., *Adenia* Forsk., *Alangium* Lam. and *Marlea* Roxb., *Albizzia* Durazz., *Alloteropsis* Presl, *Alysicarpus* Neck., *Amorphophallus* Bl., *Apodytes* E. Mey., *Aponogeton* L. f., *Arduina* Mill. and *Carissa* L., *Artabotrys* R. Br., *Asteracantha* Nees*, *Asystasia* Bl., *Azima* Lam., *Baphia* Afzel., *Blyxa* Nor., *Borassus* L., *Bothriochloa* Kuntze, *Bridelia* Willd., *Bruguiera* Lam., *Canarium* L., *Canscora* Lam., *Centipeda* Lour., *Ceriops* Arn., *Ceropegia* L., *Cheirostylis* Bl., *Cirrhopetalum* Lindl., *Cleistanthus* Hk. f., *Cnestis* Juss., *Coffea* L., *Commiphora* Jacq., *Corymbis* Thou., *Crossandra* Salisb., *Cryptolepis* R. Br. and *Ectadiopsis* Benth., *Deeringia* R. Br., *Dichrostachys* Wight et Arn., *Dicoma* Cass., *Disperis* Sw., *Dumasia* DC., *Ecbolium* Kurz., *Emilia* Cass., *Enhalus* L. C. Rich., *Enteropogon* Nees, *Ethulia* L. f., *Exacum* L., *Filicium* Thw., *Flagellaria* L., *Gaertnera* Lam., *Garcinia* L., *Gastonia* Comm., *Gelonium* Roxb., *Geniosporum* Wall., *Gerbera* Cass., *Giseckia* L., *Gloriosa* L., *Gnidia* L. and *Lasiosiphon* Fres., *Grangea* Adans., *Grewia* L., *Gymnema* R. Br., *Gynura* Cass., *Helinus* E. Mey., *Hemarthria* Munro, *Heteropholis* C. E. Hubb., *Holmskioldia* Retz., *Hugonia* L., *Hydrilla* L. C. Rich., *Hydrophylax* L. f., *Hymenodictyon* Wall., *Hypoestes* Soland., *Iodes* Bl., *Iphigenia* Kunth., *Laggera* Sch.-Bip., *Laurembergia* Berg., *Leea* L., *Lepironia* L. C. Rich.,*Lumnitzera* Willd.,*Macaranga* Thou., *Maesa* Forsk., *Medinilla* Gaudich., *Memycylon* L., *Mezoneuron* Desf.,

Micrargeria Benth., *Micrococca* Benth., *Microglossa* DC., *Moschosma* Reichb., *Mundulea* Benth., *Mussaenda* L., *Myrsine* L., *Neyraudia* Hk. f., *Nothosaerva* Wight, *Oberonia* Lindl., *Ochna* L., *Odina* Roxb., *Olax* L., *Olea* L., *Orthosiphon* Benth., *Osbeckia* L., *Paropsia* Nor., *Pavetta* L., *Pedalium* L., *Pemphis* Forst., *Peristrophe* Nees, *Phaius* Lour., *Phaylopsis* Willd., *Pleurostylia* Wight et Arn., *Pollia* Thunb., *Polyalthia* Bl., *Premna* L., *Pseudarthria* Wight et Arn., *Rhamphicarpa* Benth., *Rhinacanthus* Nees, *Rungia* Nees, *Saccolabium* Bl. and *Acampe* Lindl., *Satyrium* Sw., *Scolopia* Schreb., *Sebaea* Soland.*, *Secamone* R. Br. and *Toxocarpus* Wight et Arn., *Smithia* Ait., *Sopubia* Buch.-Ham., *Sphaeranthus* L., *Stereospermum* Cham., *Streblochaete* Hochst., *Striga* Lour., *Strophanthus* DC., *Tarenna* Gaertn., *Thunbergia* Retz., *Toddalia* Juss., *Tricalysia* A. Rich., *Tristellateia* Thou. and *Hiptage* Gaertn., *Turraea* L., *Tylophora* R. Br., *Uraria* Desv., *Urophyllum* Wall., *Vangueria* Juss., *Ventilago* Gaertn., *Vepris* Comm., *Voacanga* Thou. and *Orchipeda* Bl., *Wiesneria* M. Mich., *Woodfordia* Salisb., *Xylia* Benth.   .   142 (140)

3. The Madagascar region and Asia (often extending into Australasia and the Pacific Islands).

Actinoschoenus Benth., *Agrostophyllum* Bl., *Agyneja* L., *Anacolosa* Bl., *Apluda* L., *Atylosia* Wight et Arn., *Balanophora* Forst., *Barringtonia* Forst.*, *Bleekrodea* Bl., *Byrsophyllum* Hk. f., *Carallia* Roxb., *Cephalostachyum* Munro, *Cerbera* L., *Cipadessa* Bl., *Cymbidium* Sw., *Ellertonia* Wight, *Erythrospermum* Lam., *Euodia* Forst. and *Melicope* Forst., *Foetidia* Lam., *Geniostoma* Forst., *Givotia* W. Griff., *Hedychium* Koenig, *Melastoma* L., *Nepenthes* L., *Ochlandra* Thw., *Ochrocarpos* Thou., *Paederia* L., *Pongamia* Vent., *Pothos* L., *Samadera* Gaertn., *Sandoricum* Cav., *Soulamea* Lam., *Strobilanthes* Bl., *Thuarea* Pers., *Tropidia* L., *Vateria* L., *Wormia* Rottb., *Zoisia* Willd. 38 (38)

4. Africa and/or the Madagascar region and Australasia.

Adansonia L., *Athrixia* Ker-Gawl., *Brexia* Noronha and *Ixerba* A. Cunn., *Caesia* R. Br., *Cunonia* L., *Hibbertia* Andr., *Keraudrenia* J. Gay, *Rulingia* R. Br., *Triraphis* R. Br. 9 (8)

c. America and Asia (often extending into Australasia and the Pacific Islands).

Anaxagorea St. Hil., *Bocagea* St. Hil., *Callicarpa* L., *Capsicum* L., *Cedrela* P. Br. and *Toona* M. Roem., *Citronella* D. Don and *Chariessa* Miq., *Engelhardtia* Leschen. and *Oreomunnea* Oerst., *Enydra* Lour., *Gilibertia* R. et P., *Helicteres* L., *Ichnanthus* Beauv., *Inocarpus* Forst., *Klugia* Schlechd., *Laplacea* H., B. et K., *Lespedeza* Michx., *Linostoma* Wall. and *Lophostoma* Meissn., *Mappia* Jacq., *Meliosma* Bl., *Microtropis* Wall., *Mitreola* R. Br., *Nelumbo* Adans., *Oxybaphus* L'Hérit., *Physurus* L. C. Rich., *Roucheria* Planch., *Sageretia* Brongn., *Sapindus* L.*, *Saurauja* Willd., *Schoepfia* Schreb., *Sloanea* L. and *Echinocarpus* Bl., *Spathiphyllum* Schott, *Symplocos* Jacq., *Talauma* Juss., *Thismia* W. Griff., *Turpinia* Vent. 34 (34)

d. America and Australasia only.

Atkinsonia F. Muell. and *Gaiadendron* G. Don, *Distichlis* Raf., *Lindenia* Benth., *Nicotiana* L., *Orthosanthos* Sweet, *Trichocline* Cass.*   .   .   .   6 (6)

e. Discontinuous over a considerable part of the Tropical Zone.

Arundinaria Michx., *Byttneria* Loefl., *Calliandra* Benth., *Campnosperma* Thw., *Carapa* Aubl. and *Xylocarpus* Koenig, *Clethra* L., *Cochlospermum* Kunth, *Diplanthera* Thou., *Halophila* Thou., *Hermannia* L., *Hernandia* L., *Kalanchoe* Adans., *Lochnera* Reichb., *Lonchocarpus* H., B. et K., *Mimulus* L., *Omphalea* L., *Passiflora* L., *Protium* Burm. f., *Rhizophora* L., *Schrebera* Roxb., *Styrax* L., *Suriana* L., *Syringodium* Kütz., *Ternstroemia* Mutis, *Thalassia* Banks, *Turnera* L.   26 (26) *f.* Anomalous genera of the Tropical Zone.

Aldrovanda Monti, *Buxus* L., *Canarina* L., *Cohnia* Kunth, *Cossinia* Comm., *Cytinus* L., *Dyerophyton* O. Ktze., *Fagonia* L., *Hydrodea* N. E. Br., *Kissenia* R. Br., *Nesogenes* A. DC., *Pelargonium* L'Hérit., *Pharnaceum* L. and *Hypertelis* E. Mey., *Phylica* L., *Pilostyles* Guill., *Ruthea* Bolle, *Stillingia* L., *Weinmannia* L. 18 (17)

C. Genera found entirely or predominantly in the South Temperate Zone.

a. America and Australasia, some reaching Malaysia and Asia.

1. America, Australia and New Zealand, some reaching the Pacific Islands.

Abrotanella Cass., *Amphibromus* Nees, *Aristotelia* L'Hérit., *Colobanthus* Bartl., *Discaria* Hook., *Donatia* Forst., *Drapetes* Banks, *Drimys* Forst. and *Pseudowintera* Dandy, *Haloragis* Forst., *Hebe* Comm., *Libertia* Spreng., *Lilaeopsis* Greene, *Muehlenbeckia* Meissn., *Nothofagus* Bl., *Oreomyrrhis* Endl., *Ourisia* Comm., *Pernettia* Gaudich. and *Gaultheria* L., *Phyllachne* Forst., *Schizeilema* Domin, *Selliera* Cav., *Uncinia* Pers. 21 (21)

2. America and Australia, some reaching the Pacific Islands.

Calandrinia H. B. et K., *Eucryphia* Cav., *Gevuina* Mol., *Lebetanthus* Engl. and *Prionotes* R. Br., *Lomatia* R. Br., *Oreocallis* R. Br., *Orites* R. Br. . 7 (6)

3. America and New Zealand, some reaching the Pacific Islands.

Azorella Lam.*, *Enargea* Banks, *Fuchsia* L., *Gaimardia* Gaudich., *Griselinia* Forst., *Jovellana* R. et P., *Laurelia* Juss., *Marsippospermum* Desv., *Pseudopanax* C. Koch, *Rostkovia* Desv., *Tetrachondra* Petrie 11 (11)

b. Africa and Australasia.

Anacampseros L., *Arctotis* L. and *Cymbonotus* Cass., *Australina* Gaudich., *Bulbine* L., *Bulbinella* Kunth, *Chrysitrix* L., *Dietes* Salisb., *Helipterum* DC., *Hypolaena* R. Br., *Restio* L., *Villarsia* Vent., *Wurmbea* Thunb. . 12 (12)

c. Anomalous genera.

Carpobrotus N. E. Br., *Chevreulia* Cass., *Leptocarpus* R. Br., *Pringlea* Anders., *Tetragonia* L. 5 (5)

D. Genera found in both North and South Temperate Zones.

a. North Temperate Zone, and S. America, S. Africa and Australasia.

Erodium L'Hérit., *Frankenia* L., *Geum* L., *Koeleria* Pers., *Myosotis* L., *Myosurus* L., *Thesium* L., *Triglochin* L., *Viola* L., *Zostera* L. . . . 10 (10)

b. North Temperate Zone, S. America and Australasia.

Boisduvalia Spach, *Caltha* L., *Coriaria* L., *Daucus* L., *Eryngium* L., *Euphrasia* L., *Gentiana* L., *Glycyrrhiza* L., *Montia* L., *Myrtus* L., *Scleranthus* L. . 11 (11)

c. North Temperate Zone, S. Africa and Australasia.

Emex Neck., *Kochia* Roth., *Limonium* Mill., *Papaver* L., *Trigonella* L., *Zygophyllum* L. 6 (6)

d. North Temperate Zone and S. Africa.

Althenia Petit*, *Cryophytum* N. E. Br., *Herniaria* L., *Oligomeris* Cambess. *Pityranthos* Viv., *Seetzenia* R. Br., *Sium* L.* 7 (7)

e. North Temperate Zone and Australasia.

Angelica L., *Damasonium* Mill., *Nitraria* L., *Posidonia* Koenig, *Saussurea* DC., *Sparganium* L., *Veronica* L.* . . . . 7 (7) *f.* North Temperate Zone and S. America.

Adenocaulon Hk. f., *Antennaria* Gaertn., *Armeria* Willd., *Chrysosplenium* L., *Cicendia* Adans., *Drusa* DC.*, *Empetrum* L., *Hippuris* L., *Honkenya* Ehrh. *Hymenolobus* Nutt., *Lardizabala* R. et P. and *Parvatia* Decne., *Lepuropetalon* Elliott, *Littorella* Berg., *Phippsia* R. Br., *Primula* L., *Saxifraga* L. . 16 (17)

E. Genera of various distribution but all with outlying species in the Hawaiian Islands (excluding cosmopolitan and pan-tropical genera).

a. Entirely or predominantly Old World.

Alectryon Gaertn., *Alphitonia* Reissek., *Alyxia* Banks, *Antidesma* L., *Byronia* Endl., *Canthium* Lam., *Claoxylon* A. Juss., *Coprosma* Forst., *Cordyline* Comm., *Couthovia* A. Gr., *Cyathodes* Labill., *Cyrtandra* Forst., *Dianella* Lam., *Dracaena* L., *Elaeocarpus* Burm., *Embelia* Burm. f., *Exocarpus* Labill., *Freycinetia* Gaud., *Gahnia* Forst., *Gymnelaea* Spach, *Joinvillea* Gaudich., *Korthalsella* van Tiegh., *Metrosideros* Banks, *Myoporum* Banks et Soland., *Ochrosia* Juss., *Osteomeles* Lindl., *Pandanus* L., *Pipturus* Wedd., *Pittosporum* Banks, *Plectranthus* L'Hérit., and *Coleus* Lour., *Santalum* L., *Schizostachyum* Nees, *Strongylodon* Vog., *Suttonia* Hk. f., *Tetraplasandra* A. Gr. 35 (33)

b. Entirely or predominantly New World.

Cuphea P. Br., *Hesperocnide* Torr., *Nama* L., *Sicyos* L., *Sisyrinchium* L., *Sphacele* Benth. 6 (6)

c. Both Old and New World.

Acaena L., *Astelia* Banks et Soland., *Edwardsia* Salisb. (see special note, p. 130), *Eurya* Thunb., *Gunnera* L., *Lagenophora* Cass., *Lysimachia* L., *Nertera* Banks et Soland., *Oreobolus* R. Br., *Perrottetia* H., B. et K., *Pritchardia* Seem. et Wend., *Urera* Gaudich., *Xylosma* Forst. f. 13 (14),

Numerical Summary

A	.	.	.	.	128 (127)
B	.	.	.	.	470 (465)
C	.	.	.	.	56 (55)
D	.	.	.	.	57 (58)
E	.	.	.	.	54 (53)

765 (758)

BIBLIOGRAPHY

(Late additions are at the end)

1. ABEYWICKRAMA, B. A.: "The Origin and Affinities of the Flora of Ceylon." *Proc. 11th Ann. Sess. Ceylon Ass. Adv. Science*, 1955.
2. ABRAMS, L. R.: "The Origin and Geographical Affinities of the Flora of California." *Ecology*, **6**, 1925.
3. ADAMSON, R. S.: *The Vegetation of South Africa.* London, 1938.
4. ADAMSON, R. S.: "Some Geographical aspects of the Cape flora." *Trans. Roy. Soc. S. Africa*, **31**, 1948.
5. ADAMSON, R. S.: "The Cape as an Ancient African Flora." *The Advancement of Science*, no. 58, 1958.
6. ADAMSON, R. S., and SALTER, T. M., (ed.): *The Flora of the Cape Peninsula.* Cape Town and Johannesburg, 1950.
7. AHLMANN, H. W.: "The present climatic fluctuation." *Geog. Journ.*, **112**, 1949.
8. AHLMANN, H. W.: *Glacier Variations and Climatic Fluctuations.* New York, 1953.
9. AHRENDT, L. W. A.: "*Berberis* and *Mahonia*: a taxonomic revision." *Journ. Linn. Soc. London—Bot.*, **57**, 1961.
10. AKIYAMA, S.: "Geographical Distribution of *Carices* indigenous to the far eastern areas of Asia." *Journ. Fac. Sci. Hokkaido Univ.*, Ser V, *Bot.*, **7**, 1951.
11. ALEKHIN, V. V.: *Geography of Plants* (in Russian). Moscow, 1944.
12. ALLAN, H. H.: "Indigene versus alien in the New Zealand plant world." *Ecology*, **17**, 1936.
13. ALLAN, H. H.: "The Origin and Distribution of the Naturalized Plants of New Zealand." *Proc. Linn. Soc. London*, **150**, 1937–38.
14. ALLAN, H. H.: "Handbook of the Naturalized Flora of New Zealand." *Dept. of S. and I. Res. New Zealand*, Bull. **83**, 1940.
15. ALLAN, H. H. (ed. MOORE, L. B.): *Flora of New Zealand.* Wellington, 1961→.
16. ALLISON, J., GODWIN, H. and WARREN, S. H.: "Late-glacial deposits at Nazeing in the Lea Valley, North London." *Phil. Trans. Roy. Soc.*, B, **236**, 1952.
17. ALM, C. G., and FRIES, T. C. E.: "Monographie der Gattung *Blaeria*." *Acta Horti Bergiani*, **8**, 1925.
18. ALM, C. G., and FRIES, T. C. E.: "Monographie der Gattungen *Philippia* . . ." *K. Svenska Vetens. Handl.*, 3 ser., **4**, 1927.
19. ANDERSON, E.: "Cytology in its relation to Taxonomy." *Bot. Review*, **3**, 1937.
20. ANDERSON, E., and SAX, K.: "A cytological monograph of the American species of *Tradescantia*." *Bot. Gaz.*, **97**, 1936.
21. ANDERSSON, G.: "The Swedish Climate of the late Quaternary Period." *Rep. International Geological Congress, Stockholm*, 1910.
22. ANDREWS, C. W.: *A Monograph of Christmas Island.* London, 1900.
23. ANDREWS, E. C.: "The Geological History of the Australian Flowering Plants." *American Journ. Sci.*, **42**, 1916.
24. ANDREWS, E. C.: "Origin of the Pacific Insular Floras." *Proc. 6th Pacific Sci. Congr.*, **4**, 1939.
25. ANTEVS, E.: "The Last Glaciation." *Amer. Geog. Soc. Research Ser.*, **17**, 1928.
26. ARENS, K.: "Die kutikuläre Exkretion des Laubblattes." *Jahrb. f. wiss. Botanik*, **80**, 1934.
27. ARLDT, T.: *Die Entwicklung der Kontinente und ihre Lebenwelt.* Auf. 2, Berlin, 1938.
28. ATKINS, W. R. G.: "Some Physical and Chemical Factors which affect Plant Distribution." *Sci. Proc. Roy. Dublin Soc.*, **16**, 1922.
29. AUBRÉVILLE, A.: "Climats, forêts et désertification de l'Afrique tropicale." *Soc. d'Editions Geogr., Maritimes et Colon.*, Paris, 1949.
30. AUBRÉVILLE, A.: "Contribution à la palaéohistoire des forêts de l'Afrique tropicale." *Soc. d'Editions Geogr., Maritimes et Colon.*, Paris, 1949.
31. AUBRÉVILLE, A.: "La Disjonction Africaine dans la Flore Forestière Tropicale." *Cont. Rend. Soc. Biogeogr.*, **278**, 1955.
32. AUER. V.: "The Pleistocene of Fuego-Patagonia." *Ann. Acad. Sci. Fenn.*, A, **3**, 1958.

33. Avias, J.: "Contributions a l'Étude Stratigraphique et Paléontologique des Formations antecretacées de la Nouvelle-Calédonie Centrale." *Sciences de la Terre*, **1**, 1953.
34. Axelrod, D. I.: "Evolution of desert vegetation in western North America." *Carnegie Inst. Washington Publ.*, **590**, 1950.
35. Axelrod, D. I.: "A theory of Angiosperm evolution." *Evolution*, **6**, 1952.
36. Babcock, E. B.: *The Genus Crepis*. Berkeley and Los Angeles, 1947.
37. Babington, C. C. (ed. Wilmott, A. J.): *Manual of British Botany*. 10th ed., London, 1922.
38. Backer, C. A.: *The Problem of Krakatao as seen by a Botanist*. Weltevreden, n.d.
39. Baker, H. G.: "Self-compatability and establishment after 'long distance' dispersal." *Evolution*, **9**, 1955.
40. Baker, J. G.: *Elementary Lessons in Botanical Geography*. London, 1875.
41. Baldwin, J. T., Jnr.: "Geography of *Maschalocephalus dinklagei*." *American Journ. of Botany*, **37**, 1950.
42. Baldwin, J. T., Jnr., and Speese, B. M.: "Cytogeography of *Physalis*." *Bull. Torrey Bot. Club*, **78**, 1953.
43. Balfour, I. B.: "The Botany of Socotra." *Trans. Roy. Soc. Edin.*, **31**, 1887.
44. Balgooy, M. M. J. van: "Preliminary Plant-Geographical Analysis of the Pacific." *Blumea*, **10**, 1960.
45. Bandulska, H.: "On the cuticles of some recent and fossil Fagaceae." *Journ. Linn. Soc. London—Bot.*, **46**, 1924.
46. Bandulska, H.: "On the cuticles of some recent and fossil Myrtaceae." *Journ. Linn. Soc. London—Bot.*, **48**, 1928–31.
47. Barber, H. N.: "Evolution in the genus *Paeonia*." *Nature*, **148**, 1941.
48. Barrow, G.: "Isles of Scilly." *Mem. Geol. Survey London*, 1906.
49. Barton, L. V.: *Seed Preservation and Longevity*. London and New York, 1961.
50. Baulig, H.: "The Changing Sea-level." *Publ. Inst. Brit. Geog.*, **3**, 1935.
51. Baumann-Bodenheim, M. G.: "Fagacées de la Nouvelle-Calédonie." *Bull. Mus. Nat. d'Hist. Nat.*, **25**, 1953.
52. Baylis, G. T. S.: "A Botanical Survey of the Small Islands of the Three Kings Group." *Rec. Auckland Inst. Mus.*, **5**, 1958.
53. Beaufort, L. F. de: *Zoogeography of the land and inland waters*. London, 1951.
54. Beccari, O.: "The origin and dispersal of *Cocos nucifera*." *Philippines Journ. Sci.—Bot.*, **12**, 1917.
55. Beetle, A. A.: "The Phtyogeography of Patagonia." *Bot. Review*, **9**, 1943.
56. Bentham, G., and Hooker, J. D.: *Genera Plantarum*. London, 1862–83.
57. Bentham, G., and Hooker, J. D. (ed. Rendle, A. B.): *Handbook of the British Flora*. 7th ed., London, 1924.
58. Berg, L. S. (trans. Titelbaum, O. A.): *Natural regions of the U.S.S.R*. New York, 1950.
59. Berry, E. W.: "The Lower Cretaceous Flora of the World." *Maryland Geological Survey*, 1911.
60. Berry, E. W.: "The Origin and Distribution of the Family Myrtaceae." *Bot. Gaz.*, **59**, 1915.
61. Berry, E. W.: *Tree Ancestors*. Baltimore, 1923.
62. Berry, E. W.: "Age and Area as viewed by the Palaeontologist." *American Journal of Botany*, **11**, 1924.
63. Berry, E. W.: "Links with Asia before the Mountains brought aridity to the Western U.S.A." *The Scientific Monthly*, **25**, 1927.
64. Berry, E. W.: "The Past Climates of the North Polar Regions." *Smithsonian Miscell. Coll.*, **82**, Washington, 1930.
65. Berry, E. W.: "Tertiary Floras of Eastern North America." *Bot. Review*, **4**, 1937.
66. Bews, J. W.: "Plant Succession and Plant Distribution in South Africa." *Annals of Botany*, **34**, 1920.
67. Bews, J. W.: "Some General Principles of Plant Distribution . . ." *Annals of Botany*, **35**, 1921.
68. Bews, J. W.: "The South-East African Flora: its origin, migrations, and evolutionary tendencies." *Annals of Botany*, **36**, 1922.
69. Bews, J. W.: "Studies in the Ecological Evolution of the Angiosperms." *New Phytologist*, **26**, 1927.
70. Bilham, E. G.: "Variation in the climate of York . . ." *Quart. Journ. Roy. Meteor. Soc.*, **59**, 1933.
71. Blackburn, K. B.: "Possible Glacial survivals in our Flora." *Trans. Northern Nat. Union*, **1**, pt. I, 1931.

72. BLAKE, S. F., and ATWOOD, A. C.: "Geographical Guide to the Floras of the World, I." *U.S. Dept. Agric. Misc. Publ.*, **401**, 1942.
73. BLASDALE, W. C.: *Cyclamen persicum: its natural and cultivated forms.* Stanford, California, 1952.
74. BLUMENSTOCK, D. I., and THORNTHWAITE, C. W.: "Climate and world pattern." *U.S. Dept. Agric. Yearbook, Washington*, 1941.
75. BÖCHER, T. W.: "Nordische Verbreitungstypen." *Svensk. Bot. Tid.*, **37**, 1943.
76. BÖCHER, T. W.: "Distribution of Plants of the Circumpolar Area in relation to Ecological Changes." *Journ. of Ecology*, **39**, 1951.
77. BOND, G.: "Fixation of Nitrogen in *Coriaria myrtifolia.*" *Nature*, **193**, 1962.
78. BONYTHORN, C. W., and MASON, B.: "The Filling and Drying of Lake Eyre." *Geogr. Journ.*, **119**, 1953.
79. BOOBERG, G.: "Die Malayische Strandflora." *Engl. Bot. Jahrb.*, **66**, 1934.
80. BOUGHEY, A. S.: "The Vegetation of the Mountains of Biafra." *Proc. Linn. Soc. London*, **165**, 1955.
81. BOUGHEY, A. S.: "The Lowland Rain-forest of Tropical Africa." *Proc. and Trans. Rhodesia Sci. Assoc.*, **44**, 1956.
82. BOUGHEY, A. S.: *The Origin of the African Flora.* Oxford, 1957.
83. BOULGER, G. S.: *Plant Geography (The Temple Primers).* London, 1912.
84. BOWDEN, W. M.: "Diploidy, polyploidy and winter hardiness relationships in the flowering plants." *American Journal of Botany*, **27**, 1940.
85. BRAY, W. L.: "On the relation of the flora of the Lower Sonoran zone in N. America . . ." *Bot. Gaz.*, **26**, 1898.
86. BRENCHLEY, W. E.: "Some factors in plant competition." *Ann. Applied Biology*, **6**, 1919-20.
87. BRIDGES, E. L.: *Uttermost part of the Earth.* London, 1948.
88. BROOKS, C. E. P.: *The Evolution of Climate.* London, 1925.
89. BROOKS, C. E. P.: "The Change of Climate in the British Isles." *Meteor. Magazine*, **70**, 1935.
90. BROOKS, C. E. P.: *Climate through the Ages.* 2nd ed., London, 1949.
91. BROWN, F. B. H.: "Flora of South-eastern Polynesia." *B. P. Bishop Mus. Memoirs*, **84** and **130**, 1931 and 1935.
92. BRUCE, E. A.: "The Giant Lobelias of East Africa." *Kew Bull.*, 1934.
93. BRUNEAU DE MIRÉ, P., and QUEZEL, P.: "Sur la Présence de la Bruyère en Arbre (*Erica arborea* L.) sur les Sommets de l'Emi Koussi (Massif de Tibesti)". *Cont. Rend. Soc. Biogeogr.*, **315**, 1959.
94. BURBIDGE, N. T.: "The Phytogeography of the Australian Region." *Australian Journ. of Bot.*, **8**, 1960.
95. BURKILL, I. H., and others: "A Discussion on the biogeographical divisions of the Indo-Australian Archipelago . . ." *Proc. Linn. Soc. London*, **154**, 1941-42.
96. BUTCHER, R. W.: *A New Illustrated British Flora.* London, 1961.
97. BUTCHER, R. W., and STRUDWICK, F. E.: *Further Illustrations of British Plants.* Ashford, 1930.
98. BUTLER, H. C.: "Desert Syria." *Geog. Review*, **9**, 1920.
99. CABRERA, A. L.: "Territorios Fitogeograficos de la Republica Argentina." *Bol. Soc. Argentina de Bot.*, **4**, 1951.
100. CABRERA, A. L.: "Esquema Fitogeografico de la Republica Argentina." *Revista del Mus. de la ciudad Eva Peron*, n.s. **8**, 1953.
101. CAILLEUX, A.: *Biogéographie Mondiale.* Presses Universitaires de France, Paris, 1953.
102. CAIN, S. A.: "Pollen Analysis as a Paleo-Ecological Research Method." *Bot. Review*, **5**, 1939.
103. CAIN, S. A.: "Criteria . . . centre of origin . . ." *Torreya*, **43**, 1943.
104. CAIN, S. A.: *Foundations of Plant Geography.* New York, 1944.
105. CAIN, S. A.: "Life-forms and phytoclimate." *Bot. Review*, **16**, 1950.
106. CAMBAGE, R. H.: Presidential Address. *Proc. Linn. Soc. N.S.W.*, **50**, 1925.
107. CAMBAGE, R. H.: Presidential Address. *Austr. Assoc. Adv. Sci.* (1928), 1929.
108. CAMP, W. H.: "Distribution patterns in modern plants and the problems of ancient dispersals." *Ecological Monographs*, **17**, 1947.
109. CAMPBELL, D. H.: "Some Botanical and Environmental Aspects of Hawaii." *Ecology*, **1**, 1920.
110. CAMPBELL, D. H.: "The Vegetation of Australia and New Zealand." *The Scientific Monthly* **15**, 1922.
111. CAMPBELL, D. H.: *Outline of Plant Geography.* London, 1926.
112. CAMPBELL, D. H.: "The flora of the Hawaiian Islands." *Quart. Rev. Biol.*, **8**, 1933.

113. CAMPBELL, D. H.: "Continental Drift and Plant Distribution." *Science*, 95, 1942.
114. CAMPBELL, D. H.: "Relations of the temperate floras of North and South America." *Proc. Californian Acad. Sci.*, 4 ser., 25, 1944.
115. CAMPBELL, D. H., and others: "Effect of the introduction of exotic plant and animal forms." *Proc. 5th Pacific Sci. Congr.*, 1, 1934.
116. CANDOLLE, A. L. P. P. DE: *Géographie botanique raisonnée*. Paris, 1855.
117. CANDOLLE, A. L. P. P. DE: *Origin of Cultivated Plants*. London, 1884.
118. CAREY, S. W.: "The Orocline Concept in Geotectonics, pt. 1." *Papers and Proc. Roy. Soc. Tasmania*, 89, 1955.
119. CAREY, S. W. (ed.): *Continental Drift: a Symposium*. Hobart, 1958.
120. CARLQUIST, S.: *The Genus Fitchia (Compositae)*. Berkeley and Los Angeles, 1957.
121. CHAMBERLIN, T. C.: "Concerning the hollow curve of distribution." *American Naturalist*, 58, 1924.
122. CHANDLER, M. E. J.: "The Arctic Flora of the Cam Valley . . ." *Quart Journ. Geol. Soc.*, 77, 1921.
123. CHANDLER, M. E. J.: *The Lower Tertiary Floras of Southern England: 1. Palaeocene Floras; London Clay Flora (Supplement)*. London, 1961.
124. CHANEY, R. W.: "Paleoecological Interpretations of Cenozoic Plants in Western North America." *Bot. Review*, 4, 1938.
125. CHANEY, R. W.: "Tertiary floras and continental history." *Bull. Geol. Soc. America*, 51, 1940.
126. CHANEY, R. W.: "Tertiary centres and migration routes." *Ecological Monographs*, 17, 1947.
127. CHAPMAN, F.: "Descriptions of Tertiary plant remains from Central Australia . . ." *Trans. and Proc. Roy. Soc. S. Austr.*, 61, 1937.
128. CHAPMAN, F. M.: "The upper zonal bird life of Mts. Roraima and Duida." *Bull. Amer. Mus. Nat. Hist.*, 63, 1931.
129. CHEESEMAN, T. F.: *Manual of the New Zealand Flora*. 2nd ed., Wellington, 1925.
130. CHEVALIER, A.: "L'origine géographique et les migrations des bruyères." *Bull. Soc. Bot. France*, 70, 1923.
131. CHEVALIER, A.: "La vegetation montagnarde de L'Ouest Afrique et sa genèse." *Mem. Soc. Biogéographie*, 2, 1928.
132. CHEVALIER, A.: "Les Îles du Cap Vert: Flore de l'Archipel." *Rev. Bot. Appl.*, 15, 1935.
133. CLAPHAM, A. R.: "Check List of British Vascular Plants." *Journ. of Ecology*, 33, 1946.
134. CLAPHAM, A. R., TUTIN, T. G., and WARBURG, E. F.: *Flora of the British Isles*. Cambridge, 1952, 2nd. ed. 1962.
135. CLARK, A. H.: *The Invasion of New Zealand by Exotic Plants and Animals*. Christchurch, 1949.
136. CLARKE, W. A.: "Plant Distribution in the Western Isles." *Proc. Linn. Soc. London*, 167, 1956.
137. CLAUSEN, J., KECK, D. D., and HIESEY, W. M.: "Experimental studies in the nature of species. I. Effect of varied environments on western North American plants." *Carnegie Inst. Washington Publ.*, 520, 1940.
138. CLAUSEN, J., KECK, D. D., and HIESEY, W. M.: "Regional differentiation in plant species." *American Naturalist*, 75, 1941.
139. CLAUSEN, J., KECK, D. D., and HIESEY, W. M.: "Experimental studies in the nature of species. III. Environmental responses of climatic races of *Achillea*." *Carnegie Inst. Washington Publ.*, 581, 1948.
140. COCKAYNE, L., and ALLAN, H. H.: "An Annotated List of Groups of Wild Hybrids in the New Zealand Flora." *Annals of Botany*, 48, 1934.
141. COCKAYNE, L., SIMPSON, G., and SCOTT THOMSON, J.: "Some New Zealand indigenous-induced weeds . . ." *Journ. Linn. Soc. London—Bot.*, 49, 1932–35.
142. COCKERELL, T. D. A.: "Miocene Trees of the Rocky Mountains." *American Naturalist*, 44, 1910.
143. COCKERELL, T. D. A.: "Aspects of the Madeiran Flora." *Bot. Gaz.*, 85, 1928.
144. COLGAN, N., and SCULLY, R. W.: *Cybele Hibernica*. 2nd ed., Dublin, 1898.
145. COLLET, L. W.: *The Structure of the Alps*. 2nd ed., London, 1935.
146. COLLINSON, D. W., and RUNCORN, S. K.: "Polar Wandering and Continental Drift: evidence from palaeomagnetic observations in the U.S.A." *Bull. Geol. Soc. America*, 71B, 1960.
147. COMPTON, R. H.: "New Caledonia and the Isle of Pines." *Geog. Journ.*, 49, 1917.
148. CONWAY, V. M.: "Von Post's work on climatic rhythms." *New Phytologist*, 47, 1948.

149. COOKSON, I. C.: "Recent Additions to our Knowledge of Australian Tertiary Floras." *Comptes Rend. 8e. Intern. Bot. Congr.*, Paris 1954.
150. CORE, E. L.: "Plant migrations and vegetational history of the southern Appalachian region." *Lilloa*, 3, 1938.
151. CORNER, E. J. H.: "An Introduction to the Distribution of *Ficus*." *Reinwardtia*, 4, 1958.
152. COSTIN, A. B.: "The High Mountain Vegetation of Australia." *Australian Journ. of Botany*, 5, 1957.
153. COTTON, A. D.: "The Tree Senecios of the high African Mountains." *Proc. Linnean Soc. London*, 1932.
154. COUPER, R. A.: "The spore and pollen flora of the *Cocos*-bearing beds, Manganui, North Auckland, . . ." *Trans. and Proc. Roy. Soc. New Zealand*, 79, 1952.
155. COUPER, R. A.: "Southern Hemisphere Mesozoic and Tertiary Podocarpaceae and Fagaceae, and their palaeogeographic significance." *Proc. Roy. Soc., B*, 152, 1960.
156. COX, A., and DOELL, R. R.: "Review of Palaeomagnetism." *Bull. Geol. Soc. America*, 70, 1960.
157. CRANWELL, L. M.: "Fossil Pollen from Seymour Island, Antarctica." *Nature*, 184, 1959.
158. CRANWELL, L. M., HARRINGTON, H. J., and SPEDEN, I. G.: "Lower Tertiary Microfossils from McMurdo Sound, Antarctica." *Nature*, 186, 1960.
159. CRESSEY, G. B.: "The Climate of the Glacial Period in Eastern Asia." *Proc. 3rd Pan-Pacific Sci. Congr.*, 2, 1926.
160. CROCKER, R. L.: "Past Climatic Fluctuations and their influence upon Australian vegetation." *Monographiae Biologiae*, 8, 1959.
161. CROCKER, R. L., and WOOD, J. G.: "Some Historical influences in the development of the South Australian vegetation communities." *Trans. Roy. Soc. S. Austr.*, 71, 1947.
162. CROCKER, W. C.: "Life-span of Seeds." *Bot. Review*, 4, 1938.
163. CROIZAT, L.: "*Trochodendron, Tetracentron*, and their meaning in phylogeny." *Bull. Torrey Bot. Club*, 74, 1947.
164. CROIZAT, L.: *Manual of Phytogeography*. The Hague, 1952.
165. CROIZAT, L.: *Panbiogeography*. Caracas, 1958.
166. CUFODONTIS, G.: "Revision der afrikanischen Arten von *Pittosporum*." *Fedde Repert.*, 55, 1952.
167. CURTIS, W. M.: *The Student's Flora of Tasmania*. Hobart, 1956→
168. DAHL, E.: "On different types of unglaciated areas during the Ice Ages . . ." *New Phytologist*, 45, 1946.
169. DALY, R. A.: *The Floor of the Ocean*. Chapel Hill, 1942.
170. DANDY, J. E.: "Notes on *Kissenia* and the Geographical Distribution of the Loasaceae." *Kew Bull.*, 1926.
171. DANSEREAU, P.: "Flora and vegetation on the Gaspé Peninsula." *Wild Flower*, April, 1950.
172. DANSEREAU, P.: "Description and recording of vegetation on a structural basis." *Ecology*, 32, 1951.
173. DANSEREAU, P.: *Biography: an ecological perspective*. New York, 1957.
174. DANSEREAU, P., and LEMS, K.: "The Grading of Dispersal Types in Plant Communities and their Ecological Significance." *Cont. l'Inst. Bot. de l'Univ. Montreal*, 71, 1957.
175. DARLINGTON, P. J., Jnr.: *Zoogeography*. New York and London, 1957.
176. DARWIN, C.: *Journal of a Naturalist . . . H.M.S. Beagle*. London, 1939.
177. DARWIN, C.: *The Origin of Species*. 6th ed., London, 1872.
178. DAUBENMIRE, R. F.: *Plants and Environment: a textbook of plant autecology*. New York and London, 1947.
179. DEEVEY, E. S., junr.: "Biography of the Pleistocene." *Bull. Geol. Soc. America*, 60, 1949.
180. DE GEER, G.: "A Geochronology of the last 12,000 years." *Rep. International Geographical Congress*. Stockholm, 1920.
181. DE GEER, G.: "Geochronologica Suecica: Principles." *K. Svenska Vetens. Handl.*, 3 ser., 18, 1940.
182. DE LA RUE, E. A.: "Étude Géologique et Géographique de L'Archipel des Kerguélens." *Rev Geogr. Phys.*, 5, 1932.
183. DELPINO, G. G. F.: "Studi di geografia botanica secondo un nuovo indirizzo." *Mem. R. Accad. Bologna*, 5 ser., 7, 1898.
184. DE VRIES, H. (trans. FARMER, J. B., and DARBISHIRE, A. D.): *The Mutation Theory*. London, 1910–11.
185. DEWEY, H.: *British Regional Geology—South-West England*. London, 1935.

29

186. De Wildeman, E.: "De l'Origine de Certains Éléments de la Flore du Congo Belge . . . ." *Mem. Inst. Roy. Colon. Belge, s.* 8e., **10**, 1940.
187. Dexter, S. T., Tottingham, W. E., and Graber, L. F.: "Preliminary Results in Measuring the Hardiness of Plants." *Plant Physiology*, **5**, 1930.
188. Diels, L.: *Pflanzengeographie (Sammlung Goschen* 389). Auf. 2, Berlin, 1918.
189. Diels, L.: "Ein Beitrag zur Analyse der Hochgebirgs-Flora von Neu-Guinea". *Engl. Bot. Jahrb.* **63**, 1930.
190. Diels, L.: "Phytogeography of the south-western Pacific." *Essays in Geobotany in Honor of W. A. Setchell*, 1936.
191. Dietz, R. S.: "Continent and Ocean Basin Evolution by Spreading of the Sea Floor." *Nature*, **190**, 1961.
192. Dimirez, H.: "Ökologisches Beobachtungen uber das gemeinsame Auftreten von *Laurus nobilis* L. und *Myrtus communis* L. an Anatolens Nord- und Sudkuste." *Rev. Fac. Sci. de l'Univ. d'Istanbul, ser. B*, **21**, 1957.
193. Docters van Leeuwen, W. M.: *Krakatau, 1883–1933. A. Botany*. Leiden, 1936.
194. Donat, A.: "Zur Begrenzung der Magellanischen Florengebietes." *Ber. d. Deutsch. Bot. Ges.*, **52**, 1934.
195. Dorf, E.: "Climatic Changes of the Past and Present." *American Scientist*, **48**, 1960.
196. Douglass, A. E.: "Climatic Cycles and Tree-Growth." *Carnegie Inst. Washington Publ.*, **289**, 1919 and 1928.
197. Druce, G. C.: "The extinct and dubious plants of Britain." *Rep. Bot. Soc. and Exch. Club* (1919), 1920.
198. Druce, G. C.: *British Plant List*. 2nd ed., Arbroath, 1928.
199. Druce, G. C.: *The Comital Flora of the British Isles*. Arbroath, 1932.
200. Drude, O.: *Atlas der Pflanzenverbreitung* (Berghaus Phys. Atlas). Gotha, 1887.
201. Drude, O.: *Handbuch der Pflanzengeographie*. Stuttgart, 1890.
202. Drude, O.: "The flora of Great Britain compared with that of Central Europe." *New Phytologist*, **11**, 1912.
203. Du Rietz, G. E.: "Factors Controlling the Distribution of Species in Vegetation." *Proc. Intern. Congr. Plant Sciences*. Ithaca, 1929.
204. Du Rietz, G. E.: "Two New Species of *Euphrasia* from the Philippines . . ." *Svensk. Bot. Tid.*, **25**, 1931.
205. Du Rietz, G. E.: "Problems of Bipolar Distribution." *Acta Phytogeographica Suecica*, **13**, 1940.
206. Durocher-Yvon, F.: "Seychelles Botanical Treasure." *La Rev. Agric. de L'île Maurice*, **26**, 1947.
207. Dusén, P.: "Ueber die Tertiare flora der Seymour-Insel." *Wiss. Ergeb. Schwed. Sudpolar-Exped.*, 1901–03, **3**, 1908.
208. Du Toit, A. L.: *Our Wandering Continents*. Edinburgh and London, 1937.
209. Du Toit, A. L.: "Further remarks on continental drift." *American Journ. Sci.*, **242**, 1944.
210. Duvigneaud, P., Marlier, M. L., and Dewit, J.: "La Géographie de Caractères chez le Genre zambezien *Diplorrhynchus.*" *Bull. Soc. Roy. Bot. Belge*, **84**, 1952.
211. Edmondson, C. H.: "Viability of coconut seeds after floating in the sea." *B. P. Bishop Mus. Occ. Papers*, **16**, 1941.
212. Edwards, W. N.: "The Geographical Distribution of Past Floras." *The Advancement of Science*, **12**, 1955.
213. Egyed, L.: "A New Dynamic Conception of the Internal Constitution of the Earth." *Geol. Rundschau*, **46**, 1957.
214. Egyed, L.: "Continental Drift, Polar Wandering and the Internal Constitution of the Earth." *Act. Zool. Acad. Sci. Hungr.*, **3**, 1958.
215. Emberger, L.: "La végétation de la région Méditerranéenne." *Rev. Gen. de Bot.*, **42**, 1930.
216. Engler, A.: *Versuch einer Entwicklungsgeschichte der Pflanzenwelt* . . . Leipzig, 1872–82.
217. Engler, A.: "Über floristische Verwandschaft zwischen dem tropischen Afrika und Amerika . . ." *Sitzungsber. Königl. Preuss. Akad. Wiss.*, **6**, 1905.
218. Engler, A. (ed.): *Das Pflanzenreich*. Leipzig, 1900→
219. Engler, A., and Drude, O., (ed.): *Die Vegetation der Erde*. Auf. 1 und 2, Leipzig, 1896→
220. Engler, A., and Diels, L.: *Syllabus der Pflanzenfamilien*. Auf. 11, Berlin, 1936.
221. Engler, A., and Prantl, K., (ed.): *Die natürlichen Pflanzenfamilien*. Auf. 1, Leipzig, 1889–1915.
222. Engler, A., and Prantl, K., (ed.): *Die natürlichen Pflanzenfamilien*. Auf. 2, Leipzig, 1924→

223. ERDTMAN, G.: *An Introduction to Pollen Analysis.* Waltham, Mass., 1943.
224. ERDTMAN, G.: "Did Dicotyledonous plants exist in early Jurassic times?" *Geol. Foren. Forhandl.*, **70**, 1948.
225. ERLANSON, E. W.: "Plant colonization on two new tropical islands." *Journ. Indian Bot. Soc.*, **15**, 1936.
226. ETTINGSHAUSEN, C. VON: "Contributions to the knowledge of the fossil flora of New Zealand." *Trans. New Zealand Inst.*, **23**, 1890.
227. EVANS, W. E.: "A Revision of the genus *Diapensia*." *Notes Roy. Bot. Gard. Edinburgh*, **15**, 1927.
228. EXELL, A. W.: "Dr. Camisso's Botanical Mission to Angola." *Journ. Bot.*, **76**, 1938.
229. EXELL, A. W.: *The Vascular Plants of S. Tomé.* London, 1944.
230. EXELL, A. W.: "Discussion of the percentage relationship calculated by Dr. Williams." *Proc. Linn. Soc. London*, **158**, 1945–46.
231. EXELL, A. W.: "La Végétation de l'Afrique Tropicale Australe." *Bull. Soc. Roy. Bot. Belge*, **89**, 1957.
232. FAEGRI, K., and IVERSEN, J.: *Textbook of Modern Pollen Analysis.* Copenhagen, 1950.
233. FARRINGTON, A.: "The Level of the ocean in Glacial and Late-Glacial times." *Proc. Royal Irish Acad.*, **50** B, 1945.
234. FEDOROV, A. A.: "The Tropical Rain-forests of China." *Botanical Journal U.S.S.R.*, **43**, 1958.
235. FEDOROV, A. A.: "Woody Epiphytes and Strangling Figs in the Tropical Forests of China." *Botanical Journal U.S.S.R.*, **44**, 1959.
236. FERNALD, M. L.: "Persistence of Plants in Unglaciated Areas of Boreal America." *Mem. Amer. Acad. Arts and Sci.*, **15**, 1925.
237. FERNALD, M. L.: "Some Relationships of the Floras of the Northern Hemisphere." *Proc. Intern. Congr. Plant Sciences.* Ithaca, 1929.
238. FERNALD, M. L.: "Specific segregations and identities in some floras of eastern North America . . ." *Rhodora*, **33**, 1931.
239. FERNALD, M. L.: "Recent Discoveries in the Newfoundland Flora." *Rhodora*, **35**, 1933.
240. FERNALD, M. L.: "Must all rare plants suffer the fate of *Franklinia*?" *Journal Franklin Institute*, **226**, 1938.
241. FERNANDES, A.: "Sur la phylogenie des espèces du genre *Narcissus* L." *Bol. Soc. Broteriana*, 2 ser., **25**, 1951.
242. FITCH, W. H., and SMITH, W. G.: *Illustrations of the British Flora.* 5th ed., Ashford, 1924.
243. FLETCHER, F.: "Toxic excreta of plants." *Journ. Agric. Sci.*, **4**, 1912.
244. FLINT, R. F.: *Glacial geology and the Pleistocene epoch.* New York, 1947.
245. FLINT, R. F.: "Dating late-Pleistocene events by means of radio-carbon." *Nature*, **167**, 1951.
246. FORBES, C. N.: "Notes on the naturalized flora of the Hawaiian Islands." *B. P. Bishop Mus. Occ. Papers*, **4**, 1911.
247. FORBES, E.: "On the Connection between the Distribution of the existing Fauna and Flora of the British Isles and the Geological Changes . . ." *Mem. Geol. Survey London*, **1**, 1846.
248. FORBES, H. O.: *The Natural History of Socotra.* Liverpool and London, 1903.
249. FOSBERG, F. R.: "The American Element in the Hawaiian Flora." *Pacific Science*, **5**, 1951.
250. FOSBERG, F. R.: "Lignes biogeographiques dans l'Ouest de la Pacifique." *Cont. Rend. Soc. Biogeogr.*, **256**, 1952.
251. FOSBERG, F. R.: "Pacific forms of *Lepturus* R. Br. (Gramineae)." *B.P. Bishop Museum, Occ. Papers*, **21**, 1955.
252. FOSBERG, F. R. and ST. JOHN, H.: "Végétation et Flore de l'atoll Maria, Îles Australes." *Revue Sci. du Bourbonnais et du Centre de la France*, (1951), 1952.
253. FRIES, R. E.: "Die *Sonchus*-Arten des tropischen und südlichen Afrika." *Acta Horti Bergiani*, **8**, 1924.
254. FRIES, R. E.: "Revision der tropisch-afrikanishen *Carduus*-Arten." *Acta Horti Bergiani*, **8**, 1923.
255. FRIES, R. E.: "Zur Kenntnis der ostafrikanischen *Echinops*-Arten." *Acta Horti Bergiani*, **8**, 1923.
256. FRIES, R. E.: "Zur Kenntnis der Scrophulariaceen des tropischen Ostafrika." *Acta Horti Bergiani*, **8**, 1924.
257. FRIES, T. C. E.: "Die *Anagallis*-Arten der afrikanischen Hochgebirge." *Notizbl. Bot. Gart. Berlin-Dahlem*, **8**, 1923.
258. FRIES, T. C. E.: "Die *Swertia*-Arten der afrikanischen Hochgebirge." *Notizbl. Bot. Gart. Berlin-Dahlem*, **8**, 1923.

259. FUNKE, G. L.: "The influence of *Artemisia absinthium* on neighbouring plants." *Blumea*, **5**, 1943.
260. FUNKE, G. L.: "The influence of *Satureia hortensis* L. on *Allium Cepa* L." *Blumea*, **5**, 1943.
261. FURON, R.: *Causes de la Répartition des Êtres Vivants*. (Evolution des Sciences, no. 10), Paris, 1958.
262. GARDNER, C. A.: "The Vegetation of Western Australia, with special reference to the climate and soils." *Journ. Roy. Soc. W. Austr.*, **28**, 1941–42.
263. GATES, R. R.: "On pairs of species." *Bot. Gaz.*, **61**, 1916.
264. GEIGER, R.: *The Climate near the Ground*. Cambridge, Mass., 1950.
265. GIBBS, L. S.: "A contribution to the phyto-geography of Bellenden-Ker." *Journ. Bot.*, **55**, 1917.
266. GIBBS, L. S.: *Dutch N. W. Guinea: ... Arfak Mts., etc.* London, 1917.
267. GIBBS, L. S.: "Notes on the Phytogeography and Flora of the Mountain Summit Plateaux of Tasmania." *Journal of Ecology*, **8**, 1921.
268. GILES, N. H., junr.: "Autopolyploidy and geographical distribution in *Cuthbertia graminea*." *American Journal of Botany*, **29**, 1942.
269. GILL, E. D.: "The Climates of Gondwanaland in Kainozoic times." In *Descriptive Palaeoclimatology*, ed. Nairn, 1961.
270. GILLILAND, H. B.: "Some current problems concerning the understanding of African vegetation." *Geog. Review*, **40**, 1950.
271. GINSBERGER, A.: *Pflanzengeographisches Hilfsbuch*. Vienna, 1939.
272. GLEASON, H. A.: "Age and Area from the viewpoint of phyto-geography." *American Journal of Botany*, **11**, 1924.
273. GLEASON, H. A.: "Studies on the flora of northern South America—XIII. The Tate collection from Mt. Roraima and vicinity." *Bull. Torrey Bot. Club*, **56**, 1929.
274. GLEASON, H. A.: "Botanical results of the Tyler-Duida Expedition." *Bull. Torrey Bot. Club*, **58**, 1931.
275. GLOCK, W. S.: "Principles and Methods of Tree-ring Analysis." *Carnegie Inst. Washington Publ.*, **486**, 1937.
276. GODWIN, H.: "Pollen Analysis: an outline of the Problems and Potentialities of the Method." *New Phytologist*, **33**, 1934.
277. GODWIN, H.: "The Late-Glacial Period." *Science Progress*, **35**, 1947.
278. GODWIN, H.: "The spreading of the British flora." *Journ. of Ecology*, **37**, 1949.
279. GODWIN, H.: "Pollen Analysis (palynology)." *Endeavour*, **10**, 1951.
280. GODWIN, H.: *The History of the British Flora*. Cambridge, 1956.
281. GODWIN, H.: "Quaternary History and the British Flora." *The Advancement of Science*, **13**, 1956.
282. GOEZE, E.: *Pflanzengeographie*. Stuttgart, 1882.
283. GOOD, R.: "The Past and Present Distribution of the Magnolieae." *Annals of Botany*, **39**, 1925.
284. GOOD, R.: "On the Geographical Distribution of the Stylidiaceae." *New Phytologist*, **24**, 1925.
285. GOOD, R.: "A Summary of Discontinuous Generic Distribution in the Angiosperms." *New Phytologist*, **26**, 1927.
286. GOOD, R.: "The Genus *Empetrum*." *Journ. Linn. Soc. London—Bot.*, **47**, 1925–27.
287. GOOD, R.: "The Geography and Taxonomy of the genus *Cremanthodium*." *Journ. Linn. Soc. London—Bot.*, **48**, 1928–31.
288. GOOD, R.: "The Geography of the Genus *Coriaria*." *New Phytologist*, **29**, 1930.
289. GOOD, R.: "A Theory of Plant Geography." *New Phytologist*, **30**, 1931.
290. GOOD, R.: *Plants and Human Economics*. Cambridge, 1933.
291. GOOD, R.: "A Geographical Survey of the Flora of Temperate South America." *Annals of Botany*, **47**, 1933.
292. GOOD, R.: "On the Distribution of the Lizard Orchid." *New Phytologist*, **35**, 1936.
293. GOOD, R.: "An Account of a Botanical Survey of Dorset." *Proc. Linn. Soc. London*, 1936–1937.
294. GOOD, R.: "The Distribution of the Primrose in a Southern County." *The Naturalist*, 1944.
295. GOOD, R.: *A Geographical Handbook of the Dorset Flora*. Dorchester, 1948.
296. GOOD, R.: "Madagascar and New Caledonia; a problem in plant geography." *Blumea*, **6**, 1950.
297. GOOD, R.: "The distribution of the flowering plants in relation to theories of continental drift." *The Advancement of Science*, **8**, 1951.
298. GOOD, R.: "The evolutionary theories of Dr. J. C. Willis." *New Phytologist*, **50**, 1951.

299. GOOD, R.: "An atlas of the Asclepiadaceae." *New Phytologist*, **51**, 1952.
300. GOOD, R.: "Plant Geography." In *A Century of Progress in the Natural Sciences*. Calif. Acad. Sci., San Francisco, 1955.
301. GOOD, R.: *Features of Evolution in the Flowering Plants*. London, 1956.
302. GOOD, R.: "Some Problems of Southern Floras with special reference to Australasia." *Australian Journ. Science*, **20**, 1957.
303. GOOD, R.: "Australasian Floras." *Nature*, **179**, 1957.
304. GOOD, R.: "The Biogeography of Australia." *Nature*, **181**, 1958.
305. GOOD, R.: "On the Geographical Relationships of the Angiosperm Flora of New Guinea." *Bull. Brit. Mus. (Nat. Hist.), Botany*, **2**, 1960.
306. GOOD, R.: "On the Biological and Physical Relationship between New Guinea and Australia." *10th. Pacific Sci. Congr. Symposia*, in press.
307. GOOD, R., and WAUGH, W. L.: "The Vegetation of Redcliff Sand . . ." *Journ. of Ecology*, **22**, 1934.
308. GOODSPEED, T. H.: *The genus Nicotiana*. Chronica Botanica, Waltham, Mass., 1954.
309. GORDON, H. D.: "The problem of sub-antarctic plant distribution." *Rep. Austr. and N.Z. Assoc. Adv. Sci.*, **27**, 1949.
310. GRABAU, A. W.: *A Textbook of Geology: pt. II—Historical Geology*. Boston, New York and Chicago, 1921.
311. GRAEBNER, P.: *Lehrbuch der allgemeinen Pflanzengeographie*. Auf. 2, Leipzig, 1929.
312. GRAY, A.: ". . . Observations upon the Relationship of the Japanese Flora to that of N. America . . ." *Mem. Amer. Acad. Arts and Sci.* (new ser.), **6**, 1859.
313. GREENMAN, J. M.: "The Age and Area hypothesis with special reference to the flora of tropical America." *American Journal of Botany*, **12**, 1925.
314. GREGORY, H. E.: "Types of Pacific Islands." *Proc. 3rd Pan-Pacific Sci. Congr.*, **2**, 1926.
315. GREGORY, J. W.: "The Geological History of the Atlantic Ocean." *Quart. Journ. Geol. Soc.*, **85**, 1929.
316. GREGORY, J. W.: "The Geological History of the Pacific Ocean." *Quart. Journ. Geol. Soc.*, **86**, 1930.
317. GRIGGS, R. H.: "The ecology of rare plants." *Bull. Torrey Bot. Club*, **67**, 1940.
318. GRISEBACH, A. H. R.: *Die Vegetation der Erde*. Auf. 2, Leipzig, 1884.
319. GUILLAUMIN, A.: "Les Régions floristiques du Pacifique . . ." *Proc. 3rd Pan-Pacific Sci. Congr.*, 1926.
320. GUILLAUMIN, A.: "Les affinités de la flore des Nouvelles Hébrides." *Mém. Soc. Biogéographie*, **4**, 1934.
321. GUILLAUMIN, A.: "Compendium de la Flore Phanerogamique des Nouvelles Hebrides." *Ann. Mus. Colon. Marseille*, **6**, 1947–48.
322. GUILLAUMIN, A.: *Flore analytique et synoptique de la Nouvelle Caledonie*. Paris, 1948.
323. GULICK, A.: "Biological peculiarities of oceanic islands." *Quart. Rev. Biol.*, **7**, 1932.
324. GUPPY, H. B.: *Observations of a Naturalist in the Pacific: I. Vanua Levu*. London, 1903.
325. GUPPY, H. B.: *Observations of a Naturalist in the Pacific: II. Plant Distribution*. London, 1906.
326. GUPPY, H. B.: *Studies in Seeds and Fruits*. London, 1912.
327. GUPPY, H. B.: *Plants, Seeds and Currents in the West Indies and the Azores*. London, 1917.
328. GUPPY, H. B.: "The Island and the Continent." *Journ. of Ecology*, **7**, 1919.
329. GUPPY, H. B.: "Plant Distribution from the Standpoint of an Idealist." *Journ. Linn. Soc. London—Bot.*, **44**, 1917–20.
330. GUTENBERG, B., (ed.): *Internal Constitution of the Earth*. 2nd ed., New York, 1951.
331. GUTHRIE-SMITH, H.: *Tutira: the story of a New Zealand sheep station*. 2nd ed., Edinburgh and London, 1926.
332. HANNIG, E., and WINKLER, H., (ed.): *Die Pflanzenareale*. Jena, 1926→
333. HANSEN, A.: *Die Pflanzendecke der Erde*. Leipzig, 1920.
334. HANSEN, I.: "Die europaiishen Arten der Gattung *Erica* L." *Engl. Bot. Jahrb.*, **75**, 1950–52.
335. HARA, H.: "Contributions to the Study of Variations in the Japanese Plants closely related to those of Europe and North America." *Journ. Fac. Sci. Univ. Tokyo, Sect. iii, Bot.*, **6**, 1952.
336. HARA, H.: "Synopsis of the genus *Chrysosplenium* L. (Saxifragaceae)." *Journ. Fac. Sci. Univ. Tokyo, Sect. lii, Bot.* **7**, 1957.
337. HARA, H.: "An Outline of the Phytogeography of Japan." In Hara and Kanai, *Distribution Maps of Flowering Plants in Japan*, Tokyo, 1958, 1959.
338. HARDY, M. E.: *The Geography of Plants*. Oxford, 1925.

339. HARE, G L.: "The Arborescent Senecios of Kilimanjaro . . ." *Trans. Roy. Soc. Edinb.*, **60**, 1941.

340. HARPER, J. L. (ed.): *The Biology of Weeds: a Symposium of the British Ecological Society.* Oxford, 1960.

341. HARPER, R. M.: "A preliminary list of the endemic flowering plants of Florida." *Quart. Journ. Florida Acad. Sci.*, **11** and **12**, 1949–50.

342. HARRIS, T. M.: "Recent developments in Palaeobotany." *Science Progress*, **37**, 1949.

343. HARTLEY, W.: "The global distribution of the tribes of the Gramineae." *Australian Journ. Agr. Res.*, **1**, 1950.

344. HAUMAN, L.: "Les 'Lobelia' géants des montagnes du Congo Belge." *Mem. Inst. Roy. Colon. Belge, 8e coll.*, **1** and **2**, 1934.

345. HAYEK, A.: *Allgemeine Pflanzengeographie.* Berlin, 1926.

346. HAYWARD, W. R.: *Botanists' Pocket Book.* 18th ed., London, 1926.

347. HEDBERG, O.: "Vegetation Belts of the East African Mountains." *Svensk. Bot. Tid.*, **45**, 1951.

348. HEDBERG, O.: "A Taxonomic Revision of the genus *Sibthorpia* L." *Bot. Notiser*, **108**, 1955.

349. HEDBERG, O.: "Afro-alpine Vascular Plants: a Taxonomic Revision." *Symbolae Bot. Upsaliensis*, **15**, 1957.

350. HEDBERG, O.: "Monograph of the genus *Canarina* L. (Campanulaceae)." *Svensk. Bot. Tid.*, **55**, 1961.

351. HEDLEY, C.: "The Palaeogeographical Relationships of Antarctica." *Proc. Linn. Soc. London*, **124**, 1912.

352. HEDLEY, C.: "On the Relation of the Fauna and Flora of Australia to those of New Zealand." *Natural Science*, **3**, 1893.

353. HEGI, G. (trans. DEANS, W. M.): *Alpine Flowers.* London and Glasgow, 1930.

354. HEILPRIN, A.: *The Distribution of Animals.* London, 1894.

355. HEMSLEY, W. B.: "Report on . . . Insular Floras." *Reports Voyage H.M.S. "Challenger,"* Botany, **1**, London, 1885.

356. HEMSLEY, W. B.: "The Flora of Lord Howe Island." *Annals of Botany*, **10**, 1896.

357. HERBERT, D. A.: "Present day distribution and the geological past." *Victorian Nat.*, **66**, 1950.

358. HESS, H. H.: "Drowned ancient islands of the Pacific basin." *American Journ. Sci.*, **244**, 1946.

359. HILL, A. W.: "The genus *Lilaeopsis:* a Study in Geographical Distribution." *Journ. Linn. Soc. London—Bot.*, **47**, 1925–27.

360. HILL, A. W.: "Antarctica and problems of geographical distribution." *Proc. Intern. Congr. Plant Sciences.* Ithaca, 1929.

361. HOBBS, W. H.: *Fortress Islands of the Pacific.* Ann Arbor, 1945.

362. HØEG, O.A.: "The Present and Past Vegetation of Spitzbergen." *Proc. Linn. Soc. London*, **166**, 1956.

363. HOLDGATE, M.: "Biological Routes between the Southern Continents." *The New Scientist*, 1961.

364. HOLLAND, T. H.: "The Theory of Continental Drift." *Proc. Linn. Soc. London*, **155**, 1942–43.

365. HOLLICK, A.: "The Upper Cretaceous Floras of Alaska." *U.S. Geol. Survey Prof. Papers*, **159**. Washington, 1930.

366. HOLLICK, A.: "The Tertiary Floras of Alaska." *U.S. Geol. Survey Prof. Papers*, **182**. Washington, 1936.

367. HOLMES, A.: *The Age of the Earth.* London, 1939.

368. HOLMES, A.: "A revised estimate of the age of the earth." *Nature*, **159**, 1947.

369. HOLMES, A.: "The Construction of a Geological Time-scale." *Trans. Geol. Soc. Glasgow*, **21**, 1947.

370. HOLTTUM, R. E.: *Plant Life in Malaya.* London, 1954.

371. HOOKER, J. D.: *Introductory Essay to the Flora of New Zealand.* London, 1853.

372. HOOKER, J. D.: *On the Flora of Australia . . . being an introductory essay to the Flora of Tasmania.* London, 1859.

373. HOOKER, J. D.: "Outlines of the Distribution of Arctic Plants." *Trans. Linn. Soc. London*, **23**, 1861.

374. HOOKER, J. D.: "Lecture on Insular Floras." *Gard. Chron.* London, January, 1867.

375. HOOKER, J. D.: *The Student's Flora of the British Islands.* 3rd ed., London, 1884.

376. HOOKER, J. D.: "Sketch of the botany of British India." *Imperial Gazetteer of India*, **1**, Oxford, 1909.

377. HOOKER, J. D., and JACKSON, B. D., etc.: *Index Kewensis.* Oxford, 1895→

378. HOOPER, K. J. TEN, and SCHMIDT, F. H.: "Recent climatic variations in Malaysia." *Nature*, **168**, 1951.

379. HOSOKAWA, T.: "Phytogeographical relationship between the Bonins and the Marianne Islands . . ." *J. Soc. Agric. Taikoku Univ. Taiwan*, **6**, 1934.
380. HOSPERS, J.: "Rock Magnetism and Polar Wandering." *Journ. of Geology*, **63**, 1955.
381. HOWELL, J. T.: "The genus *Scalesia*." *Proc. Californian Acad. Sci.*, **22**, 1941.
382. HU, H. H.: "A comparison of the ligneous floras of China and eastern North America." *Bull. Chinese Bot. Soc.*, **1**, 1935.
383. HUDSON, W. H.: *Far Away and Long Ago*. London and Toronto, 1918.
384. HULTÉN, E.: "On the American component in the flora of Eastern Siberia." *Svensk. Bot. Tid.*, **22**, 1928.
385. HULTÉN, E.: *Outline of the History of Arctic and Boreal Biota during the Quaternary Period*. Stockholm, 1937.
386. HULTÉN, E.: *Atlas over vaxternas utbredning i Norden*. Stockholm, 1950.
387. HULTÉN E.: "The Amphi-Atlantic plants and their Phytogeographical Connections." *K. Svenska Vet. Handl.*, *ser.* 4, **7**, 1958.
388. HULTÉN, E.: "The Circumpolar Plants: vol. I." *K. Svenska Vet. Handl.*, *ser.* 4, **8**, 1962.
389. HUMBERT, H.: "Vegetation des hautes montagnes de Madagascar." *Mém. Soc. Biogéographie*, **2**, 1928.
390. HUMBOLDT, A. VON: *De distributione geographica plantarum*. Paris, 1817.
391. HUMPHREYS, G. N.: "Ruwenzori: flights and further exploration." *Geog. Journ.*, **82**, 1933.
392. HUNTINGTON, E., and VISHER, S. S.: *Climatic Changes*. . . . Yale and London, 1922.
393. HUTCHINSON, A. H.: "Limiting factors in relation to specific ranges of tolerance . . ." *Bot. Gaz.*, **66**, 1918.
394. HUTCHINSON, J.: *The Families of Flowering Plants*. London, 1926 and 1934. 2nd ed., Oxford, 1959.
395. HUTCHINSON, J.: *A botanist in southern Africa*. London, 1946.
396. HUXLEY, J. S.: *Evolution: the . . . synthesis*. London, 1942.
397. HUXLEY, L.: *Life and Letters of Sir J. D. Hooker*. London, 1918.
398. IRMSCHER, E.: "Pflanzenverbreitung und Entwicklung der Kontinente." *Mitt. Inst. allgem. Botanik Hamburg*, **5**, 1922.
399. IRVING, E.: "The Magnetization of the Mesozoic Dolerites of Tasmania." *Papers and Proc. Roy. Soc. Tasmania*, **90**, 1956.
400. IRVING, E.: "Palaeomagnetic and Palaeoclimatological aspects of Polar Wandering." *Geofisica Purae Appl.*, **33**, 1956.
401. IRVING, E., and GREEN, R.: "Polar Movement relative to Australia." *Geophys. Journ.*, **1**, 1958.
402. JACCARD, P.: "Sur le coéfficient générique." *Chronica Botanica*, **6**, 1941.
403. JEANNEL, R.: "Au Seuil de l'Antarctique . . ." *Mus. d'Hist. Nat. Paris Publ.*, no. 5, 1941.
404. JENSEN, I. H.: "The geology of New Caledonia." *Proc. Pan-Pacific Sci. Congr.*, **2**, 1923.
405. JEPSON, W. L.: "Centres of plant endemism in California . . ." *Proc. 6th Intern. Bot. Congr.*, Leiden, **1**, 1936.
406. JEPSON, W. L.: *A Manual of the Flowering Plants of California*. Berkeley and Los Angeles, 1951.
407. JESSEN, K.: "*Rhododendron ponticum* in the Irish inter-glacial flora." *Irish Naturalist's Journ.*, **9**, 1948.
408. JESSEN, K.: "Studies in late Quaternary deposits and flora-history of Ireland." *Proc. Roy. Irish Acad.*, **52B**, 1949.
409. JOHNSON, H.: "Sun, earth and ice ages; methods for criticising suggested causes of the Quaternary cold periods." *Science Progress*, **37**, 1949.
410. JOHNSON, L. A. S.: "A Review of the family Oleaceae." *Cont. N.S.W. Nat. Herb.*, **2**, 1957.
411. JOHNSTON, I. M.: "The Flora of the Revillagigedo Islands." *Proc. Californian Acad. Sci.*, 4 ser., **20**, 1931.
412. JOLY, J.: *The Surface History of the Earth*. Oxford, 1925.
413. JONES, G. N.: "On the number of species of plants." *Scientific Monthly*, **72**, 1951.
414. JONES, W. NEILSON: "Organic soils and epinastic response." *Nature*, **136**, 1935.
415. JOYCE, J. R. F.: "The relationship of the *Scotia* arc to Pangaea." *The Advancement of Science*, **8**, 1951.
416. JUST, T.: "Geology and Plant Distribution." *Ecological Monographs*, **17**, 1947.
417. JUST, T.: "Gymnosperms and the Origin of Angiosperms." *Bot. Gaz.*, **110**, 1948.
418. KANEHIRA, R.: "On the Flora of Micronesia." *Bull. Biogeograph. Soc. Japan*, **5**, 1935.
419. KANEHIRA, R.: "On the phytogeography of Micronesia." *Proc. 6th Pacific Sci. Congr.*, **4**, 1940.
420. KARSTEN, G., and SCHENCK, H., (ed.): *Vegetationsbilder*. Jena, 1903→

421. KAUSIK, S. B.: "The Distribution of the Proteaceae; past and present." *Journ. Indian Bot. Soc.*, **22**, 1943.
422. KEAY, W. R. G.: "Montane Vegetation and Flora of the British Cameroons." *Proc. Linn. Soc. London*, **165**, 1955.
423. KENDREW, W. G.: *Climatology*. 2nd ed., Oxford, 1957.
424. KING, L. C.: "Basic Palaeogeography of Gondwanaland during the late Palaeozoic and Mesozoic eras." *Quart. Journ. Geol. Soc.*, **114**, 1958.
425. KINGDON-WARD, F.: "The geography and botany of Tibet." *Journ. Linn. Soc. London—Bot.*, **50**, 1935–37.
426. KINGDON-WARD, F.: *Burma's Icy Mountains*. London, 1949.
427. KLAGES, K. H. W.: *Ecological Crop Geography*. New York, 1942.
428. KNOWLTON, F. H.: *Plants of the Past*. Princeton, 1927.
429. KOIDZUMI, G.: "The vegetation of Jaluit Island." *Bot. Mag. Tokyo*, **29**, 1915.
430. KOMAROV, V. L., (ed.): *Flora U.R.S.S.* Moscow and Leningrad, 1934→
431. KOPPEN, W. P. and GEIGER, R.: *Handbuch der Klimatologie*, vol. I, pt. A. Berlin, 1930.
432. KOSKIMIZU, T.: "The *Crinum* line in the flora of Japan." *Bot. Mag. Tokyo*, **52**, 1938.
433. KRAUSEL, R.: "Zur Geschichte der Angiospermen." *Bot. Mag. Tokyo*, **69**, 1956.
434. KROEBER, A. L.: "Floral relations among the Galapagos Islands." *Univ. California Publ. Botany*, **6**, 1916.
435. KRYLOV, P.: "Phyto-statistische ubersicht vom alpinen gebiet der Altai." *Bot. Archiv*, **31**, 1931.
436. KRYSHTOFOVICH, A. N.: "Principal features of evolution of the flora of Asia in the Tertiary period." *Proc. 4th Pacific Sci. Congr.*, 1930.
437. LAING, R. M.: "A revised list of the Norfolk Island flora." *Trans. New Zealand Inst.*, **47**, 1915.
438. LAM, H. J.: "Some Remarks on the Genetic Phytogeography of the Malay Archipelago." *Ann. Bot. Gard. Buitenzorg*, **37**, 1927.
439. LAM, H. J.: "The Burseraceae of the Malay Archipelago and Peninsula." *Bull. Jard. Bot. Buitenzorg*, 3 *ser.*, **12**, 1932.
440. LAM, H. J.: "Materials towards a study of the flora of the Island of New Guinea." *Blumea*, **1**, 1934.
441. LAM, H. J.: "On the relation of taxonomy, phylogeny and biogeography." *Blumea*, **3**, 1938.
442. LAM, H. J.: "Contributions to our knowledge of the flora of Celebes. . . ." *Blumea*, **5**, 1945.
443. LAM, H. J.: "Notes on the historical phytogeography of Celebes." *Blumea*, **5**, 1945.
444. LAM, H. J., and VAROSSIEAU, W. W.: "Revision of the Sarcospermaceae." *Blumea*, **3**, 1938.
445. LANG, R.: *Verwitterung und Bodenbildung als Einführung in die Bodenkunde*. Stuttgart, 1920.
446. LANGDON, L. M.: "The comparative morphology of Fagaceae. 1. The genus *Nothofagus*." *Bot. Gaz.*, **108**, 1946–47.
447. LAUTERBACH, C.: "Neuere Ergebnisse der pflanzengeographischen Erforschung Neu-Guineas." *Engl. Bot. Jahrb.*, **45**, Beib. 103, 1911.
448. LAWRENCE, G. H. M.: *Taxonomy of Vascular Plants*. New York, 1951.
449. LAWSON, A. A.: "The origin of endemism in the Angiosperm flora of Australia." *Proc. Linn. Soc. N.S.W.*, **55**, 1930.
450. LEANDRI, J.: "Progrès récents des Recherches Botaniques à Madagascar." *Bull. Soc. Bot. France*, **99**, 1952.
451. LÉEMANN, A. C.: "Contribution a l'étude du *Dichapetalum cymosum* (Hook.) Engl. . . ." *Bull. de la Soc. Bot. de Genève*, 2 *ser.*, **5**, 29, 1936–37.
452. LEMÉE, A.: *Dictionnaire descriptif et synonymique des genres de plantes phanérogames*. Brest, 1929–43→
453. LEVYNS, M. R.: "Some evidence bearing on the past history of the Cape flora." *Trans. Roy. Soc. S. Africa*, **26**, 1938.
454. LEVYNS, M. R.: "Clues to the Past in the Cape Flora of Today." *South African Journ. Sci.*, **49**, 1952.
455. LEVYNS, M. R.: "Some Geographical Features of the family Polygalaceae in Southern Africa." *Trans. Roy. Soc. South Afr.*, **34**, 1955.
456. LEVYNS, M. R.: "The Phytogeography of Members of the Proteaceae in Africa." *Journ. of South Afr. Botany*, **24**, 1958.
457. LEWIS, L. F.: "Variations of Temperature at Oxford, 1815–1934." *Prof. Notes Meteor. Office, London*, **5**, no. 77, 1937.
458. LI, H. L.: "Floristic relationships between Eastern Asia and Eastern North America." *Trans. American Phil. Soc., new ser.*, **42**, 1952.

459. LI, H. L., and KENG, H.: "Phytogeographical affinities of southern Taiwan." *Taiwania*, **1** (2/4), 1950.
460. LIBBY, W. F.: "Radio-carbon dating." *Endeavour*, **13**, 1954.
461. LINNÆUS, C.: *Species Plantarum.* Holmiae, 1753.
462. LIVINGSTON, B. E., and SHREVE, F.: "The Distribution of the Vegetation of the United States . . ." *Carnegie Inst. Washington Publ.*, **284**, 1921.
463. *London Catalogue of British Plants.* 11th ed., London, 1925.
464. LONGWELL, C. R.: "The mobility of Greenland." *American Journ. Sci.*, **242**, 1944.
465. LONGWELL, C. R., and BAILEY WILLIS: "Some thoughts on the evidence for continental drift." *American Journ. Sci.*, **242**, 1944.
466. LOUSLEY, J. E.: "Recent research and additions to the British Flora." *Nature*, **168**, 1951.
467. LOUSLEY, J. E. (ed.).: *The Study of the Distribution of British Plants.* Arbroath and Oxford, 1951.
468. LOUSLEY, J. E. (ed.).: *The Changing Flora of Britain.* Arbroath, 1953.
469. LÖVE, A., and LÖVE, D.: "The Geobotanical significance of polyploidy: I. Polyploidy and Latitude." *Portugaliae Acta Biol., A ser., R. B. Goldschmidt vol.*, 1949.
470. LÖVE, A., and LÖVE, D.: "Arctic Polyploidy." *Proc. Genet. Soc. Canada*, **2**, 1957.
471. LÖVE, A., and LÖVE, D.: "The American element in the Flora of the British Isles." *Bot. Notiser*, **111**, 1958.
472. LYSGAARD, L.: "Recent Climatic Fluctuations." *Nature*, **161**, 1948.
473. MACCAUGHEY, V.: "A Survey of the Hawaiian Land Flora." *Bot. Gaz.*, **64**, 1917.
474. MCLENNAN, E. I.: "*Thismia rodwayi* F. Muell. and its endophyte." *Australian Journ. Bot.*, **6**, 1958.
475. MCLUCKIE, J., and MCKEE, H. S.: *Australian and New Zealand Botany.* Sydney, 1954.
476. MCNAIR, R. B.: "The geographical distribution in North America of poison ivy and allies." *American Journal of Botany*, **12**, 1925.
477. MADAUS, G.: *Deutsche Medizinische Wochenschrift*, H. **26, 27**. Leipzig, 1938.
478. MADAUS, G.: *Madaus Jahresbericht*, **1**, 1937. Radebeul, 1938.
479. MAIRE, R.: "Origine de la Flore des Montagnes de l'Afrique du Nord." *Mém. Soc. Biogéographie*, **2**, 1928.
480. MALTHUS, T. R.: *An Essay on Population.* (*Everyman's Library.*) London, 1927.
481. MANGELSDORF, P. C.: "The origin and evolution of Maize." *Advances in Genetics*, **1**, 1947.
482. MANLEY, G.: "Recent Antarctic discoveries and some speculations thereon." *Quart. Journ. Roy. Meteor. Soc.*, **72**, 1946.
483. MANLEY, G.: "The Range of variation in the British Climate." *Geog. Journ.*, **117**, 1951.
484. MANTON, I.: "The cytological history of Watercress, *Nasturtium officinale* R. Br." *Zeitschr. f. Indukt. Abstam. u. Vererb.*, **69**, 1935.
485. MARIE VICTORIN, Frère: "Le Dynamisme dans la Flore du Québec." *Cont. Lab. Bot. de l'Université de Montréal*, **13**, 1929.
486. MARIE VICTORIN, Frère: "Some Evidence of Evolution in the Flora of North-Eastern America." *Journ. Bot.*, **68**, 1930.
487. MARIE VICTORIN, Frère: "Quelques Resultats Statistiques Nouveaux concernants la Flore Vasculaire de Québec." *Cont. Lab. Bot. de l'Université de Montréal*, **26**, 1935.
488. MARIE VICTORIN, Frère: "Phytogeographical Problems of Eastern Canada." *The American Midland Naturalist*, **19**, 1938.
489. MARKGRAF, F.: "Genetische beziehungen der Mittelmeerflora." *Ber. d. Deutsch. Bot. Ges.*, **52**, 1934.
490. MARLOTH, R.: "Stone-shaped Plants." *Journ. S. African Biol. Soc.*, **6**, 1929.
491. MARSH, G. P.: *The Earth as modified by Human Action.* London and New York, 1874.
492. MASAMUNE, G.: "On the importance of the Osumi Strait as a phytogeographical demarcation line." *Jap. Journ. Bot.*, **24**, 1949.
493. MASON, H. L.: "The Principles of Geographic Distribution as applied to Floral Analysis." *Madrono*, **3**, 1936.
494. MASON, H. L.: "Distribution, history and fossil record of *Ceanothus*." In van Rensselaer and McMinn, *Ceanothus*, a publication of the Santa Barbara Botanic Garden, 1942.
495. MASON, H. L.: "Plant Geography in the Delimitation of Genera." *Chronica Botanica*, **14**, 1953.
496. MASON, H. L.: "Migration and Evolution in Plants." *Madrono*, **12**, 1954.
497. MASON, H. L., and STOUT, P. R.: "The Role of Plant Physiology in Plant Geography." *Annual Review of Plant Physiology*, **5**, 1954.

498. MATHEW, W. D.: "Climate and evolution" (2nd edition). *Spec. Publ. N.Y. Acad. Sci.*, **1**, 1939.
499. MATHIAS, M. E., and CONSTANCE, L.: "The Genus Oreomyrrhis (Umbelliferae) . . ." *Univ. California Publ., Bot.*, **27**, 1955.
500. MATTHEWS, J. R.: "The Distribution of Certain Portions of the British Flora: I." *Annals of Botany*, **37**, 1923.
501. MATTHEWS, J. R.: "The Distribution of Certain Portions of the British Flora: II." *Annals of Botany*, **38**, 1924.
502. MATTHEWS, J. R.: "The Distribution of Certain Portions of the British Flora: III." *Annals of Botany*, **40**, 1926.
503. MATTHEWS, J. R.: "Geographical Relationships of the British Flora." *Journ. of Ecology*, **25**, 1937.
504. MATTHEWS, J. R.: *Origin and Distribution of the British Flora.* London, 1955.
505. MAXIMOV, N. A.: "The Theoretical Significance of Vernalization." *Imp. Bureau of Plant Genetics*, Herbage Publication Series, *Bull*. **16**, Aberystwyth, 1934.
506. MAYR, E.: "Wallace's line in the light of recent zoogeographic studies." *Quart. Rev. Biol.*, **19**, 1944.
507. MAYURANATHAN, P. V.: "The original home of the coconut." *J. Bombay Nat. Hist. Soc.*, **40**, 1938.
508. MEINERTZHAGEN, R.: "Some Biological Problems connected with the Himalaya." *The Ibis*, 1928.
509. MELLISS, J. C.: *St. Helena.* London, 1875.
510. MERRILL, E. D.: "The . . . elements in the Philippine Flora." *Ann. Bot. Gard. Buitenzorg*, 2 *ser.*, 3rd supp., pt. I, 1910.
511. MERRILL, E. D.: "The influence of the Australian flora on the flora of the Philippines . . ." *Proc. Pan-Pacific Sci. Congr.*, **1**, 1923.
512. MERRILL, E. D.: "The correlation of geographical distributions with the geological history of Malaysia." *Proc. Pan-Pacific Sci. Congr.*, **2**, 1923.
513. MERRILL, E. D.: "Bibliography of Polynesian Botany." *B. P. Bishop Mus. Bull.*, **13**, 1924.
514. MERRILL, E. D.: *Plant life of the Pacific world.* New York, 1946.
515. MERRILL, E. D., and WALKER, F. H.: "A botanical bibliography of the islands of the Pacific." *Cont. U.S. Nat. Herb.*, **30**, 1947.
516. MEUSEL, H.: *Vergleichende Arealkunde.* Berlin, 1943.
517. MEYEN, F. J. F. (trans. JOHNSTON, M.): *Outlines of the Geography of Plants.* London, 1846.
518. MILL, H. R., (ed.): *The International Geography.* 3rd ed. London, 1903.
519. MILLER, A. A.: "Climatic requirements of some major vegetational formations." *The Advancement of Science*, **7**, 1950.
520. MILLSPAUGH, C. F.: "Flora of the Alacran Reef." *Publ. Field Mus. Bot.*, **2**, 1916.
521. MILNE-REDHEAD, E.: "Distributional Ranges of Flowering Plants in Tropical Africa." *Proc. Linn. Soc. London*, **165**, 1954.
522. MOLINIER, R., and MÜLLER, P.: "La Dissemination des Espéces Vegetales." *Rev. Gén. Bot.*, **50**, 1938.
523. MOLISCH, H.: "Über der Einfluss einer Pflanze auf die andere . . ." *Anz. Akad. d. wiss. Wien*, **74**, 1937.
524. MOORE, D. M.: "Chromosome numbers of Flowering Plants from Macquarie Island." *Bot. Notiser*, **113**, 1960.
525. MOREAU, R. E.: "Africa since the Mesozoic: with particular reference to certain biological problems." *Proc. Zool. Soc. London*, **121**, 1952.
526. MOREAU, R. E.: "Ecological Changes in the Palaeoarctic Region since the Pliocene." *Proc. Zool. Soc. London*, **125**, 1955.
527. MÜLLER, P.: "Verbreitungsbiologie der Blutenpflanzen." *Veroff. Geobot. Inst. Rubel Zurich*, **30**, 1955.
528. MUNTZING, A.: "The evolutionary significance of autopolyploidy." *Hereditas*, **21**, 1936.
529. MUNZ, P. A.: "A revision of the genus *Fuchsia*." *Proc. Californian Acad. Sci.*, 3 *ser.*, **25**, 1943.
530. MUNZ, P. A., and KECK, D. D.: *A Californian Flora.* Berkeley and Los Angeles, 1959.
531. MURNEEK, A. E., WHYTE, R. O., and others: *Vernalization and photoperiodism: a symposium.* Waltham, Mass., 1948.
532. MURRAY, J.: "On the Height of the Land and the Depth of the Ocean." *Scot. Geog. Mag.*, **4**, 1888.
533. NAIRN, E. A. M.: "Relevance of Palaeomagnetic Studies of Jurassic Rocks to Continental Drift." *Nature*, **178**, 1956.

534. NAIRN, E. A. M.: "Palaeomagnetic Results from Europe." *Journ. of Geol.*, **68**, 1960.
535. NAIRN, E. A. M., (ed.): *Descriptive Palaeoclimatology*. New York and London, 1961.
536. NEL, G. C.: *Lithops*. Stellenbosch, 1946.
537. NICHOLSON, R. J.: "A note on hollow curves." *New Phytologist*, **50**, 1951.
538. NOVAK, F. A.: "Quelques remarques. . . ." *Preslia*, **6**, 1928.
539. OLIVER, W. R. B.: "The Vegetation of the Kermadec Islands." *Trans. New Zealand Inst.*, **42**, 1909–10.
540. OLIVER, W. R. B.: "Biogeographical Relations of the New Zealand Region." *Journ. Linn. Soc. London—Bot.*, **47**, 1925–27.
541. OLIVER, W. R. B.: "The Genus *Coprosma*." *B. P. Bishop Mus. Bull.*, **132**, 1935.
542. OLIVER, W. R. B.: "The Plants of New Zealand." *New Zealand Official Year-book*, 1936.
543. OLIVER, W. R. B.: "The genus *Coriaria* in New Zealand." *Rec. of the Dominion Mus.*, **1**, 1942.
544. OLIVER, W. R. B.: "The flora of the Three Kings Islands." *Rec. Auckland Inst. Mus.*, **3**, 1948.
545. OPDYKE, N. D., and RUNCORN, S. K.: "Wind Direction in the western U.S.A. in the late Palaeozoic." *Bull. Geol. Soc. America*, **71**, 1960.
546. OSBORN, F., (ed.): *The Pacific World*. London, 1945.
547. OSTENFELD, C. H.: "The Present State of Knowledge on Hybrids between Species of Flowering Plants." *Journ. Roy. Hort. Soc.*, **53**, 1928.
548. OSTENFELD, C. H.: "On the origin of the flora of Greenland." *Proc. Intern. Congr. Plant Sciences*. Ithaca, 1929.
549. OSVALD, H.: "Equipment of plants in the struggle for space." *Vaxtodlung (Plant Husbandry)*, **2**, 1947.
550. PALMGREN, A.: "Die Artenzahl als Pflanzengeographische Charakter." *Acta Bot. Fennica*, **1**, 1925.
551. PEARSON, G. A.: "Factors Controlling the Distribution of Forest Types." *Ecology*, **1**, 1920.
552. PENCK, A., and BRÜCKNER, E.: *Die Alpen im Eiszeitalter*. Leipzig, 1901–9.
553. PERRIER DE LA BATHIE, H.: "Au sujet de la distribution géographique des Chlaenacées." *Bull. Soc. Bot. France*, **67**, 1920.
554. PERRIER DE LA BATHIE, H.: *Biogéographie des Plantes de Madagascar*. Paris, 1936.
555. PERRING, F. H., and WALTERS, S. M., (ed.): *Atlas of the British Flora*. London and Edinburgh, 1962.
556. PETTERSSON, H.: "The chronology of the ocean floor." *The Advancement of Science*, **7**, 1950.
557. PHILLIPS, E. P.: "The Genera of South African Flowering Plants." *Bot. Survey South Africa Mem.*, **10**, 1926. 2 ed., *Mem.*, **25**, 1951.
558. PICHI-SERMOLLI, R. E. G., "Flore e vegtazione delle serpentine . . . valle de Tevere (Toscana)." *Webbia*, **6**, 1948.
559. PICKERING, S.: "The effect of grass on apple trees." *Journ. Agric. Sci.*, **6**, 1914.
560. PIGOTT, C. D., and WALTERS, S. M.: "On the Interpretation of the Discontinuous Distribution shown by British species of open habitats." *Journ. of Ecology*, **42**, 1954.
561. PILLANS, N. S.: "The genus *Phylica* Linn." *Journ. of South Afr. Botany*, **8**, 1942.
562. POLE-EVANS, I. B.: "The Vegetation of South Africa" in *South Africa and Science*. Johannesburg, 1929.
563. POLUNIN, N.: "Botany of the Canadian Eastern Arctic: pt. III." *Nat. Mus. Canada Bull.*, **104**, 1948.
564. POLUNIN, N.: "The real Arctic: suggestions for its delimitation, subdivision and characterization." *Journ. of Ecology*, **39**, 1952.
565. POLUNIN, N.: *Circumpolar Flora*. Oxford, 1959.
566. POLUNIN, N.: *Introduction to Plant Geography and some Related Sciences*. London, 1960.
567. POPOV, G. B.: "The Vegetation of Socotra." *Journ. Linn. Soc. London, Bot.*, **55**, 1957.
568. PORSILD, A. E.: "Plant life in the Arctic." *Canadian Geog. Journ.*, March, 1951.
569. POST, L. VON: "The prospect of pollen analysis in the study of the earth's climatic history." *New Phytologist*, **45**, 1946.
570. PRAEGER, R. LL.: "Irish Topographical Botany." *Proc. Roy. Irish Acad.*, 3 ser., **7**, 1901 and supp.
571. PRAEGER, R. LL.: "The Canarian *Sempervivum*-flora . . ." *Journ. Bot.*, **66**, 1928.
572. PRAEGER, R. LL.: "Recent views bearing on the problem of the Irish flora and fauna." *Proc. Roy. Irish Acad.*, **41B**, 1932.
573. PRAEGER, R. LL.: *The Botanist in Ireland*. Dublin, 1934.
574. PRAEGER, R. LL.: "Recent Advances in Irish Field Botany." *Journ. Bot.*, **73**, 1935.
575. PRAEGER, R. LL.: "The relations of the Flora and Fauna of Ireland to those of other countries." *Proc. Linn. Soc. London*, **151**, 1938–39.

576. PRAIN, D., and BURKILL, I. H.: "An account of the genus *Dioscorea* in the East." *Ann. Roy. Bot. Gard. Calcutta*, **14**, 1936–39.
577. RAISTRICK, A.: "The Glacial Maximum and Retreat." *Trans. Northern Nat. Union*, **1**, pt. I, 1931.
578. RAO, C. V.: "Cytotaxonomy of the Proteaceae." *Proc. Linn. Soc. N.S.W.*, **82**, 1957.
579. RASTALL, R. H.: "On Continental Drift and Cognate Subjects." *Geol. Magazine*, **66**, 1929.
580. RASTALL, R. H.: "Palaeozoic, Mesozoic and Kainozoic: a geological disaster." *Geol. Magazine*, **81**, 1944.
581. RAUNKIAER, C. (ed. TANSLEY, A. G.): *The Life Forms of Plants and Statistical Plant Geography*. Oxford, 1934.
582. RAUP, H. M.: "Botanical Problems of Boreal America." *Bot. Review*, **7**, 1941.
583. RAUP, H. M.: "Some natural floristic areas in boreal America." *Ecological Monographs*, **17**, 1947.
584. REID, C.: *The Origin of the British Flora*. London, 1899.
585. REID, C.: *Submerged Forests*. Cambridge, 1913.
586. REID, C.: "The Plants of the late Glacial deposits of the Lea Valley." *Quart. Journ. Geol. Soc.*, **71**, 1915.
587. REID, C., and REID, E. M.: "The Pre-glacial Flora of Britain." *Journ. Linn. Soc. London— Bot.*, **38**, 1908.
588. REID, E. M.: "A Comparative Review of Pliocene Floras . . ." *Quart Journ. Geol. Soc.*, **76**, 1920.
589. REID, E. M.: "The late glacial flora of the Lea Valley." *New Phytologist*, **48**, 1949.
590. REID, E. M., and CHANDLER, M. E. J.: *Catalogue of Cainozoic Plants: The Bembridge Flora*. London, 1926.
591. REID, E. M., and CHANDLER, M. E. J.: "Palaeobotany." *Encyclopaedia Britannica*. 14th ed., London and New York, 1929.
592. REID, E. M., and CHANDLER, M. E. J.: *The London Clay Flora*. London, 1933.
593. RIDLEY, H. N.: "Some notes on the acclimatisation of plants." *Agr. Bull. Str. and Fed. Mal. States*, **6** and **7**, 1907–08.
594. RIDLEY, H. N.: "On Endemism and the Mutation Theory." *Annals of Botany*, **30**, 1916.
595. RIDLEY, H. N.: "The Distribution of Plants." *Annals of Botany*, **37**, 1923.
596. RIDLEY, H. N.: *The Dispersal of Plants throughout the World*. Ashford, 1930.
597. RIVALS, P.: "*Études sur la Végétation Naturelle de l'Île de la Réunion*." Toulouse, 1952.
598. ROBYNS, W.: "Considérations sur . . . des feux de brousse . . ." *Bull. Inst. Roy. Colonial Belge*, **9**, 1938.
599. ROBYNS, W.: "Statistiques de nos connaissances sur les Spermatophytes du Congo Belge et du Ruanda-Urundi." *Bull. Jard. Bot. de l'Etat*, Brussels, **18**, 1946.
600. ROCK, J. F.: "Vegetation der Hawaii-Inseln." *Engl. Bot. Jahrb.*, **53**, 1915.
601. RODWAY, L.: "The endemic Phanerogams of Tasmania." *Proc. Pan-Pacific Sci. Congr.*, **1**, 1923.
602. ROGER, J. G.: "*Diapensia lapponica* L. in Scotland." *Trans. and Proc. Bot. Soc. Edinb.*, **36**, 1952.
603. ROSA, D.: *L'Ologénèse*. Paris, 1931.
604. ROTHMALER, W.: *Allgemeine Taxonomie und Chorologie der Pflanzen*. Jena, 1950.
605. RÜBEL, E.: "Ecology, plant geography and geobotany, their history and aim." *Bot. Gaz.*, **84**, 1927.
606. RUNCORN, S. K.: "The Permanent Magnetization of Rocks." *Endeavour*, **14**, 1955.
607. RUNCORN, S. K.: "Palaeomagnetic Comparisons between Europe and North America." *Proc. Geol. Assoc. Canada*, **8**, 1956.
608. RUNCORN, S. K.: "Palaeomagnetism, Polar Wandering and Continental Drift." *Geologie en Mijnbouw*, n.s. **18**, 1956.
609. RUNCORN, S. K.: "Towards a Theory of Continental Drift." *Nature*, **193**, 1962.
610. RUNE, O.: "Plant life on serpentines and related rocks in the north of Sweden." *Acta Phytogeographica Suecica*, **31**, 1953.
611. RUSSELL, R. J.: "Climatic change through the Ages." *U.S. Dept. Agric. Yearbook*, Washington, 1941.
612. SAHNI, B.: "Wegener's theory . . . in the light of palaeobotanical evidence." *Journ. Indian Bot. Soc.*, **15**, 1936.
613. SAHNI, B.: "Revolutions in the Plant World." *Pres. Address, Bot. Sec., Indian Science Congr.*, 1938.

614. SALISBURY, E. J.: "The Geographical Distribution of Plants in Relation to Climatic Factors." *Geog. Journ.*, **67**, 1926.
615. SALISBURY, E. J.: "East Anglian Flora." *Trans. Norfolk and Norwich Nat. Soc.*, **13**, 1931–32.
616. SALISBURY, Sir E. J.: *Weeds and Aliens.* London, 1961.
617. SARASIN, F., and ROUX, J.: *Nova Caledonia, vol.* 1, *Botany* 3. Berlin and Wiesbaden, 1921.
618. SCHIMPER, A. F. W.: *Die Indo-Malayische strandflora.* Jena, 1891.
619. SCHIMPER, A. F. W. (trans. FISHER, W. R.): *Plant Geography upon a Physiological Basis.* Oxford, 1903–4.
620. SCHIMPER, A. F. W., and FABER, F. C. VON: *Pflanzen-Geographie auf physiologischer Grundlage.* Auf. 3, Jena, 1935.
621. SCHLECHTER, R.: "Pflanzengeographische Gliederung der Insel Neu-Caledonien." *Engl. Bot. Jahrb.*, **36**, 1905.
622. SCHONLAND, S.: "On the Theory of Age and Area." *Annals of Botany*, **38**, 1924.
623. SCHOUW, J. F.: *Grundzüge einer allgemeinen Pflanzengeographie.* Berlin, 1823.
624. SCHOVE, D. J.: "The Climatic Fluctuation since A.D. 1850 in Europe and the Atlantic." *Quart. Journ. Roy. Meteor. Soc.*, **76**, 1950.
625. SCHROETER, C.: *Genetische Pflanzengeographie.* Auf. 2, Jena, 1934.
626. SCHUBERT, C.: "Gondwana land bridges." *Bull. Geol. Soc. America*, **43**, 1932.
627. SEALY, J. R.: "*Arbutus unedo*." *Journ. of Ecology*, **37**, 1949.
628. SEARS, P. B.: "Glacial and Postglacial Vegetation." *Bot. Review*, **1**, 1935.
629. SEIN, K. M.: "*Nothofagus* pollen in the London Clay." *Nature*, **190**, 1961.
630. SELLING, O. H.: "On the late Quaternary history of the Hawaiian vegetation." *B. P. Bishop Mus. Spec. Publ.*, **39**, 1948.
631. SENN, H. A.: "Chromosome number and relationship in the Leguminosae." *Bibliographia Genetica*, **12**, 1938.
632. SETCHELL, W. A.: "Geographical distribution of the marine spermatophytes." *Bull. Torrey Bot. Club*, **47**, 1920.
633. SETCHELL, W. A.: "Phytogeographical notes on Tahiti, I." *Univ. California Publ. Botany*, **12**, 1926.
634. SETCHELL, W. A.: "Migration and endemism with reference to Pacific Insular floras." *Proc. 3rd Pan-Pacific Sci. Congr.*, **1**, 1926.
635. SETCHELL, W. A.: "Pacific insular floras and Pacific palaeogeography." *American Naturalist*, **69**, 1935.
636. SEWARD, A. C.: "Arctic Vegetation; past and present." *Journ. Roy. Hort. Soc.*, **50**, 1925.
637. SEWARD, A. C.: "The Cretaceous plant-bearing rocks of western Greenland." *Phil. Trans. Roy. Soc. London*, **215**, 1926.
638. SEWARD, A. C.: "Greenland: as it is and as it was." *Nature*, **123**, 1929.
639. SEWARD, A. C.: *Plants: what they are and what they do.* Cambridge, 1932.
640. SEWARD, A. C.: *Plant Life through the Ages.* 2nd ed., Cambridge, 1933.
641. SEWARD, A. C.: "An Extinct Malayan Flora in England." *Science Progress*, 1934.
642. SEWARD, A. C., and CONWAY, V.: "A Phytogeographical Problem: Fossil Plants from the Kerguelen Archipelago." *Annals of Botany*, **48**, 1934.
643. SEYMOUR SEWELL, R. B.: "The Continental Drift Theory and the Distribution of the Copepods." *Proc. Linn. Soc. London*, **166**, 1956.
644. SHAPLEY, H., (ed.): *Climatic Change.* Cambridge, Mass., 1953.
645. SHARP, A. J.: "Relationships between the floras of California and South-eastern United States." *Cont. Dudley Herb.*, Stanford, **4**, 1951.
646. SHEPARD, F. P.: *Submarine Geology.* New York, 1948.
647. SHREVE, F.: "The Rôle of Winter Temperature in determining the Distribution of Plants." *American Journal of Botany*, **1**, 1914.
648. SHULL, A. E.: "Toxicity of root excretions." *Plant Phys.*, **7**, 1932.
649. SIMPSON, G.: "A revision of the genus *Carmichaelia*." *Trans. and Proc. Roy. Soc. New Zealand*, **75**, 1945.
650. SIMPSON, G. C.: "Past Climates." *Quart. Journ. Roy. Met. Soc.*, **53**, 1927.
651. SIMPSON, G. C.: "Possible Causes of Change of Climate and their Limitations." *Proc. Linn. Soc. London*, **152**, 1939–40.
652. SIMPSON, J. B.: "Fossil pollen in Scottish Jurassic coal." *Nature*, **139**, 1937.
653. SIMPSON, J. B.: "The Tertiary pollen Flora of Mull and Ardnamurchan." *Trans. Roy. Soc. Edinburgh*, **64**, 1960–61.
654. SINNOTT, E. W.: "Comparative rapidity of evolution in various plant types." *American Naturalist*, **50**, 1916.

655. SINNOTT, E. W.: "The 'Age and Area' Hypothesis and the Problem of Endemism." *Annals of Botany*, **31**, 1917.
656. SINNOTT, E. W.: "Age and Area and the history of species." *American Journal of Botany*, **11**, 1924.
657. SKOTTSBERG, C.: "A Botanical Survey of the Falkland Islands." *Kungl. Svenska Vet. Handl.*, **50**, 1913.
658. SKOTTSBERG, C.: *The Natural History of Juan Fernandez and Easter Island*, **2**. Upsala, 1922.
659. SKOTTSBERG, C.: "Juan Fernandez and Hawaii." *B. P. Bishop Mus. Bull.*, **16**, 1925.
660. SKOTTSBERG, C.: "Remarks on the Relative Interdependency of Pacific Floras." *Proc. 3rd Pan-Pacific Sci. Congr.*, 1926.
661. SKOTTSBERG, C.: "On some arborescent species of *Lobelia* from Tropical Asia." *Medd. Göteborgs Bot. Trädgård*, **4**, 1928.
662. SKOTTSBERG, C.: "The Flora of the high Hawaiian Volcanoes." *Medd. Göteborgs Bot. Trädgård*, **6**, 1930.
663. SKOTTSBERG, C.: "Zur pflanzengeographie Patagoniens." *Ber. d. Deutsch. Bot. Ges.*, **49**, 1931.
664. SKOTTSBERG, C.: "Studies in the genus *Astelia* Banks et Solander." *Kungl. Svenska Vet. Handl.*, 3 ser., **14**, 1934.
665. SKOTTSBERG, C.: "Le peuplement des îles pacifiques du Chili." *Mem. Soc. Biogéographie*, **4**, 1934.
666. SKOTTSBERG, C.: "Antarctic Plants in Polynesia." *Essays in Geobotany in Honor of W. A. Setchell*, 1936.
667. SKOTTSBERG, C.: "Flora of the Desventuradas Islands." *Göteborgs Kungl. Vetensk. Vitterh. Samhalles Handl.*, ser. B, **5**, 1937.
668. SKOTTSBERG, C.: "Geographical isolation as a factor in species formation . . ." *Proc. Linn. Soc. London*, **150**, 1937–38.
669. SKOTTSBERG, C.: "Remarks on the Hawaiian Flora." *Proc. Linn. Soc. London*, **151**, 1938–39.
670. SKOTTSBERG, C.: "Nagra drag av den antarktiska kontinentens biologiska historia." *K. Norske Vid. Selsk. Skr.*, **12**, 1940.
671. SKOTTSBERG, C.: "Weitere Beiträge zur flora der Insel San Ambrosio. . . ." *Arkiv för Botanik*, new ser., **1**, 1952.
672. SLEDGE, W. A.: "The distribution and ecology of *Scheuchzeria palustris* L." *Watsonia*, **1**, 1949.
673. SLEUMER, H.: "Rev. der Gattung *Pernettya*." *Notizbl. Bot. Gart. Berlin*, **12**, 1935.
674. SLEUMER, H.: "Proteaceae americanae." *Engl. Bot. Jahrb.*, **76**, 1954.
675. SLOOTEN, D. F. VAN: "The Stylidiaceae of the Netherlands Indies." *Bull. Jard. Bot. Buitenzorg*, 3 ser., **14**, 1936.
676. SMIT SIBINGA, G. L.: "The Malay double (triple) orogen, i, ii, iii." *Proc. Kon. A. K. Wet.*, **36**, 1933.
677. SMITH, A. C.: "Geographical distribution of the Winteraceae." *Journ. Arnold Arbor.*, **26**, 1945.
678. SMITH, A. C.: "The families Illiciaceae and Schisandraceae." *Sargentia*, **7**, 1947.
679. SMITH, A. C.: "Studies of Pacific Island plants, VII. Further notes on Fijian flowering plants." *Journ. Arnold Arbor.*, **31**, 1950.
680. SMITH, A. C.: "The Vegetation and Flora of Fiji." *The Scientific Monthly*, **73**, 1951.
681. SMITH, A. C.: "Studies of Pacific Island Plants, XV. The genus *Elaeocarpus* in the New Hebrides, Fiji, Samoa and Tonga." *Cont. U.S. Nat. Herb.*, **30**, 1953.
682. SMITH, A. C.: "Phanerogam genera with Distributions terminating in Fiji." *Journ. Arnold Arbor.*, **36**, 1955.
683. SMITH, C. M.: "Changed and Changing Vegetation." In *Science in New Zealand*, Wellington, 1957.
684. SMITH, L. B.: "Geographical evidence on the lines of evolution in the Bromeliaceae." *Engl. Bot. Jahrb.*, **66**, 1934.
685. SOLMS-LAUBACH, H. von: *Die leitenden Gesichtspunkte einer allgemeinen Pflanzengeographie . . .* Leipzig, 1905.
686. SØRENSEN, T.: "Summary of botanical investigations in N.E. Greenland." *Medd. om Grønland*, **144**, 1945.
687. SPRAGUE, T. A.: "Some aspects of organic evolution." *Proc. Cotteswold Nat. Field Club*, **29**, 1948.
688. ST. JOHN, H.: "Endemism in the Hawaiian flora . . ." *Proc. Californian Acad. Sci.*, **25**, 1946.
689. ST. JOHN, H.: "Sandalwood in Oahu, Hawaiian Islands." *Pacific Science*, **1**, 1947.

690. St. John, H.: "The Distribution of *Pisonia grandis* (Nyctaginaceae)". *Webbia*, **8**, 1951.
691. St. John, H., and Hosaka, E. Y.: "Notes on Hawaiian species of *Lobelia*." *B. P. Bishop Mus. Occ. Papers*, **14**, 1938.
692. Stapf, O.: "The Southern Element in the British Flora." *Engl. Bot. Jahrb.*, **50**, *Supp.*, 1914.
693. Stapf, O.: "A cartographic study of the southern element in the British flora." *Proc. Linn. Soc. London*, **129**, 1916–17.
694. Stauffer, H. U.: "Revisio Anthobolearum." *Mitt. Bot. Mus. Univ. Zurich*, **213**, 1959.
695. Stearn, W. T.: "*Epimedium* and *Vancouveria* (Berberidaceae), a monograph." *Journ. Linn. Soc. London—Bot.*, **51**, 1938.
696. Stearn, W. T.: "The floristic regions of the U.S.S.R. with reference to the genus *Allium*." *Herbertia*, **11** (1944), 1946.
697. Stebbins, G. L., junr.: "The significance of polyploidy in plant evolution." *American Naturalist*, **74**, 1940.
698. Stebbins, G. L., junr.: *Variation and Evolution in Plants*. London, 1950.
699. Steenis, C. G. G. J. van: *Malayan Bignoniaceae*. Amsterdam, 1927.
700. Steenis, C. G. G. J. van: "On the Origin of the Malaysian Mountain Flora." *Bull. Bot. Gard. Buitenzorg*, 3 *ser.*, **13–14**, 1934–36.
701. Steenis, C. G. G. J. van: "A new botanical hypothesis on the origin of deserts." *Bull. Jard. Bot. Buitenzorg*, 3 *ser.*, **14**, 1936.
702. Steenis, C. G. G. J. van, (ed.): *Flora Malesiana*. Batavia and Djakarta, 1948→
703. Steenis, C. G. G. J. van: "Preliminary account of Papuan *Nothofagus*." *Blumea*, **7**, 1952.
704. Steenis, C. G. G. J. van: "Papuan *Nothofagus*." *Journ. Arnold Arbor.*, **34**, 1953.
705. Steenis, C. G. G. J. van: "Additional Notes on *Nothofagus*." *Journ. Arnold Arbor.*, **35**, 1954.
706. Stefanoff, B.: "Researches . . . relic distribution of plants." *Spiss. Bulgar. Acad. Nauk.*, **53**, 1936.
707. Steffen, H.: "Ueber die floristischen beziehungen der beiden Polargebiete zuneinander." *Beih. Bot. centralbl.*, **59b**, 1939.
708. Stern, F. C.: *A Study of the genus Paeonia*. London, 1946.
709. Stewart, A.: "A Botanical Survey of the Galapagos Islands." *Proc. Californian Acad. Sci.*, 4 *ser.*, **1**, 1911.
710. Stojanoff, N.: "Versuch . . . relikten elements . . . Balkan halbinsel." *Engl. Bot. Jahrb.*, **63**, 1930.
711. Stomps, J. T.: "A Contribution to our Knowledge of the British Flora." *Rec. Trav. Bot. Néerlandais*, **20**, 1923.
712. Summerhayes, V. S.: "An enumeration of the Angiosperms of the Seychelles Archipelago." *Trans. Linn. Soc. London*, **19**, 1931.
713. Summerhayes, V. S.: *The Wild Orchids of Britain*. London, 1951.
714. Supan, A.: *Grundzuge der Physiche Erdkunde*. Auf. 7, Leipzig, 1927–30.
715. Svenson, H. K.: "Vegetation of the coast of Ecuador and Peru and its relation to the Galapagos Islands." *American Journ. of Botany*, **33**, 1946.
716. Szymkiewicz, D.: "Contributions statistiques a la Géographie floristique." *Acta Soc. Bot. Polon.*, **11–15**, 1934–38.
717. Takhtajan, A. L.: "On the Origin of the Temperate Flora of Eurasia." *Botanical Journal U.S.S.R.*, **42**, 1957.
718. Tansley, A. G.: *The British Islands and their Vegetation*. 2nd ed., Cambridge, 1950.
719. Tate, G. H. H.: "Notes on the Mt. Roraima region." *Geog. Review*, **20**, 1930.
720. Tate, G. H. H., and Hitchcock, C. B.: "The Cerro Duida region of Venezuela." *Geog. Review*, **20**, 1930.
721. Taylor, B. W.: "An Example of Long-distance Dispersal." *Ecology*, **35**, 1954.
722. Taylor, B. W.: "The Flora, Vegetation and Soils of Macquarie Island." *Australian Nat. Antarctic Res. Exped. Rep.*, B, **2**, 1955.
723. Taylor, G.: *An Account of the genus Meconopsis*. London, 1934.
724. Taylor, G.: "The British Museum Expedition to the Mountains of East Africa." *Proc. Linn. Soc. London*, **149**, 1936–37.
725. Taylor, G.: "Some observations on British Potamogetons." *The South-eastern Nat. and Antiquary*, **54**, 1949.
726. Taylor, N.: "A quantitative study of Raunkiaer's growth forms . . . species of Long Island, N.Y." *Brooklyn Bot. Gard. Mem.*, **1**, 1918.
727. Taylor, N.: "Endemism in the Bahama Flora." *Annals of Botany*, **35**, 1921.
728. Taylor, W. R.: *Plants of Bikini and other northern Marshall Islands*. Ann Arbor, 1950.

729. THACKER, A. G.: "Some statistical aspects of geographical distribution." *Biol. Rev. Camb. Phil. Soc.*, **1**, 1923–25.
730. THISELTON-DYER, W. T.: "Plants: distribution." *Encyclopaedia Britannica.* 11th ed., London, 1910–11.
731. THODAY, D.: "The Geographical Distribution and Ecology of the genus *Passerina.*" *Annals of Botany*, **39**, 1925.
732. THOMAS, H. H.: "Palaeobotany and the origin of the Angiosperms." *Bot. Review*, **2**, 1936.
733. THOMSON, G. M.: *The Naturalization of Animals and Plants in New Zealand.* Cambridge, 1922.
734. THONNER, F.: *Die Blütenpflanzen Afrikas.* Berlin, 1908.
735. THORNTHWAITE, C. W.: "The climates of the earth." *Geog. Review*, **23**, 1933.
736. TISCHLER, G.: "Die Bedeutung der Polyploidie für die Verbreitung der Angiospermen." *Engl. Bot. Jahrb.*, **67**, 1935.
737. TURNAGE, W. V., and HINCKLEY, A. L.: "Freezing weather in relation to plant distribution in the Sonoran desert." *Ecological Monographs*, **8**, 1938.
738. TURRILL, W. B.: *The Plant Life of the Balkan Peninsula.* London, 1929.
739. TURRILL, W. B., etc.: "A Discussion on the Present State of the Theory of Natural Selection." *Proc. Roy. Soc. London, B*, **121**, 1937.
740. TURRILL, W. B.: "The principles of plant geography." *Kew Bull.*, 1939.
741. TURRILL, W. B.: "On the Flora of St. Helena." *Kew Bull.*, 1948.
742. TURRILL, W. B.: "Pioneer Plant Geography: the Phytogeographical Researches of Sir Joseph Dalton Hooker." *Lotsya*, **4**, The Hague, 1953.
743. TUTIN, T. G.: "A note on species pairs in the Gramineae." *Watsonia*, **1**, 1950.
744. TUYAMA, T.: "Outline of the genus *Haloragis* . . ." *Jap. Journ. Bot.*, **16**, 1940.
745. UMBGROVE, J. H. F.: *The Pulse of the Earth.* 2nd ed., The Hague, 1947.
746. VALENTIN, H.: "Present Vertical Movements in the British Isles." *Geogr. Journ.*, **119**, 1953.
747. VARMA, S. C.: "On the nature of competition between plants in the early phases of their development." *Annals of Botany*, N.S., **2**, 1938.
748. VAVILOV, N. I.: "The Problem of the Origin of the World's Agriculture . . ." *Science at the Cross Roads.* London, 1931.
749. VERDOORN, F., (ed.): *Plants and Plant Science in Latin America.* Chronica Botanica, Waltham, Mass., 1945.
750. VESTER, H.: "Die areale und arealtypen der Angiospermen-familien." *Bot. Archiv*,. **41**, 1940.
751. VIROT, R.: "La Végétation canaque." *Mem. Mus. Nat. d'Hist. Nat.*, ser. *B*, **7**, 1956.
752. WACE, N. M.: "The Botany of the Southern Oceanic Islands." *Proc. Roy. Soc., B*, **152**, 1960.
753. WACE, N. M.: "The Vegetation of Gough Island." *Ecological Monographs*, **31**, 1961.
754. WACE, N. M., and HOLDGATE, M. W.: "The Vegetation of Tristan da Cunha." *Journ. of Ecology*, **46**, 1958.
755. WALLACE, A. R.: *The Malay Archipelago.* 3rd ed., London, 1872.
756. WALLACE, A. R.: *Island Life* . . . 2nd ed., London, 1892.
757. WALTER, H.: *Allgemeine Pflanzengeographie Deutschlands.* Jena, 1927.
758. WALTON, J.: *An Introduction to the Study of Fossil Plants.* 2nd ed., London, 1953.
759. WANGERIN, W.: "Florenelemente und Arealtypen (Beitrage zur Arealgeographie der deutschen Flora)." *Beih. Bot. Centralbl.*, **49** (Enganzungsband), 1932.
760. WATSON, H. C.: *Outlines of the geographical distribution of British Plants.* Edinburgh, 1832.
761. WATSON, H. C.: *Remarks on the geographical distribution of British Plants.* London, 1835.
762. WATSON, H. C.: *Cybele Britannica, and Compendium.* London, 1847–70.
763. WATSON, H. C.: *Topographical Botany.* 2nd ed. and supplements, London, 1883→
764. WATSON, L. "A peculiar Ericalean pollen grain." *Nature*, **194**, 1962.
765. WEBB, D. A.: "Hybridization and variation in the Robertsonian Saxifrages." *Proc. Roy. Irish Acad.* **53B**, 1950.
766. WEBB, D. A.: "The Biological flora of the British Isles: *Saxifraga* L." *Journ. of Ecology*, **38**, 1950.
767. WEGENER, A. (trans. SKERL, J. G. A.): *The Origin of Continents and Oceans.* London, 1924.
768. WEIMARCK, H.: *Monograph of the genus Clifortia.* Lund, 1934.
769. WEIMARCK, H.: "Monograph of the genus *Aristea.*" *Lund. Univ. Arrsk.*, N.F., 2 ser., **36**, 1940.
770. WEIMARCK, H.: "Phytogeographical groups . . . within the Cape flora." *Kungl. Fysiograf. Sältskapets Handl.*, N.F., **52**, 1941.
771. WEIMARCK, H.: "Studies in Juncaceae . . ." *Svensk. Bot. Tid.*, **40**, 1946.
772. WHITE, A., and SLOANE, B. L.: *The Stapelieae.* 2nd ed., Pasadena, 1937.
773. WHITE, O. E.: "Geographical Distribution and the cold-resisting characters . . ." *Brooklyn Bot. Gard. Rec.*, **15**, 1926.

774. WHITE, O. E.: "Mutation, Adaptation to Temperature Differences, and Geographical Distribution in Plants." *Verhandl. des V. Intern. Kongr. für Vererbungswissenschaft*, Berlin, 1927.
775. WHITE, O. E.: "Temperature reaction, mutation, and geographical distribution in plant groups." *Proc. 8th American Sci. Congr.*, **3**, 1940.
776. WHYTE, R. O.: "Phasic development of plants." *Biol. Reviews*, **14**, 1939.
777. WHYTE, R. O., and HUDSON, P. S.: "Vernalization." *Imp. Bureaux of Plant Genetics, Bull.* **9**. Cambridge and Aberystwyth, 1933.
778. WILD, H.: "Some Records of Phytogeographical Interest from Southern Rhodesia." *Proc. Rhodesian Sci. Assoc.*, **43**, 1951.
779. WILDER, G. P.: "Makatea." *B. P. Bishop Mus. Bull.*, **120**, 1934.
780. WILLIAMS, C. B.: "Area and number of species." *Nature*, **152**, 1943.
781. WILLIAMS, C. B.: "A diagrammatic method of analysing the inter-relationships of the fauna and flora of several different localities." *Proc. Linn. Soc. London*, **158**, 1945–46.
782. WILLIAMS, C. B.: "The logarithmic series and the comparison of island floras." *Proc. Linn. Soc. London*, **158**, 1945–46.
783. WILLIS, B.: "Isthmian Links." *Bull. Geol. Soc. Amer.*, **43**, 1932.
784. WILLIS, J. C. *Age and Area*. Cambridge, 1922.
785. WILLIS, J. C.: *A Dictionary of the Flowering Plants and Ferns*. 5th and 6th eds., Cambridge, 1925 and 1931.
786. WILLIS, J. C.: *The Course of Evolution by Differentiation or Divergent Mutation rather than by Selection*. Cambridge, 1940.
787. WILLIS, J. C.: *The Birth and Spread of Plants*. Geneva, 1949.
788. WILLS, L. J.: *A Palaeogeographical Atlas*. London and Glasgow, 1951.
789. WILMOTT, A. J.: "Concerning the History of the British Flora." *Mém. Soc. Biogéographie*, **3**, 1930.
790. WILMOTT, A. J.: "Changes in the British Flora during the past 50 years." *Proc. Linn. Soc. London*, **148**, 1935–36.
791. WILMOTT, A. J., (ed.): *British Flowering Plants and modern systematic methods*. London, 1949.
792. WILMOTT, A. J., SALISBURY, E. J., etc.: "Discussion on the Origin and Relationship of the British Flora." *Proc. Roy. Soc. London*, *B*, **118**, 1935.
793. WILSON, J. T.: "Evidence from Islands on the Spreading of Ocean Floors." *Nature*, **197**, 1963.
794. WIMMER, F. E.: *Das Pflanzenreich, Campanulaceae*—Lobelioideae, 1. Leipzig, 1943. Lobelioideae, 2. Berlin, 1953.
795. WOMERSLEY, J. S., and McADAM, J. B.: *The Forests and Forest Conditions in the Territories of Papua and New Guinea*. Port Moresby, 1957.
796. WOODHEAD, T. W.: "History of the Vegetation of the Southern Pennines." *Journ. of Ecology*, **17**, 1929.
797. WOOD-JONES, F.: *Coral and Atolls*. London, 1910.
798. WRIGHT, W. B.: *The Quaternary Ice Age*. 2nd ed., London, 1937.
799. WRIGHT SMITH, W.: "Plant invaders." *Yearbook of the Roy. Soc. Edinb.*, 1946.
800. WULFF, E. V.: "Introduction to the Historical Geography of Plants." *Bull. Appl. Bot. Genetics and Plant Breeding*, Supp. **52**, Leningrad, 1932 (in Russian with English summary).
801. WULFF, E. V.: "Essay on Dividing the World into Phytogeographic Regions . . ." *Bull. Appl. Bot. Genetics and Plant-breeding*, 1 *ser.*, **2**, Leningrad, 1934 (in Russian with German summary).
802. WULFF, E. V. (trans. BRISSENDEN, E.): *An Introduction to Historical Plant Geography*. Waltham, Mass., 1943.
803. WULFF, E. V.: *History of the floras of the world*. Moscow and Leningrad, 1944 (in Russian).
804. WYNNE-EDWARDS, V. C.: "Isolated arctic-alpine floras in eastern North America . . ." *Trans. Roy. Soc. Canada*, **31**, 1937.
805. ZEUNER, F. E.: *The Pleistocene Period. Its climate, chronology and faunal succession*. London, 1945.
806. ZEUNER, F. E.: *Dating the Past*. 2nd ed., London, 1950.
807. ZIMMERMAN, E. C.: *Insects of Hawaii: Vol. I, Introduction*. Honolulu, 1948.
808. ZOTOV, V. D.: "Some Correlations between Vegetation and Climate in New Zealand." *N.Z. Journ. of Sci. and Tech.*, **19**, 1938.
809. —— "Plant Breeding in the Soviet Union." *Imp. Bureaux of Plant Genetics, Bull.* **13**, Cambridge and Aberystwyth, 1933.
810. —— "Vernalization and Phasic Development of Plants." *Imp. Bureaux of Plant Genetics, Bull.* **17**. Cambridge and Aberystwyth, 1935.

30

811. —— "Sir T. H. Holland." *Obit. Notes Royal Society*, **6. 17**, 1948.
812. BADER, F. J. W.: "Die Verbreitung borealer und subantarktischer Holzgewächse in der Gebirgen des Tropengürtels." *Nova Acta Leopoldina*, n.s. **23**, 1960.
813. CHANDLER, M. E. J.: *The Lower Tertiary Floras of Southern England*, 2. *Flora of the Pipe-Clay series of Dorset (Lower Bagshot)*. London, 1962.
814. EGYED, L.: "The Expanding Earth?" *Nature*, **197**, 1963.
815. EYRE, S. R.: *Vegetation and Soils: a world picture*. London, 1963.
816. GIRDLER, R. W.: "Rift valleys, continental drift and convection in the earth's mantle." *Nature*, **198**, 1963.
817. GOLD, T.: "Instability of the Earth's Axis of Rotation." *Nature*, **175**, 1955.
818. GREENE, S. W. and GREENE, D. M.: "Check-list of the Sub-antarctic and Antarctic Vascular Flora." *The Polar Record*, **11**, 1963.
819. HULTÉN, E.: "The Circumpolar Plants, part 1." *K, Svenska Vet. Handl.*, ser. 4, **8**, 1962.
820. KRAUSE, E. B.: "Recent Climatic Changes." *Nature*, **181**, 1958.
821. MANUM, S.: *Studies in the Tertiary Flora of Spitzbergen. . . .: A Palynological Investigation*. Oslo, 1962.
822. NAIRN, A. E. M. and RUNCORN, S. K.: "Palaeoclimates." *Nature*, **198**, 1963.
823. NOLDEKE, A. M. and HOWELL, J. T.: "Endemism and a California Flora." *Leaflets of Western Botany*, **9**, 1960.
824. PLUMSTEAD, E. P.: "Ancient Plants and Drifting Continents." *S. Afr. Journ. Sci.*, **57**, 1961.
825. POELLNITZ, K. VON: "*Anacampseros* L." *Engl. Bot. Jahrb.*, **65**, 1933.
826. RUNCORN, S. K.: "Ancient Climates of the Earth." *The Times*, 1 July 1963.
827. SCHLITTLER, J.: "Monographie die Liliaceengattung *Dianella* Lam." *Mitt. Bot. Mus. Univ. Zürich*, **163**, 1940.
828. SMITH, G. L. and NOLDEKE, A. M.: "A Statistical Report on a California Flora." *Leaflets of Western Botany*, **9**, 1960.
829. STEENIS, C. G. G. VAN: "The Land-bridge Theory in Botany." *Blumea*, **11**, 1962.
830. WILSON, J. T.: "Evidence from Islands on the Spreading of Ocean Floors." *Nature*, **197** 1963.
831. WILSON, J. T.: "Hypothesis of Earth's Behaviour." *Nature*, **198**, 1963.
832. AXELROD, D. I.: "The Evolution of Flowering Plants." *Evolution after Darwin*, vol. 1, Chicago, 1960.
833. CHARLSWORTH, J. K.: *The Quaternary Era*. London, 1957.
834. FRENGUELLI, J,: "Restos de *Casuarina* en el Mioceno de El Mirador, Patagonia central." *La Plata Univ. Nac. Mus., Notas*, **8**, 1943.
835. HAMILTON, E. L.: "Sunken Islands of the Mid-Pacific Mountains." *Geol. Soc. America Mem.*, **64**, 1956.
836. JOHNSON, L. A. S. and BRIGGS, B. G.: "Evolution in the Proteaceae." *Australian Journ. of Bot.*, **11**, 1963
837. KALKMAN, C.: "A Plant-geographical Analysis of the Lesser Sunda Islands." *Acta. Bot. Neerland.*, **4**, 1955.
838. STEENIS, C. G. G. J. VAN: "The Distribution of Mangrove Plant Genera and its Significance for Palaeogeography." *Proc. Kon. Ak. Vet. Amsterdam*, Ser. C, **65**, 1962.

INDEX OF SUBJECTS

Acclimatisation, 426, 427, 431
Age and Area, Theory of 38–42, 209, 340, 419
Andesite, 403
Andesite line, 215, 257, 265
Angiosperms, origin of, 310, 314, 315
Animals, dipersal by, 374–376
Annual rings, 386
Antarcto-Tertiary flora, 319, 323, 324
Apomixis, 178
Archaean rocks, 396
Archaeozoic era, 308, fig. 73
"Arctic beds," 272
Arcto-Tertiary flora, 319, 322
Astronomical Theory of Glaciation, 393
Barriers, 336, 337
Bipolar distributions, 247, 355
Birds, dispersal by, 374–376
Blytt-Sernander scheme, 330
British flora, 268–294
    Atlantic and Lusitanian element of, 291, 293
Bush fires, 252, 359
Caenozoic era, 308–311
Cambrian period, 308, fig. 73
Carboniferous period, 308, 319, fig. 73
Changes of climate, 341, 384–394
    geological, 341, 395–414
Climate, changes of, 341, 384–394
    factors of, 333–335, 350–360
    regional classification of, 360
    zonation of, 350
Climatic Cycles, Theory of, 409
Climatic Migrations, Theory of, 416 et seq.
Competition, 341–345
Continental Drift, 267, 401 et seq.
Continents, 11, 12
Coombe rock, 271
Cretaceous period, 310, 311, 315–317, 319, 322,
    323, 327, 384, 391, 405, 413, 433, fig. 73
Cromer forest bed, 268
Cromerian, 268, 322
Definitions, 20
Demarcation lines and knots, 25, 348
Désertification, 160, 200, 332, 385
Deserts, 17–19
Devonian period, 308, fig. 73
Differentiation, Theory of, 38–40, 392
Discontinuity, 47, 48, 395
Dispersal (dissemination) of plants, 335–337,
    369–383
    by animals, 374–376
    by dust seeds, 370
    by explosive fruits, 377
    by human agencies, 378
    by ice, river and flood, 372
    by jactitation, 370
    by plumed fruits and seeds, 371
    by rain wash, 372
    by sea, 373
    by special mechanisms, 376
    by tumble weeds, 369
    by viscid adhesion, 377

Dispersal (dissemination) of plants, by water,
    372–374
    by winged fruits and seeds, 371
    by woolly seeds, 372
Divergent Dichotomous Mutation, Theory of,
    41
Dorset, 295–306, 319
Earth, convection currents in, 413
Earth, expansion of, 412
Earthworms, 368
Ecesis, 429
Edaphic factors, 334, 361–368
Effects of one species on another, 344
Endemism, 45, 391
Eocene subperiod, 311, 318, 319, 323, 384
Epibiotics, 46
Epicontinental seas and islands, 12, 396, 397, 409
Equator, theoretical positions of, 411, fig. 85
Equiformal Progressive Areas, Theory of, 179
Ete, 147
Eustatic change, 246, 398
Evolution, 33 et seq., 332, 395, 432 et seq.
Factors of distribution, summaries, 346, 347
Families, anomalous, 69
    cosmopolitan and subcosmopolitan, 52–57
    discontinuous, 62–64
    distribution of, 49–83
    endemic, 64–69
    number and size, 49, 50
    southern, 67–71, 243 et seq.
    temperate, 60
    tropical, 57–60
Floras, of the past, 316–323
    statistical comparison of, 161
Floristic units, classification of the world into,
    30–32
Flowering Plants, classification of, 5–8
    geological history of, 307–331
    nomenclature of, 8
Foraminifera, 329
Fossil plants, 311–323, 386, 430
    identification of, 311–316
Frost, 353, 365
Genera, cosmopolitan and subcosmopolitan,
    87–89
    discontinuous, 104–131, 439–444
    distribution of, 86–153
    endemic, 132–153
    number and size of, 84–86
    other wide, 94–103
    pantropical, 89–91
    temperate, 91–93
Generic Cycles, Theory of, 43, 44
Genes, 36, 425, 428
Genorheitron, 41
Geological time scale, the, 307–311, fig. 73
Glaciation, 271 et seq., 323–331, 348, 384, 385,
    387, 388, 391, 398, 399, 409, 428, 433,
    434
    chronology of, 329, 330, fig. 81
    extent of, 324, 325, figs. 78–80

Gondwanaland, 402
Granite, 384, 405
Greensand, 304
Growth forms, 353, 354
Günz glaciation, 324, fig. 81
Guyots, 15
Heredity, 35
Hologenesis, Theory of, 41
Hybridisation, 36
Ice Ages, the, 246, 268, 275, 280, 293, 322–331, 393, 435
Igapo, 147
Individuals, numbers of, 234
Inselberge, 202
Islands, 12–15
Isochores, 179
Isoflors, 315
Isostasy, 400
Jurassic period, 308, 310, fig. 73
Land and sea, distribution of, 243, 388
Land-bridges, Theory of, 404 et seq.
Land surfaces, statistics of, 383–385
Laurasia, 402, 411
Length of day, 23, 177, 261, 358, 393, 409
Light, 357, 358
"Little Ice Age," 388
Loma, 356
London Clay, 314, 318, 319
Lower Bagshots, 319
Madro–Tertiary flora, 319
Map projections, 19, 266
Maquis, 135, 197
Melanesian "continent," 265, 405
Mesozoic era, 308, 309, 310, 315, 406, 432, fig. 73
Meyer Ratio, 356
Microspecies, 85, 282, 283
Mid-Atlantic swell, 405
Mindel glaciation, 324, 329, fig. 81
Miocene subperiod, 100, 311, 320, 322, 391, 399, fig. 73
Montane floras, of Africa, 202–206, 244, 355
    of Malaysia, 211, 355
Mountain building, 391, 398
Mountains, 15, 17, 339, 356
Mutations, 36
Mycorrhiza, 368
Natural selection, 341
    Theory of, 34–36
Naturalisation of plants in New Zealand, 380–383
Neotropical-Tertiary flora, 319
Nitrogen fixation, 120
Norman Britain, 277
Norse period in Greenland, 189, 387
Northern March of Empire, the, 3
Nunataks, Theory of, 199, 271, 272
Obliquity of the ecliptic, 177, 350, 358, 392, 393
Ocean currents, 351
Oceanic islands, types of, 14, 215, 404
Oceanic ridges, 413
Oceans, 11, 12
Oligocene subperiod, 311, 319, 320, 322, fig. 73
Ordovician period, 308, fig. 73
Orocline Concept, the, 411
Palaeomagnetism, 267, 410
Palaeotropical–Tertiary flora, 319
Palaeozoic era, 308, 309, 385, fig. 73

Paleocene, 311
Palynology, see Pollen analysis
Pangaea, 402
Pangenesis, 35
Permian period, 308, 390, fig. 73
Perturbations, 393
Phasic development in plants, 429
Phytohormones, 344
Plant geography, history of, 9, 10
    principles of, 423, 424
Plant migrations, 204, 347–349
Pleistocene subperiod, 57, 141, 144, 149, 191, 194, 197, 199, 246, 268 et seq., 289, 311, 323–331, 385, 388, 390, 391, 413, 428, 435, figs. 73, 78
Pliocene subperiod, 73, 144, 216, 269, 311, 322, 391, 392, 399, 421, 431, fig. 73
Poles, movement of the, 409, 410, 411
Pollen analysis, 273, 275, 314, 329, 330
Polychrony, 37, 38
Polyploidy, 36, 178
Polytopy, 37, 38
Post-glacial changes, 273, 275, 276, 329, 330, fig. 81
Precipitation, 355–357
Precipitation-evaporation Ratio, 356
Proterozoic era, 308, fig. 73
Quaternary subperiod, 179, 308, 311, figs, 73, 84
Radio-carbon, 273, 330
Rainfall, distribution of, 356, 357
Rainfall/temperature equation, 356
Recent subperiod, 311, fig. 73
Reuverian, 320
Riss glaciation, 324, 329, fig. 81
Roman Britain, 275, 277
Serpentine, 252, 254, 365
Serpentinomorphosis, 365
Sial, 400, 405, fig. 83
Silurian period, 308, fig. 73
Sima, 400, 405, 409, fig. 83
Soils, 361, 362
    acidity of, 366, 367
    bacterial content of, 368
    chemistry of, 365
    constituents of, 364–366
    depth of, 362
    in relation to rainfall, 361, fig. 82
    temperature of, 364, 365
    texture of, 363
    water in, 364
Species, concentration of, 170–173
    cosmopolitan and very wide, 174, 175
    density of, 157–160
    discontinuous, 180, 226–230
    distribution within genera, 161 et seq.
    endemic, 189 et seq.
    endemic species of Britain, 289
    narrowly restricted, 234–237
    numbers of, 154 et seq.
    other wide, 177 et seq.
    pantropical, 175–177
    paucity in tropical Africa, 159, 160
    status of, 280, 281, 379
    vicarious, 230–234
Species pairs, 230–234
Sunspot cycle, 387
Teglian, 322
Temperature, 350–355

Tertiary period, 141, 160, 177, 197, 205, 213–216, 267, 308, 309, 311, 317, 318, 319, 384, 385, 391, 409, 410, 413, 433, fig. 73
Tethys Sea, 319
Theory of Age and Area, 38–42, 340, 419
    Climatic Cycles, 409
    Climatic Migrations, 416 *et seq.*
    Continental Drift, 267, 400 *et seq.*
    Differentiation, 38–40, 392
    Divergent Dichotomous Mutation, 41
    Equiformal Progressive Areas, 179
    Generic Cycles, 43, 44
    Glaciation (Astronomical), 393
    Hologenesis, 41
    Land-bridges, 404 *et seq.*
    Natural Selection, 34–36, 341

Theory of Tolerance, 415 *et seq.*
Tolerance, Theory of, 415 *et seq.*
Toxic reactions, 344
Transitions regions, 29, 245, 348, 349
Triassic period, 308, 310, fig. 73
Varves, 329
Vegetation, main types of, 2
    zonation of, 22–24
Vernalisation, 429, 430
Viability, 337
Vicarious species, 230–234
Wallace's line, 141
Wind, 358, 359
    effect of, 359
Würm glaciation, 324, 329, fig. 81

INDEX OF PLANT NAMES

Abelia, 440
Abronia, 136
Abrotanella, 443
Abrus precatorius, 176
Abutilon asiaticum, 176
  crispum, 176
  grandiflorum, 202
  hirtum, 176
  indicum, 176
  pannosum, 208
Acacia, 74, 85, 90, 201, 220, 248, 249, 250, 252, 256, 259
  abyssinica, 201
  aneura, 221
  caven, 219
  dealbata, 220
  farnesiana, 176, 220
  giraffae, 207
  harpophylla, 201
  heterophylla, 252
  karroo, 207
  koa, 212
  loderi, 232
  senegal, 201
  sowdeni, 232
Acaena, 125, 246, 247, 444
  anserinifolia, 229
Acalypha sanderiana, 210
Acampe, 442
Acanthaceae, 50 57, 105, 221, 251, 254, 255
Acanthophippium, 100
Acanthosicyos horrida, 207
Acanthus mollis, 197
Acer, 92, 198
  negundo, 198
  rubrum, 226
  saccharum, 198
Aceraceae, 60
Achariaceae, 68
Achasma, 97
Achatocarpaceae, 66
Achillea millefolium, 285
  ptarmica, 286
Achimenes grandiflora, 216
  longiflora, 216
Achlys, 439
Achras zapota, 216
Achyranthes aspera, 176
  indica, 176
Achyrospermum, 441
Acianthus, 101
Aciphylla, 102, 259
Ackama, 101
Aconitum, 85
  excelsum, 192
Acorus calamus, 305
Acridocarpus, 441
Acrocephalus, 441
Actaea, 231
Actinidia, 97
  callosa, 184
  chinensis, 196

Actinidiaceae, 68
Actinoschoenus, 442
Actinotus, 102
Adansonia, 442
  digitata, 186
Adenanthera, 441
  pavonina, 184
Adenia, 441
Adenocarpus, 98
Adenocaulon, 444
Adenostemma, 377
Adesmia, 94, 246
Adina, 441
Adinandra, 248, 441
Adonis annua, 305
Adoxa, 93
  moschatellina, 182, 287
Adoxaceae, 60
Aechmea fulgens, 218
Aegialitis, 99
Aegicerataceae, 63
Aegle, 441
  marmelos, 209
Aegopodium podagraria, 304
Aerva javanica, 183
Aeschynomene, 90, 360
Aesculus, 439
Aetanthus mutisii, 28
Aethionema, 135
Aextoxicaceae, 67
Afraegle, 441
Aframomum melegueta, 201
Afrormosia elata, 233
  laxiflora, 233
Afrovivella, 138
Afzelia bijuga, 183
Afzeliella, 206
Agapanthus africanus, 208
Agastachys, 150
Agatea, 102
Agathosma, 139, 248
Agauria, 96
Agavaceae, 58
Agave, 94, 146, 236
Agdestidaceae, 66
Ageratum, 90
  conyzoides, 176
Aglaia, 99, 256
Agonis, 101
Agropyron, 88
  repens, 344, 381
Agrostis, 88, 206
  magellanica, 224, 229
Agrostiphyllum, 442
Agyneja, 442
Aichryson, 135
Ailanthus, 99
Airosperma, 102
Aizoaceae, 58, 72, 131, 248
Aizoon canariense, 230
Akaniaceae, 69
Akebia, 134

Alangiaceae, 63
Alangium, 441
Alberta, 96
Albertinia, 147
Albizzia, 441
  fastigiata, 208
  lebbek, 228
Alchemilla, 205
  javanica, 228
alder, 276
Aldrovanda, 113, 443
Alectra arvensis, 228
Alectryon, 444
Aletris, 440
Aleurites, 98
Alismataceae, 56
Allamanda cathartica, 218
Allenrolfea occidentalis, 232
  patagonica, 232
  vaginata, 232
Allium, 85, 92
  porrum, 197
  sibiricum, 194
  vineale, 299
Alloteropsis, 441
Alnus, 92
Aloe, 98, 248
  abyssinica, 201
  candelabrum, 208
aloes, 250
Alopecurus geniculatus, 286
alpenrosen, 169, 233
Alphandia, 102, 143
Alphitonia, 99, 444
  excelsa, 220
Alpinia, 256
Alseuosmia, 152
Alstonia, 441
  plumosa, 229
Alstroemeria, 94
  aurantiaca, 218
Alstroemeriaceae, 66
Alternanthera repens, 176
  sessilis, 176
Althaea officinalis, 303
  rosea, 227
Althenia, 443
Althoffia, 142
Alysicarpus, 441
Alyxia, 253, 444
  olivaeformis, 212
Amanoa, 440
Amaracarpus, 100
Amaranthaceae, 57, 177, 219, 256, 376
Amaranthus, 88
  angustifolius, 175
  caudatus, 176
  spinosus, 176
  tristis, 176
Amaroria, 145
Amaryllidaceae, 57
Amaryllis bella-donna, 208
Amborellaceae, 69
Amherstia nobilis, 210, 234
Ammannia auriculata, 174
Ammophila, 363, 439
Amorphophallus, 441
  campanulatus, 184
  titanum, 210

Ampelocissus, 90
Ampelopsis veitchii, 196
Amperea, 150
Amphibromus, 102, 443
Amphicome, 140
Amsonia, 440
Amyema, 101
Anabasis aretioides, 201
Anacampseros, 249, 443
Anacardiaceae, 57, 151, 255
Anacardium occidentale, 176
Anacolosa, 442
Anagallis, 74, 88, 205
  arvensis, 299, 381
  tenella, 205
Anamirta cocculus, 210
Ananas, 94
  comosus, 217
  sativus, 217
Anaphalis, 88
Anastatica, 135
  hierocuntica, 201, 370
Anaxagorea, 442
Ancistrocladaceae, 63
Ancistrocladus, 441, fig. 31
  heyneanus, fig. 30
  tectorius, 185
Andira, 440
  inermis, 227
Andropogon, 88
  gayanus, 201, 228
Androsace, 74, 75, 92
  chamaejasme, 191
  helvetica, 192, 370
  umbellata, 184
  villosa, 227
Andruris, 98
Aneilema, 90
  nudiflora, 176
Anemone, 85, 88, 230, 371, 377
  alpina, 191
  coronaria, 197
  japonica, 196
  multifida, 226
  nemorosa, 231
  quinquefolia, 231
  sumatrana, 185
Anemopsis, 134, 440
Anerincleistus, 142
Angelica, 443
Angianthus, 150
Angophora, 150
Angraecum, 96
  sesquipedale, 206
Anigozanthos, 151
Anisopus, 137
Anisotome, 259
Anneslea, 97
Annona, 260
  cherimolia, 218
  muricata, 216
  reticulata, 216
Annonaceae, 58, 255
Anodendron paniculatum, 210
Anodopetalum, 150
Anogeissus,, 441
  leiocarpus, 231
  pendulus, 231
Anopterus, 150

Anotis wightiana, 228
Anplectrum, 142
Antennaria, 444
Anthephora, 440
Antholoma, 102
Anthoxanthum odoratum, 381
Anthurium, 85
Anthyllis, 134
   vulneraria, 299
Antiaris, 441
   toxicaria, 210
Antiaropsis, 102
Antidesma, 444
   membranacea, 233
   venosa, 233
Antigonon leptopus, 216
Antonia, 147
Antoniaceae, 58
Antrocaryon, 440
Apetahia, 80, 145
Aphania, 441
Aphanomyrtus, 142
Aphanopetalum, 100
Aphelandra squarrosa, 218
Apios, 440
Apium, 88
   nodiflorum, 300
Apluda, 442
   mutica, 228
Apocynaceae, 50, 57, 130, 144, 251–255, 372
Apocynum, 439
   androsaemifolium, 187
Apodytes, 441
Aponogeton, 441
   fenestralis, 206
Aponogetonaceae, 63
Apostasiaceae, 68
Aptandra, 440
Aptandraceae, 58
Aquifoliaceae, 57
Aquilariaceae, 63
Aquilegia, 92
   formosa, 200
Arabis, 92, 289
   alpina, 226
   brownii, 287
Araceae, 50, 57, 253, 255
Arachis, 147
   hypogaea, 218
Aralia, 440
   chinensis, 196
Araliaceae, 53, 57, 73, 144, 213, 252, 253, 255, 256
Arborescent Compositae, 74, 82, 83, 145, 260
Arbutoideae, 55
Arbutus, 439
   menziesii, 200
   unedo, 287, 293, fig. 66
Archeria, 102
Archontophoenix, 150
Arctagrostis, 132
Arctium, 376
   lappa, 381
Arctostaphylos, 272
Arctotideae, 248, 250
Arctotis, 443
   stoechadifolia, 208
Arduina, 441
Areca, 99
   catechu, 184

Areceae, 72, 253
Arenaria, 88
   ciliata, 287
   marcescens, 231
   obtusiloba, 231
   uliginosa, 286
Arenga saccharifera, 210
Arethusa,440
Argania, 135
Argemone mexicana, 176
Argophyllum, 102
Argostemma, 441
Argyroxiphium, 83
Aristea, 96
Aristolochia, 88
   grandiflora, 216
Aristolochiaceae, 57
Aristotelia, 443
   peduncularis, 229
   racemosa, 222
Armeria, 444
   vulgaris, 230
Arnica montana, 191
aroids, 100, 220, 252, 259
Arrhenatherum elatius, 381
Artabotrys, 441
Artanema, 441
Artemisia, 92
   absinthium, 382
   campestris, 192
   capillare, 184
   norvegica, 286
   tridentata, 200
   vulgaris, 344
Arthraxon lancifolius, 183
Arthroclianthus, 144, 253
Arthropodium, 101
   paniculatum, 186
Arthrostylidium schomburgkii, 217
Artocarpus, 317
   communis, 210
   incisa, 210
   integer, 184
   nobilis, 209
arum-lily, 185
Arundinaria, 82, 442
   alpina, 202
Arundinella hispida, 228
Arundo saccharoides, 217
Asarum, 92
Ascarina, 93
Asclepiadaceae, 50, 57, 137, 140, 147, 170–173, 221, 246, 248, 372
Asclepias, 85, 440
   curassavica, 175
Ascolepis, 440
   gracilis, 232
   setigera, 232
ash, 370
Asimina triloba, 428
Aspalathus, 139, 248
Asparagus, 85, 98
   asiaticus, 183
   cochinchinensis, 184
   officinalis, 192
   plumosus, 208
   racemosus, 228
Asperula cynanchica, 301
Aspidistra, 134

Aspidistra elatior, 196
Aspidosperma quebracho, 219
Astelia, 125, 253, 444, fig. 50
Aster, 26, 85, 198, 256
Asteracantha, 441
Asteranthaceae, 66
Asteriscus pygmaeus, 200
Asterolinon, 74, 75, 98
Asteropeia, 138
Astilbe, 440
    japonica, 196
Astragalus, 26, 85, 92, 246
    glycyphyllos, 287
    tragacantha, 186
Astrantia, 133
Astrocarpus, 135
Astrocaryum jawari, 217
Astronidium, 102
Asystasia, 441
Atherosperma moschatum, 220
Atherospermaceae, 64
Athrixia, 442
Atkinsonia, 150, 442
Atragene alpina, 191
Atriplex, 88
Atropa, 134
    bella-donna, 304, 344
Attalea compta, 218
    excelsa, 217
Atylosia, 442
Aubretia, 135
    deltoidea, 197
Aucuba japonica, 196
Aulacocarpus crassifolius, 236
Aulonemia quexo, 217
Australina, 249, 443
    pusilla, 187
Austrobaileyceae, 69
Avena, 88
    pratensis, 287
Avicennia, 91
    alba, 240
    balanophora, 241
    eucalyptifolia, 241
    lanata, 240
    marina, 240
    nitida, 240
    resinifera, 241
    sphaerocarpa, 240
    tomentosa, 241
Axonopus compressus, 176
Azara, 149
Azima, 441
Azorella, 247, 443
    multifida, 218
    selago, 224
Babbagia, 151
Babiana, 95
Baccharis, 246
    tola, 218
Backhousia, 101
bacteria, 368
Bactris, 76
    aristata, 218
Baeckea, 99, 256
    virgata, 186
Baikiea insignis, 211
Baissea, 441
Balanitaceae, 69

Balanites aegyptiaca, 231
    roxburghii, 231
Balanophora, 442
Balanophoraceae, 58, 151
Balanops, 102, 254, 264, 314
Balanopsidaceae, 69
balm trees, 26
Balsaminaceae, 70
Balsamodendron myrrha, 200
    opobalsamum, 200
bamboos, 81, 82, 160, 251, 253
Bambusa, 82
Bambuseae, 74, 81
bananas, 22, 23
Banksia, 101, 150, 220
Baphia, 441
    nitida, 186
Baptisia, 136
Barbacenia, 440
Barbarea vulgaris, 230
Barbeuiaceae, 68
Barbeyaceae, 67
Barclaya, 97
Barjonia, 147
Barleria, 90
barley, 3
Barringtonia, 442
    speciosa, 242
Barringtoniaceae, 58, 63
Bartsia, 205, 440
    alpina, 182, 191
    viscosa, 305
Basellaceae, 63
Batidaceae, 66
Batis maritima, 242
Bauera, 150
Baueraceae, 69
Bauhinia, 89, 220
    purpurea, 210
    splendens, 218
bay, 428
Beaufortia, 151
    grandiflora, 209
Beaumontia, 96
beech, 5, 117, 276, 330, 362
Begonia, 85–90, 236, 370
    annobonensis, 164
    arborescens, 164
    aspleniifolia, 164
    boliviensis, 164
    burbidgei, 164
    carpinifolia, 164
    cladocarpa, 164
    columnaris, 164
    comoroensis, 164
    conophylla, 164
    diptera, 164
    evansiana, 164
    ferruginea, 164
    fiebrigii, 164
    foliosa, 164
    franconis, 164
    handelii, 164
    hirsuticaulis, 164
    malabarica, 164
    maurandiae, 164
    meyer-johannis, 164
    micrantha, 164
    microphylla, 164

Begonia mollis, 148
  oxyloba, 164
  perpusilla, 164
  prismatocarpa, 164
  pseudolateralis, 164
  renifolia, 164
  rex, 210
  roxburghii, 164
  salaziensis, 164
  sanguinea, 164
  scandens, 164
  semperflorens, 218
  thomeana, 164
  tricuspidata, 164
Begoniaceae, 58
Beilschmiedea tawa, 222
Bellendena, 150
Belliolum, 102, 143
Bellis, 135
  perennis, 193, 285, 381
Beloperone guttata, 216
Bembicia, 138
Bennettiodendron leprosipes, 228
Bentinckiopsis, 145
Berberidaceae, 60, 74, 80, 131
Berberidopsis, 148
Berberis, 80, 81, 92, fig. 17
  buxifolia, 222
  darwinii, 218
  vulgaris, 382
Berchemia, 440
Bergenia, 133
  cordifolia, 194
  crassifolia, 194
Berlinia baumii, 202
Berrya, 100
Bertholletia excelsa, 217
Bertiera, 440
Beta vulgaris, 344
Betula humilis, 227
  nana, 272, 273
Betulaceae, 60
Bidens, 83, 376
  hyperborea, 199
  pilosa, 176
Bifora, 439
Bigelovia, 136
Bignoniaceae, 58, 147, 251, 252, 371
Bikkia, 100
Billardiera, 150
Billbergia nutans, 218
Biophytum, 90
birch, 275, 276, 330
Bixa orellana, 188
Bixaceae, 66
blackberries, 282, 382
black walnut, 427
bladder senna, 372
Blaeria, 96, 205, 206
  tenuifolia, 205
Blandfordia, 150
Bleekeria, 102
Bleekrodea, 442
Blepharistemma, 140
Bletia purpurea, 216
Blighia sapida, 201
Blyxa, 441
Bobea, 144
Bocagea, 442

Bocconia frutescens, 187
Boea hygroscopica, 220
Boehmeria nivea, 184
Boerhaavia diffusa, 176
Boerlagiodendron, 142
Boisduvalia, 439, 443
  glabella, 230
Bolax glebaria, 222
Bombacaceae, 58
Bombax malabaricum, 209
Boninia, 145
Bonnetiaceae, 63
Bontia, 140
Boraginaceae, 53, 246, 258
Borassus, 74, 441
  aethiopicum, 201
Borderea, 165
Borodinia, 133
Boroneae, 254
Boronia, 150, 249, 256, 259
  megastigma, 220
  semialata, 220
Borreria verticillata, 176
Boschniakia, 439
Bosea, 439
Bossiaea, 150
Boswellia, 98
  carteri, 200
Bothriochloa, 441
Bouchardatia, 101
Bouchea, 440
Bougainvillea spectabilis, 218
Bousigonia, 140
Boutonia, 138
Bouvardia, 146
Bowringia, 441
Boykinia, 439
Brabejum stellatifolium, 208
Brachychiton acerifolium, 220
Brachycome iberidifolia, 220
  linearifolia, 220
Brachyglottis, 83
Brachylophon, 441
Brachypodium, 88
  sylvaticum, 192, 381
Brachypterys, 440
Brachystegia, 202
  spicaeformis, 208
Brackenridgea, 441
Brandzeia, 138
Brasenia, 439
Brassavola nodosa, 188
Brassica oleracea, 303, 344, 382
Braya, 190
  purpurascens, 182
Bretschneideraceae, 68
Brexia, 439, 442
Bridelia, 441
  micrantha, 186
Brighamia, 144
broad bean, 382
Bromelia, 94
Bromeliaceae, 63, 64, 66, 345
Bromheadia finlaysonia, 184
Bromus, 88
Brosimum galactodendron, 217
Broussonetia, 97
Browallia speciosa, 218
Brownea grandiceps, 217

Brownea macrophylla, 218
Brucea, 206, 441
Bruguiera, 441
Brunelliaceae, 66
Bruniaceae, 68, 248
Brunnichia, 371
Brunoniaceae, 69
Bryanthud, 95, fig. 58
Bryocarpum, 74, 75
Bryonia, 133
    dioica, 368
Bryonopsis, 441
    laciniosa, 183
Bryophyllum pinnatum, 176
Bubbia, 101
Bucklandia populnea, 185
Buckleya, 440
Buddleja, 85
    globosa, 218
Buddlejaceae, 57
Buforrestia, 440
Bulbine, 249, 443
Bulbinella, 249, 443
Bulbocodium, 133
Bulbophyllum, 85, 90, 254, 256, 258
    grandiflorum, 210
bulbous buttercup, 9
Buphthalmum speciosum, 193
Buraeavia, 102, 143
Burkea africana, 202
Burmannia disticha, 184
Burmanniaceae, 58
Bursera gummifera, 187
Burseraceae, 58
Butea frondosa, 209
Butomaceae, 56
Butomus umbellatus, 192, 300
buttercups, 9
Butyrospermum parkii, 186
Buxaceae, 70
Buxus, 443
    macowani, 208
Byblidaceae, 69
Byblis, 150
Byronia, 444
Byrsophyllum, 442
Bythophytum indicum, 185
Byttneria, 442
Cabombaceae, 58
Cacoucia, 440
Cactaceae, 26, 50, 64, 66, 148, 171, 173, 246
cacti, 353, 380, 386
Caesalpinia, 90
    bonduc, 176
    echinata, 218
    major, 228
    pulcherrima, 176
Caesalpiniaceae, 58, 89, 177
Caesia, 442
Cajanus, 441
    cajan, 175
Cajophora, 149
Cakile, 439
    alacranensis, 236
    maritima, 241
Caladenia, 259
Calamagrostis epigejos, 287
Calamintha ascendens, 304
Calamus, 76, 85, 441

Calamus australis, 220
    draco, 210
Calandrinia, 247, 443
    menziesii, 230
Calanthe mexicana, 216
    veratrifolia, 184
Calceolaria, 26, 85, 118, 247
    integrifolia, 218
Caleana, 102
Calliandra, 442
Callicarpa, 442
Calligonum comosum, 200
Callistemon, 256, 259
    speciosus, 220
Callistephus, 134
    chinensis, 196
Callitrichaceae, 56
Callitriche, 88
    antarctica, 224
Calluna, 279
    vulgaris, 301, 381
Calochilus, 101
Calochortus, 136
Calodendron capense, 208
Calogyne, 99
Calophyllum inophyllum, 242
Calotropis gigantea, 209
    procera, 200
Caltha, 98, 443
    palustris, 182
Calycacanthus, 102
Calycanthaceae, 63
Calycanthus, 440
Calyceraceae, 67
Calypso, 93
Calystegia, 88
    sepium, 174
    soldanella, 233, 241
Calythrix, 150
Cambessedesia, 147
Camelina, 344
Camellia, 26, 97
    japonica, 196
Camoensia maxima, 201
Campanula, 85
    barbata, 191
    glomerata, 192, 301
    jacobaea, 198
    rotundifolia, 366
    scheuchzeri, 191
    thyrsoides, 192
    trachelium, 192
    uniflora, 182
    vidalii, 197, 236
Campanulaceae, 53, 248
Campnosperma, 442
Campsis, 440
Campynema, 102, 254
Canacomyrica, 144
Cananga odorata, 210
Canarina, 113, 442
    canarienaia, 198
Canarium, 441
    commune, 184
    luzonicum, 210
Canavalia ensiformis, 175
    maritima, 175
Canellaceae, 63
Canna indica, 188

Cannabinaceae, 60
Cannabis, 135
  sativa, 344
Cannaceae, 66
Canscora, 441
  decussata, 228
  diffusa, 183
Canthium, 444
Cantua buxifolia, 218
Caperonia, 440
Capillipedium, 441
Capparidaceae, 53, 57
Capparis spinosa, 197
Caprifoliaceae, 55, 56, 151
Capsella, 382
  bursa-pastoris, 175, 285, 380
Capsicum, 442
  annuum, 187
  frustescens, 176
Caragana, 133
  arborescens, 196
  versicolor, 196
Carallia, 442
Caralluma, 98, 171, 173
  winkleri, 235
Carapa, 442
  moluccensis, 183
Cardamine, 88
  hirsuta, 380
cardoon, 219
Carduus, 205
  tenuiflorus, 294
Carex, 53, 85, 87, 205, 230, 259, 288
  brunnea, 228
  graeffeana, 229
  lapponica, 182
  misandroides, 231
  petricosa., 231
  trifida, 224
  uncinata, 229
Carica papaya, 187
Caricaceae, 63
Caricoideae, 213
Carissa, 441
  arduina, 207
Carlina, 133
  acaulis, 192
Carludovica palmata, 218
Carmichaelia, 102, 151, 258, 260
Carnarvonia, 150
Carnegiea gigantea, Plate 6
Carpha, 205, 439
Carpinus, 439
Carpobrotus, 119, 249, 442
Carpodetus, 102
Carpodinus, 137
Carpodiptera, 440
Carronia, 101
Carruthersia, 100
Cartonema, 101
  incana, 106
Cartonemataceae, 69
Carum verticillatum, 304
Carya, 187, 198
Caryocar, 146
  villosum, 217
Caryocaraceae, 66
Caryophyllaceae, 26, 50, 53
Caryopteris, 134

Caryota, 99
  urens, 209
Casearia tomentosa, 184
Cassia, 85, 90
  absus, 176
  mimosoides, 176
  nodosa, 210
  senna, 201
  tora, 176
Cassinopsis, 96
Cassiope, fig. 58
  hypnoides, 182
  lycopodioides, 182
Cassipourea, 90, 440
Cassytha, 90
  filiformis, 176, 242
Castanospermum, 101, 254
  australe, 220
Castelnavia, 147
Castilla elastica, 216
Castilleja, 95
  coccinea, 199
Casuarina, 99, 100, 221, 250, 254, 259, 314
  equisetifolia, 100, 242
  torulosa, 220
Casuarinaceae, 69, 72
Catalpa, 371, 440
  bignonioides, 198
Catesbaea, 146
Catha, 98
  edulis, 200
Catharanthus, 90, 176
  roseus, 176
Cattleya, 146
  labiata, 218
Caulophyllum, 440
Caustis, 150
Cayratia, 439, 441
Caytoniales, 310
Ceanothus, 94
  caeruleus, 216
  thyrsiflorus, 200
Cecropia, 146
  peltata, 188
Cedrela, 442
  odorata, 187
Celastraceae, 26, 55, 255
Celastrus, 92, fig. 21
Celmisia, 102, 151, 259
  coriacea, 222
Celosia, 88, 90
  argentea, 176
  trigyna, 185
Celtis, 254
Cenarrhenes, 150
Cenchrus echinatus, 176
Centaurea, 85, 88
  cretica, 227
  cyanus, 305, 381
Centaurium umbellatum, 381
Centipeda, 441
Centotheca, 441
Centranthus, 135
  calcitrapa, 198
Centrolepidaceae, 63
Centrolepis, 99
Centropogon, 80
Centrosema pubescens, 188
Centunculus, 74, 75

Cephaelis ipecacuanha, 218
Cephalanthera damasonium, 301
  grandiflora, 301
Cephalocereus, 146
Cephalostachyum, 82, 442
Cephalotaceae, 69
Cephalotus, 151
Cerastium, 88
  triviale, 205
  vulgatum, 285, 380
Ceratiola, 136, fig. 43
Ceratopetalum 88
  gummiferum, 220
Ceratophyllaceae, 56
Ceratophyllum, 88
  demersum, 174
Ceratostylis, 100, 256
Cerbera, 254, 442
Cercidiphyllaceae, 68
Cercis, 439
  siliquastrum, 197
Cereus, 94
Ceriops, 441
  candolleana, 240
Ceropegia, 98, 441
  fusca, 188
  sandersonii, 208
  woodii, 208
Ceroxylon andicola, 218
Chaetostoma, 147
Chailletiaceae, 58
Chamaedorea, 76
Chamaelaucieae, 250
Chamaelaucium, 151
  uncinatum, 220
Chamaenerion angustifolium, 378
Chamaepericlymenum, 231, 232, fig. 59
Chamaerhodos, 95
Chamaesaracha, 439
Chambeyronia, 102, 143
Chariessa, 442
Chaydaia, 97
Cheirostylis, 441
Chelidonium majus, 304
Chenopodiaceae, 56, 134, 151, 249, 250, 255
Chenopodium, 83, 88, 219
  album, 176, 381
  quinoa 218
Chevreulia, 443
  stolonifera, 229
chickweed, 337
Chiloglottis, 102
Chimonanthus, 134, 440
Chiogenes, 109, 440
  hispidula, 199
Chionanthus, 440
Chionodoxa, 135
Chionographis, 134
  japonica, 196
Chitonanthera, 255
Chlaenaceae, 68, 138, 251
Chloanthaceae, 69, 249
Chloraea, 246
Chloranthaceae, 63
Chorocodon whitei, 186
Chlorophora, 440
  tinctoria, 187
Choisya, 136
  ternata, 200

Chorisia ventricosa, 218
Chorizanthe commissuralis, 230
Chorizema, 220
Chrysanthemum arcticum, 190
  coronarium, 197
  leucanthemum, 301, 381
  parthenium, 304
Chrysitrix, 443
Chrysobalanaceae, 58
Chrysobalanus, 440
  icaco, 188
Chrysocoma, 139
  tenuifolia, 208
Chrysoglossum, 100
Chrysophyllum, 90
  cainito, 187
Chrysosplenium, 444
  alternifolium, 287
  oppositifolium, 303
Cicendia, 444
Cicer, 135
Cichoriaceae, 26
Cichorium intybus, 381
Cimicifuga foetida, 227
Cinchona, 26, 146
  succirubra, 218
Cinna, 439
Cinnamomum, 317
  camphora, 210
Cipadessa, 442
Circaea lutetiana, 377
Circaeasteraceae, 68
Cirrhopetalum, 441
Cirsium, 92
  arvense, 285, 381
  mingaanense, 235
  palustre, 285
  vulgare, 285, 381
Cistaceae, 26, 62
Cistanche, 98
  lutea, 200
Cistus, 135
  monspeliensis, 198
Citriobatus, 99
Citronella, 442
Citropsis, 441
Citrus, 210
Cladium, 88
  angustifolium, 231
  mariscus, 174, 304
  scorpoideum, 231
Cladopus, 97
Cladrastis, 440
Claoxylon, 253, 444
Clarkia elegans, 200
Clausena, 441
Claytonia, 95
Cleidion, 90
Cleistachne, 441
Cleistanthus, 441
Cleistochloa, 101
Cleistoyucca arborescens, 200
Clematis, 88, 279, 371
  montana, 195
  simensis, 185
  vitalba, fig. 70
  welwitschii, 202
Clematopsis, 96
  scabiosifolia, 186

Cleome hirta, 186
  monophylla, 183
  spinosa, 186
Clermontia, 80, 144
Clerodendrum, 85
  fallax, 210
  macrosiphon, 202
  paniculatum, 210
  splendens, 201
  thomsonae, 186
Clethra, 113, 442, fig. 35
  arborea, 198
  tomentosa, fig. 34
Clethraceae, 64
Clianthus dampieri, 221
  puniceus, 222
Clidemia hirta, 187
Cliffortia, 96, 248
Clintonia, 107, 439
  borealis, 233
  umbellulata, 233
Clitorea ternata, 184
Cloezia, 100
club-mosses, 308
Clymenia, 145
Cneoraceae, 67
Cnestis, 441
Cobaea scandens, 216
Cobaeaceae, 66
Coccinia, 441
Coccolobis uvifera, 188, 242
Cochlearia, 289
Cochlioda, 148
Cochlospermaceae, 64
Cochlospermum, 442
cocoa, 195, 217
Cocconerion, 144
coconut, 373
Cocos, 90
  coronata, 218
  nucifera, 373
Codia, 144
Codiaeum variegatum,
  211
Codonopsis, 134
Coelopleurum, 95
Coffea, 441
  arabica, 201
  liberica, 201
coffee, 195
Cohnia, 113, 253, 443
Coix, 90
  lacryma-jobi, 176
Cola, 137
  acuminata, 201
  nitida, 186
Coldenia, 90
Colensoa, 151
Coleus, 85, 444
  barbatus, 235
  blumei, 210
  elongatus, 235
  thyrsoideus, 185
Collomia grandiflora, 200
Collospermum. fig. 50
  montanum, fig. 49
Colmeiroa, 144, 151, 261
Colobanthus, 116, 443, fig. 36
  crassifolius, 223, 224

Colocasia, 96
  esculenta, 210
Colpodium fulvum, 190
Columelliaceae, 67
Colutea arborescens, 370
Colvillea racemosa, 206
Comandra, 439
Comarum palustre, 182
Combretaceae, 58, 131
Combretum, 90, 360, 370
  rupicola, 218
Comesperma, 150
Cometes, 98
Commelina, 90
  diffusa, 176
Commelinaceae, 57, 253
Commidendron, 83, 139
Commiphora, 441
Compositae, 8, 26, 49, 50, 52, 53, 74, 82, 89, 95,
  105, 130, 136, 139, 144, 147, 151, 177, 198,
  205, 212, 213, 246–251, 253, 255–257, 260,
  371, 372, 376, 377
Congea velutina, 210
Coniferae, 6, 22, 23, 133
Conium maculatum, 192
Connaraceae, 58
Connaropsis, 142
Conocarpus, 440
Conospermum, 150
Conostephium, 150
Conostylis, 157
Convallaria majalis, 287, 305
Convolvulaceae, 55, 255
Convolvulus, 88
  arvensis, 381
Conyza aegyptiaca, 183
Copaifera, 440
Copernicia, 217
  cerifera, 218
Coprosma, 125, 126, 214, 215, 236, 257, 261,
  444, fig. 48
  nitida, fig. 47
  pumila, 336
Coralliokyphos, 145
Corallospermum crassicaule, 222
Corchorus, 89
  capsularis, 209
Cordia, 90
  gerascanthus, 216
  sebestana, 187
  subcordata, 242
Cordyline, 258, 444
  australis, 222
Corema, 107, 269, 439, fig. 43
Coriaria, 126, 259, 443, fig. 42
  japonica, fig. 41
  ruscifolia, 222, 229
Coriariaceae, 64
Coris, 74, 75
Cornaceae, 49, 64, 71
Cornulaca, 136
Cornus, 93, 231, 232
  canadensis, 182, 231, 232, fig. 39
  florida, 198
  nuttallii, 200
  suecica, 182, 231, 232, fig. 59
  unalaschkensis, 231, 232, fig. 59
Corokia, 132, 214
Coronanthera, 144

Coronantherinae, 260
Coronopus, 88
Corozo, 76, 440
Correa, 150
Corrigiola, 440
Corsiaceae, 63
Cortaderia selloana, 219
Cortusa, 74, 75
Corydalis claviculata, 287, 304
Corylaceae, 60
Corymbis, 441
Corynanthe, 138
Corynocarpaceae, 69
Corynocarpus, 101
Corypha umbraculifera, 209
Cosmos, 146
    bipinnatus, 216
Cossinia, 115, 253, 443
Costus, 89
    giganteus, 202
Cotoneaster, 92
    frigida, 196
    integerrima, 286
cotton, 372
Cotula, 258
    plumosa, 224
Couma utilis, 217
Couroupita guianensis, 188
Couthovia, 100, 444
cowslip, 381
Coxella, 151
crab apple, 304
Crambe, 98
Craniotome versicolor, 228
Craspedia, 102
Crassula, 249
    falcata, 208
    lycopodioides, 208
    moschata, 224
Crassulaceae, 55, 198, 248
Crataegus, 85, 199, 235, 382
    oxyacantha, 193
Crataeva, 90
    tapia, 187
Cratoxylon, 97
creeping buttercup, 9
Cremanthodium, 134
Cremocarpus, 138
Crepis, 37, 40, 92
    capillaris, 381
Crescentieae, 253
Cressa cretica, 176
Crinum, 88
    asiaticum, 242
Criosanthes, 440
Crithmum, 133
Crocosmia crocosmiaeflora, 208
Crocus, 135
    albiflorus, 192
    veneris, 227
Croomia, 440
Crossandra, 441
Crossosomataceae, 66
Crossostylis, 143
Crotalaria, 90
    incana, 176
    uncea, 209

Crotalaria retusa, 176
Croton, 85, 90
    cascarilla, 216
    lacciferus, 210
Cruciferae, 26, 50, 53, 84, 95, 133, 134, 135, 136, 151, 246, 255
Cruddasia, 140
Cryophytum, 443
Cryptandra, 256
Cryptanthus zonatus, 218
Cryptogams, 5
Cryptolepis, 441
    elegans, 185
Crypteroniaceae, 68
Cryptostegia grandiflora, 206, 234
Cryptostylis, 97
Cryptotaenia, 440
Ctenolophon, 441
Ctenolophonaceae, 63
Cucurbitaceae, 57, 138
Cunonia, 109, 442
    capensis, fig. 7
Cunoniaceae, 63, 73, 109, 253, fig. 8
Cupaniopsis, 101
Cuphea, 125, 444
Cupuliferae, 140
Curatella americana, 217
Curculigo orchioides, 184
Curcuma zedoaria, 210
Cuscuta, 88
Cuscutaceae, 53
Cusparia febrifuga, 217
Cyanastraceae, 67
Cyanea, 80, 144
Cyanotis, 441
Cyathodes, 444
    acerosa, 186
    tameiameiae, 229
Cyathula achyranthoides, 187
    prostrata, 176
Cycadophyta, 310
Cyclamen, 74, 75
    persicum, 197
Cyclanthaceae, 66
Cyclophyllum, 102, 143
Cycnogeton, 101
Cylindrocline, 138
Cymbidium, 442
    grandiflorum, 209
Cymbonotus, 443
Cymbopogon citratus, 183
    giganteus, 186
Cymodocea ciliata, fig. 61
Cynanchum, 57, 85, 88
    multiflorum, 187
Cynara carduncellus, 219
    scolymus, 197
Cynocrambaceae, 64
Cynodon, 88
    dactylon, 175
Cynoglossum, 88
    officinale, 368
Cynometra cauliflora, 184
Cynomoriaceae, 67
Cynosurus cristatus, 381
Cyperaceae, 50, 53, 152, 175, 187, 223, 246, 248, 257, 376
Cyperus, 53, 88, 256
    alternifolius, 206

Cyperus flavescens, 174
  haspan, 175
  longus, 304
Cypholophus, 100
Cyphomandra betacea, 218
Cypripedium, 98
  calceolus, 192
  guttatum, 182
  reginae, 226
Cyrillaceae, 66
Cyrtandra, 129, 130, 214, 236, 254, 256, 444
Cyrtandroidea, 145
Cyrtandromoea, 142
Cyrtandropsis, 255
Cytrococcum, 441
Cyrtostachys renda, 211
Cyrtostylis, 102
Cytinus, 443
Cytisus battandieri, 197
  canariensis, 198
Daboecia azorica, 197
  cantabrica, 287, fig. 67
  polifolia, 287, fig. 67
Dactylanthus, 151
Dactylis glomerata, 286, 381
Dactyloctenium, 90
Daemia, 137
  extensa, 200
Daemonorops, 76, 96
Dalhia, 146
  variabilis, 216
Dalbergia, 89
  ecastophyllum, 227, 342
  nigra, 218
Dalechampia, 90
  roezliana, 216
  scandens, 228
Dalhousiea, 441
Dallachya, 141
Damasonium, 122, 443
Damnacanthus indicus, 228
Dampiera, 150
Danae, 135
dandelion, 371
Danthonia intermedia, 227
Daphnandra, 101
Daphniphyllaceae, 68
Daphniphyllum, 97
Darlingia, 150
Darlingtonia, 136
Darwinia, 150
Dasypogon, 151
date palm, 200
Datisca, 439
Datiscaceae, 63
Datura, 88
  metel, 209
  suaveolens, 218
Daucus, 443
  carota, 299, 381
Davidia, 134
Davidsoniaceae, 69
Daviesia, 150, 156
Deckenia, 139
Decumaria, 440
Deeringia, 253, 441
  amaranthoides, 184
Degeneria, 145
Degeneriaceae, 69, 257

Deherainia smaragdina, 216
Deinacanthon, 148
Delarbrea, 102
Delissea, 80, 144
Delonix regia, 206, 234
Delphinium grandiflorum, 194
Dendrobium, 85, 99, 253, 254
  crumenatum, 184
  nobile, 209
  superbiens, 236
  superbum, 211
Dendrocalamus, 97
  giganteus, 211, Plate 22
Dendromecon, 136
Dendroseris, 83, 148
Dendrosicyos, 83, 138
  socotrana, 201
Denea, 144
Deschampsia, 89
  antarctica, 223, 224
  caespitosa, 174, 299
Desfontainia, 148
Desfontainiaceae, 66
Desmodium adscendens, 187
  triflorum, 176
  umbellatum, 176
Desmos, 100
Desmostachya bipinata, 183
Dialypetalanthaceae, 66
Dianella, 129, 253, 444
  ensifolia, 183
  javanica, 184
  nemorosa, 183
  odorata, 184, 212
Dianthus, 85, 90
  alpinus, 193
  caesius, 286
  gratianopolitanus, 286
  superbus, 192
Diapensia, 93, 191
  himalaica, 191,
  lapponica, 191, 286
  purpurea, 191
  wardii, 191
Diapensiaceae, 60
Diarrhena, 440
Diascia, 248
Dicentra, 439
  spectabilis, 196
Dichanthium, 441
  annulatum, 183
Dichapetalaceae, *see* Chailletiaceae
Dichapetalum, 360
Dichelachne, 101
Dichondra repens, 176
Dichroa, 96
Dichromena ciliata, 188
Dichrostachys, 441
Diclidanthera, 147
Diclidantheraceae, 66
Dicoma, 441
  tomentosa, 183
Dicorypha, 138
Dicotyledons, 6, 49, 154, 221, 314, 407
Dictamus, 344
  albus, 192
Dictyanthus, 146
Didierea, 138
Didiereaceae, 68, 251

Didiscus procumbens, 229
Didymocarpus perditus, 234
Dieffenbachia seguine, 188
Diervilla, 440
 florida, 195
Dietes, 443
Digitalis purpurea, 193, 381, 427
Digitaria sanguinalis, 176
Dilkea, 147
Dilleniaceae, 58, 73, 256
Dillwynia, 150
Dilobeia, 78
Dimorphanthera moro, 257
Dimorphotheca, 208
Dinisia excelsa, 218
Dionaea, 136
Dioncophyllaceae, 67
Dionysia, 74, 75,
Dioscorea, 85, 89, 162, 165, 371
 adenocarpa, 165
 altissima, 165
 amazonica, 165
 balcanica, 165
 bulbifera, 165
 campestris, 165
 caucasica, 165
 cirrhosa, 165
 collettii, 165
 convolvulacea,, 165
 elephantipes, 165, 207
 esculenta, 165
 glabra, 165
 glandulosa, 165
 lanata, 165
 megalantha, 165
 nipponica, 165
 nummularia, 165
 occidentalis, 165
 pilosiuscula, 165
 polifolia, 165
 polyclades, 165
 quartiniana, 165
 triphylla, 165
Dioscoreaceae, 57
Diospyros, 85, 90
 ebenum, 209
 kaki, 196
 quaesita, 209
Diphylleia, 440
Diplachne fusca, 183
Diplanthera, 442
Diplolaena, 151
Diplusodon, 147
Dipsacaceae, 69
Dipsacus fullonum, 299
 sylvestris, 299
Dipteranthemum, 151
Dipterocarpaceae, 63, 96, 140, 371
Dipterocarpus, 96
 turbinatus, 210
Dipteryx odorata, 217
Dirca, 136
Disa, 96, 205
 grandiflora, 208
Discaria, 443
Dischidia, 99
 rafflesiana, 184
Discocalyx, 100
Disperis, 441

Disphyma australis, 229
Disporum, 440
Dissiliaria, 442
Distichlis, 442
Dittoceras, 140
Dizygotheca, 102, 143,
Dodecania, 140
Dodecatheon, 74, 75, 95
 meadia, 187
Dodonaea, 91
 viscosa, 176, 242
dogwood, 273
Dolicholobium, 100
Dombeya wallichii, 206
Donatia, 443
 fascicularis, 232
 novae-zelandiae, 231
Dorema, 135
Doronicum, 95
Dorstenia, 83, 90
 gigas, 201
 indica, 209
Doryanthes 150
 excelsa, 220
Doryphora, 150
double coconut, 373
Douglasia, 74, 75, 439
Dovyalis, 441
Dowingia, 80
Draba, 92
 incana, 230
Dracaena, 444
 cinnabari, 201
 draco, 198
Dracocephalum, 93
Dracophyllum, 101, 258, 260
Drakaea, 101
Drakebrockmania, 138
Drapetes, 443
Drepanocarpus, 440
 lunatus, 227, 242
Drimys, 118, 443
 lanceolata, 220
 winteri, 218, fig. 4
Droogmansia, 441
Drosera, 85, 165, 166, 187, 256, 259, 300, 367
 fig. 18
 adelae, 166
 angelica, 166
 arcturi, 166
 banksii, 166
 brevifolia, 166
 burkeana, 166
 burmanni, 166, 184
 capensis, 166
 capillaris, 166
 filiformis, 166
 gigantea, 166
 glanduligera, 166
 indica, 165, 183
 intermedia, 166
 longifolia, 166, 227, 234
 madagascariensis, 166
 montana, 166
 myriantha, 166
 natalensis, 166
 peltata, 166
 petiolaris, 166

31

Drosera pygmaea, 166
  rotundifolia, 166, 234
  sessilifolia, 166
  spathulata, 166, 184
  stenopetala, 166
  stenophylla, 166, 231
  uniflora, 166, 232
  whittakeri, 166
Droseraceae, 56, 73, 256
Drosophyllum, 135
Drusa, 444
Dryandra, 151, 220
Dryas, 93, 273, 371
  octopetala, 191
Drymophlaeus, 100
Dryobalanops, 142
  aromatica, 211
Duabanga, 97
Duboisia, 218
  myoporoides, 186
Dubouzetia, 102
Duchesnea indica, 185
duckweeds, 373
Duguetia quitarensis, 217
Dumasia, 441
  villosa, 228
Dupontia fischeri, 190
Durandea, 99
Duranta plumieri, 188
Durio, 142
  zibethinus, 184
Duvalia, 140
Dyerophyton, 443
Dysoxylum, 99
  fraserianium, 220
Dysphaniaceae, 69
Earina, 202
Ebenaceae, 58
ebony, 209
Ecballium, 135, 377
Ecbolium, 441
Eccremocarpus, 148
Echeveria, 94, 216
Echinocactus, 94, 246
Echinocarpus, 442
Echinochloa crus-galli, 175
  crus-pavonis, 227
Echinopanax, 439
  horridum, 182
Echinops, 98, 204
Echium, 138
  vulgare, 298
Eclipta prostrata, 176
Ectadiopsis, 441
  oblongifolia, 186
Ectrosia, 101
edelweiss, 193
Edithcolea, 138
Edwardsia, 130, 444, fig. 40
  grandiflora, 212
Ehretia, 90
Ehretiaceae, 58
Eichhornia, 90, 440
  crassipes, 176
Eleaganaceae, 60
Elaeis, 76, 440
  guineensis, 201
Elaeocarpaceae, 64, 73, 254, 256

Elaeocarpus grandis, 129, 220, 252, 253, 256, 439, 444
  persicaefolius, 186
Elatinaceae, 56
Elatine, 88
  americana, 230
Elatostema, 256, 441
elder, 273
Elegia, 139
Eleocharis, 88
  chaetaria, 175
  geniculata, 175
Elephantopus scaber, 176
Elephantorrhiza, 360
  burchellii, 207
Elettaria cardamomum, 209
  repens, 209
Elettariopsis, 142
Eleusine corocana, 209
  indica, 176
Elimgamita, 151
Elisma natans, 227
Ellertonia, 442
Elliottia, 439, 440
elm, 276, 370
Elodea canadensis, 380
Elsholtzia, 441
Elyonurus royleanus, 228
Elythranthe tetrapetala, 222
Elytropappus rhinocerotis, 208
Elytrophorus, 441
  spicatus, 183
Embadium, 151
Embelia, 440
Emblingia, 151
Embothrium coccineum, 218
  grandiflorum, fig. 15
Emex, 443
Emilia, 441
  coccinea, 176
  sonchifolia, 176
Empetraceae, 62, fig. 43
Empetrum, 122, 444, fig. 43
  nigrum, 305
  rubrum, 223, 224
Enargea, 443
  marginata, 229
Endiandra, 318
Endospermum, 100
Enemion, 439
Engelhardtia, 442
Englerastrum, 441
Enhalus, 441
Entada sudanica, 201
Entelea, 151
  arborescens, 222
Enteropogon, 441
Enydra, 442
Epacridaceae, 26, 55, 63, 72, 220, 249, 250 254–256, 258
Epacris, 101
  longiflora, 220
Epiblastus, 101
Epidendrum, 85
  fragrans, 187
  nocturnum, 187
  polybulbon, 216
  rigidum, 187

Epigaea, 440
  asiatica, 231
  repens, 231
Epilobium, 98, 187, 221, 257, 259, 372
  angustifolium, 378
  hirsutum, 300, 355
  junceum, 229
  tetragonum, 230
Epimedium, 439
Epipactis, 92
  latifolia, 303
Epipogium aphyllum, 286
  roseum, 184
Episcia fulgida, 218
Epithema, 441
Eragrostis, 95
  aspera, 228
  tef, 201
Eranthis, 147
Ercilla volubilis, 218
Erechtites arguta, 184
  hieracifolia, 187
Eremanthus, 142
Eremophila, 150, 249, 256
Eremosynaceae, 69
Eremurus, 133
Eria, 256
Erica, 85, 98, 169, 205, 208, 248, 250, 279, 371
  arborea, 169, 198, 205, 228
  azorica, 169, 197
  ciliaris, 169, 293, 297, 304, fig. 65
  cinerea, 169, 301, fig. 65
  mackaiana, 287, 293
  mackaii, 287
  mediterranea, 169, 287, fig. 65
  tetralix, 169, 229, fig. 65
  vagans, 169, fig. 65
Ericaceae, 50, 53, 72, 139, 248, 250, 256
Ericeae, 205
Ericoideae, 55, 72
Erigeron, 88
  canadensis, 175
  multiradiatus, 196
Erinus, 133
  alpinus, 193
Erioblastus, 95
Eriobotrya, 96
Eriocaulaceae, 57
Eriocaulon, 88
  bipetalum, 227
  septangulare, 182, 293, 294
Eriocephalus, 139
  umbellatus, 208
Eriochilus, 150
Eriochrysis, 440
Eriodendron anfractuosum, 176
Eriogonum, 85
Eriophorum latifolium, 192
Eriosema, 90, 360
Eriostemon, 249, 256
Erisma, 440
Erismadelphus, 440
Eritrichium villosum, 192
Erodium, 88, 377, 443
Eryngium, 120, 443
Erythrina, 89
  caffra, 208
  corallodendron, 187
  crista-galli, 218

Erythrina excelsa, 201
  velutina, 188
Erythrocephalum, 137
Erythronium, 93
  grandiflorum, 200
Erythropalaceae, 68
Erythrophlaeum, 441
Erythrospermum, 442
Erythroxylaceae, 58
Erythroxylum, 90
  coca, 218
Escallonia, 26, 94
  micrantha, 218
Escalloniaceae, 63, 73
Eschscholzia, 85, 136
  californica, 200, 381
Espeletia, 218
Ethulia, 441
Eucalyptus, 26, 74, 85, 99, 100, 101, 186, 220, 221, 250–254, 259, 314, fig. 22
  alba, 100
  ampupa, 101
  confertiflora, 101
  deglupta, 100
  ficifolia, 220
  hemiphloia, 220
  marginata, 220
  oleosa, 220
  papuana, 101
  pilularis, 220
  polycarpa, 101
  regnans, 220, Plate 10
  tereticornis, 101
Eucharis grandiflora, 218
Euchlaena, 146
Euclasta, 440
  cordylotricha, 227
Euclea, 95
  undulata, 208
Eucommiaceae, 68
Eucryphia, 443, fig. 37
  cordifolia, 218
  glutinosa, fig. 38
Eucryphiaceae, 63
Eugenia, 85, 89, 246, 253, 254, 256
  caryophyllata, 210
  malaccensis, 212
Eugonia, 206
Eulophia, 90
Eulophidium, 440
Euodia, 253, 442
Euonymus, 92, fig. 21
Eupatorium, 85, 88
Euphorbia, 55, 85, 87, 171, 248
  abyssinica, 201
  buxifolia, 242
  canariensis, 198
  caput-medusae, 209
  cooperi, 208
  cyparissias, 344
  fulgens, 206
  helioscopia, 175
  ingens, Plate 8
  leucocephala, 216
  origanoides, 206
  peplus, 381
  pulcherrima, 216
  tetragona, 207
  tirucalli, 202

Euphorbiaceae, 50, 55, 57, 130, 140, 147, 219, 246, 248, 249, 251–256, 257
Euphorbieae, 248
Euphrasia, 289, 443
Eupomatia, 101
Eupomatiaceae, 69
Euptelea, 134
Eupteleaceae, 68
Euroschinus, 101
Eurotia, 439
Eurya, 390
Eurycentrum, 102
Euryops, 205
   tenuissima, 208
Eustrephus, 101
Euterpe edulis, 218
Evolvulus alsinoides, 176
Ewartia, 102
Exacum, 441
   affine, 201
Excoecaria agallocha, 210
Exocarpus, 126, 214, 444, fig. 51
Exochorda, 135
Exorrhiza, 102, 145
Exospermum, 144
Faba vulgaris, 382
Fadogia, 95
Fagaceae, 62
Fagonia, 443
   californica. 232
   chilensis, 232
Fagraea, 99
Fagus, 117, 439
   sieboldii, 196
   sylvatica, 193
Fargesia, 139
Farsetia aegyptiaca, 200
Fascicularia, 148
Fatsia, 134
   japonica, 196
Faurea, 78, 96
Feijoa sellowiana, 218
Fenzlia, 101
ferns, 6, 308
Fernseea, 147
Feronia elephantipes, 209
Feroniella, 97
Festuca, 88
Ficus, 85, 90, 253, 254, 256, 317
   bengalensis, 209
   carica, 197
   columnaris, 214
   elastica, 209
   pumila, 196
Fieldia australis, 220
figs, 22, 23, 253
Filicium, 441
Filipendula hexapetala, 287, 297
   ulmaria, 273
Fingerhuthia, 441
Finlaysonia obovata, 184
Finschia, 102
Firmiana, 441
Fitchia, 83
Fittonia argyronema, 218
Fitzalania, 150
Flacourtia, 441
   flavescens, 231
   indica, 231

Flacourtiaceae, 58
Flagellaria, 441
Flagellariaceae, 63, 72
Flaveria contrayerba, 187
Flemingia, 441
   saccifera, 176
Fleurya, 89
Flindersia, 99
Fluggea, 441
Foeniculum vulgare, 381
Foetidia, 442
Fontanea pancheri, 186
Foraminifera, 6, 329
Forstera, 102, fig. 3
Forsythia, 439
   suspensa, 196
Fortuynia, 136
Fothergilla, 439
Fouquieria splendens, 200
Fouquieriaceae, 66
Fragariopsis, 147
Francoa, 148
Francoaceae, 67
Frankenia, 88, 120, 443
   pulverulenta, 230
Frankeniaceae, 62
Franklandia, 151
Franklinia, 136, 236
   alatamaha, 234
Freesia, 140
   refracta, 208
Fremontia californica, 200
Frerea, 172, 173, fig. 56
Freycinetia, 129, 130, 256, 444
   arnotti, 212
Fritillaria, 92
   camschatcensis, 182
   imperialis, 196
   meleagris, 305
Fuchsia, 118, 247, 443
   coccinea, 218
   magellanica, 222
   procumbena, 118, 222
   rosea, 218
Fuirena umbellata, 175
Fumaria, 289
Fumariaceae, 60
fungi, 5, 368
Funtumia elastica, 261
Furcraea, 146
Gaertnera, 441
Gagea lutea, 192
Gahnia, 444
   gaudichaudii, 229, 231
   javanica, 231
Gaiadendron, 442
Gaillardia, 94
   aristata, 198
Gaimardia, 443
   australis, 232
   setacea, 231
Galanthus, 135
   nivalis, 305
Galeandra beyrichii, 188
Galega, 135
   officinalis, 344
Galeopsis tetrahit, 286
Galieae, 55
Galinsoga parviflora, 176

Galium, 88, 206
  aparine, 205, 377
  cruciata, 287
  mollugo, 299
  triflorum, 182
  verum, 299
Galphimia glauca, 216
Galtonia, 140
  candicans, 208
Ganophyllum, 441
Garcinia, 441
  cochinchinensis, 210
  mangostana, 210
Gardenia jasminoides, 210
Garrya, 136
  elliptica, 200
Garryaceae, 66
Gasteria, 139, 208, 248
Gastonia, 441
Gatesia, 136
Gaultheria, 246, 259, 443
  depressa, 187, 229
  leucocarpa, 184
  procumbens, 199
  shallon, 200
Gaura lindheimeri, 198
Gazania, 208
Gearum, 147
Geigera, 101
Geissaspis, 360, 441
Geissois, 102
Geissolomataceae, 68
Geitonoplesium, 101
Gelonium, 441
Gelsemium, 440
Geniosporum, 441
Geniostoma, 253, 442
  densiflora, 186
Genista anglica, 287
  dalmatica, 227
Genisteae, 248
Genlisea, 440
Gentiana, 85, 202, 235, 257, 259, 443, fig. 46
  acaulis, 193
  acuta, 182, 231
  amarella, 231, 301
  farreri, 196
  lutea, 193
  nivalis, 182, 191
  pneumonanthe, 293
  prostrata, 230
  purpurea, 191
  sino-ornata, 196
Gentianaceae, 53, 131, 258
Geodorum, 99
Geoffroea decorticans, 219
Geonoma, 76
  macroclona, 218
Geophila, 89
Geosiridaceae, 68
Geraniaceae, 55, 72
Geranium, 55, 88, 212
  ardjunense, 229
  caroliniense, 188
  dissectum, 230
  molle, 381
  pilosum, 184
  pratense, 192, 287
  robertianum, 381

Gerbera, 441
  jamesoni, 208
Gesneria cinnabarina, 216
Gesneriaceae, 57, 151, 193, 220, 253–256, 260
Geum, 371, 377, 443
  chiloense, 218
  montanum, 193
  rivale, 182, 230
  urbanum, 230
Gevuina, 78, 439, 443
giant water-lily, 217
Gibbaeum album, Plate 11
Gigantochloa, 97
Gilia, 382
  pusillia, 230
Gilibertia, 442
Gillbeea, 101
Gillespiea, 145
Giseckia, 441
Givotia, 442
Gladiolus, 85, 98, 208, 248
Glaucidium, 440
Glaux, 74, 75
Glecoma hederacea, 382
Gleditsia, 439
  aquatica, 428
Glehnia, 439
Glinus, 90
Globularia cordifolia, 193
Globulariaceae, 67
Glomera, 254, 256
Gloriosa, 441
  superba, 228
  virescens, 185
Glossonema, 137
Gloxinia, 146
Glyceria, 88
  fluitans, 174
Glycine max, 196
  soya, 196
Glycyrrhiza, 443
Gnaphalium, 88
  luteo-album, 175
Gnetaceae, 58
Gnetum, 90
  gnemon, 184
  macrostachyum, 211
Gnidia, 206, 441
Godetia, 94, 200
Gomortegaceae, 67
Gomophocarpus, 440
Gompholobium, 101, 150
Gomphrena globosa, 176
Goniocladus, 145
Goniosperma, 145
Gonolobus, 94
Gonystylaceae, 69
Goodenia, 150, 249, 256
  pinnatifida, 186
Goodeniaceae, 63, 72, 220, 249, 254, 256
Gordonia, 440
gorse, 377
Gossypium, 90
  arboreum, 176
  barbadense, 187
  hirsutum, 227
  peruvianum, 176
Goupiaceae, 66
Gramineae, 50, 52, 53, 89, 95, 144, 152, 177, 187, 205, 213, 223, 241, 248, 249, 251, 253–257

Grammatophyllum, 100
Grammatotheca, 80
Grangea, 441
grape vine, 194
grapple plant, 377
Graptophyllum pictum, 211
grasses, 2, 3, 6, 53, 148, 212, 213, 220, 224, 225, 233, 286, 353, 371, 376
grass-trees, 250
Greslania, 82, 144
Grevillea, 99, 186, 249, 254, 256
　robusta, 220
Grevilleoideae, 78
Grewia, 441
　villosa, 183
Greyiaceae, 68
Grias cauliflora, 216
Grisebachia, 139
Griselinia, 443
　litoralis, 222
Grossulariaceae, 60
ground-nut, 147
Grubbiaceae, 68
Guajacum, 146
　officinale, 188
Guamia, 145
Guarea, 440
Guettarda speciosa, 242
Gulubia, 100
Gunnera, 128, 246, 444, fig. 52
　chilensis, 218, Plate 9
　petaloides, 212
　scabra, 222
Gunneraceae, 63
Guttiferae, 58
Guya, 139
Gymnanthera nitida, 184
Gymnelaea, 127, 439, 444
Gymnema, 441
　stenophylla, 229
　sylvestre, 183
Gymnocladus, 440
　canadensis, 199
Gymnosperms, 6, fig. 73.
Gymnostachys, 156
Gynandropsis, 90
　gynandra, 176
Gynerium sagittatum, 188
Gynocardia odorata, 209
Gynotroches, 142
Gynura, 441
Gypsophila, 135
Gyrocarpus, 89
　jacquinii, 176
Gyrostemonaceae, 69
Haastia, 151
　pulvinaria, 222
Habenaria, 85
Haberlea fernandii-corburgii, 193
　rhodopensis, 193
Hachettea, 144
Haematoxylum capechianum, 216
Haemodoraceae, 64, 73
Haemodorum, 101, 150
Hagenia, 138
Hagenia abyssinica, 202
hairy buttercup, 9
Hakea, 150, 220, 249, 256
Halesia, 440

Halfordia, 101
Hallieracantha, 142
Halopegia, 441
Halopeplis perfoliata, 200
Halophila, 442
　baillonis, 232
　decipiens, 232
　ovalis, 212, 240, 423
Haloragaceae, 56, 73, 259
Haloragis, 99, 117, 246, 443
　micrantha, 184
Haloxylon ammodendron, 196
　salicornicum, 200
Hamamelidaceae, 64, 314
Hamamelis, 440
　japonica, 196
　vernalis, 448
　virginiana, 198
Hammarbya paludosa, 304
Hancornia speciosa, 218
Haplocarpha, 205
Haplopappus, 246
harebell, 366
Harpagophytum, 377
Harrimanella, 439, fig. 58
Harrisonia, 441
Harungana madagascariensis, 185
Haworthia, 208
hazel, 276, 330
heather, 105, 343
heaths, 105, 169, 343, 382
Hebe, 117, 221, 222, 257, 259, 443, fig. 37
Hebenstreitia, 205
Heberdenia, 439
Hedera, 95
　helix, 285
Hedstromia, 145
Hedycarya, 101
Hedychium, 442
　coronarium, 184
　gardnerianum, 210
Hedyosmum arborescens, 188
Hedyotis adscensionis, 206
Hedysareae, 253
Hedysarum obscurum, 191
Hedyscepe, 144
Heisteria, 440
Helenium, 94
　autumnale, 198
Heliamphora, 147, 235
　nutans, 235
Helianthemum, 439
　nummularium, 303
　vulgare, 303
Helianthus, 94
Helichrysum, 85, 205, 206, 208, 256
　bracteatum, 220
　vestitum, 209
Helicia, 78, 99
Heliconia binai, 188
Helicopsis, 78
Helicteres, 442
Helictotrichon pratense, 287
Helinus, 441
Heliophila, 139, 248
Heliotropium, 88
　indicum, 176
　peruvianum, 218

Helipterum, 220, 443
Helleborus, 135
Helmholtzia, 101
Helwingia, 134
Helxine, 135
Hemarthria, 441
Hemiandra, 151
Hemidesmus indicus, 185
Hemiphues, 102, 150
  suffocatus, 187
Hemiscolopia trimera, 228
hemp, 344
Hepatica triloba, 231
Heracleum sphondylium, 192
Heritiera, 441
Hermannia, 90, 248, 442
Herminium monorchis, 304
Hermodactylus tuberosus, 197
Hernandia, 253, 442, fig. 33
  peltata, fig. 32
Hernandiaceae, 58
Herniaria, 443
  hemistemon, 200
Herpolirion, 102
Herpysma, 97
Hesperocnide, 444
Hesperomannia, 82
Hetaeria, 235
Heteradelphia, 137
Heteranthera, 440
Heteropholis, 439, 441
Heteropogon contortus, 176
Heteropteris, 440
Heteropyxidaceae, 68
Heterosmilax, 97
Heterospathe, 100
Heterostylaceae, 67
Heuchera, 94
Hevea, 147
  brasiliensis, 217
Hewardia, 150
Heylandia, 140
Hibbertia, 73, 109, 249, 252, 253, 254, 256, 259, 442, fig. 27
  volubilis, fig. 26
Hibiscus, 85, 89
  abelmoschus, 209
  aristivalvis, 183
  caesius, 183
  cannabinus, 176
  diversifolius, 227
  lobatus, 228
  micranthus, 228
  panduriformis, 183
  rosa-sinensis, 211
  sabdariffa, 176
  schizopetalus, 202
  surattensis, 183
  tiliaceus, 242
  trionum, 183
hickories, 198
Hieracium, 81, 283, 284, 287, 288, 289
Hierochloe, 88
Hillebrandia, 144
Himantandra, 101
Himantandraceae, 69
Himantochilus, 96
Himantoglossum hircinum, 304, 389

Hippeastrum, 94
Hippocastanaceae, 63
Hippocastanum, 439
Hippocratea, 90
Hippocrateaceae, 58
Hippocrepis, 135
  comosa, 303
Hippomane mancinella, 188, 242
Hippuridaceae, 62
Hippuris, 444
Hiptage, 442
Hirtella, 440
Hitchenia, 140
Hodgsonia, 96
Hoffmanseggia, 440
Hoheria, 151
  populnea, 221
Holarrhena, 441
Holcus, 98
  lanatus, 192, 286, 381
Holmbergia, 148
Holmskioldia, 441
  sanguinea, 209
Homalanthus, 99
Homogyne alpina, 286
Homonoia riparia, 185
Honkenya, 123, 444
hop, 370
Hopea, 96
Hoplestigmataceae, 67
Hordeum, 92
  nodosum, 301
  vulgare, 196
horizontal, 150
hornbeam, 371
Hortonia, 140
  angustifolia, 209
Hosta, 134
  plantaginea, 196
Hottonia, 74, 75, 439
  palustris, 305
Houttuynia, 440
Hovenia, 134
Howea, 144
  forsteriana, 214
Howellia, 80
Hoya, 85, 99, 256
  carnosa, 184
Huacaceae, 67
Hudsonia, 136
  montana, 235
Hugonia, 318, 441
Hugoniaceae, 58
Humbertiaceae, 68
Humblotidendron, 138
Humboldtia laurifolia, 209
Humea, 150
  elegans, 220
Humiriaceae, 63
Hunteria, 441
Hura, 146
  crepitans, 187, 377
Hyacinthus orientalis, 197
Hybanthus, 90
Hydatella, 102
Hydnocarpus, 96
Hydnophytum, 100
Hydnora, 96

Hydnoraceae, 63
Hydrangea, 440
    macrophylla, 196
    oblongifolia, 228
Hydrangeaceae, 63
Hydranthelium, 440
Hydrastis, 440
    canadensis, 198
Hydriastele, 101
Hydrilla, 441
Hydrocaryaceae, 64
Hydrocharitaceae, 56
Hydrocotyle, 88
    umbellata, 227
    verticillata, 228
    vulgaris, 286, 301
Hydrodea, 443
Hydrolea, 70
Hydrophylax, 441
Hydrophyllaceae, 69, 70
Hydrostachyaceae, 67
Hydrotriche, 138
Hymenaea courbaril, 188
Hymenanthera, 102
Hymenocardia, 441
    acida, 186
Hymenodictyon, 441
Hymenolobium, 147
Hymenolobus, 444
Hymenospermum, 101
Hyophorbe, 139
    amaricaulis, 236
Hyoscyamus, 98
Hyparrhenia rufa, 227
Hypecoum 95
    procumbens, 269
Hypericaceae, 53
Hypericum, 88, 205
    androsaemum, 303, 380
    coris, 232
    empetrifolium, 232
    gramineum, 186
    hirsutum, 287
    lalandii, 183
    lanceolatum, 185, 202
    mysorense, 228
    peplidifolium, 218
    roeperianum, 186
Hypertelis, 115, 443
Hyphaene crinita, 208
    thebaica, 201
Hypochaeris radicata, 381
Hypodiscus, 139
Hypoestes, 441
Hypogynium, 440
    spathiflorum, 227
Hypolaena, 443
    fastigiata, fig. 11
Hypopitys, 439
Hypoxidaceae, 57, 73
Hypoxis, 90
    pusilla, 187
Hypsela, 80
Hyptis, 80
    capitata, 176
    lobata, 228
    pectinata, 176
Hyssopus officinalis, 196
Icacinaceae, 58, 255

Ichnanthus, 442
Ilex paraguayensis, 218
Illecebraceae, 56
Illiciaceae, 63
Illicium, 440
Illigera, 441
Impatiens, 85, 88, 377
Imperata cylindrica, 183
Incarvillea delavayi, 196
Indigofera, 85, 90, 248
    tinctoria, 209
Indorouchera, 97
Inga vera, 187
Inocarpus, 442
Inula helenium, 304
    salicina, 287
Inuleae, 248, 250
Iodes, 318, 441
Iphigenia, 441
Ipomoea, 85, 90
    horsfalliae, 209
    pes-caprae, 233, 242
Iresine celosia, 176
Iridaceae, 57, 205, 248
Iris, 92
    ensata, 195
    halophila, 196
    sibirica, 194
    stylosa, 197
    susiana, 197
Irvingia, 439, 441
Irvingiaceae, 63
Isoplexis, 135
Isopogon, 150
Isotoma longiflora, 176
Itatiaea, 147
Itea, 440
Itoa, 97
Ixerba, 151, 439, 442
    brexioides, 222
Ixia, 208
Ixonanthaceae, 58
Ixora, 90
    coccinea, 210
Jacaranda, 146
    mimosaefolia, 188
Jacksonia, 150
Jacobinia, 146
Jankaea heldrichii, 193
Jasione, 135
Jasminum, 85, 90
    grandiflorum, 209
    nudiflorum, 196
    officinale, 196
    rex, 210
Jatropha curcas, 187
    pungens, 187
Jeffersonia, 440
Jodina, 148
Joinvillea, 444
Jovellana, 118, 247, 443, fig. 37
Juania, 148
Jubaea, 148
    spectabilis, 218
Juglandaceae, 60
Juglans, 92
    nigra, 198, 227
Julianiaceae, 66
Jumella, 250

Juncaceae, 53, 258
Juncaginaceae, 62, 73
Juncus, 88, 186, 258, 301, 377
  acutus, 163
  andicola, 163
  antarcticus, 163
  articulatus, 163
  biglumus, 163
  bufonius, 163
  bulbosus, 163
  capitatus, 163
  communis, 224
  compressus, 163
  conglomeratus, 163, 285
  dichotomus, 163
  dudleyi, 293
  effusus, 285
  falcatus, 163
  gerardii, 163
  inflexus, 163
  lomatophyllus, 164
  marginatus, 163
  maritimus, 163
  pauciflorus, 163
  planifolius, 163
  prismatocarpus, 163
  scheuchzerioides, 224
  stygius, 182
  tenuis, 163, 293
  triglumis, 163
  xiphioides, 163
Jussieua erecta, 227
  peruviana, 187
  repens, 176
  suffruticosa, 176
Justicia, 85, 89
Kadua, 144
Kaempferia, 441
Kalanchoe, 113, 442
  blossfeldiana, 206
  coccinea, 185
  daigremontiana, 206
  uniflora, 206
Kalmia, 94
  latifolia, 98
kapok, 372
Kedrostis, 441
Kennedya, 150
Kentia, 101
Keraudrenia, 442
Kerguelen cabbage, 119
Kermadecia, 102
Kerria, 134
  japonica, 196
Khaya, 137
  senegalensis, 201
Kibara, 99
Kibessia, 142
Kielmeyera, 147
Kigelia aethiopica, 201
Kingia, 151
  australis, 220
Kingiodendron, 100
Kirengeshoma, 134
Kissenia, 115, 443
Kissodendron, 101
Kleinia neriifolia, 198
  scottii, 201
Klugia, 442

Knightia, 102, 258
  excelsa, 222
Kniphofia, 98, 205, 208
Knoxia, 99
Kobresia tibetica, 196
Kochia, 443
Koeberliniaceae, 66
Koeleria, 443
  cristata, 205
Koenigia islandica, 286
Kolkwitzia, 134
  amabilis, 196
Korthalsella, 253, 444
  opuntia, 185
Krameria, 94
  triandra, 218
Krameriaceae, 66
Kraunhia, 440
Labiatae, 26, 50, 53, 221, 246, 255, 256, 259, 376
Labichea, 150
Labordea, 144
Laburnum, 133
  anagyroides, 193
  vulgare, 193
Lachenalia, 139, 248
Lacistemaceae, 66
Lactoridaceae, 67, 260
Lactoris, 148
Lactuca alpina, 191
Laelia, 146
Lagenandra, 140
Lagenophora, 444
  billardierii, 184
  forsteri, 222
Lagerstroemia indica, 210
Lagetta, 146
  lagetto, 216
Laggera, 441
Lagunaria, 102, 144
Laguncularia, 440
  racemosa, 240
Lambertia, 150
  formosa, 220
Lamium, 95
  album, 192, 381
  purpureum, 381
Landolphia, 440
  owariensis, 201
Lannea, 318, 360
Lantana camara, 216
  mixta, 176
Lapageria, 148
  rosea, 218, fig. 9
Laplacea, 442
Laportea, 90
Lardizabala, 148, 444
Lardizabalaceae, 62
Larrea divaricata, 218
  mexicana, 216
Lasianthus, 441
Lasiosiphon, 441
Lastarriaca chilensis, 230
Latania loddigesii, 236
Lathyrus, 92
  maritimus, 182
  odoratus, 382
  palustris, 287
  pratensis, 192
  sylvestris, 287

Latipes senegalensis, 183
Lauraceae, 57, 160 256
Laurelia, 443
    aromatica, 218
    novae-zealandiae, 222
laurels, 22, 23
Laurembergia, 441
Laurentia, 80
Laurus canariensis, 198
    nobilis, 197, 227, 428
Lautea, 145
Lavandula, 135
    rotundifolia, 198
    spica, 197, 428
Lavoisiera, 147
Lawsonia inermis, 200
Lebeckia, 139
Lebetanthus, 152, 443
Lecanthus, 441
Lechenaultia, 101, 150
Lecythidaceae, 66
Ledocarpaceae, 66
Ledothamnus, 147
Leeaceae, 63
Leersia, 88
Legenere, 80
Leguminosae, 50, 89, 130, 147, 177, 213, 221, 241
Leiocarpus, 148
Leiphaimos, 440
Leitgebia, 147
Leitneria floridana, 428
Leitneriaceae, 66
Lemna, 88, 174, 375, 376
Lemnaceae, 56
Lennoaceae, 66
Lentibulariaceae, 56
Leonotis leonurus, 186
    nepetifolia, 176
Leontopodium, 439
    alpinum, 193
Leopoldinia piassaba, 218
    pulchra, 217
Lepidium, 88
    sativum, 344, 382
Lepidobotryaceae, 67
Lepidosperma, 99
Lepinia, 102
Lepironia, 441
Lepistemon, 441
Leptadenia, 137
    pyrotechnica, 200
Leptarrhena, 95
Leptocarpus, 248, 443
Leptocladus, 440
Leptonychia, 441
Leptospermoideae, 73, 250, 254
Leptospermum, 99
    flavescens, 184
    scoparium, 186, 222
Leptotes, 147
Lepturus cylindricus, 230
Lepuropetalon, 444
Lespedeza, 91, 442
Leucadendron, 139, 248
    argenteum, 209
Leucas martinicensis, 176
Leucogenes, 151
Leucojum vernum, 305
Leucopogon, 318

Leucospermum conocarpum, 209
Levenhookia, fig. 3
Lewisia, 136
    rediviva, 200
Leycesteria, 134
    formosa, 382
Liatris, 93
    pycnostachya, 198
Libertia, 443
    pulchella, 186
Licuala, 76, 99
Lightfootia, 96
Liguliflorae, 83
Ligustrum, 439
lilac, 305
Lilaeopsis, 117, 443
    lineata, 229
Liliaceae, 50, 53, 130
lilies, 6
Lilium asiaticum, 196
    candidum, 197
    chalcedonicum, 197
    longiflorum, 196
    philadelphicum, 198
    tigrinum, 196
lime, 276, 371
Limnanthaceae, 66
Limnanthemum, 88
Limnocharis flava, 176
Limonia, 441
Limonium, 88, 289, 443
    guyonianum, 200
    suworowii, 196
Limosella, 88
Linaceae, 55
Linaria alpina, 193
    vulgaris, 303
Lindackeria, 444
Lindenia, 442
    vitiensis, 136
Linnaea borealis, 355
Linospadix, 101
Linostoma, 442
Linum, 55, 85, 88, 272, 273
    bienne, 298
    catharticum, 286
    usitatissimum, 304, 382
Liparis, 254, 256
    loeselii, 182
Liparophyllum, 102, 254, 256
Lippia citriodora, 218
Liquidambar, 107, 439
Liriodendron, 109, 312, 313, 440, fig. 74
    tulipifera, Plate 18
Liriope, 134
Lissocarpa, 147
Lissocarpaceae, 66
Listera cordata, 182
    ovata, 192
Litchi, 134
Lithops, 207
Litsea, 318
Littorella, 123, 444
    uniflora, 231
Livistona, 77, 99
    chinensis, 196
lizard orchid, 389
Lloydia serotina, 286
Loasaceae, 63

Lobelia, 80, 85, 88, 204, 205
  aberdarica, 204
  anceps, 229
  bambuseti, 204
  bequaertii, 204
  burttii, 204
  cardinalis, 198
  columnaris, 204
  conraui, 204
  deckenii, 204
  dortmanna, 182
  elgonensis, 204
  erinus, 208
  fulgens, 216
  gibberoa, 204
  inflata, 198
  keniensis, 204
  lanuriensis, 204
  lechenaultii, 209
  longisepala, 204
  lugwangulensis, 204
  mildbraedii, 204
  nicotianifolia, 209
  petiolata, 205
  rhynchopetalum, 204, Plate 13
  sattimae, 204
  stricklandae, 204
  suavibracteata, 205
  telekii, 204
  trichandra, 209
  usafuensis, 204
  utshungwensis, 204
  volkensii, 204
  wollastonii, 204
Lobeliaceae, 52, 57, 74, 78, 144, 212, 248
Lobelioideae, 49
Lochnera, 90, 176, 442
Lodoicea, 139, 373
Loeflingia, 439
Loesneriella, 99
Loganiaceae, 49, 58
Loiseleuria, 93
Lolium, 88
  perenne, 286
Lomandra, 101, 150
Lomatia, 78, 443
Lomatophyllum, 138
Lonchocarpus, 442
  latifolius, 188
Londesia, 136
Lonicera nitida, 196
  persica, 196
Lophira alata, 201, 233
  procera, 233
Lophophora williamsii, 266
Lophoschoenus, 253
Lophostoma, 442
Loranthaceae, 57, 255
Loranthus, 85, 98
  acaciae, 201
  estipitatus, 185
  falcatus, 184
Lotus corniculatus, 233, 286, 299
  uliginosus, 233
Loudetia, 440
  flammula, 232
  phragmitoides, 232
Lowiaceae, 69
Loxocarpus, 235

Lucuma mammosa, 188
Ludwigia, 88
  palustris, 227
  parviflora, 174
Luffa aegyptiaca, 209
Lumnitzera, 441
Lunaria, 133
Lunasia, 142
Lupinus, 439
  arboreus, 200
  luteus, 344
  nootkatensis, 200
  polyphyllus, 200
Luronium natans, 227
Luzula, 88, 377
  campestris, 174, 224
  pilosa, 231
  saltuensis, 231
Lyallia, 152
Lycaste, 146
  skinneri, 216
Lychnis dioica, 370
  flos-cuculi, 286
  fulgens, 194
Lychnophora, 147
Lycopersicon esculentum, 218
Lycopsis arvensis, 303
Lycoris, 134
Lyperanthus, 104
  gigas, 186
Lysiana, 102
Lysichiton, 231
Lysimachia, 74, 75, 85, 88, 444
Lytanthus, 135
Lythraceae, 55
Maba foliosa, 186
Macadamia, 99
Macaranga, 256, 441
Macarthuria, 150
Macgregoria, 151
Machaerium firmum, 218
Mackinlaya, 101
Maclura aurantiaca, 199
  pomifera, 199, 428
Macrolobium, 440
Macropiper, 102
Macropodium, 133
Macrosolen avenis, 185
  cochinchinensis, 185
Maddenia, 134
Madia sativa, 187
Maerua, 98
  dupontii, 236
Maesa, 441
  lanceolata, 185
Maesobotrya, 137
Magallana, 152
Magnolia, 25, 109, 318, 440
  campbellii, 196
  grandiflora, 198, 428
  kobus, 196
Magnoliaceae, 63, 131, 160
Magnolieae, fig. 23
Mahonia, 80, 81, 439, fig. 17
  aquifolium, 200
Maianthemum bifolium, 231
  canadense, 231
maize, 3
Malaisia tortuosa, 184

Malaxis, 254, 256
  paludosa, 304
Malcolmia heudelotiana, 233
  macrophylla, 233
Malesherbiaceae, 66
Mallotus, 441
Malope, 135
  trifida, 197
Malouetia, 440
Malpighia glabra, 188
Malpighiaceae, 58
Malus pumila, 193
Malva moscata, 194
  rotundifolia, 380
  sylvestris, 304
Malvaceae, 55, 177
Malvales, 372
Malvaviscus grandiflora, 188
Mammea americana, 188
Mammillaria vivipara, 353
Mandevilla suaveolens, 218
Mandragora officinarum, 197
Manettia bicolor, 218
Mangifera, 96
  indica, 184
mangroves, 91, 240–242
Manicaria, 147
  saccifera, 216
Manihot glaziovii, 218
Maniltoa gemmipara, 211
Manisuris, 441
Mansonia, 441
Mantanoa bipinnatifolia, 216
Mantisia saltatoria, 210
maple, 273, 370
Mappia, 442
Maprounea, 440
maranta, 146
  arundinacea, 188
Marantaceae, 58
Marantochloa cuspidata, 210
Marcgravia nepenthoides, 216
Marcgraviaceae, 66
Margaretta, 137
Marlea, 441
Marsdenia, 90
Marsippospermum, 443
Martynia, 146, 377
Martyniaceae, 66
Mathurina, 139
Matricaria discoidea, 305
  matricarioides, 305, 371, 382
Matthaea, 128
Maurandia barclayana, 216
Mauritia, 216
  flexuosa, 216
  vinifera, 218
Mauritiella, 147
Maxwellia, 144
Mayaca, 440
Mayacaceae, 63
Mazus pumilio, 187
Mecomischus, 136
Meconopsis, 107, 134, 439
  baileyi, 196
  betonicifolia, 196
Medicago, 135
  arabica, 298
Medinilla, 254, 256, 441

Medusagynaceae, 68
Medusagyne, 139
Medusandraceae, 67
Meehania, 136
Melaleuca, 99, 249, 252, 256, 259
  acuminata, 221
  leucadendron, 360
Melampyrum pratense, 300
Melandrium dioicum, 370
Melanodendron, 83, 139
Melanorrhoea usitata, 210
Melanoselinum, 83, 135
Melasma, 440
Melastoma, 253, 442
Melastomataceae, 26, 50, 58, 147, 206, 251,
  254–256
Melhania, 98
Meliaceae, 58, 131, 254, 256
Melianthaceae, 67, 72
Melicope, 442
Melicytus, 102
  ramiflorus, 229
Melinis minutiflora, 218
Meliosma, 318, 442
Melissa parviflora, 228
Melittis, 133
  melissophyllum, 304
Mellisea, 139
Melothria, 89
Memecylon, 441
  umbellatum, 209
Menispermaceae, 57, 255
Menispermum, 107, 440
  canadense, 199
Mentha, 88
  pulegium, 381
Mentzelia, 94
  albicans, 230
Menyanthaceae, 56
Menyanthes, 92
  trifoliata, 182
Menziesia, 95
Merckia, 95
Merrilliodendron, 102
Mertensia maritima, 182
Meryta, 102
Mesembryanthemum, 26, 84, 85, 119, 140, 200
  248, 250
  forskahlei, 208
Mesua, 96
Metalasia, 139
  muricata, 209
Metaplexis, 134
Metastelma, 94
  parviflora, 188
Metatrophis, 145
Metrosideros, 128, 444, fig, 53
  polymorpha, 128
  robusta, 222
Metroxylum, 100
  rumphii, 210
Mezoneuron, 441
Michaelmas daisies, 198
Michauxia, 135
Michelia, 97
  champaca, 210
Miconia, 85
Micraira, 150
  subulifolia, 220

Micrargeria, 442
Microcarpaea muscosa, 184
Micrococca, 442
Microdesmis, 441
Microglossa, 442
　pyrifolia, 176
Microlaena, 101
　stipoides, 229
Microtea, 440
Microtis, 99
　parvifolia, 186
Microtropis, 442
Mikania, 90
　scandens, 176
Milium effusum, 182
milk thistle, 219
Millettia, 441
Milligania, 150
Miltonia, 146
Mimetes, 140
　lysigera, 209
Mimosa, 85, 90
　pudica, 176
Mimosaceae, 50, 57, 89, 177, 248, 249
Mimulus, 442
　guttatus, 304
　moschatus, 200
Mimusops, 89
　balata, 184
Minuartia arctica, 182
Mirabilis jalapa, 188
Mirbelia, 150
mistletoe, 377
Mitchella, 440
Mitella, 439
　nuda, 182
Mitragyna, 441
Mitrasacme, 99
　montana, 187
Mitrastemon kawasasakii, 228
Mitreola, 442
Moenchia erecta, 304
Mourenhoutia, 102
Molinia caerulea, 286, 301, fig. 72
Molluginaceae, 58
Mollugo verticillata, 188
Molucella laevis, 196
Momordica charantia, 176
Monarda, 94
　fistulosa, 198
Monimiaceae, 58, 64, 73
Monochoria, 441
Monococcus, 150
Monocotyledons, 6, 49, 129, 144, 154, 201, 206, 212, 221, 248, 250, 304, 314, 407
Monodora myristica, 201
Monotaxis, 150
Monotes, 137
Monotoca, 150
Monotropa, 439
　hypopithys, 301
Monotropaceae, 60
Monstera, 146
　deliciosa, 216
Montbretia, 208, 305
Montia, 88, 443
　fontana, 174, 224
　lamprosperma, 182

Montiniaceae, 67
Montrichardia arborescens, 217
Montrouzeria, 144
Moraceae, 57, 254–256, 258
Moraea, 249
Morettia, 138
Morina, 95
Morinda, 90
　citrifolia, 184
Moringaceae, 69
Morus alba, 196
Moschosma, 442
Mosla dianthera, 228
mosses, 5, 26
Mostuea, 440
Mucuna pruriens, 176, *bennettii*, 211
　urens, 227
Muehlenbeckia, 443
　axillaris, 186
Muiria hortenseae, Plate 11
Mulgedium alpinum, 191
Mulinum spinosum, 222
Mundulea, 442
　sericea, 228
Muntingia culubura, 188
Murraya koenigii, 209
Musa, 441
　acuminata, 210
　balbisiana, 210
　cavendishii, 183
　coccinea, 210
　holstii, 202
　paradisiaca, 183
　textilis, 210
Musaceae, 63
Muscari, 135
Mussaenda, 442
　erythrophylla, 202
Musschia, 135
mustards, 344
Mutisia, 94
　clematis, 218
　viciaefolia, 218
Myoporaceae, 49, 64, 256
Myoporum, 253, 444
Myosotidium, 151
Myosotis, 257, 376, 443
　alpestris, 182, 191
　antarctica, 229
　arvensis, 368, 376
　palustris, 192
　versicolor, 286
Myosurus, 120, 443
　aristatus, 229
Myrcia, 85
Myrianthemum, 206
Myrica, 85
　cerifera, 216
　faya, 198
　gale, 301
Myricaceae, 70
Myricaria prostrata, 196
Myriophyllum, 56, 88
　elatinoides, 224
　spicatum, 174
Myristica fragrans, 210
Myristicaceae, 58
Myrmecodia, 99
Myrothamnaceae, 67

Myrothamnus, 96
    flabellifer, 186
Myrsinaceae, 58, 253, 255
Myrsine, 442
    africana, 185
Myrtaceae, 50, 58, 73, 142, 144, 213, 246, 249, 250, 252, 254–256, 259
Myrteae, 254
myrtles, 22, 23, 428
Myrtus, 443
    communis, 227, 428
    nummularia, 222
Myzodendraceae, 67
Myzodendron, 149
Nablonium, 150
Najadaceae, 56
Najas, 88
    marina, 174
    minor, 269
Nama, 444
Nandina, 134
    domestica, 196
Nannoseris, 205
Napoleona, 137
Narcissus, 135, 197
    biflorus, 305
    jonquilla, 197
    poeticus, 193
    pseudo-narcissus, 194
Nardosmia glacialis, 190
Nardostachys, 134
    jatamansi, 209
Naregamia, 441
Nargedia, 140
Narthecium, 439
    ossifragum, 301
Nassauvia, 149, 246
Nasturtium, 88
    officinale, 380, 381
Nauclea, 99
Nautonia, 147
Nectandra antillana, 216
    rodioei, 217
Nectaropetalaceae, 68
Negria, 144, 260
Neillia thyrsiflora, 228
Nelumbo, 113, 442, fig. 77
    nucifera, fig. 76
Nemesia, 208
Nemophila menziesii, 200
Nengella, 255
Neocinnamomum caudatum, 228
Neomarica northiana, 218
Neoschroetera tridentata, 216
Neosepicaea, 101
Neotinea intacta, 287, fig. 66
Neottia, 95
Neoveitchia, 145
Nepenthaceae, 63
Nepenthes, 105, 252, 253, 442, fig. 25
    gracilis, fig. 24
    mirabilis, 211
Nepeta cataria, 304
    mussinii, 196
Nephelium lappaceum, 184
Nephrodesmus, 253
Nephrophyllidium, 439
Neptunia oleracea, 188
Nerine bowdenii, 207

Nerium oleander, 197
Nertera, 126, 444
    depressa, 244, 248
Nervilia aragoana, 184
Nesiota, 139
Nesogenes, 443
Neurada, 136
    procumbens, 200
Neuropheltis, 441
Neurotheca, 440
    loeselioides, 227
Neviusia, 136
    alabamensis, 235
Newcastlia, 151
New Zealand flax, 260
Neyraudia, 442
    madagascariensis, 228
Niaouli, 252, 360
Nicandra physalodes, 218
Nicotiana, 113, 442
    affinis, 219
    debaryi, 113
    fragrans, 113
    suaveolens, 220
    tabacum, 218
Nidularium, 147
Niederlinia, 152
Nigella, 135
    damascena, 197
Nigritella, 133
    nigra, 191
Nipa, 99, 318, fig. 75, Plate 19
    fruticans, 242, 373
Nitraria, 443
    schoeberi, 230
Nolanaceae, 67
Nolina, 136
Nomocharis, 134
Nonnea alba, 233
    ventricosa, 233
Norantea guianensis, 118
Nothocestrum, 144
Nothofagus, 117, 118, 246, 247, 314, 443, fig. 37
    betuloides, 222
    cunninghamii, 220
    fusca, 222
    pumila, 222
Nothosaerva, 442
Notonerium gossei, 235
Notothlaspi, 151
Nuytsia, 151
    floribunda, 220
Nyctaginaceae, 57, 377
Nymphaea, 88
    caerulea, 186
    mexicana, 428
    odorata, 428
Nymphaeaceae, 56
Nyssa, 440
    aquatica, 199
Nyssaceae, 63
oak, 273, 276, 330, 337
oats, 3
Oberonia, 254, 256, 442
Oceanopapaveraceae, 69
Ochlandra, 82, 442
    stridula, 209
Ochna, 442
Ochnaceae, 58

Ochradenus, 136
Ochrocarpos, 442
Ochroma, 146, 318
  lagopus, 188
Ochrosia, 253, 318, 444
Ochthocharis, 142
Ochthocosmos, 440
Ocimum, 89
  basilicum, 183
Ocotea, 317
  bullata, 208
  leucoxylon, 216
Octoknema, 137
Octoknemataceae, 68
Odina, 317, 442
Odontadenia grandiflora, 210
Oenothera, 94
Olacaceae, 58, 131
Olax, 318, 442
Oldenburgia, 139
Oldenlandia herbacea, 176
Oldfieldia, 137
Olea, 442
  chrysophylla, 202
  europaea, 197
  verrucosa, 208
Oleaceae, 55, 131
Olearia, 83, 85, 101, 257
  haastii, 222
  nitida, 220
  paniculata, 222
Oligomeris, 122, 443
Oliniaceae, 68, 72
Olyra, 440
Omania, 136
ombu tree, 219
Omphalea, 442
  triandra, 242
Onagraceae, 53, 257
Oncidium, 85, 146
  luridum, 188
  papilio, 218
  pulchellum, 188
Oncoba, 318
  spinosa, 185
Oncostemon, 138, 250
Oncotheca, 144
Onobrychis, 304
Ononis spinosa, 287
Ophrys, 135
  sphegodes, 304
Opilia, 441
Opiliaceae, 58,
Oplismenus hirtellus, 176
Opophytum forskahlei, 200
Opuntia, 94, Plate 6
  darwinii, 222
  missouriensis, 353
  vulgaris, 382
Orchidaceae, 49, 52, 53, 57, 89, 147, 187, 213, 221, 246, 248, 249, 251, 252, 254–257
orchids, 144, 146, 160, 211, 214, 216, 258, 259
Orchipeda, 442
Orchis elodes, 303
  ericetorum, 303
  fuchsii, 303
  kerryensis, 287
  occidentalis, 287
  traunsteinerioides, 287

Orchis ustulata, 304
Oreobolus, 444
  obtusangulus, 229
Oreocallis, 78, 443
  grandiflora, fig. 15
Oreodaphne foetens, 198
Oreodoxa oleracea, 188
  regia, 216
Oreomunnea, 442
Oreomyrrhis, 18, 443, fig. 39
Oreophyton, 137
Oreostylidium, 151, fig. 3
Oricia, 137
Origanum, 135
Orites, 78, 443
Ormocarpum sennoides, 228
Ornithogalum umbellatum, 305
Ornithopus perpusillus, 287
Orobanchaceae, 62
Orobanche, 88
Oropetium, 441
Orthanthera, 441
Orthoceras, 101
  strictum, 186
Orthosanthos, 442
Orthosiphon, 442
Oryza coarctata, 209
Osbeckia, 442
Osbornia, 101
Osmanthus, 439
  delavayi, 196
Osmelia, 96
Osteomeles, 444
  anthyllidifolia, 184
Osteospermum, 205
Ostrearia, 64
Ostrowskia, 135
Ostrya, 439
  virginiana, 226
Ottochloa, 441
Ourisia, 443
Oxalidaceae, 55, 72, 246
Oxalis, 55, 85, 88, 246, 247, 248, 377
  acetosella, 182, 231, 286
  enneaphylla, 222
  lactea, 231
  magellanica, 232
  montana, 231
  rosea, 176
Oxera, 144
Oxybaphus, 442
Oxylobium, 150
Oxyria digyna, 182, 272
Oxytenanthera, 82, 441
  abyssinica, 186
Oxytheca dendroides, 230
Oxytropis foliosa, 227
Pachira insignis, 216
Pachygone, 99
Pachynema, 150
Pachypodium namaquanum, 207
Pachysandra, 440
Pachystigma, 360
Paederia, 442
Paeonia, 107, 439
  officinalis, 197
Paeoniaceae, 63
Paepalanthus, 440
  lamarckii, 227

Palaquium gutta, 184
Palaua, 145
Palmae, 50, 58, 73, 74, 75–77, 145, 236, 251, 253–255, 258, 373, fig. 14
palms, 22, 23, 26, 75–77, 148, 160, 214, 217, 218, 220, 233, 251, 253, 257, 260, 310
Pamphilea, 147
Panax, 440
  schinseng, 195
Pancheria, 144
Pandaceae, 68
Pandanaceae, 63, 72, 256, 258
Pandanus, 129, 130, 214, 444
  tectorius, 220
  vandermeeschii, 236
Pangium, 100, 142
Panicoideae, 89
Panicum, 85, 88
  decompositum, 186
  maximum, 228
pansies, 7
Papaver, 122, 370, 443
  aculeatum, 229
  orientale, 196
  rhoeas, 381
Papaveraceae, 62
Paphia, 101
Papilionaceae, 50, 52, 53, 89, 139, 177, 246, 248, 249, 251, 253–256, 259
Pappophorum nigricans, 186
Para rubber, 147, 217
Parabarium, 140
Paraboea, 142
Paracryphia, 144
Paradisea liliastrum, 193
Paragulubia, 115
Paralinospadix, 255
Paratheria, 440
  prostrata, 227
Parentucellia viscosa, 305
Parietaria, 88
Parinari, 360
  excelsa, 227
Paris, 95
  quadrifolia, 192, 287
Parkia bicolor, 233
  filicoidea, 233
  roxburghii, 184
Parkinsonia, 440
Parmentiera cerifera, 216
Parnassia palustris, 305
Parnassiaceae, 60
Parochetus, 441
  communis, 183
Paropsia, 442
Parrotia, 439
Parrya, 132
  nudicaulis, 182
Parsonsia, 99, 253
Parthenocissus tricuspidata, 196
Parvatia, 144
Paspalum distichum, 175
Passerina, 422
Passiflora, 85, 442
  caerulea, 218
  edulis, 218
  foetida, 176
Passifloraceae, 58, 151
Patersonia, 99

Paullinia, 440
  cupana, 217
  pinnata, 227
  sorbilis, 217
Paulownia, 134
  tomentosa, 196
Pavetta, 90, 442
Pavonia, 90
  schimperiana, 183
Payena, 97
peach, 384
pecans, 198
Peckelia, 202
Peckeliopanax, 102
Pectinaria, 140
Pedaliaceae, 69
Pedalium, 442
Pedicularis, 85, 190
  rosea, 227
  sudetica, 182
Pedilanthus, 441
  tithymaloides, 188
Peganum, 439
  harmala, 200
Pelagodoxa, 145
Pelargonium, 85, 115, 205, 248, 249, 443
  acerifolium, 208
  australe, 224
  inodorum, 187
  zonale, 381
Pelea, 143, 253
Pelletiera, 74, 75
Pellicieraceae, 66
Peltandreae, 252
Pemphis, 442
  acidula, 242
Penaeaceae, 68
Pennantia, 102
Pennisetum glaucum, 209
  purpureum, 186
Penstemon, 85, 95, 187
  heterophyllus, 200
Pentace, 370
Pentachondra, 102
Pentaclethra, 440
Pentadesma butyracea, 186
Pentadiplandraceae, 68
Pentaphragmataceae, 68
Pentaphylacaceae, 68
Pentas lanceolata, 202
Pentasacme, 97, 141
Penthoraceae, 63
Penthorum, 440
Pentodon, 440
Pentzia, 248
Peperomia, 85, 89
  hispidula, 188
  reflexa, 176
  rotundifolia, 188
Pereskia, 173
  aculeata, 216
Periploca graeca, 197
  laevigata, 198
Periplocaceae, 60
Peripterygiaceae, 68
Peristeria elata, 216
Peristrophe, 442
Pernettia, 219, 247, 259, 443
  howellii, 219

Pernettia mucronata, 222
Perotis, 444
Perottetia, 444
Persea americana, 216
  indica, 198
Persoonia, 102, 256, 259
Persoonioideae, 78, 250
Petalidium, 441
Petermanniaceae, 69
Petersianthus, 441
Petiveriaceae, 64, 73
Petraea arborea, 188
Petrobium, 83, 139
Petrophila, 150
  sessilis, 220
Petrosavia sakuraii, 228
Petrosaviaceae, 68
Petroselinum crispum, 197
Petunia, 94, 219
  parviflora, 382
Phacelia, 85, 200
Phacellothrix, 101
Phajus, 442
  tankervillae, 184
Phalaris arundinacea, 174
  canariensis, 381
Pharnaceum, 115, 443
  acidum, 234
Phaseolus lunatus, 218
  multiflorus, 188, 216
  vulgaris, 218
Phaylopsis, 442
Phebalium, 102, 259
Phelipaea, 135
Phenakospermum, 441
Philadelphaceae, 60
Philadelphus, 439
  coronarius, 196
Philbornea, 142
Philesia buxifolia, 222
Philesiaceae, 63, 73, figs. 9, 10
Philippia, 96, 205
  excelsa, 205
Phillyrea, 135
Philydraceae, 64, 72
Philydrum, 99
Phippsia, 444
  algida, 190
Phleum, 88
  alpinum, 224
  pratense, 381
Phlomis lanata, 227
Phlox, 95
  subulata, 198
Phoebe barbusana, 198
Phoenix, 76
  dactylifera, 200
  reclinata, 201
Pholidota imbricata, 184
Phoradendron, 94
Phormium, 102, 151, 260
  tenax, 222
Photinia, 440
Phragmites, 88
  communis, 174, 371
Phreatia, 254
Phryma, 440
Phrymaceae, 63
Phygelius capensis, 208

Phylica, 111, 443, fig. 45
Phyllachne, 118, 443, fig. 3
Phyllanthus, 89, 253
  caroliniensis, 188
  distichus, 176
  reticulatus, 228
Phyllis, 135
Phyllocosmos, 440
Phyllodinae, 250, 252, 254, 259
Phyllodoce, 93, fig. 58
  caerulea, 180, 182
Phyllospadix, 237, 439
  scouleri, fig. 60
Phyllostegia, 143
Physalis peruviana, 176
Physocarpus, 95
Physokentia, 145
Physospermum, 133
Physurus, 442
Phytelephas, 146
  macrocarpa, 218
Phytolacca, 382
  dioica, 219
Phytolaccaceae, 58
Picrella trifoliata, 234
Picris echioides, 298, 301, fig. 71
Picrodendraceae, 66
Piliocalyx, 102, 143
Pilostyles, 443
Pimelea, 249, 256, 257
Pimenta officinalis, 216
Pimia, 145
Pinanga, 76
pine, 275, 276
Pinguicula, 92, 367, fig. 64
  alpina, fig. 64
  grandiflora, 287, fig. 64
  lusitanica, 287, 301, fig. 64
  vulgaris, 182, 305, fig. 64
Piper, 85, 90, 254, 256
  aduncum, 188
  betle, 184
  cubeba, 184
  longum, 209
  nigrum, 209
Piperaceae, 26, 50, 58, 256, 258
Piptadenia africana, 201
  peregrina, 188
Piptocalyx, 101, 150
Pipturus, 444
  velutinus, 228
Piriqueta, 440
Pirola, 92
  japonica, 228
  media, 192
  minor, 304
Pirolaceae, 60
Pisonia aculeata, 176
  grandis, 377
Pistacia, 439
Pistia, 90
  stratiotes, 176
Pisum, 135
  sativum, 382
Pitcairnea, 440
Pithecellobium, 90
  dulce, 216
  saman, 188
Pittosporaceae, 63, 72, 259, fig. 6

32

Pittosporum, 125, 253, 257, 444
  coriaceum, 198
  tenuifolium, 222
Pityranthos, 443
Plagianthus, 102
  betulinus, 222
plane, 310
Plantaginaceae, 53
Plantago, 83, 88, 162, 163, 246, 382
  amplexicaulis, 162
  asiatica, 162
  aucklandica, 163
  canescens, 162
  coronopus, 381
  crassifolia, 162
  depressa, 162
  durvillei, 162
  erosa, 162
  fernandezia, 163, 231
  gunnii, 163
  hedleyi, 163
  heterophylla, 162
  hirtella, 162
  lanceolata, 162, 381
  lanigera, 162
  macrocarpa, 162
  major, 162, 175, 377, 381
  maritima, 162
  media, 162
  ovata, 162
  palustris, 163
  pentasperma, 163
  picta, 163
  principis, 231
  rapensis, 163
  robusta, 163
  rupicola, 163
  stauntoni, 163
  triantha, 162
  trimenta, 162
Platanaceae, 63
Platanthera chlorantha, 300, 304
Platanus, 107, 317, 439
  occidentalis, 199
  orientalis, 196
Platostoma, 441
Platycodon, 134
Plectomirtha, 151
  baylisiana, 236
Plectranthus, 85, 444
Pleea, 136
Pleiocarpa mutica, 201
Pleione hookeriana, 196
Pleiotaxis, 137
Plerandra, 102
Pleurophyllum, 151
Pleuropogon sabinii, 190
Pleurostylia, 442
Pleurothallis, 85
  pruinosa, 188
Plocama, 135
Plocospermaceae, 66
Pluchea dioscoridis, 176
  indica, 184
Plumbaginaceae, 56, 221
Plumbago capensis, 208
Plumeria acutifolia, 216
Poa, 88, 225, 257
  altaica, 196

Poa annua, 175, 286, 381
  caespitosa, 222
  cookii, 224, 225
  flabellata, 222, 225
  foliosa, 225
  hamiltonii, 225
  litorosa, 225
  novarae, 225
  pratensis, 286, 381
Podalyria, 139
  calyptrata, 209
Podalyrieae, 250, 259
Podoaceae, 68
Podophyllaceae, 60
Podophyllum, 440
  peltatum, 198
Podostemaceae, 58
Pogonia, 440
Pogostemon patchouly, 184
Poinciana regia, 206
Poinsettia pulcherrima, 216
Polemoniaceae, 60, 69
Polemonium, 93
Polianthes, 146
  tuberosa, 216
Pollia, 442
Polyalthia, 442
polyanthus, 381
Polycarpon, 88
Polygala, 55, 85, 87
  erioptera, 183
  senega, 198
Polygalaceae, 55
Polygonaceae, 53, 55
Polygonum, 88
  arifolium, 226
  aviculare, 175, 381
  baldschuanicum, 196
  plebeium, 183
  virginicum, 226
  viviparum, 182, 191
Polyosma, 99
Polypogon monspeliensis, 381
Polyscias, 253
Pomaderris, 101
Pomatosace, 74, 75
Poncirus, 134
Pongamia, 442
  glabra, 242
Pontederia cordata, 199
Pontederiaceae, 57
poplars, 372
Porana volubilis, 184
Poranthera, 102
Portlandia grandiflora, 216
Portulaca, 88
  oleracea, 175
  quadrifida, 183
Portulacaceae, 55, 74
Posidonia, 237, 443
Posidoniaceae, 62
Poskea, 138
Posoqueria trinitatis, 216
Potaliaceae, 58
Potamogeton, 56, 88, 273
  crispus, 174
  lanceolatus, 289
  pectinatus, 174
Potamogetonaceae, 56

Potaninia, 135
Potentilla apennina, 227
  argentea, 304
  erecta, 301
  fruticosa, 182, 226
Pothos, 442
Pottsia cantonensis, 185
Poupartia, 138
Pourouma cecropiaefolia, 217
Prainea, 142
Prasophyllum, 101
Pratia, 80
  angulata, 231
  repens, 232
Premna, 442
Prevostea, 440
Priestleya, 139
  villosa, 209
primrose, 296, 381, fig. 69
Primula, 74, 75, 85, 381, 444
  auricula, 193
  bulleyana, 196
  elatior, fig. 63
  farinosa, 230, fig. 63
  florindae, 196
  glutinosa, 193
  imperialis, 228
  japonica, 196
  malacoides, 196
  obconica, 196
  scotica, fig. 63
  sinenis, 196
  veris, 301, fig. 63
  vulgaris, 194, 297, figs. 63, 69
Primulaceae, 26, 53, 74, 75, 221
Principina, 137
Pringlea, 119, 152, 443
  antiscorbutica, 224
Prionotes, 150, 443
Prioria copaifera, 216
Prismatocarpus, 140
Pritchardia, 143, 233, 444
Pritchardiopsis, 145
Priva, 440
  cordifolia, 185
Procris pedunculata, 228
Promenaea, 147
Prosopis alba, 219
  juliflora, 230
Prostanthera, 150, 256
Prostanthereae, 250
Protea, 78, 96, 205
  abyssinica, 228
  angolensis, 228
  cynaroides, Plate 12
  grandiflora, 209
  mellifera, 209
Proteaceae, 50, 63, 73, 74, 77, 248–250, 252,
  254–256, 259, 314, 372, fig. 16
Protium, 442
Prunella, 88
  vulgaris, 174, 286, 381
Prunus, 92
  cerasus, 194
  communis, 196
  laurocerasus, 197, 233
  lusitanica, 233
  persica, 381
  serotina, 199

Psathyranthes amazonicus, 217
Pseudagrostistachys, 137
Pseudarthria, 442
Pseudelephantopus spicatus, 176
Pseudopanax, 443
Pseudowintera, 118, 443
Psidium galapageium, 217
  quajava, 188
Psoralea argophylla, 370
Psychotria, 85, 90, 254
Pteridium, 279
Pteridophyllum, 134
Pterisanthes, 142
Pterocarpus erinaceus, 202, *echinatus*,
  211
  officinalis, 188
  santolinus, 209
Pterocarya, 439
Pterolobium, 441
Pteronia, 248
Pterostemonaceae, 66
Pterostylis, 101, 258
Pterygopappus, 150
Pterygota, 441
Ptilotus, 99, 150, 256
Ptychococcus, 102
Ptychopetalum, 440
Ptychosperma, 101
Pulicaria vulgaris, 304
Pullea, 101
Pulmonaria, 133
  longifolia, 304
Pultenaea, 150, 249, 256
Punica, 98
Punicaceae, 67
Puya raimondii, 218, Plate 7
Pycnospora hedysaroides, 184
Pygeum, 441
Pygmaeorchis, 147
Pyracantha coccinea, 197
Pyrenacantha, 441
Pyrostria, 139
Pyrularia, 440
Pyrus baccata, 194
  communis, 194
  glandulosa, 185
  malus, 194
  pulcherrima, 196
Quamoclit, 90
Quassia, 440
  amara, 218
Quercus, 85
  chrysolepis, 200
  humboldtiana, 218
  ilex, 197
  infectoria, 200
  suber, 197
Quinaceae, 66
Quillaja saponaria, 218
Quisqualis, 441
  indica, 210
Radiola linoides, 205
Rafflesia, 142
  arnoldi, 211
Rafflesiaceae, 58
Rafnia, 139, 248
Raillardia, 144
Ramonda, 133
  myconi, 193

Ramonda nathaliae, 193
  pyrenaica, 193
  serbica, 193
Ramondia pyrenaica, 193
Ranalisma, 441
Randia, 90
Ranunculaceae, 50, 53, 257
Ranunculus, 9, 85, 88, 187, 205, 211, 221, 259, 377
  abortivus, 233
  acris, 192, 286
  allegheniensis, 233
  biternatus, 224
  bulbosus, 9
  crassipes, 224
  ficaria, 422
  flammula, 231
  glacialis, 191
  hederaceus, 286
  hirsutus, 9
  hyperboreus, 272
  laxicaulis, 231
  lyallii, 222
  nivalis, 182
  pallasii, 190
  parviflorus, 230
  pygmaeus, 191
  repens, 9, 286, 380
Raoulia, 101, 258, 259
Rapateaceae, 63, 147
Raphia, 76, 440
  ruffia, 206
  vinifera, 201
Rapinia collina, 236
Ravenala, 251, 441
  madagascariensis, 206
Ravenea, 138
Readea, 145
red clover, 381
Redowskia, 133
reed, 174
Reevesia, 134
Rehderophoenix, 145
Rehmannia, 134
Relhania, 139
Remirea, 91
Remusatia, 441
Renealmia, 440
Reptonia, 136
Reseda, 98
  lutea, 233
  luteola, 233
  muricata, 200
  odorata, 197
Resedaceae, 64
Restio, 85, 118, 248, 443
Restionaceae, 63, 73, 118, 139, 248, 250, 252, 254, 255, 259, 314, fig. 12
Retama rhaetam, 200
Rhabdothamnus, 151
Rhagodia, 101
Rhamnaceae, 55, 131, 255
Rhamnus, 88, 92, 279
Rhamphicarpa, 442
Rhazya stricta, 200
Rheedia, 441
Rhetinodendron, 83, 148
Rheum, 133
  rhaponticum, 196

Rhigozum trichotomum, 207
Rhinacanthus, 442
Rhipsalis megalantha, 236
Rhizanthella, 151
Rhizophora, 91, 442
  mangle, 240
  racemosa, 240
Rhizophoraceae, 58, 131
Rhodamnia, 99
Rhodochiton atrosanguineum, 216
Rhodochlaena, 138
Rhododendroideae, 55
Rhododendron, 85, 168, 169, 170, 220, 254, 256, 259, 371, fig. 54
  anthopogon, 169
  californicum, 200
  ferrugineum, 169, 233
  hirsutum, 169, 233
  lapponicum, 169
  lochae, 168
  maximum, 199
  ponticum, 169, 197, 227, 293
  retusum, 168
Rhodoleia, 97
Rhodotypos, 134
Rhoeo discolor, 216
Rhoipteleaceae, 68
Rhopalocarpaceae, 68
Rhopalocnemis phalloides, 228
Rhopalostylis, 102, 151, 260
  sapida, 222
Rhus, 85, 91
  simaroubaefolius, 186
  tomentosa, 209
  toxicodendron, 199, 344
  typhina, 198
  vernix, 199
Rhynchelytrum repens, 208
Rhynchosia, 89
Rhynchospora, 88
  corymbosa, 175
  fusca, 287
Rhyticaryum, 255
Ribes, 92, fig. 20
  aureum, 200
  grossularia, 304
  rubrum, 300, 303
  sanguineum, 200
  speciosum, 200
  uva-crispa, 304, 382
rice, 3, 210
Richea, 150
Ricinocarpus, 102
Ricinodendron, 137
Ricinus communis, 186
Riedelia, 256
Rinorea, 90
Ripogonum, 101
Ritchiea, 137
Rivina humilis, 188
Robinia, 136
  pseudo-acacia, 198
Robinsonia, 83
Rochea, 140
  coccinea, 208
Rodetia, 439
Rodgersia, 134
Roella, 140
Rohdea, 134

Rollandia, 80, 144
Romanzoffia, 95
Romneya, 136
Romulea, 98
Rondeletia odorata, 216
Roridula, 140
Roridulaceae, 68
Rosa, 92, 285, 289
  banksiae, 196
  canina, 382
  centifolia, 194
  multiflora, 196
  nutkana, 200
  omeiensis, 196
  rubiginosa, 382
  rugosa, 195
  wichuriana, 196
Rosaceae, 50, 53
Roscoea cautleoides, 196
Rosmarinus, 135
Rostkovia, 443
Rotala mexicana, 174
Rothia, 441
Rottboellia exaltata, 183
Roucheria, 442
Roupala, 78
Roureopsis, 441
Roussea, 138
Roxburghiaceae, 63
rubber plants, 210
rubber tree, 147, 217
Rubia peregrina, 287, 293, 298
Rubiaceae, 50, 55, 57, 130, 144, 145, 213, 219, 246, 248, 249, 251–257, 360
Rubus, 85, 88, 211, 283, 288, 289
  alpinus, 188
  australis, 222
  fruticosus, 382
  humulifolius, 192
  lineatus, 228
  niveus, 228
  spectabilis, 227
Rudbeckia, 194
  hirta, 198
Ruellia, 89
Rulingia, 442
Rumex, 88, 285
  acetosa, 286
  acetosella, 286, 381
  crispus, 286, 299, 381
  nepalensis, 183
  obtusifolius, 286, 381
Rungia, 442
Ruppia, 88
Ruppiaceae, 56
Ruscaceae, 67
Ruscus, 135
  hypophyllus, 198
Russellia equisetiformis, 216
Rutaceae, 57, 73, 131, 144, 248, 249, 252–256
Ruthea, 443
Rutidosis, 151
rye, 3
Ryssopterys, 99
Sabal, 318
  palmetto, 199
Sabiaceae, 63
Sabicea. 440
Saccoglottis, 440

Saccolabium, 442
Saccolepis curvata, 228
Sageretia, 442
Sagina, 88
  procumbens, 380
Sagittaria sagittifolia, 300
Saintpaulia, 138
  ionantha, 138
Salaxis, 139
Salicaceae, 60
Salicornia, 88
  europaea, 175
Salix, 85, 88, 190, 285
  arctica, 190
  herbacea, 191, 276, 279
  nummularia, 190
  polaris, 190
Salpichroa rhomboidea, 219
Salpiglossis, 94
  sinuata, 218
Salsola, 88
  arbuscula, 196
  kali, 241
Saltia, 136
Salvadora, 98
Salvadoraceae, 69
Salvia, 26, 85
  fulgens, 216
  splendens, 218
Samadera, 442
  indica, 242
Sambucus, 88, 92
  adnata, 228
  ebulus, 304
  maderensis, 198
  nigra, 299, 382
  racemosa, 382
Samolus, 74, 88
  valerandi, 174
Samydaceae, 58
Sandoricum, 442
Sanguinaria, 136
Sanicula, 88
  europaea, 192, 203, 355, 377
Sansevieria, 441
  zeylanica, 210
Santalaceae, 55
Santalodes, 441
Santalum, 127, 444
  album, 127
  insulare, 128
  pyrularium, 212
Santiria, 441
Santiriopsis, 441
Santolina, 135
Sapindaceae, 58
Sapindus, 442
  saponaria, 216
Saponaria ocymoides, 193
Sapotaceae, 57, 253, 258
Sapria, 141
Sapucaya, 147
Saracha indica, 209
Sararanga, 102
Sarcanthinae, 252
Sarcanthus, 100
Sarcocaulon, 140
  patersonii, 207
Sarcocephalus, 441

Sarcodes, 136
Sarcolobus, 100
Sarcopygme, 145
Sarcosperma, 97
Sarcospermataceae, 68
Sargentodoxaceae, 68
Sarothamnus scoparius, 381
Sarracenia, 136
Sarraceniaceae, 67
Saruma, 134
Satureja, 88, 205
Satyrium, 442
    carneum, 209
Saurauja, 254, 256, 442
Sauraujaceae, 63, 256
Sauromatum, 441
Saururaceae, 63
Saururus, 440
    cernuus, 199
Saussurea, 443
    tridactyla, 196
Sauvagesia, 90
    erecta, 227
Savia, 440
Savignya, 136
Saxifraga, 287, 444
    aizodes, 191
    cernua, 286
    hirsuta, 298, 291, fig. 67
    magellanica, 230
    oppositifolia, 182, 191
    retusa, 227
    sarmentosa, 196
    spathularis, 287
    stellaris, 182
Saxifragaceae, 60, 71, 131
Saxifragella, 152
saxifrages, 26
Scabiosa, 26, 371
    columbaria, 287
Scaevola, 91, 254, 256
    koenigii, 242
Scalesia, 83, 148, 219, 233
Schaueria, 440
Schefflera, 256
Schelhammera, 101
Scheuchzeria, 231
Scheuchzeriaceae, 60
Schiedea, 144
Schinus molle, 218
Schisandra, 440
    elongata, 228
Schisandraceae, 63
Schismatoglottis, 142
Schismus barbatus, 183
Schizanthus, 148
    pinnatus, 218
Schizeileman, 443
Schizocapsa, 140
Schizochlaena, 234
Schizopetalon walkeri, 218
Schizophragma, 134
    hydrangeoides, 196
Schizostachyum, 82, 444
    glaucifolium, 82
Schlumbergeria, 147
Schoenefeldia, 441
Schoenus, 88, 249, 256
Schoepfia. 442

Schrebera, 442
Schultesia, 440
Schumacheria, 140
    castaneifolia, 209
Scilla non-scripta, 370, 382
Scirpus, 87, 174, 258
    nodosus, 224
    setaceus, 227
    sylvaticus, 182
Scitamineae, 26
Scleranthus, 443
Scleria lithosperma, 175
Sclerocarpus, 440
Sclerocephalus arabicus, 200
Sclerotheca, 80, 145
Scolopia, 442
Scolymus hispanicus, 197
Scoparia dulcis, 176
Scorzonera humilis, 256, 304
Scrophularia, 93
    aquatica, 233
    marilandica, 231
    nodosa, 231, 233
Scrophulariaceae, 50, 53, 130, 246, 248, 249, 255, 257
Scutellaria, 88
    luzonica, 185
    minor, 301
    mociniana, 216
Scutinanthe, 97
Scyphiphora, 99
Scyphochlamys, 139
Scyphogyne, 139
Scyphostegiaceae, 69
Scytopetalaceae, 68
sea-grasses, 212, 232, 237–241
seaweeds, 5
Sebaea, 442
    ovata, 187
Secale cereale, 344
Secamone, 442
    elliptica, 184
Sechium edule, 188
sedges, 26, 212, 371
Sedum, 85, 92, 205
    telephium, 304
Seetzenia, 443
    prostrata, 230
Selaginaceae, 67, 72
Selago, 96
Selliera, 443
    radicans, 229
Semecarpus, 99
    atra, 186
Semele, 135
    androgyna, 198
Semepervivum, 26, 198
    arachnoideum, 193
    spathulatum, 198
Senecio, 82, 85, 199, 203, 205, 246, 248, 257
    articuLatus, 208
    cineraria, 197
    cruentus, 198
    erucifolius, 301
    greyii, 222
    jacobaea, 192, 299, 381
    keniodendron, Plate 14
    palustris, 205

Senecio resedifolius, 227
  vulgaris, 381, 382
sequoias, 386
Seraphyta diffusa, 188
Sericolea, 255
Seris, 147
Serratula tinctoria, 301
Serruria, 248
Sesamum, 441
  indicum, 209
Sesuvium distylium, 236
  portulacastrum, 176
Setaria verticillata, 175
Shorea, 96
  robusta, 209
Shortia, 440
  galacifolia, 235
Shuteria, 441
Sibthorpia, 122, 123, 440, fig. 44
  europaea, 205
Sicyos, 444
Sida, 90
  cordifolia, 176
  linifolia, 227
  rhombifolia, 176
  spinosa, 177
  urens, 177
  veronicifolia, 177
Sidalcea, 136
Sideroxylon marmulano, 198
Sigesbeckia orientalis, 177
Silaum silaus, 301
Silaus pratensis, 301
Silene, 92, 212, 272, 273
  quinquevulnera, 380
silver tree, 372
Silybum marianum, 219
Simarouba amara, 188
Simaroubaceae, 58, 131
Simethis planifolia, 305
Simocheilus, 139
Sinapis alba, 344
Sindora, 142
Sinningia, 147
  speciosa, 218
Siphocampylus, 80
Siphodontaceae, 68
Sison amomum, 301
Sisyrinchium, 444
  angustifolium, 287
  bermundiana, 287, 293, 294
Sium, 443
  sisarum, 195
Skimmia, 96
  japonica, 168
Sloanea, 442
  jamaicensis, 216
Smilacaceae, 57
Smilacina, 95
Smilax, 85, 88, 217
  herbacea, 226
  medica, 216
Smithia, 442
Smyrnium olusatrum, 304
Soaresia, 147
Solanaceae, 50, 55, 221, 246, 247
Solanum, 85, 87, 246
  aculeatissimum, 177
  aviculare, 187, 229

Solanum dulcamara, 192
  melongena, 183
  nigrum, 175
  pseudocapsicum, 183
  tuberosum, 218
Solandra macrantha, 216
Soldanella, 74, 75, 133, 193
  alpina, 193
  carpatica, 193
  hungarica, 193
  montana, 193
  villosa, 193
Solidago, 26, 93, 187
  anticostensis, 235
  victorinii, 235
Sollya, 151
Sonchus, 88, 204, 205
  arvensis, 381
  oleraceus, 175, 381
Sonneratia apetala, 240
Sonneratiaceae, 68
Sophora (Tetrapterae), 130, fig. 40
Sopubia, 442
Sorbus, 289
  maderensis, 198
Sorghum arundinaceum, 186
  caffrorum, 186
  guineense, 186
  subglabrescens, 183
  verticilliflorum, 185
Soulamea, 253, 442
Sparganiaceae, 62
Sparganium, 443
  simplex, 227
Sparganophorus, 440
Sparattosyce, 144
Sparrmannia, 96
  africana, 186
Spartina, 439
Spathelia, 146
  sorbifolia, 216
Spathicarpa, 147
Spanthiphyllum, 442
Spanthodea campanulata, 201
Spathoglottis vieillardii, 184
Specularia, 439
  hybrida, 303
Spergula, 88
  arvensis, 380
Spergularia, 88, 371
Sphacele, 444
Sphaeralcea, 440
Sphaeranthus, 442
  africanus, 183
  indicus, 183
Sphaerosepalum, 102
Sphenocleaceae, 67
Sphenostemon, 102
Sphinctacanthus, 141
Spigelia anthelmia, 188
Spigeliaceae, 64
Spilanthes acmella, 177
spinach, 344
Spinacia, 135
  oleracea, 186, 344
Spiraea, 92
Spiraeanthemum, 101
Spiranthes gemmipara, 287, 293
  romanzoffiana, 182, 293

Spiridium, 150
Spondias, 318
　lutea, 216
　mombin, 216
　purpurea, 188
Sporobolus, 88
Squamellaria, 145
squirting cucumber, 377
Stachys, 88
　lanata, 194
　sieboldii, 195
　sylvatica, 192
Stachyurus, 134
Stachyuraceae, 68
Stachytarpheta guianensis, 177
　jamaicensis, 177
Stackhousia, 99
　intermedia, 184, 229
Stackhousiaceae, 69, 72
Stapelia, 26, 96
Staphelianthus, 138
Stapelieae, 170–173, 208, 235, 248, 252, figs. 55–57
Staphylea, 439
Staphyleaceae, 63
Statice, 289
　suworowii, 196
Staudtia gabonensis, 201
Stegnospermataceae, 66
Stellaria, 88
　media, 175, 380
　palustris, 192
Stemona, 99
Stemonoporus, 140
Stemonurus, 99
Stenanthella, 439
Stenocarpus, 101, 254
Stenogyne, 144
Stenomeridaceae, 69
Stenopadus, 147
Stephanandra tanakae, 196
Stephania, 441
　abyssinica, 186
Stephanotis floribunda, 206
Sterculia, 90
Sterculiaceae, 49, 58, 131, 255
Stereospermum, 442
Stewartia, 440
Stifftia chrysantha, 218
Stilbeaceae, 68
Stillingia, 143
Stimpsonia, 74, 75
Stipa, 88, 376
Stipularia africana, 201
Stirlingia, 151
Stoebe, 96, 205
stone-plants, 207, Plate 11
Storckiella, 102, 143
　vitiensis, 186
storks-bill, 377
Strangea, 150
Stranvaesia, 134
Strasburgeriaceae, 69
Stratiotes, 133
　aloides, 422
Streblochaete, 442
Streblorrhiza, 144
　speciosa, 236
Strelitzia 140

Strelitzia angusta, 208
Strelitziaceae, 63, 74
Streptocaulon griffithii, 185
Streptopus streptopoides, 227
Striga, 442
　asiatica, 228
Strobilanthes, 209, 442
Strobilopanax, 102, 143
Strombosia, 441
Strongylocaryum, 145
Strongylodon, 253, 444
　lucidum, 212
Strophanthus, 372, 442
　hispidus, 201
　maingayi, 234
　sarmentosus, 201
Struthiola, 248
Strychnaceae, 57
Strychnos, 85, 89
　ignatii, 211
　spinosa, 185
Stylidiaceae, 63, 72, 118, 220, 254, 256, 259, fig. 3
Stylidium, 99, 211, 249, 256, fig. 3
　alsinoides, 211
　inconspicuum, 211
　javanicum, 211
　kunthii, 211
　pedunculatum, 211
　pycnanthum, fig. 2
　scandens, fig. 2
　schizanthum, 211
　tenellum, fig. 2
　uliginosum, 211
Stylophorum, 440
Stypandra, 102
Styphelia, 99, 249, 256
Styracaceae, 63
Styrax, 113, 442
Suaeda, 88
　maritima, 175
Subularia, 92
sugar maples, 198
Sukunia, 145
sundews, 165
Suriana, 91, 442
Suttonia, 139, 444
Swainsona, 102, 150, 259
　greyana, 221
Swartzia simplex, 216
Swertia, 88, 205
　bimaculata 228
　perennis, 1,2
Swietenia, 1468
sycamore, 370
Symbegonia, 255
Symmeria, 440
Symphonia, 440, fig. 28
　globulifera, 227, fig. 29
Symphoricarpos, 94, 440
　albus, 187
Symphytosiphon, 138
Sympieza, 139
Symplocaceae, 63
Symplocarpus, 440
　foetidus, 226
Symplocos, 85, 160, 318, 442
Synadenium, 138
Synandrospadix, 148

Synedrella nodosa, 177
Syngonanthus, 440
Syringa, 95
   vulgaris, 305
Syringodium, 442
Syzygium, 253, 254
Tacca, 89
   leontopetaloides, 183
Taccaceae, 58
Tacsonia mixta, 218
Taeniophyllum, 99, 254, 256
Tagetes, 94
   erecta, 216
   minor, 344
   patula, 216
Tahitia, 145
Talauma, 442
Talinum, 440
Tamaricaceae, 69
Tamarindus indica, 176
Tamus, 135
   edulis, 198
Tapeinosperma, 101, 253
Tapura, 440
Taraxacum, 88
   officinale, 175, 286
Tarenna, 442
Taveunia, 145
tea, 195, 210
Tecoma, 146
   stans, 188
Tecomanthe, 99
   speciosa, 236
Tecophilaea, 148
Tecophilaeaceae, 62
Tecticomia, 101
   cinerea, 185
Tectona, 96
   grandis, 184
Teesdalia nudicaulis, 287
Telfairea pedata, 186
Telopea, 150
   speciosissima, 220
Telosma, 441
   extensa, 186
Tenagocharis, 441
Tephrosia, 90
Terminalia, 90, 370
Ternstroemia, 442
Tetracarpaea, 150
Tetracentraceae, 68
Tetracentron, 71
Tetracera, 90, 135, 318, 360
Tetrachondra, 443
Tetrachondraceae, 63
Tetraena, 135
Tetragonia, 247, 443
   expansa, 229
Tetrameristaceae, 69
Tetrapathaea, 151
Tetraplandra, 147
Tetraplasandra, 444
Tetrastigma, 99
Tetratheca, 150
Tetraulacium, 147
Teucrium, 88
Thalassia, 442
Thalassia testudinum, 237
Thalia, 440
   33

Thalictrum, 92, 289
   javanicum, 228
   rhynchocarpum, 228
Thamnochortus, 139
Thamnoseris, 148
Thamnosma, 440
Theaceae, 58
Thelepogon, 441
Theligonum, 439
Thelymitra, 99, 186, 258, 259
Themeda triandra, 201
Theobroma, 146
   cacao, 217
   pentagona, 216
Theophrastaceae, 66
Thermopsis, 439
Thesium, 248, 443
Thespesia populnea, 242
Thismia, 442
   americana,, 234
   rodwayi, 234
Thismiaceae, 58
thistles, 26
Thladiantha, 97
Thomasia, 150
Thozetia, 150
Threlkeldia, 151
Thuarea, 442
   involucrata, 228
Thunbergia, 85, 442
   alata, 177
Thunbergianthus, 137
Thurniaceae, 66
Thymelaeaceae, 55, 72, 248, 256, 259
Thymus serpyllum, 286
Thysanotus, 99
Tiarella, 439
Tibouchina, 85
   semidecandra, 218
Tigridia pavonia, 216
Tilia, 439
Tiliaceae, 57
Tiliacora, 441
Tillaea, 88
Tillandsia usneoides, 428
Timonius, 256
Tinospora, 318, 441
Tipularia, 440
Tirania, 140
Tithonia diversifolia, 177
Toddalia, 442
Toechima, 101
Tofieldia palustris, 182
Tolmiea, 136
   menziesii, 200
Toona, 318, 442
Torenia fournieri, 210
Torrenticola, 101
touch-me-not, 377
Tournefortia argentea, 242
   sarmentosa, 228
Tovaria, 99, 140
Tovariaceae, 66
Toxocarpus, 442
Trachycarpus fortunei, 186
Trachymene, 99
   caerulea, 220
Trachymene saniculaefolia, 228
Trachypogon, 440

Tradescantia virginiana, 198
Tragus racemosus, 177
Trapa natans, 238, 269
Trautvetteria, 440
tree ferns, 22, 23, 272
tree heath, 169
Trema micrantha, 188
Tremandraceae, 69, 249
Trematolobelia, 144
Tremblya, 147
Trianosperma, 440
Tribulus, 91
    cistoides, 188
Tricalysia, 442
Trichadenia, 97
Trichilia, 440
Trichocaulon, 96
Trichochilus, 145
Trichocline, 442
Trichodesma africanum, 183
    indicum, 228
    zeylanicum, 183
Tricholaena rosea, 208
Trichopodaceae, 63
Trichopus zeylanicus, 185
Trichotoria, 142
Tricomaria, 148
Tricoryne, 101
Tricyrtis, 134
Trientalis, 74, 75
Trifolium, 92, 205, 286
    alpinum, 193
    fragiferum, 299
    lupinaster, 192
    pratense, 381
    squamosum, 298
Triglochin, 120, 230, 443
    bulbosa, 230
    maritima, 230
    palustris, 230
    striata, 230
Trigonella, 443
Trigoniaceae, 63
Trigoniastrum, 142
Trilliaceae, 60
Trillium, 170, 187, 439
Trimenia, 102
Triodia irritans, 186
Triosteum, 440
Tripetaleia, 439, 440
Tripetalum, 102
Triplachne, 135
Triplaris, 371
    surinamensis, 217
Triplostegia, 97, 134
Triptilium, 149
Triraphis, 442
Trisepalum, 140
Tristachya, 440
    chrysothrix, 227
Tristellateia, 253, 442
Tristicha, 440
Tristichaceae, 58
Trithrinax campestris, 219
Triticum, 196
Triumfetta subpalmata, 242
Triuridaceae, 58
Trochocarpa, 101
Trochodendraceae, 68

Trochodendron, 71, 134
Trollius, 92, 287
    europaeus, 194
Tropaeolaceae, 66, fig. 13
Tropaeolum, 94
    majus, 218, 381
    peregrinum, 218
    speciosum, 218
Tropidia, 442
Trukia, 145
tulip-tree, 312
Tulipa, 95
    gesneriana, 196
    sylvestris, 305
tumble-weeds, 370
Tupeia, 102
Turnera, 113, 442
Turneraceae, 63
Turpinia, 442
Turraea, 442
Tussilago farfara, 301
Tylophora, 442
Typha, 88
    angustifolia, 174
    latifolia, 174
Typhaceae, 56
Ulbrichia, 146
Ulex, 135
    europaeus, 380
Uldina, 150
Ullucus tuberosus, 218
Ulmaceae, 57
Ulmus, 289
    fulva, 198
Umbelliferae, 26, 53, 95, 134, 250, 255, 257
Umbellanthus, 138
Umbellularia, 136
Umbilicus pendulinus, 205
Uncaria, 90
    africana, 201
    gambier, 184
Uncinia, 258, 443
    riparia, 184
Uraria, 442
Urena, 90
    lobata, 177
Urera, 443
Urochloa panicoides, 183
Urophyllum, 442
Ursinia, 96
Urtica, 92
    dioica, 175, 268, 381
    urens, 381
Urticaceae, 55, 254–256
Utleria, 140
Utricularia, 85, 345, 347
    intermedia, 287
    monanthos, 187
    nelumbifolia, 218
Uvularia, 136
Vacciniaceae, 55, 60, 254, 256
Vaccinium, 85, 88, 92, 215, 254, 256, fig. 19
    cylindraceum, 197
    macgillivrayi, 186
    peleanum, 231
    varingiifolium, 231
Vahlia, 98
Vahlia oldenlandioides, 228
Vahliaceae, 69

Valeriana hardwickii, 228
Valerianaceae, 62
Vallisneria, 88
   americana, 231
   spiralis, 231
Valvanthera, 58
Vancouveria, 439
Vanda, 99
   caerulea, 209
   tricolour, 211
Vandasia, 101
Vangueria, 442
Vanilla, 89
   planifolia, 216
Vateria, 442
Veitchia, 143
Velleia, 101, 150
Vellozia, 440
   candida, 218
Velloziaceae, 63
Venidium fastuosum, 207
Ventilago, 442
Vepris, 442
Veratrilla, 134
Veratrum, 92
   album, 192
Verbascum, 135
   nigrum, 297
   thapsus, 192, 368, 382
Verbena, 85, 246
   bonariensis, 218
   erinoides, 218
   officinalis, 381
Verbenaceae, 55, 255
Vernonia, 85, 90
   arborea, 82
   cinerea, 177
Veronica, 221, 222, 257, 443
   americana, 182
Verticordia, 150
Viburnum, 92
   rugosum, 198
   tinus, 197
Vicia, 92, 133
   bithynica, 298
   sativa, 344, 381
Victoria amazonica, 217
   regia, 217
Vigna marina, 177
Villarsia, 443
Vinca, 133
   minor, 304
Viola, 55, 166–168, 211, 232, 443
   albanica, 167
   altaica, 167
   arcuata, 167
   arguta, 167
   athois, 167
   bertolonii, 167
   betonicifolia, 167
   biflora, 191
   blanda, 167
   canina, 167
   celebica, 167
   cheiranthifolia, 167
   collina, 167
   cunninghamii, 187
   dacica, 167
   decumbens, 167

Viola diffusa, 167
   domingensis, 167
   etbaica, 167
   forrestiana, 167
   fragrans, 167
   hederacea, 220
   hirta, 167
   humboldtii, 167
   incognita, 167
   jalapensis, 167
   javanica, 167
   kashmiriana, 167
   lanceolata, 167
   langsdorffii, 167
   lunata, 167
   maculata, 167
   magellensis, 167
   mirabilis, 167
   occidentalis, 167
   odorata, 167, 381
   ovalifolia, 167
   palmensis, 167
   palustris, 166, 304
   paradoxa, 167
   pedata, 167
   pinnata, 167
   reichenbachiana, 167
   riviniana, 167
   rostrata, 167
   rubella, 167
   sarmentosa, 167
   scandens, 167
   selkirkii, 166
   sentiformis, 167
   serpens, 167
   somalensis, 167
   splendida, 167
   stipularis, 167
   tricolor, 167, 344, 382
Violaceae, 55
violets, 7
Viscum, 98
Vismia, 440
Vitaceae, 57
Vitex, 89
   negundo, 209
Vitiphoenix, 145
Vitis, 91, 318
   labrusca, 199
   vinifera, 194, 344
Vivianiaceae, 67
Voacanga, 442
Voandzeia, 95
   subterranea, 186
Vochysiaceae, 63
Vomitra, 138
Vossia, 441
Voyria, 147, 440
Wahlenbergia, 248
   gracilis, 230
   linifolia, 206
Wallenia, 146
Walsura, 96
Waltheria, 90
   americana, 177
Warszewiczia coccinea, 216
Washingtonia filifera, 200, Plate 25
water-lily, 310
Watsonia rosea, 209

wattles, 250
Wedelia trilobata, 177
Weigela, 440
    florida, 195
Weihea, 440
Weinmannia, 113, 236, 253, 443, fig. 8
    camaguiensis, 236
    comoroensis, 236
    denhami, 236
    fraxinea, 236
    macgillivrayi, 236
    spiraeoides, 236
    vitiensis, 236
Wenzelia, 100
wheat, 3
Wiesneria, 442
Wightia, 97
Wilkesia, 83
Willdenowia, 139
willows, 7, 272, 372
Winteraceae, 63, 257, fig. 5
Wisteria, 440
    sinensis, 196
Wolffia, 88
Woodfordia, 442
Wormia, 442
Wulfenia, 439
Wunderlichia, 147
Wurmbea, 443
Xanthium, 376
    chinense, 177
Xanthoceras, 134
Xanthophytum, 100
Xanthorrhoea, 150, Plate 17
    preissii, 220
Xanthorrhoeaceae, 69, 250, 259
Xanthosia, 150
Xanthosiinae, 250
Xanthostemon, 253, 256
Xeronema, 102, 258
Xerotes, 254
Xerotia, 136
Xylia, 442
Xylocarpus, 442
Xylomelum, 150
Xylopia aethiopica, 202
Xylosma, 442
Xyridaceae, 57

Xyris, 90
    indica, 183
yams, 165
Yucca, 136
    aloifolia, 216
    filamentosa, 428
Zalacca edulis, 211
Zaluzyanskya, 248
Zannichellia, 88
    palustris, 174
Zannichelliaceae, 56
Zantedeschia aethiopica, 185
Zanthoxylum, 440
Zataria, 136
Zea mays, 216, 344
Zebrina pendula, 216
Zelkova, 439
    serrata, 196
Zeylanidium, 140
Zieria, 102
Zilla, 136
    spinosa, 200
Zingiber officinale, 210
Zingiberaceae, 58
Zinnia, 136
    elgans, 216
Zizania, 440
Ziziphus, 90
    mucronatus, 202
Zoisia, 442
    matrella, 184
Zostera, 237, 443
    asiatica, 237
    caespitosa, 237
    capensis, 237
    capricorni, 237
    caulescens, 237
    japonica, 237
    marina, 237
    muelleri, 237
    nana, 237
    novazelandica, 237
    tasmanica, 237
Zosteraceae, 63
Zygadenus, 95
Zygophyllaceae, 58, 73
Zygophyllum, 443
    simplex, 230

INDEX OF PERSONS AND PLACES

Aberdare Mts., 204, 205
Abrams, L. R., 200
Abruzzi, 167
Abyssinia, 17, 31, 78, 113, 136, 138, 169, 185, 203, 204, 205
Aconcagua, Mt., 16
Adamson, R. S., 209
Aden, 136, 239
Afghanistan, 16, 96, 136, 167
African Subkingdom, 31
Ahaggar, Mts., 203
Ahlmann, H. W., 388, 389
Ahrendt, L. W. A., 80
Alabama, 317, 427
Alacran Reef, 236
Alaska, 13, 16, 30, 95, 163, 189, 237, 317, 318, 356, 365, 390, 411
Albania, 165, 167
Aldabra Is., 13, 20, 138, 230, 236
Aleutian Is., 13, 30, 215
Alice Springs, 77
Allan, H. H., 71, 221
Allard, H. A., 394
Alleghenies, 81
Alps, the, 16, 26, 28, 30, 75, 190, 191, 192, 193, 227, 233, 324, 327, 329, 388, 399
Altai Mts., 30, 191, 194
Amazon R., 147, 174, 201
Amazon Region, 29, 32, 147, 153, 217
Amsterdam I., 13, 115, 163, 223, 225, 413, Plate 3
Andaman Is., 13, 77, 140, 141, 210
Andean Region, 32, 147, 148, 218, 219
Anderson, E., 178
Andes, the, 16, 17, 26, 32, 62, 80, 118, 120, 146, 147, 148, 149, 152, 162, 164, 167, 188, 202, 217, 222, 244, 339, 355, 390, 400
Andrews, E. C., 149
Angkor, 389
Angola, 31, 137, 138, 202, 360
Annam, 126
Annobon I., 159, 164
Antarctica, 11, 13, 17, 19, 24, 26, 28, 52, 53, 70, 71, 115, 117, 222, 246, 323, 324, 327, 390, 409, 410, 411, 413
Antevs, E., 323
Antipodes Is., 13, 222
Apennines, 16, 192, 193
Appalachians, the, 16, 192, 193
Arabia, 13, 16, 18, 19, 26, 28, 31, 67, 69, 81, 98, 115, 136, 172, 173, 185, 200, 239, 319, 356, 385, 396, 398, 405
Arabian Sea, 183
Ararat, Mt., 16
Arctic, the, 12, 19, 26, 52, 191
Arctic and Subarctic Region, 30, 132, 189
Arctic North American Archipelago, 397
Arctic Ocean, 11, 12, 132, 327, 410
Arfak Mts., 235
Argentina, 18, 19, 28, 32, 113, 148, 149, 152, 153, 164, 165, 167, 230
Arizona, 156, 158

Arldt, T., 15, 395, 396
Armenia, 30, 134
Aru Is., 31, 77, 141, 142, 211, fig. 62
Ascension I., 13, 15, 159, 206, 405, 413, Plate 3
Ascension and St. Helena, Region of, 13, 139, 206
Asia Minor, 135, 191, 193, 196, 197, 398
Assam, 31
Atacama Desert, 32
Atamaha R., 136
Athos, Mt., 167
Atlantic North American Region, 29, 30, 136, 153, 198
Atlantic Ocean, the, 12, 20, 28, 179, 223, 242, 351, 397, 405, 406, 410
Atlas Mts., 17, 197, 227
Aubréville, A. 160, 233, 385
Auckland Is., 13, 32, 125, 159, 163, 222, 225, 257, Plate 3
Auer, V. 323
Austral Is., 128
Australasia, 11, 20, 55, 58, 59, 60, 63, 64, 69, 72, 73, 74, 81, 88, 89, 94, 97, 98, 99, 101, 103, 109, 115, 117, 120, 142, 163, 166, 183, 184, 185, 223, 224, 229, 230, 240, 243, 245–249, 251–253, 258, 262, 263, 265, 348, 422, 441–443, fig. 62
Austria, 157
Axelrod, D. I., 52
Azores, the, 13, 15, 20, 30, 107, 123, 135, 136, 159, 169, 197, 198, 236, 405, Plate 3
Babcock, E. B., 37, 40
Babington, C. C., 283
Baffinland, 12
Bahamas, the, 12, 32, 159, 215, 236, 397
Baker, H. G., 336
Balfour, Sir I. B., 201
Balgooy, M. M. J. van, 26, 143
Bali, I., 141
Balkans, the, 16, 146, 158, 192, 193, 227, 233, 397
Baluchistan, 411
Barbados, I., 77
Barber, H. N., 107
Barghoorn, E. S., 318
Barton, L. V., 337
Batgan, I., 77
Bear, I., 12
Beata I., 146
Beaufort, L. F. de, 142
Bechuanaland, 207
Becker, C., 166
Beetle, A. A., 152, 222
Belgian Congo, 204
Bellenden-Ker, Mt., 168, 220, 235
Bembridge, 320
Ben Lawers, 286
Bennett, W., 289
Bentham, G., 49, 283, 289
Bering Strait, the, 94, 95, 167, 179, 227, 231, 397
Bermudas, the, 12, 15, 32, 77, 146, 159, 216, Plate 3

Bernal, J. D., 412
Berry, E. W., 317
Bews, J. W., 392, 409
Beyer, H., 344
Billiton, I., 77
Bird, I., 77
Bismarck Archipelago, 12, 13, 20, 21, 77, 78,
    101, 105, 215, 244
Black Sea, the 227
Blackburn, K. B., 271
Blake, S. T., 100
Böcher, T. W., 180
Bolivia, 28, 123, 148, 164
Bonin Is., 13, 128, 145, 214, 215, Plate 3
Borneo, 12, 13, 17, 31, 97, 118, 125, 126, 129,
    141, 142, 158, 160, 164, 168, 184, 185, 211,
    228, 238, 397
Bosphorus, the 16
Botel Tobago, 29, 141, 143
Bougainville, I., 77
Bowden, W. M., 178
Bray, W. L., 230
Brazil, 13, 16, 25, 28, 29, 32, 78, 113, 146, 147,
    159, 160, 164, 165, 166, 167, 188, 230, 235,
    356, 406
Brenchley, W. E., 343
Bridges, E. L., 222
British Columbia, 30
British East Africa, 202
British Isles, the, 5, 13, 25, 57, 135, 156, 169,
    175, 192, 197, 221, 268–294, 295, 366, 370,
    371, 376, 396, 398, 430
Brittany, 293
Brooks, C. E. P., 361, 384, 388, 389, 390,
    392
Brown, F. B. H., 214
Bruce, E. A., 203
Brückner, E., 324
Bulgaria, 227
Burbidge, N. T., 149
Burkill, I. H., 165
Burma, 17, 31, 69, 97, 100, 120, 129, 140, 159,
    164, 165, 168, 171, 173, 184, 185, 194, 195,
    209, 231, 234, 349, 356
Buru, I., 141, fig. 62
Butcher, R. W., 283
Butler, H. C., 388
Cabrera, A. L., 144, 222
Caicos Is., 215
Cailleux, A., 160, 216, 340, 375
Cain, S. A., 45, 170, 178, 233, 424
Cairns, 113
California, 28, 30, 62, 81, 113, 125, 136, 157,
    158, 162, 200, 227, 230, 231, 237, 262, 357,
    386, 423
Camagui Is., 236
Cambage, R. H., 149
Cambodia, 389
Cambridgeshire, 272, 366
Cameroon Mt., 17, 203, 204
Cameroons, the, 31, 204, 205, 228
Camp, W. H., 71
Campbell, D. H., 230
Campbell Is., 13, 32, 125, 159, 222, 225, 257,
    Plate 3
Canada, 30, 58, 167, 188, 327, 352, 353, 365,
    396, 397
Canada, Eastern Arctic, 157
Canada, North West Territory, 157

Canary Is., 12, 20, 30, 64, 113, 135, 136, 159,
    162, 167, 198, 228, 230, 397, Plate 3
Cancer, Tropic of, 13, 60, 183
Candolle, A. L. L. P. de, 427
Cape Farewell, 387
Cape Horn, 16, 261
Cape of Good Hope, 17, 18, 98, 115, 120, 125,
    139, 160, 163, 167, 171, 185, 205, 220, 357,
    392
Cape Peninsula, the, 157, 208
Cape Province, 17, 31, 139, 247
Cape Region, 32, 46, 139, 150, 166, 169, 208,
    248
Cape Verde Is., 12, 20, 30, 135, 198, 228, 230,
    Plate 3
Capricorn, Tropic of, 11, 55, 70, 72, 81, 244,
    247, 249
Carey, S. W., 410, 411
Caribbean Region, the, 28, 32, 146, 215–217
Caribbean Sea, 13, 232, 238, 244, 329
Carolina, 317
Caroline Is., 13, 77, 101, 102, 145, 159, 214, 229,
    Plate 3
Carpathians, 16, 191, 192, 193
Caspian Sea, 113, 388
Caucasus Mts., 16, 30, 107, 134, 165, 192, 194,
    198
Celebes, 12, 31, 129, 141, 142, 164, 167, 168,
    211, 212
Central America, 26, 62, 64, 73, 76, 80, 95, 107,
    118, 120, 146, 152, 160, 165, 167, 188, 212,
    215, 216, 217, 228, 244, 388, 406
Central Asia, 16, 64, 75, 80, 96, 120, 135, 162,
    167, 192, 227, 356, 357, 398, 439
Central Australian Region, 32, 56, 151, 221, 257
Ceram, 77, 141, 165, fig. 62
Cevennes, the, 193
Ceylon, 12, 13, 16, 31, 80, 96, 129, 130, 140, 157,
    159, 162, 164, 185, 209, 211, 235, 238, 239,
    241
Chagos Is., 13, 29
Chamberlin, T. C., 41
Chandler, M. E. J., 307, 318, 319, 320
Chaney, R. W., 315, 317, 319
Channel Islands, 285, 293
Charlesworth, J. K., 323
Chatham Is., 13, 32, 120, 125, 130, 151, 152,
    167, 222, 229, 236, 257, Plate 3
Cheddar, 286
Cheeseman, T. F., 221, 259
Chevalier, A., 198, 205
Chicago, 234
Chile, 13, 15, 18, 19, 28, 32, 46, 62, 64, 82, 118,
    119, 120, 136, 147, 148, 152, 157, 162, 167,
    218, 219, 230, 247, 260, 317, 355
China, 13, 16, 17, 26, 28, 30, 31, 75, 80, 96, 97,
    98, 99, 100, 107, 109, 120, 129, 130, 133, 134,
    135, 140, 153, 159, 162, 164, 165, 166, 167,
    168, 183, 184, 185, 192, 194, 195, 196, 198,
    211, 228, 318, 348
Christmas I., 13, 14, 29, 77, 212, 236, 377
    Plate 3
Claiborne, 317
Clanwilliam, 208
Clapham, A. R., 283
Clark, A. H., 379
Clausen, J., 418
Cochin, 340
Cockerell, T. D. A., 197

Cocos I., 77, Plate 3
Cocos-Keeling Is., 13, 14, 212, Plate 3
Colgan, N., 281
Collinson, D. W., 410
Colombia, 28, 32, 81, 147, 148, 164, 165
Colorado, 81, 158, 317
Comoro Is., 13, 20, 31, 77, 138, 164, 236, 239, Plate 3
Compton, R. H., 213
Congo Basin, 31, 379
Congo R., 201
Constance, L., 118
Continental South East Asiatic Region, 31, 129, 130, 140, 153, 160, 184, 185, 210, 211, 228, 232, 240, 241
Cook Is., 13, 186, Plate 3
Cook Mt., 17
Coral Sea, 265
Core, E. L., 348
Corisco I., 77
Cornwall, 286, 293
Corsica, 12, 135, 159, 167, 191, 193, 197
Costa Rica, 81, 164, 216
Cotton, A. D., 204
Couper, R. A., 314
Cox, A., 410
Crete, 12, 159, 167, 169, 227
Crimea, 327
Crocker, R. L., 149
Croizat, L., 39, 42, 71, 72, 310
Croker, I., 77
Cromer, 268
Crozet Is., 13, 119, 223, 225, Plate 3
Cuba, 12, 81, 146, 157, 158, 160, 216, 267, 397
Cyprus, 12, 159, 227
Cyrenaica, 198
Dakota, 317
Dalmatia, 193
Daly, R. A., 396
Damaraland, 31
Dandy, J. E., 109, 115
Dansereau, P., 199, 369
Danube Basin, 30
Darlington, P. J., jr., 215, 406
Darwin, C., 10, 14, 34, 35, 36, 70, 77, 174, 310, 368, 376
Daubenmire, R. F., 361
Daydon Jackson, B., 37
Deccan, 31
Deevey, E. S., jr., 272, 323
De Geer, G., 329
De Wildeman, E., 379
Delpino, G. G. F., 27
Desventuradas Is., 148, 219, Plate 3
Devonshire, 219, 271, 272, 288
Dexter, S. T., 427
Diels, L., 107, 165
Dietz, R. S., 412, 413
Dimiriz, H., 227
Disco I., 318
Docters van Leeuwen, W. M., 340
Doell, R. R., 410
Donat, A., 152
Dorchester, 297
Dorset, 156, 286, 288, 295 et seq., 319, 366
Dover, Straits of, 269, 293
Douglass, A. E., 386
Druce, G. C., 281, 283
Drude, O., 10, 291

Duida, Mt., 217
Du Rietz, G. E., 71, 229, 346, 355
Dusén, P., 323
Du Toit, A., 266, 401, 402, 407, 411
Dutch-Prussian Border, 320, 322
East Africa, 31, 60, 81, 113, 138, 171, 172, 230, 238, 240, 241, 348, 390, 405
East African Island Region, 29
East African Mountains, 31, 81, 123, 192, 202–206, 228, 235
East African Steppe Region, 31, 137, 200, 201, 202
East Anglia, 269, 272, 322
East Cape I., 163
East Yorkshire, 272
Easter I., 13, 21, 130, 159, 214, 215, 236, Plate 3
Ecuador, 13, 148, 164, 167, 219
Edwards, W. N., 310
Egyed, L., 412
Egypt, 30, 200
Elgon, Mt., 17, 203, 204
Ellesmere Land, 352
Ellice Is., 13
England, 271, 273, 277, 286, 287, 288, 291, 297, 298, 303, 318, 320, 322, 368, 380
Engler, A., 10, 27, 49, 422
Enquist, F., 293
Erdtman, G., 310
Eritrea, 31, 78, 137
Erlanson, E. W., 340
Ethiopia, see Abyssinia
Euro-Siberian Region, 29, 30, 133, 177, 191
Evans, W. E., 191
Everest, Mt., 16
Exell, A. W., 25, 161, 202, 360
Eyre, S. R., 361
Faber, F. C. von, 350
Falkland Is., 13, 26, 32, 81, 117, 118, 123, 152, 159, 167, 222, 223, 225, 229, 359, 357
Farrer, R., 195
Fedorov, A. A., 134
Fernald, M. R., 199, 235, 271
Fernando Noronha I., 13, 147, 218, 236
Fernando Po, 12, 77, 137, 159, 164, 203, 204, 205, 228, Plate 3
Fiji Is., 13, 15, 20, 21, 30, 69, 72, 77, 78, 82, 100, 101, 102, 109, 115, 120, 127, 129, 143, 145, 159, 164, 184, 185, 186, 214, 215, 229, 236, 244, 245, 252, 254, 257, 259, 264, 265, 267, 405, Plate 3, fig. 62
Finland, 57
Fleet, the, 303
Fletcher, F., 344
Flinders Range, 232
Flint, R. F., 323, 330
Flores, 100
Florida, 28, 32, 397
Florida Stream, 351
Florissant, 320
Forbes, E., 280, 282, 289
Forbes, C. N., 212
Formosa, 12, 13, 16, 29, 31, 68, 80, 81, 107, 118, 130, 134, 140, 141, 143, 157, 162, 165, 169, 185, 210, 211, 377
Forrest, G., 195
Fort Union, 317
France, 26, 157, 288, 291, 293
French Guinea, 78
French Polynesia, 214

Fuegia, 13, 26, 32, 118, 167, 222, 224, 225, 247, 323, 357, 397, 409
Funke, G. L., 344
Gaboon, 164
Galaland, 31
Galapagos Is., 13, 15, 32, 46, 75, 83, 125, 148, 159, 217, 218, 219, 233, 242, Plate 3
Galway, 293
Gambier I., 128
Ganges Plain, 31, 159
Gardner, C. A., 149, 356
Gaspé Region, 199
Gates, R. R., 233
Geiger, R., 350, 393
Georgia, 136
Germany, 157, 194, 288
Gilbert Is., 13
Giles, N. H., jr., 178
Gill, E. D., 267
Gilliland, H. B., 385
Girdler, R. W., 413
Gobi Desert, the, 18, 19
Godwin, H., 268, 272, 273, 295, 330
Gold, T., 410
Good, R., 109
Goodspeed, T. H., 113
Gordon, H. D., 71
Gorgona I., 236
Gough I., 13, 130, 223, 223, Plate 3
Grabau, A. W., 395
Grand Chaco, 32
Gray, A., 107, 227
Great Basin, the, 18, 30
Great Britain, 12, 155, 348, 379, 380, 389, 397, 399, 425, 426, 428
Great Lakes, the 30
Great Orme, the, 286
Great Rift Valley, the, 203, 413
Greater Antilles, 215
Greece, 123, 169, 193
Greenland, 12, 16, 30, 132, 189, 194, 231, 237, 271, 272, 316, 317, 318, 321, 323, 327, 387, fig. 77
Green Mountain, 206
Grenada, 77
Griggs, R. H., 237
Grisebach, A., 10
Grummer, G., 344
Guadalupe I., 146
Guadeloupe, 77, 165
Guatemala, 32, 136, 164
Guiana, 28, 164, 165, 166, 188, 351
Guillaumin, A., 213, 214
Gulf Coast, 30
Gulf of Aden, 413
Gulf of California, 413
Gulf of Guinea, 13, 137, 202
Gulf of St. Lawrence, 199, 235, 271
Gulf Stream, 57, 133, 351
Guppy, H. B., 39, 80, 129, 197, 213, 214, 315, 316, 336, 373, 391, 392
Gutenberg, B., 396, 414
Guthrie-Smith, H., 279
Hainan, 31, 140, 210
Haiti, 12, 146, 167
Halmahera, 141, 215, fig. 62
Hampshire, 304
Handel-Mazzetti, H., 193
Hansen, A., 22

Hara, H., 107, 134, 145, 194, 231
Hartley, W., 353
Hawaiian Is. (Hawaii), 13, 14, 17, 46, 52, 76, 77, 80, 82, 83, 107, 125–130, 143, 144, 145, 152, 159, 162, 166, 167, 183, 185, 186, 212, 213, 214, 219, 226, 227, 228, 229, 231, 233, 240, 241, 252, 260, 330, 356, 376, 406, 413, 444, Plate 3
Hawaiian Region, 31, 144, 212
Hayek, A., 37, 193, 346, 357, 365
Hayward, W. R., 283
Heard I., 13, 119, 223, 225, Plate 3
Hedberg, O., 113, 123, 205
Hedley, C., 265
Hegi, G., 191, 192, 193
Heilprin, A., 311
Henderson I., 128
Henry, A., 195
Herekopere I., 236
Hiesey, W. M., 418
Hill, Sir A. W., 117
Himalayas, the 16, 17, 26, 31, 80, 95, 107, 120, 134, 140, 141, 143, 159, 162, 167, 169, 170, 185, 190, 191, 194, 196, 202, 226, 228, 351, 355, 356, 357, 400
Himalayan-Burmese Mts., 164
Høeg, O. A., 318
Holderness, 362
Holdgate, M., 223
Holland, Sir T. H., 410
Holmes, A., 308
Holttum, R. E., 235
Hong Kong, 165
Honimo I., 236
Hooker, Sir J. D., 10, 40, 49, 70, 71, 77, 140, 189, 209, 272, 283, 289, 382, 395, 426
Hospers, J. 410
Howell, J. T., 219
Hudson, W. H., 148
Hultén, E., 179
Huntington, E., 384
Hutchinson, A. H., 423
Hutchinson, J., 49
Huxley, T. H., 10
Iberian Peninsula, the, 135, 227, 291
Iceland, 12, 14, 16, 190
Illinois, 158
Inaccessible I., 223
Inagua, I., 236
India, 13, 26, 28, 31, 57, 64, 69, 78, 80, 81, 96, 97, 98, 99, 100, 113, 115, 129, 134, 140, 141, 153, 159, 164, 165, 167, 168, 172, 173, 183, 185, 195, 200, 209, 211, 228, 230, 231, 239, 240, 241, 340, 349, 356, 396, 400, 405, 411
Indian Ocean, the, 13, 28, 223, 237, 238, 242, 359, 400, 405, 410
Indian Region, 31, 140, 141, 209
Indiana, 158
Indo-Australian Monsoon Province, 184, 201, 213, 357
Indo-China, 17, 31, 97, 140, 168, 185
Indo-Malaysia, 60, 96, 99, 100, 113, 254, 318
Indo-Malaysian Subkingdom, 31
Indo-Pacific Ocean, the, 232
Indus Plain, 159, 388
Iran, see Persia
Ireland, 12, 271, 281, 285, 287, 288, 291, 293, 327, 330, 396, 397
Irish Sea, the, 293

Irmscher, E., 113, 164
Irving, E., 410, 411
Isle of Pines, 77, 113
Isle of Wight, 157, 272, 314, 320
Israel, see Palestine
Isthmus of Kra, 20
Italian Somaliland, 157, 158
Italy, 26, 167, 227
Itatiaya, Mt., 235
Jaccard, P., 161
Jackson, 317
Jaluit, 215
Jamaica, 12, 14, 146, 164, 267
Jan Mayen, 12
Japan, 12, 13, 16, 26, 28, 30, 58, 64, 68, 78, 80,
    95, 96, 97, 98, 99, 107, 109, 113, 117, 120,
    129, 133, 134, 145, 153, 163, 164, 165, 166,
    167, 168, 169, 184, 185, 191, 192, 193, 194,
    196, 198, 227, 228, 231, 240, 317, 322, 397,
    440
Java, 12, 13, 17, 31, 77, 80, 97, 100, 125, 127,
    128, 141, 142, 160, 162, 164, 165, 167, 168,
    184, 185, 211, 212, 227, 228, 229, 231, 339,
    377, 397
Jeannel, R., 223, 405, 413
Jevel Akhdar, 16
Jebel Marra, 203
Jersey, 212
Jessen, K., 293
Johanna I., 164, 236
Johnson, L. A. S., 100
Johnston, I. M., 216
Joly, J., 409
Jones, G. N., 155
Joyce, J. R. F., 409
Juan Fernandez, 13, 15, 46, 77, 81, 83, 117, 125,
    128, 130, 159, 162, 163, 229, 231, 233, 242,
    244, 260, 261, Plate 3
Juan Fernandez, Region of, 32, 148, 219
Kai I., 141, 142, fig. 62
Kalahari Desert, 18, 31, 207
Kamchatka, 13, 16, 30, 162, 191
Kanehira, R., 214
Karroo Desert, 18, 31, 207, 208
Kausik, S. B., 314
Keay, W. R. G., 206
Keck, D. D., 418
Kendrew, W. G., 350
Kent, 286
Kenya, 138
Kenya, Mt., 17, 203, 204
Kerguelen Is., 13, 14, 119, 152, 158, 159, 223,
    225, 405, Plate 3
Kermadec Is., 13, 15, 32, 77, 120, 125, 214, 229,
    233, 236, 257, 258, Plate 3
Key I., 77
Kharga Oasis, 388
Kilimanjaro, Mt., 17, 203, 204
Kimberley District, 219
Kinabalu, Mt., 17, 125
Kingdon-Ward, F., 195, 231
Klebs, G., 429
Knowlton, F. H., 317, 220
Knuth, R., 165
Koidzumi, G., 215
Koppen, W. P., 360, 393
Korea, 16, 30, 107, 130, 134, 157, 196, 237
Kosciusko, Mt., 17
Krakatau, I., 339, 340

Krause, K., 389
Krausel, R., 310
Kroeber, A. L., 219
Kurile Is., 13, 82, 157
Kuro Siwo Current, 351
Labrador, 199
Laccadive Is., 13, 210
Lake Chad, 388
Lake Constance, 320
Lake Eyre, 388
Lake Victoria, 17
Lam, H. J., 211, 410
Lang, R., 361, fig. 82
Lauterbach, C., 211
Lawson, A. A., 149
Lea Valley, 272, 273
Lemée, A., 49, 85, 147, 154
Lems, K., 369
Lesser Antilles, 215
Lesser Sunda Is., 17, 101, 141, 184, 211
Levyns, M. R., 209
Libby, W. F., 330
Libya, 30
Linnaeus, C., 8, 9
Livingston, B. E., 350
Lizard Point, 286
Logan, Mt., 16
Lombok, I., 141
London Basin, 318
Longwell, C. R., 402
Lord Howe I., 12, 13, 15, 20, 31, 77, 102, 113,
    125, 127, 130, 144, 151, 152, 159, 163, 187,
    213, 214, 236, 244, 260, 261, 262, Plate 3,
    fig. 62
Löve, A. and Löve, D., 178, 294
Lower California, 15, 216
Loyalty Is., 113, fig. 62
Lusitania, 130
Luzon, 12
Lyell, Sir C., 395
Lysenko, T. D., 429, 430
Lysgaard, L., 389
Macaronesia, 20, 26, 28, 95, 98, 125, 133, 135,
    163, 167, 169, 197, 228
Macaronesian Region, 30, 55, 135, 197
Macassar Strait, 141
Macdonald I., 223
Macdonnell Range, 77
Macquarie I., 13, 125, 151, 159, 178, 223, 225,
    260, 336, Plate 3
Madagascar, 12, 13, 14, 15, 17, 20, 31, 55, 60,
    64, 67, 72, 76, 77, 78, 82, 89, 90, 92, 96, 98,
    109, 115, 125, 128, 129, 138, 152, 157, 160,
    162, 164, 165, 166, 171, 174, 183, 205, 206,
    213, 234, 239, 356, 359, 405
Madagascar Region, 29, 31, 63, 68, 72, 73, 74,
    76, 95, 96, 109, 113, 138, 206, 227, 228, 238,
    239, 240, 244, 245, 250–252, 253, 254, 262,
    440, 441, 442
Madeira, 12, 15, 20, 30, 64, 80, 113, 123, 135,
    159, 162, 167, 197, 198, 228, Plate 3
Madura, 101
Magdalen Is., 199
Magellansland, 167
Malabar Coast, 31
Malay Peninsula, 17, 20, 31, 130, 141, 142,
    158, 160, 168, 184, 185, 209, 211, 235, 355,
    397
Malaya, 13, 20, 127, 134

Malayan Archipelago, 12, 13, 17, 20, 96, 97, 100, 118, 128, 129, 141, 143, 167, 184, 215, 228, 229, 240, 241, 339
Malaysia, 11, 14, 16, 20, 25, 26, 28, 29, 55, 58, 60, 62, 64, 68, 69, 72, 76, 92, 96, 97, 98, 99, 100, 113, 125, 126–129, 130, 140, 141, 142, 149, 150, 152, 159, 168, 170, 183, 184, 185, 192, 202, 210, 213, 214, 220, 228, 235, 240, 241, 244, 245, 257, 259, 264, 266, 267, 314, 318, 348, 351, 355, 356, 357, 397, 398, 410, 427, 443, fig. 62
Malaysian Region, 27, 31, 141, 210–212
Maldive Is., 13, 210
Malthus, T. R., 34, 341
Manchuria, 16, 30, 165, 184, 196, 396
Mangareva, I., 145
Manton, I., 178
Manum, S., 318
Marianne Is., 13, 101, 102, 145, 183, 215, Plate 3
Marie Victorin, Fr., 199, 235, 271
Marion I., 13, 119, 223, 225, Plate 3
Marquesa Is., 13, 113, 126, 128, 130, 143, 145, 214, Plate 3
Marsh, G. P., 332
Marshall Is., 13, 215
Martin, P., 344
Martinique, 77
Maryland, 317
Masafuera, 81, 130, 148
Masatierra, 130, 148, 163, 236
Mascarenes, the, 13, 20, 28, 31, 64, 76, 96, 98, 113, 115, 129, 138, 183, 252
Mason, H. L., 365, 423, 424
Mathew, W. D., 395
Mathias, M. E., 118
Matthews, J. R., 268, 272, 288, 289, 290, 291, 293
Mauritius, 13, 15, 76, 77, 115, 126, 139, 159, 164, 206, 237, 239, Plate 3
Mayas, 388
McAdam, J. B., 211
McKinley, Mt., 16
McLennan, E. I., 234
Mediterranean, the, 26, 28, 62, 64, 67, 80, 98, 107, 123, 135, 162, 163, 164, 205, 227, 228, 237, 238, 262, 319, 357, 397
Mediterranean Region, 30, 55, 56, 58, 75, 98, 107, 113, 120, 122, 133, 135, 153, 167, 169, 192, 196, 197, 230, 290, 291
Melanesia, 20, 30, 143, 245, 254, 264, 266, fig. 62
Melanesia and Micronesia, Region of, 31, 145, 214, 215
Melliss, J. C., 83, 206, 234
Mendel, G., 35, 36
Mercator, G., 19
Mergui Is., 77
Merrill, E. D., 29, 142, 211, 214, 242
Meru, Mt., 204
Mesopotamia, 31, 135, 200, 388
Metzel, D. H., 323
Meusel, H., 180
Mexico, 13, 16, 18, 26, 28, 30, 32, 64, 81, 107, 117, 120, 123, 136, 146, 162, 164, 167, 215, 230, 406
Micronesia, 30, 143, 159, 184
Midway I., 377
Milankovitch, M., 393
Miller, A. A., 356
Mindanao, 12

Mindoro Strait, 141
Minnesota, 427
Mississippi Basin, 30
Molinier, R., 369
Mollweide, K. B., 20, 266
Moluccas, 31, 128, 129, 141, 142, 168, 184, 236
Mongolia, 18, 19, 30, 95, 136
Moore, D. M., 178
Moreau, R. E., 160, 323
Morocco, 26, 30, 136
Mull, 314, 318
Müeller, P., 365, 369
Muntzing, A., 178
Murneek, A. E., 394, 429
Murray, Sir J., 437
Nairn, E. A. M., 384, 410
Namaqualand, 31
Natal, 17, 31, 207
Nearctic, the, 30, 189
Nepal, 129
Nevada, 158
New Britain, 29, 100, fig. 62
New Caledonia, 12, 14, 15, 17, 20, 52, 64, 69, 72, 73, 76, 77, 78, 82, 100, 101, 102, 109, 113, 115, 117, 118, 126, 127, 128, 129, 143, 144, 150, 152, 157, 158, 159, 166, 184, 185, 186, 213, 214, 220, 229, 230, 236, 244, 245, 252–254, 255, 257, 258, 259, 260, 262, 263, 264, 265, 267, 359, 360, 377, 407, Plate 3, fig. 62
New Caledonia, Region of, 31, 144, 213, 214
Newfoundland, 12, 107, 163, 199, 397
New Guinea, 12, 17, 21, 28, 29, 31, 64, 69, 76, 78, 83, 92, 97, 99, 100, 101, 102, 109, 117, 118, 120, 125, 126, 127, 128, 129, 130, 141, 142, 143, 149, 150, 152, 162, 164, 166, 167, 168, 170, 184, 185, 211, 212, 213, 214, 215, 220, 227, 229, 235, 244, 248, 252, 254–256, 257, 258, 259, 264, 265, 266, 267, 355, 359, 397, figs. 8, 62
New Hebrides, 13, 17, 20, 21, 69, 101, 102, 120, 125, 127, 129, 143, 145, 159, 184, 185, 186, 214, 215, 236, 244, 252, 254, 257, 264, 265, Plate 3, fig. 62
New Ireland, fig. 62
New Jersey, 107, 317
New Mexico, 81, 156, 158, 317
New South Wales, 17, 18, 130, 150, 151, 157, 163, 220, 228, 258, 265
New Zealand, 12, 13, 15, 16, 17, 20, 25, 26, 57, 58, 62, 64, 68, 69, 72, 77, 78, 82, 83, 100, 101, 102, 113, 116, 117, 118, 120, 122, 125, 126, 127, 128, 129, 130, 150, 152, 153, 162, 163, 164, 166, 167, 178, 184, 186, 187, 213, 214, 215, 221, 222, 223, 224, 225, 228, 229, 230, 231, 232, 234, 235, 236, 237, 240, 244, 245, 247, 248, 249, 250, 253, 254, 256, 257–259, 261, 262, 263, 264, 265, 267, 272, 317, 323, 336, 355, 356, 357, 379, 380, 381, 382, 409, figs. 3, 62
New Zealand Region, 32, 151, 221, 222
Ngongoro Mts., 204
Niagara Falls, 329
Nicholson, R. J., 41
Nicobar Is., 13, 77, 140, 141, 210
Niger R., 201
Nigeria, 157
Nightingale I., 223
Nile R., 388

Norfolk, 288
Norfolk I., 13, 15, 20, 31, 77, 101, 125, 126, 127, 144, 159, 186, 187, 214, 229, 232, 236, 244, 260, 261, 262, Plate 3, fig. 62
Normans, the, 275
North Africa, 13, 18, 26, 64, 80, 82, 135, 156, 198, 200, 319, 357, 398, 399
North African-Indian Desert Region, 31, 136, 137, 153, 200, 230, 352, 392
North and East Australian Region, 32, 150, 152, 219, 220
North-east African Highland and Steppe Region, 31, 137, 138, 201
North Cape, New Zealand, 222
North I., New Zealand, 32, 151, 221, 240
North Pole, 194, 243, 317, 318, 412
North Sea, 269
Northern Territory of Australia, 18
Norway, 12, 16, 191
Nossi Bé, 77, 138, 164
Novaia Zemlya, 190
Novak, F. A., 365
Nubia, 167
Nyasa, 138
Oahu I., 233
Obi, 141
Oceania, 26
Oeningen, 320
Oligonesia, 28
Oliver, W. R. B., 125, 221, 229, 236
Opdyke, N. D., 410
Orange Free State, 31, 207
Orange R., 385
Oregon, 28, 30, 158
Orinoco Basin, 32
Orizaba, Mt., 16
Osborn, F., 29
Ostenfeld, C. H., 237
Osvald, H., 344
Pacaraima, Mt., 235
Pacific Islands, the, 14, 21, 29, 64, 69, 73, 76, 77, 82, 83, 94, 97, 98, 99, 100, 103, 113, 125, 130, 143, 163, 165, 183, 186, 212, 213, 214, 228, 229, 238, 240, 241, 441, 442, 443
Pacific North American Region, 30, 136, 153, 200
Pacific Ocean, the, 13, 14, 15, 20, 28, 94, 98, 113, 129, 130, 179, 192, 237, 238, 241, 242, 257, 260, 261, 264, 265, 351, 356, 357, 405
Pakistan, 129, 159
Palaerarctic, the, 189
Palau I., 13, 69, 77, 78, 159, 215, Plate 3
Palawan-Calamian Is., 141
Palestine, 227
Palma, I., 167
Palmyra I., 144
Pampas Region, 32, 148, 219
Panama, 32, 157
Panama, Isthmus of, 406
Paraguay, 28, 147, 162, 164, 165
Patagonia, 26, 28, 32, 55, 100, 123, 148, 149, 152, 162, 163, 167, 222
Patagonian Region, 30, 32, 152, 222
Pax, F., 74
Pearson, G. A., 334
Penck, A., 324, 329
Pennines, the 271, 273, 275
Perrier de la Bathie, H., 138, 250, 251
Persia, 16, 18, 19, 30, 31, 134, 136, 196, 200

Persian Gulf, 13, 200, 240
Peru, 18, 19, 28, 146, 148, 164, 165
Philippine Is., 12, 13, 17, 29, 31, 69, 80, 81, 97, 100, 120, 125, 126, 129, 130, 141, 142, 143, 158, 160, 164, 165, 167, 168, 184, 185, 211, 212, 214, 228, 229, 236, 397
Phillip I., 236
Phillips, E. P., 139, 169, 247
Pichi-Sermolli, R., 365
Pickering, S., 344
Pigott, C. D., 273
Pilger, R., 162
Pillans, N. S., 115
Pitcairn I., 13, 125, 236, 377, Plate 3
Polunin, N., 189
Polynesia, 26, 28, 30, 76, 100, 143, 184, 378
Polynesia, Region of, 31, 145, 214, 215
Polynesian Subkingdom, 31, 143
Poole Harbour, 295, 301
Poona, 172
Popocatepetl, Mt., 16
Popov, G. B., 201
Porsild, A. E., 189
Port Elizabeth, 208
Porto Rico, 12, 146
Portugal, 12, 15, 26, 107, 157, 169, 288
Portuguese East Africa, 30, 201, 247
Post, L. von, 330
Potomac R., 317
Praeger, R. Ll., 198, 281, 287, 291
Prain, Sir D., 165
Prince Edward I., 223
Principe I., 157, 159
Provinces, floristic, 30–32
Puget, 317
Purbeck, 303, 304
Pyrenees, the 16, 17, 165, 192, 193, 291
Queensland, 21, 32, 58, 60, 64, 69, 82, 100, 101, 118, 126, 144, 149, 150, 157, 166, 168, 235, 250, 254, 256, 259, 260, 264, 265, 380
Rademacher, B., 344
Raiatea, I., 128, 145, 236
Raistrick, A., 271
Rapa, I., 117, 125, 126, 127, 128, 130, 145, 151, 152, 163, 214, 236, Plate 3
Raritan, 317
Rarotonga, I., 145, 214, 236
Raton, 317
Raunkiaer, C., 353
Raup, H. M., 179, 199
Red Sea, 17, 137, 172, 239, 413
Regel, C., 231
Reid, C., 273, 322
Reid, E. M., 305, 318, 320, 322
Réunion, I., 13, 15, 113, 115, 126, 130, 139, 159, 206, 252, Plate 3
Revilla Gigedo Is., 13, 15, 146, 216, Plate 3
Rhine R., 269, 320
Rhodesia, 31, 129, 169, 183, 202, 204, 410
Ridley, H. N., 174, 175, 234, 369–374, 378, 380, 427
Rio de Janeiro, 164, 236
Ritigala, Mt., 235
Riukiu Is., 13, 31, 75, 140, 141, 165, 210, 237, 238
Rivals, P., 206
Robyns, W., 201
Rocky Mountains, the, 16, 18, 30, 120, 190, 191, 244, 318, 339

Rodriguez, I., 13, 15, 139, 159, Plate 3
Romans, the, 275, 277, 388
Roraima, Mt., 217, 235
Rosa, D., 41
Runcorn, S. K., 384, 410
Rune, O., 365
Rungwe Mts., 204
Russell, R. J., 384
Russia, 30, 134, 290, 430
Rutland, 208
Ruwenzori, 17, 137, 203, 204, 355
S. Ambrosio I., 148
S. Felix I., 148
S. Tomé, I., 12, 13, 137, 159, 164, Plate 3
Sahara Desert, 17, 18, 19, 31, 57, 82, 136, 156,
    169, 185, 200, 207, 385, 388
Sahni, B., 311
Sahul Shelf, 141
St. Elias, Mt., 16
St. Helena, 13, 14, 15, 25, 68, 80, 83, 115, 120,
    139, 159, 163, 164, 206, 234, 244, 260, 262,
    413, Plate 3
St. John, H., 127
St. Kitts, 77
St. Marie de Madagascar, I., 77
St. Paul I., 13, 163, 223, 224, 225, 413, Plate 3
St. Paul's Rocks, 218
St. Thomas (W.I.), 77
St. Vincent, 77
Sakhalin, 12, 134, 157, 237, 397
Salisbury, Sir E. J., 273, 280, 289, 422
Samoa, 13, 14, 77, 78, 82, 101, 102, 120, 129,
    145, 159, 214, 229, 241, 257, Plate 3
San Domingo, 146
San Sebastian I., 236
Santa Cruz Is., 13
Sardinia, 12, 135, 159, 167, 193, 197
Sax, K., 178
Scandinavia, 30, 70, 180, 273, 288, 315, 329,
    330, 396
Scania, 310
Schimper, A. F. W., 350, 423
Schlechter, R., 213
Schlittler, J., 129
Schouw, J. F., 26, 27
Scilly Is., 271
Scotia arc, 409
Scotland, 180, 286, 287, 288, 310
Scully, R. W., 281
Sealy, J. R., 293
Sein, K. M., 314
Selling, O. H., 330
Senegal, 12, 171, 173
Senegambia, 31, 238
Senn, H. A., 178
Setchell, W. A., 240, 336, 422
Severn R., 271, 327
Seward, Sir A. C., 107, 307, 316
Seychelles, 13, 14, 20, 31, 68, 76, 77, 109, 113,
    138, 139, 159, 206, 373, 405, Plate 3
Seymour I., 323
Seymour Sewell, R. B., 410
Shapley, H., 323, 384, 390, 392
Sharp, A. J., 231
Shepard, F. P., 396
Shreve, F., 350, 353
Shull, A. E., 344
Siam, 16, 17, 31, 98, 130, 140, 168, 185, 397

Siberia, 16, 17, 30, 133, 162, 192, 194, 226, 351,
    352, 398
Sicily, 12, 26, 135, 159
Sierra Leone, 157
Sierra Nevada, 30, 136
Sikkim, 78
Simpson, J. B., 310, 314
Simpson, Sir G. C., 384
Singapore, 234
Sino-Himalayan Mts., 16, 30, 75, 107, 133, 134,
    164, 168, 210
Sino-Japanese Region, 30, 97, 133, 177, 194, 197
Sitka, 30
Skottsberg, C., 71, 116, 148, 152, 212, 219, 222,
    229, 231, 232, 323, 324
Slooten, D. F. van, 211
Smit Sibinga, G. L., 410
Smith, A. C., 54, 214, 257
Smith, C. M., 379
Snowdon Range, 286
Society Is., 13, 80, 102, 118, 129, 143, 145, 186,
    214, Plate 3
Socorro I., 216
Socotra, 13, 31, 64, 67, 95, 129, 138, 159, 165,
    185, Plate 3
Solander Is., 236
Solomon Is., 12, 13, 17, 21, 69, 77, 82, 101, 102,
    129, 143, 145, 168, 214, 215, 244, 264, 265,
    Plate 3, fig. 62
Somaliland, 13, 31, 81, 115, 137, 138, 167, 198
South Africa, 26, 46, 55, 60, 62, 64, 67, 68, 71,
    72, 73, 78, 82, 95, 96, 98, 109, 115, 118, 119,
    120, 122, 128, 139, 140, 149, 150, 152, 160,
    162, 163, 164, 165, 170, 171, 172, 173, 183,
    200, 204, 206, 228, 229, 230, 235, 237, 244,
    247–249, 250, 251, 252, 260, 261, 262, 348,
    356, 357, 385, 420, 443
South African Region, 29, 31, 139, 156, 207
South Australia, 18, 32, 157, 232, 235, 237, 388
South Brazilian Region, 29, 32, 147, 153, 217,
    218
South Dakota, 427
South Georgia, I., 13, 223, 225, Plate 3
South I., New Zealand, 17, 32, 225
South Pole, 243, 410, 411
South Shetland Is., 223
South Temperate Oceanic Islands, 13, 15, 117,
    125, 244, 260, 261
South Temperate Oceanic Islands, Region of,
    32, 152, 222–225
South Trinidad I., 147, 218
South West Africa, 18, 138, 207, 247
South-west Australian Region, 32, 46, 150, 152,
    160, 220, 357, 392
Spain, 26, 75, 107, 135, 157, 233, 288, 293
"Spice Islands," 210
Spitzbergen, 12, 190, 318, 352
Sprague, T. A., 52
Stapf, O., 291
Stauffer, H. U., 126
Steenis, C. G. G. J. van, 25, 141, 159, 185, 211,
    212, 355, 385, 406, 427
Steffen, H., 229, 230
Stern, F. C., 107
Stewart I., 120
Stockholm, 329
Stomps, J. T., 269
Stour R., 295
Stout, P. R., 365, 423

Sudan, 31, 82
Sudanese Park Steppe Region, 31, 137, 200
Sumatra, 12, 17, 31, 77, 80, 81, 97, 128, 141, 142, 164, 167, 168, 184, 185, 211, 212, 227, 228, 397
Sumba, I., 100, 211
Sunda Is., 31, 141, 164
Sunda Sea, 141
Sunda Shelf, 141
Supan, A., 360
Sussex, 273, 286
Svenson, H. K., 219
Sweden, 329
Switzerland, 157
Sydney, 113
Syria, 30, 135, 388
Szymkiewicz, D., 155
Tahiti, 14, 126, 128, 145, 159, 214, 229
Taimyr Peninsula, 190
Taiwan, see Formosa
Takhtajan, A. L., 134
Tanganyika, 81, 113, 169
Tansley, Sir A. G., 275
Tasmania, 12, 17, 32, 58, 62, 64, 70, 117, 118, 125, 126, 127, 128, 129, 149, 150, 157, 163, 167, 187, 219, 220, 221, 229, 230, 234, 237, 250, 256, 261, 262, 265, 410, fig. 3
Tasman Sea, 265
Taylor, B. W., 336
Taylor, Sir G., 107, 203
Taylor, N., 236
Tehuantepec, Isthmus of, 406
Teneriffe, 167
Ternate I., 77
Texas, 158, 166, 427
Thacker, A. G., 42
Thailand, see Siam
Thames R., 269, 271, 327
Thiselton-Dyer, Sir W. T., 71
Thoday, D., 422
Thomas, H. H., 310
Thomson, Sir J. A., 346
Thomson, G. M., 380, 382
Thonner, F., 159
Thornthwaite, C. W., 356
Three Kings I., 151, 186, 222, 236
Thursday I., 236
Tibesti, Mts., 109, 203, 228
Tibet, 16, 17, 18, 19, 30, 64, 134, 157, 168, 195, 196, 348
Timor, 100, 101, 113, 127, 141, 143, 185, 210, 211
Timor Laut (Tanimbar), 141, 142, fig. 62
Tischler, G., 178
Tobago, 77, 146, 165, 215
Tonga I., 13, 20, 101, 102, 113, 129, 159, 214, 215, 229, 241, 357, Plate 3
Torres Strait, 236, 245, 266, 267, 348
Tortoise Is., see Galapagos Is.
Trans-Baikalia, 30
Trans-Caspia, 30
Transvaal, the, 17, 31, 207, 360
Trinidad, 12, 77, 146, 159, 215, 216
Tristan da Cunha, 13, 14, 62, 115, 123, 126, 159, 223, 224, 228, 229, 260, 375, Plate 3
Tsoong, P. C., 130
Tuamotu Is., 13, 77, 214, 236, Plate 3
Tunis, 30
Turkestan, 18, 19, 30

Turks Is., 215
Turrill, W. B., 10, 206, 233
Tuscaloosa, 317
Tutin, T. G., 233, 283
Tutira, 379
Tuyama, T., 117
Uluguru Mts., 204
Umbgrove, J. H. F., 311, 396
Union of South Africa, 139, 158, 169
United States of America, 18, 58, 113, 122, 136, 227, 230, 231, 318, 352, 427
Upper Guinea, 31
Upper Nile-land, 31
Upper Teesdale, 271
Ural Mts., 16, 133, 191, 327
Uruguay, 28, 32, 162
Usambara, 204
U.S.S.R., 159
Utah, 158
Utshungwe Mts., 204
Vancouver, 12
Varma, S. S., 344
Vavilov, N. I., 195
Venezuela, 32, 147, 164, 165, 167, 188, 217, 235
Venezuela and Guiana, Region of, 32, 146, 153, 217
Vester, H., 52, 70
Victoria, 101, 118, 157, 220, 234, 258, 265
Vierhapper, F., 163, 193
Vietnam, see Indo-China
Virginia, 317
Virot, R., 213
Virunga Mts., 204
Visher, S. S., 384
Wales, 280, 288
Wallace, A. R., 10, 211, 212, 265, 289, 391, 406
"Wallacea," 141
Walters, S. M., 273
Walton, J., 310
Wangerin, W., 194
Warburg, E. F., 283
Washington, 30
Watson, H. C., 279–282, 285, 286
Weber, M., 141
Wegener, A., 266, 400, 401, 402, 408, 409
Weimarck, H., 164, 209
West Africa, 64, 66, 78, 138, 232, 240, 241, 406
West African Rain-forest Region, 31, 137, 201
West and Central Asiatic Region, 30, 56, 134, 196
West Indies, 12, 26, 32, 64, 76, 136, 146, 153, 165, 167, 188, 201, 215, 216, 217, 230, 234, 397
West Pakistan, 18, 19, 31, 69
Western Australia, 18, 157, 238, 356
Wettar, 100
Weymouth, 302, 303, 304
White, O. E., 427, 428
White Mts., 191
Whyte, R. O., 394, 429
Widdybank Fell, 286
Wilcox, 317, 320
Williams, C. B., 25, 155, 156, 161
Willis, B., 215
Willis, J. C., 39, 40, 41, 42, 209, 235
Wills, L. J., 269
Wilmott, A. J., 272, 273, 289
Wilson, J. T., 412, 413

Wiltshire, 297
Wimmer, F. E., 78, 204
Wolbach, J., 390
Womersley, J. S., 211
Wood, J. G., 149
Woodhead, T. W., 273
Wright, W. B., 323
Wright Smith, Sir W., 71
Wulff, E. V., 155, 159, 190, 422, 423
Wynne Edwards, V. C., 199

Yap, I., 13, 69, 215
Yemen, 31
Yorkshire, 213, 253, 310, 362
Yucatan, 236, 397
Yunnan, 134, 185
Zanzibar, I., 13
Zeuner, F. E., 275, 323, 329, 393
Zimmerman, E. C., 144, 213, 369, 413
Zollinger, H., 141
Zotov, V.D., 350